Teacher's Edition

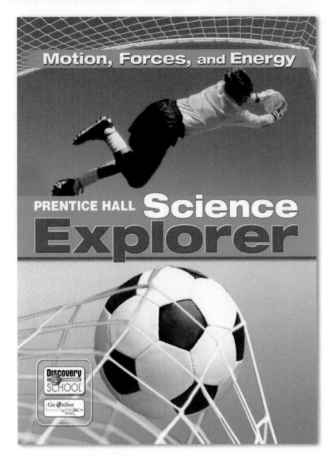

Motion, Forces, and Energy

PRENTICE HALL **Science Explorer**

PEARSON

Boston, Massachusetts • Chandler, Arizona • Glenview, Illinois • Upper Saddle River, New Jersey

13-digit ISBN   978-0-13-366853-7
10-digit ISBN   0-13-366853-3
4 5 6 7 8 9 10 V0ZN 13 12 11 10

Pacing Options

PRENTICE HALL
TeacherEXPRESS™
Plan · Teach · Assess

Lab zone™

SCIENCE EXPLORER offers many aids to help you plan your instruction time, whether regular class periods or block scheduling. Section-by-section lesson plans for each chapter include suggested times for Student Edition activities. TeacherExpress™ and the Lab zone™ Easy Planner CD-ROM will help you manage your time electronically.

Pacing Chart

	PERIODS	BLOCKS		PERIODS	BLOCKS
Careers: Understanding Nature's Designs	1–2	$1/_2$–1	**Chapter 4 Work and Machines**		
Chapter 1 Motion			Chapter 4 Project *The Nifty Lifting Machine*	Ongoing	Ongoing
Chapter 1 Project *Show Some Motion*	Ongoing	Ongoing	1 What Is Work?	1–2	$1/_2$–1
1 Describing and Measuring Motion	4–5	2–$2^1/_2$	2 Integrating Mathematics: How Machines Do Work	3–4	$1^1/_2$–2
2 Integrating Earth Science: Slow Motion on Planet Earth	1–2	$1/_2$–1	3 Simple Machines	4–5	2–$2^1/_2$
3 Acceleration	3–4	$1^1/_2$–2	Chapter 4 Review and Assessment	1–2	$1/_2$–1
Chapter 1 Review and Assessment	1–2	$1/_2$–1	**Chapter 5 Energy**		
Chapter 2 Forces			Chapter 5 Project *Coasting on Energy*	Ongoing	Ongoing
Chapter 2 Project *Newton Scooters*	Ongoing	Ongoing	1 What Is Energy?	1–2	$1/_2$–1
1 The Nature of Force	2–3	1–$1^1/_2$	2 Forms of Energy	2–3	1–$1^1/_2$
2 Friction and Gravity	2–3	1–$1^1/_2$	3 Energy Transformations and Conservation	3–4	$1^1/_2$–2
3 Newton's First and Second Laws	1–2	$1/_2$–1	4 Integrating Earth Science: Energy and Fossil Fuels	1–2	$1/_2$–1
4 Newton's Third Law	3–4	$1^1/_2$–2	Chapter 5 Review and Assessment	1–2	$1/_2$–1
5 Integrating Space Science: Rockets and Satellites	1–2	$1/_2$–1	**Chapter 6 Thermal Energy and Heat**		
Chapter 2 Review and Assessment	1–2	$1/_2$–1	Chapter 6 Project *In Hot Water*	Ongoing	Ongoing
Chapter 3 Forces in Fluids			1 Temperature, Thermal Energy, and Heat	2–3	1–$1^1/_2$
Chapter 3 Project *Staying Afloat*	Ongoing	Ongoing	2 The Transfer of Heat	2–3	1–$1^1/_2$
1 Pressure	3–4	$1^1/_2$–2	3 Integrating Chemistry: Thermal Energy and States of Matter	1–2	$1/_2$–1
2 Floating and Sinking	3–4	$1^1/_2$–2	4 Uses of Heat	1–2	$1/_2$–1
3 Pascal's Principle	1–2	$1/_2$–1	Chapter 6 Review and Assessment	1–2	$1/_2$–1
4 Tech & Design: Bernoulli's Principle	1–2	$1/_2$–1	Interdisciplinary Exploration: Bridges—From Vines to Steel	2–3	1–$1^1/_2$
Chapter 3 Review and Assessment	1–2	$1/_2$–1			

Research-Based and Proven to Work

As the originator of the small book concept in middle school science, and as the nation's number one science publisher, Prentice Hall takes pride in the fact that we've always listened closely to teachers. In doing so, we've developed programs that effectively meet the needs of your classroom.

As we continue to listen, we realize that raising the achievement level of all students is the number one challenge facing teachers today. To assist you in meeting this latest challenge, Prentice Hall has combined the very best author team with solid research to create a program that meets your high standards and will ensure that no child is left behind.

With Prentice Hall, you can be confident that your students will not only be motivated, inspired, and excited to learn science, but that they will also achieve the success needed in today's environment of the No Child Left Behind (NCLB) legislation and testing reform.

On the following pages, you will read about the key elements found throughout *Science Explorer* that truly set this program apart and ensure success for you and your students.

As we continue to listen, we realize that raising the achievement level of all students is the number one challenge facing teachers today.

A Science Program Backed by Research

In developing Prentice Hall *Science Explorer*, we used research studies as a central, guiding element. Research on *Science Explorer* indicated key elements of a textbook program that ensure students' success: support for reading and mathematics in science, consistent opportunities for inquiry, and an ongoing assessment strand. This research was conducted in phases and continues today.

1. Exploratory: Needs Assessment

Along with periodic surveys concerning state and national standards as well as curriculum issues and challenges, we conducted specific product development research, which included discussions with teachers and advisory panels, focus groups, and quantitative surveys. We explored the specific needs of teachers, students, and other educators regarding each book we developed in Prentice Hall *Science Explorer*.

2. Formative: Prototype Development and Field-Testing

During this phase of research, we worked to develop prototype materials. Then we tested the materials by field-testing with students and teachers and by performing qualitative and quantitative surveys. In our early prototype testing, we received feedback about our lesson structure. Results were channeled back into the program development for improvement.

3. Summative: Validation Research

Finally, we conducted and continue to conduct long-term research based on scientific, experimental designs under actual classroom conditions. This research identifies what works and what can be improved in the next revision of Prentice Hall *Science Explorer*. We also continue to monitor the program in the market. We talk to our users about what works, and then we begin the cycle over again. The next section contains highlights of this research.

A Science Program With Proven Results

In a year-long study in 2000–2001, students in six states using Prentice Hall *Science Explorer* outscored students using other science programs on a nationally normed standardized test.

The study investigated the effects of science textbook programs at the eighth-grade level. Twelve eighth-grade science classes with a total of 223 students participated in the study. The selected classes were of similar student ability levels.

Each class was tested at the beginning of the school year using the TerraNova CTBS Basic Battery Plus, and then retested at the end of the school year. The final results, shown in the graph, show a significant improvement in test scores from the pre-test to the post-test evaluation.

• All tests were scored by CTB/McGraw-Hill, the publisher of the TerraNova exam. Statistical analyses and conclusions were performed by an independent firm, Pulse Analytics, Inc.

In Japan, Lesson Study Research has been employed for a number of years as a tool for teachers to improve their curriculum. In April 2003, Prentice Hall adapted this methodology to focus on a lesson from this edition. Our goal was to test the effectiveness of lesson pedagogy and improve it while in the program development stage. In all three classrooms tested, student learning increased an average of 10 points from the pre- to the post-assessment.

• Detailed results of these studies can be obtained at **www.PHSchool.com/research.**

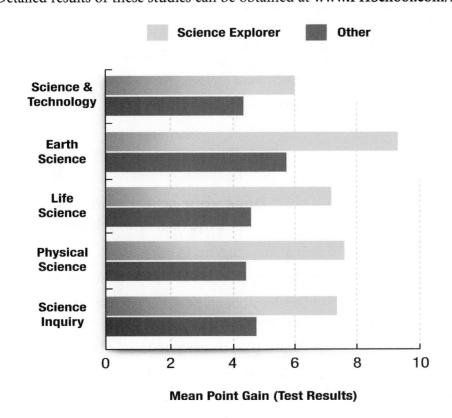

Mean Point Gain (Test Results)

Foundational Research:
Inquiry in the Science Classroom

"How do I know if my students are inquiring?" "If students are busy doing lots of hands-on activities, are they using inquiry?" "What is inquiry, anyway?" If you're confused, you are not alone. Inquiry is the heart and soul of science education, with most of us in continuous pursuit of achieving it with our students!

Defining Science Inquiry

What is it? Simply put, inquiry is the intellectual side of science. It is thinking like a scientist—being inquisitive, asking why, and searching for answers. The National Science Education Content Standards define inquiry as the process in which students begin with a question, design an investigation, gather evidence, formulate an answer to the original question, and communicate the investigative process and results. Since it is often difficult to accomplish all this in one class period, the standards also acknowledge that at times students need to practice only one or two inquiry components.

Understanding Inquiry

The National Research Council in Inquiry and the National Science Education Standards (2000) identified several "essential features" of classroom inquiry. We have modified these essential features into questions to guide you in your quest for enhanced and more thoughtful student inquiry.

1. *Who asks the question?* In most curricula, these focusing questions are an element given in the materials. As a teacher you can look for labs that, at least on a periodic basis, allow students to pursue their own questions.

2. *Who designs the procedures?* To gain experience with the logic underlying experimentation, students need continuous practice with designing procedures. Some labs in which the primary target is content acquisition designate procedures. But others should ask students to do so.

3. *Who decides what data to collect?* Students need practice in determining the data to collect.

4. *Who formulates explanations based upon the data?* Students should be challenged to think—to analyze and draw conclusions based on their data, not just copy answers from the text materials.

5. *Who communicates and justifies the results?* Activities should push students not only to communicate but also to justify their answers. Activities also should be thoughtfully designed and interesting so that students want to share their results and argue about conclusions.

Making Time for Inquiry

One last question—Must each and every activity have students do all of this? The answer is an obvious and emphatic "No." You will find a great variety of activities in *Science Explorer*. Some activities focus on content acquisition, and thus they specify the question and most of the procedures. But many others stress in-depth inquiry from start to finish. Because inquiry is an intellectual pursuit, it cannot merely be characterized by keeping students busy and active. Too many students have a knack for being physically but not intellectually engaged in science. It is our job to help them engage intellectually.

Michael J. Padilla, Ph.D.
Program Author of *Science Explorer*
Associate Dean and Director
Eugene T. Moore
School of Education
Clemson University
Clemson, South Carolina

"Because inquiry is an intellectual pursuit, it cannot merely be characterized by keeping students busy and active."

Evaluator's Checklist

Does your science program promote inquiry by—

✔ Enabling students to pursue their own questions

✔ Allowing students to design their own procedures

✔ Letting students determine what data are best to collect

✔ Challenging students to think critically

✔ Pushing students to justify their answers

Inquiry in *Science Explorer*

Science Explorer offers the most opportunities to get students to think like a scientist. By providing inquiry opportunities throughout the program, *Science Explorer* enables students to enhance their understanding by participating in the discovery.

Student Edition Inquiry

Six lab and activity options are included in every chapter, structured from directed to open-ended—providing you the flexibility to address all types of learners and accommodate your class time and equipment requirements. As Michael Padilla notes, some activities focus on content acquisition, and thus the question and most of the procedures are specified. But many others stress in-depth inquiry from start to finish. The graph below shows how, in general, inquiry levels are addressed in the Student Edition.

Science Explorer encourages students to develop inquiry skills across the spectrum from teacher-guided to open-ended. Even more opportunities for real-life applications of inquiry are included in Science & Society, Technology & Society, Careers in Science, and Interdisciplinary Exploration features.

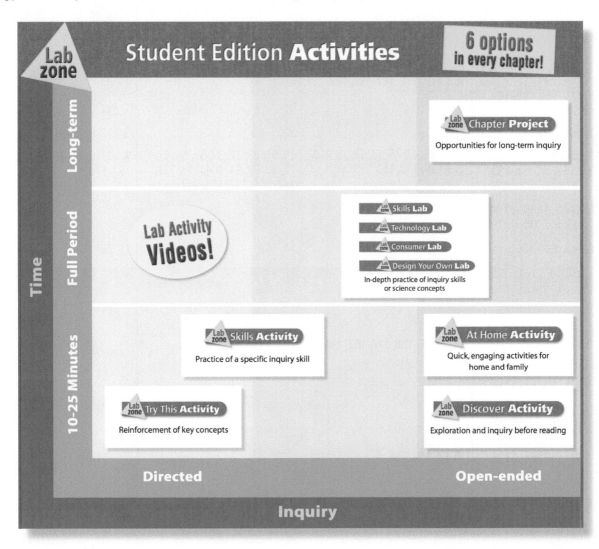

Inquiry Skills Chart

SCIENCE EXPLORER provides comprehensive teaching, practice, and assessment of science skills, with an emphasis on the process skills necessary for inquiry. This chart lists the skills covered in the program and cites the page numbers where each skill is covered.

Basic Process SKILLS

	Student Text: Projects and Labs	Student Text: Activities	Student Text: Caption and Review Questions	Teacher's Edition: Extensions
Observing	40–41, 188–189	36, 51, 90, 146, 162, 176, 183, 193	56, 130, 152, 155, 159	66, 96, 152, 185, 192
Inferring	40–41, 164–165, 182	6, 22, 52, 76, 95, 111, 151, 153, 186, 190	46, 52, 54, 61, 67, 70, 75, 80, 104, 111, 115, 121, 135, 169, 172, 187, 198	
Predicting	35	42, 48, 59, 82, 124	21, 26, 27, 39, 50, 61, 65, 84, 91, 104, 142, 148, 153, 186, 199	82, 197
Classifying	16–17, 81	159, 196	23, 50, 70, 135, 142, 155, 187, 191	13, 19
Making Models	35, 73, 136–137, 145, 182	127		7, 19, 20, 38, 60, 92, 126, 129, 161
Communicating	5, 16–17, 28–29, 35, 40–41, 62–63, 73, 81, 88–89, 107, 123, 136–137, 145, 156–157, 164–165, 175, 182, 188–189	13, 21, 31, 39, 50, 67, 69, 87, 94, 99, 103, 131, 132, 135, 141, 155, 163, 169, 171, 187, 194, 199, 201		13, 198
Measuring	5, 16–17, 164–165, 182	21	32	9, 11, 46, 131, 177
Calculating	5, 16–17, 28–29, 62–63, 107, 136–137, 156–157, 188–189	9, 10, 25, 47, 48, 53, 58, 75, 112, 119, 120, 148, 153, 179	15, 21, 27, 32, 37, 39, 54, 61, 70, 80, 87, 94, 104, 113, 121, 142, 155, 172, 181, 202	9, 11, 19, 21, 25, 37, 59, 110, 120, 152, 179, 181
Creating Data Tables	5, 16–17, 28, 40–41, 62–63, 88, 122–123, 136, 156, 165, 188–189			
Graphing	16–17, 62–63, 164–165	93, 119, 153, 168, 180	14, 142	14, 26

Advanced Process SKILLS

	Student Text: Projects and Labs	Student Text: Activities	Student Text: Caption and Review Questions	Teacher's Edition: Extensions
Posing Questions	137			
Developing Hypotheses	40–41, 164–165	55, 74, 96, 108, 116, 167, 195	104, 135, 202	
Designing Experiments	17, 41, 63, 81, 89, 123, 157, 165, 175, 189		70	85
Controlling Variables	28–29, 35, 40–41, 81, 88–89, 122–123, 145, 164–165			
Forming Operational Definitions		18, 64, 114, 166		

Advanced Process SKILLS (continued)

	Student Text: Projects and Labs	Student Text: Activities	Student Text: Caption and Review Questions	Teacher's Edition: Extensions
Interpreting Data	28–29, 40–41, 62–63, 81, 88–89, 122–123, 136–137, 156–157, 188–189	93, 119, 180	32, 85, 142, 202	
Drawing Conclusions	16–17, 28–29, 40–41, 88–89, 122–123, 136–137, 156–157, 164–165	44, 48, 86, 93, 119, 158, 180, 184	104, 109, 135, 147, 155, 169, 172, 202	

Critical Thinking SKILLS

Comparing and Contrasting			8, 11, 15, 39, 47, 49, 50, 80, 83, 87, 94, 99, 121, 133, 172, 181, 194, 199	10, 75, 114, 118, 128, 133, 153, 154, 179, 184
Applying Concepts		39, 87, 99, 135, 163, 169, 194	7, 15, 27, 32, 50, 54, 61, 67, 70, 78, 80, 87, 98, 99, 104, 113, 119, 121, 129, 142, 150, 162, 172, 177, 187, 193, 194, 202	
Interpreting Diagrams, Graphs, Photographs, and Maps		48, 93, 119, 153, 180	14, 19, 20, 21, 24, 32, 39, 43, 57, 60, 66, 80, 97, 142, 149, 150, 160, 163, 168, 172, 178, 181, 185, 187, 194, 197, 202	7, 8, 12, 18, 19, 49, 57, 78, 93, 116, 119, 125, 133, 153, 180
Relating Cause and Effect			61, 67, 70, 76, 94, 96, 99, 110, 125, 127, 142, 163, 181, 194, 202	98, 198
Making Generalizations			45, 50, 98, 104, 121, 163, 199	
Making Judgments			101, 139, 187	
Problem Solving	73, 107, 175		32, 54, 59, 70, 92, 104, 113, 139, 150, 172	

Informational Organizational SKILLS

Concept Maps			31, 171, 201	30, 61, 68, 102, 140, 170, 200
Compare/Contrast Tables			69, 141, 176	129, 140
Venn Diagrams				
Flowcharts			103	163
Cycle Diagrams			195	160

The *Science Explorer* program provides additional teaching, reinforcement, and assessment of skills in the *Inquiry Skills Activities Book* and the *Integrated Science Laboratory Manual*.

A National Look at Science Education

Project 2061 was established by the American Association for the Advancement of Science (AAAS) to define a "common core of learning"—the knowledge and skills we want all students to achieve. Project 2061 published *Science for All Americans* in 1989 and followed this with *Benchmarks for Science Literacy* in 1993. *Benchmarks* recommends what students should know and be able to do by the end of grades 2, 5, 8, and 12.

The National Research Council (NRC) used *Science for All Americans* and *Benchmarks* to develop the National Science Education Standards (NSES).

Michael Padilla, the program author of *Science Explorer*, guided one of six teams of teachers whose work led to the publication of *Benchmarks*. He also was a contributing writer of the National Science Education Standards. Under his guidance, *Science Explorer* has implemented these standards through its inquiry approach, a focus on student learning of important concepts and skills, and teacher support aligned with the NSES teaching standards.

Meeting the National Science Education Standards

MOTION

Science as Inquiry (Content Standard A)

● **Use appropriate tools and techniques to gather, analyze, and interpret data** Students identify the motion of several objects and calculate how fast each moves. Students investigate how the steepness of a ramp affects how fast an object rolling off it moves. Students investigate several factors to decide the location of a basketball court. *(Chapter Project; Skills Lab—Inclined to Roll; Skills Lab—Stopping on a Dime)*

● **Use mathematics in all aspects of scientific inquiry** You can calculate the speed of an object if you know the distance it travels in a certain amount of time. To determine the acceleration of an object moving in a straight line, calculate the change in speed per unit of time. *(Describing and Measuring Motion; Acceleration)*

Physical Science (Content Standard B)

● **Motions and forces** An object is in motion if it changes position relative to a reference point. Acceleration refers to increasing speed, decreasing speed, or changing motion. *(Describing and Measuring Motion; Acceleration)*

Earth and Space Science (Content Standard D)

● **Structure of the Earth system** Earth's landmasses have changed position over time because they are part of slowly moving plates. *(Slow Motion on Planet Earth)*

Science and Technology (Content Standard E)

● **Understandings about science and technology** The speed of transportation has increased over the years. *(Tech & Design in History)*

FORCES

Science as Inquiry (Content Standard A)

● **Use appropriate tools and techniques to gather, analyze, and interpret data** Students use sneakers to investigate friction. Students use skateboards to investigate how unbalanced forces cause acceleration. *(Consumer Lab; Skills Lab)*

Physical Science (Content Standard B)

● **A force is described by its strength and by the direction in which it acts.** Friction and gravity affect many motions on Earth. Isaac Newton proposed three basic laws of motion. A rocket can rise because the gases it expels with a downward force exert an equal but opposite upward force on the rocket. *(The Nature of Force; Friction and Gravity; Newton's First and Second Laws; Newton's Third Law; Rockets and Satellites)*

Science and Technology (Content Standard E)

● **Design a solution or product** Students design and build a vehicle that moves without an outside force acting on it. *(Chapter Project)*

● **Understandings about science and technology** Artificial satellites are designed for many useful purposes. *(Rockets and Satellites)*

FORCES IN FLUIDS

Science as Inquiry (Content Standard A)

● **Design and conduct a scientific experiment** Students investigate factors that affect the speed of rotation of a lawn sprinkler. Students investigate buoyant force. *(Design Your Own Lab; Skills Lab)*

Physical Science (Content Standard B)

● **Motions and forces** Pressure refers to a force exerted over an area. The buoyant force acts in the direction opposite to the force of gravity. When force is applied to a confined area, the change in pressure is transmitted equally to all parts of the fluid. As the speed of a moving fluid increases, the pressure within the fluid decreases. *(Pressure; Floating and Sinking; Pascal's Principle; Bernoulli's Principle)*

A National Look at Science Education (continued)

Science and Technology (Content Standard E)

● **Design a solution or product** Students design and construct a boat that can float and carry cargo. *(Chapter Project)*

● **Understandings about science and technology** Hydraulic systems are used for a variety of functions. Bernoulli's principle helps explain how planes fly. *(Pascal's Principle; Bernoulli's Principle)*

Science in Personal and Social Perspectives (Content Standard F)

● **Risks and benefits** Students weigh the advantages and disadvantages of helicopters. *(Technology and Society)*

WORK AND MACHINES

Science as Inquiry (Content Standard A)

● **Design and conduct a scientific investigation** Students investigate the relationship between distance and weight for a balanced seesaw. *(Skills Lab—Seesaw Science)*

● **Develop descriptions, explanations, predictions, and models using evidence** Students investigate how the steepness of a wheelchair-access ramp affects its usefulness. *(Skills Lab—Angling for Access)*

Physical Science (Content Standard B)

● **Motions and forces** Work is done on an object when the object moves in the same direction in which the force is exerted. A machine makes work easier by changing force, distance, or direction. *(What Is Work?; How Machines Do Work; Simple Machines)*

Science and Technology (Content Standard E)

● **Design a solution or product** Students design and build a lifting machine. *(Chapter Project)*

● **Understandings about science and technology** There are six basic kinds of simple machines. Simple machines have been used to create some of the most beautiful and useful structures in the world. *(Simple Machines; Science and History)*

Science in Personal and Social Perspectives (Content Standard F)

● **Science and technology in society** Students analyze the benefits and drawbacks of automation. *(Science and Society)*

ENERGY

Science as Inquiry (Content Standard A)

● **Use appropriate tools and techniques to gather, analyze, and interpret data** Students investigate power and exercise. *(Skills Lab—Can You Feel the Power?)*

● **Develop descriptions, explanations, predictions, and models using evidence** Students use a model to investigate the relationships between gravitational potential energy and elastic potential energy *(Skills Lab—Soaring Straws)*

Physical Science (Content Standard B)

● **Motions and forces** Whether energy is kinetic or potential depends on whether an object is moving or not. Mechanical energy is associated with the position and motion of an object. *(What Is Energy?; Forms of Energy)*

● **Transfer of energy** Work is the transfer of energy; power is the rate at which energy is transferred. Forms of energy associated with the particles of objects include thermal, electrical, chemical, nuclear, and electromagnetic energy. Most forms of energy can be transformed into other forms. Fossil fuels contain energy from the sun. (*What Is Energy?; Forms of Energy; Energy Transformations and Conservation; Energy and Fossil Fuels*)

Science and Technology (Content Standard E)

● **Design a solution or product** Students design a roller coaster that uses kinetic and potential energy to move. *(Chapter Project)*

● **Understandings about science and technology** Fossil fuels can be burned to release chemical energy, which can be used to produce electrical energy. *(Energy and Fossil Fuels)*

THERMAL ENERGY AND HEAT

Science as Inquiry (Content Standard A)

● **Develop descriptions, explanations, predictions, and models using evidence** Students use a model calorimeter to investigate the transfer of thermal energy. *(Skills Lab)*

Physical Science (Content Standard B)

● **Properties and changes in properties in matter** Most matter on Earth exists in three states—solid, liquid, and gas. *(Thermal Energy and States of Matter)*

● **Transfer of energy** Heat is transferred by conduction, convection, and radiation. Matter will change from one state to another if thermal energy is absorbed or released. *(Temperature, Thermal Energy, and Heat; The Transfer of Heat; Thermal Energy and States of Matter)*

Science and Technology (Content Standard E)

● **Design a solution or product** Students design and build a container that keeps water hot. Students design and build a thermometer. *(Chapter Project; Technology Lab)*

● **Understandings about science and technology** The three common scales for measuring temperature are the Fahrenheit, Celsius, and Kelvin scales. Heat engines transform thermal energy to mechanical energy; a refrigerator transfers thermal energy from its inside to the outside. *(Temperature, Thermal Energy, and Heat; Technology Lab; Uses of Heat)*

Note: To see how the benchmarks are supported by *SCIENCE EXPLORER,* go to **PHSchool.com.**

Reading

Reading Comprehension in the Science Classroom

Q&A

Q: Why are science texts often difficult for students to read and comprehend?

A: In general, science texts make complex literacy and knowledge demands on learners. They have a more technical vocabulary and a more demanding syntax, and place a greater emphasis on inferential reasoning.

Q: What does research say about facilitating comprehension?

A: Studies comparing novices and experts show that the conceptual organization of experts' knowledge is very different from that of novices. For example, experts emphasize core concepts when organizing knowledge, while novices focus on superficial details. To facilitate comprehension, effective teaching strategies should support and scaffold students as they build an understanding of the key concepts and concept relationships within a text unit.

Q: What strategies can teachers use to facilitate comprehension?

A: Three complementary strategies are very important in facilitating student comprehension of science texts. First, guide student interaction with the text using the built-in strategies. Second, organize the curriculum in terms of core concepts (e.g., the **Key Concepts** in each section). Third, develop visual representations of the relationships among the key concepts and vocabulary that can be referred to during instruction.

Nancy Romance, Ph.D.
Professor of Science Education
Florida Atlantic University
Fort Lauderdale, Florida

"Effective teaching strategies should support and scaffold students as they build an understanding of the key concepts and concept relationships within a text unit."

Reading Support in *Science Explorer*

The latest research emphasizes the importance of activating learners' prior knowledge and teaching them to distinguish core concepts from less important information. These skills are now more important than ever, because success in science requires students to read, understand, and connect complex terms and concepts.

Before students read—
Reading Preview introduces students to the key concepts and key terms they'll find in each section. The **Target Reading Skill** is identified and applied with a graphic organizer.

During the section—
Boldface Sentences identify each key concept and encourage students to focus on the big ideas of science.

Reading Checkpoints reinforce students' understanding by slowing them down to review after every concept is discussed.

Caption Questions draw students into the art and photos, helping them connect the content to the images.

After students read—
Section Assessment revisits the **Target Reading Skill** and encourages students to use the graphic organizer.

Each review question is scaffolded and models the way students think, by first easing them into a review and then challenging them with increasingly more difficult questions.

Evaluator's Checklist

Does your science program promote reading comprehension with—

✔ Text structured in an outline format and key concepts highlighted in boldface type

✔ Real-world applications to activate prior knowledge

✔ Key concepts, critical vocabulary, and a reading skill for every section

✔ Sample graphic organizers for each section

✔ Relevant photos and carefully constructed graphics with questions

✔ Reading checkpoints that appear in each section

✔ Scaffolded questions in section assessments

Math in the Science Classroom

Why should students concern themselves with mathematics in your science class?

Good science requires good data from which to draw conclusions. Technology enhances the ability to measure in a variety of ways. Often the scientist must measure large amounts of data, and thus an aim of analysis is to reduce the data to a summary that makes sense and is consistent with established norms of communication— i.e., mathematics.

Calculating measures of central tendency (e.g., mean, median, or mode), variability (e.g., range), and shape (graphic representations) can effectively reduce 500 data points to 3 without losing the essential characteristics of the data. Scientists understand that a trade-off exists between precision and richness as data are folded into categories, and so margins of error can be quantified in mathematical terms and factored into all scientific findings.

Mathematics is the language used by scientists to model change in the world. Understanding change is a vital part of the inquiry process. Mathematics serves as a common language to communicate across the sciences. Fields of scientific research that originated as separate disciplines are now integrated, such as happened with bioengineering. What do the sciences have in common? Each uses the language of mathematics to communicate about data and the process of data analysis. Recognizing this need, *Science Explorer* integrates mathematics practice throughout the program and gives students ample opportunity to hone their math skills.

Clearly, mathematics plays an important role in your science classroom!

William Tate, Ph.D.
Professor of Education and
Applied Statistics and
Computation
Washington University
St. Louis, Missouri

"Mathematics is the language used by scientists to model change in the world."

Integrated Math Support

In the Student Edition

The math instruction is based on principles derived from Prentice Hall's research-based mathematics program.

Sample Problems, Math Practice, Analyzing Data, and a Math Skills Handbook all help to provide practice at point of use, encouraging students to Read and Understand, Plan and Solve, and then Look Back and Check.

Color-coded variables aid student navigation and help reinforce their comprehension.

In the Teacher's Edition

Math teaching notes enable the science teacher to support math instruction and math objectives on high-stakes tests.

In the Guided Reading and Study Workbook

These unique worksheets help students master reading and enhance their study and math skills. Students can create a record of their work for study and review.

Evaluator's Checklist

Does your science program promote math skills by—

✔ Giving students opportunities to collect data

✔ Providing students opportunities to analyze data

✔ Enabling students to practice math skills

✔ Helping students solve equations by using color-coded variables

✔ Using sample problems to apply science concepts

Technology and Design

Technology and Design in the Science Classroom

Much of the world we live in is designed and made by humans. The buildings in which we live, the cars we drive, the medicines we take, and often the food we eat are products of technology. The knowledge and skills needed to understand the processes used to create these products should be a component of every student's basic literacy.

Some schools offer hands-on instruction on how technology development works through industrial arts curricula. Even then, there is a disconnect among science (understanding how nature works), mathematics (understanding data-driven models), and technology (understanding the human-made world). The link among these fields of study is the engineering design process—that process by which one identifies a human need and uses science knowledge and human ingenuity to create a technology to satisfy the need. Engineering gives students the problem-solving and design skills they will need to succeed in our sophisticated, three-dimensional, technological world.

As a complement to "science as inquiry," the National Science Education Standards (NRC, 1996) call for students at all age levels to develop the abilities related to "technology as design," including the ability to identify and frame a problem and then to design, implement, and evaluate a solution. At the 5–8 grade level, the standards call for students to be engaged in complex problem-solving and to learn more about how science and technology complement each other. It's also important for students to understand that there are often constraints involved in design as well as trade-offs and unintended consequences of technological solutions to problems.

As the *Standards for Technological Literacy* (ITEA, 2000) state, "Science and technology are like conjoined twins. While they have separate identities they must remain inextricably connected." Both sets of standards emphasize how progress in science leads to new developments in technology, while technological innovation in turn drives advances in science.

Ioannis Miaoulis, Ph.D.
President
Museum of Science
Boston, Massachusetts

"Engineering gives students the problem-solving and design skills they will need to succeed in our sophisticated, three-dimensional, technological world."

Evaluator's Checklist

Does your science program promote technology and design by—

✔ Incorporating technology and design concepts and skills into the science curriculum

✔ Giving students opportunities to identify and solve technological design problems

✔ Providing students opportunities to analyze the impact of technology on society

✔ Enabling students to practice technology and design skills

Technology and Design

Technology and Design in *Science Explorer*

How often do you hear your students ask: "Why do I need to learn this?" Connecting them to the world of technology and design in their everyday life is one way to help answer this question. It is also why so many state science curricula are now emphasizing technology and design concepts and skills.

Science Explorer makes a special effort to include a technology and design strand that encourages students to not only identify a need but to take what they learned in science and apply it to design a possible solution, build a prototype, test and evaluate the design, and/or troubleshoot the design. This strand also provides definitions of technology and engineering and discusses the similarities and differences between these endeavors and science. Students will learn to analyze the risks and benefits of a new technology and to consider the tradeoffs, such as safety, costs, efficiency, and appearance.

In the Student Edition

Integrated Technology & Design Sections

Sections throughout *Science Explorer* specifically integrate technology and design with the content of the text. For example, students not only learn how seismographs work but also learn what role seismographs play in society and how people use the data that are gathered.

Technology Labs

These labs help students gain experience in designing and building a device or product that meets a particular need or solves a problem. Students follow a design process of Research and Investigate, Design and Build, and Evaluate and Redesign.

Chapter Projects

Chapter Projects work hand-in-hand with the chapter content. Students design, build, and test based on real-world situations. They have the opportunity to apply the knowledge and skills learned to building a product.

Special Features

This technology and design strand is also reflected in Technology & Society and Science & Society features as well as Science & History timelines and Tech & Design in History timelines. These highly visual features introduce a technology and its impact on society. For example, students learn how a hybrid car differs from a traditional car.

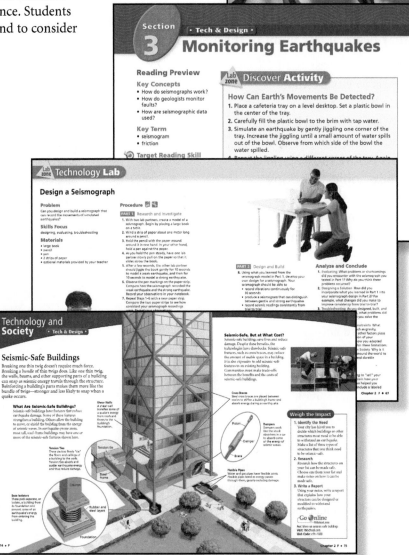

Assessment in the Science Curriculum

No Child Left Behind clearly challenges school districts across the nation to raise expectations for all students with testing of student achievement in science beginning in 2007–2008.

A primary goal of NCLB is to provide classroom teachers with better data from scientifically valid assessments in order to inform instructional planning and to identify students who are at risk and require intervention. It has been a common practice to teach a science lesson, administer a test, grade it, and move on. This practice is a thing of the past. With the spotlight now on improving student performance, it is essential to use assessment results as a way to identify student strengths and challenges. Providing student feedback and obtaining student input is a valuable, essential part of the assessment process.

Assessment is a never-ending cycle, as is shown in the following diagram. Although you may begin at any point in the assessment cycle, the basic process is the same.

An important assessment strategy is to ensure that students have ample opportunities to check their understanding of skills and concepts before moving on to the next topic. Checking for understanding also includes asking appropriate, probing questions with each example presented. This enables students and teachers to know whether the skills or concepts being introduced are actually understood.

Eileen Depka
Supervisor of Standards
and Assessment
Waukesha, Wisconsin

"Meeting the NCLB challenge will necessitate an integrated approach to assessment with a variety of assessment tools."

Use a variety of assessment tools to gain information and strengthen student understanding.

Implement the plan with a focus on gathering and using assessment information throughout.

Analyze assessment results to create a picture of student strengths and challenges.

IMPLEMENT · ASSESS · ANALYZE · TARGET · STRATEGIZE

Identify strategies to achieve the target, create a plan for implementation, and choose assessments tools.

Choose a target to create a focused path on which to proceed.

Evaluator's Checklist

Does your science program include assessments that—

- ✔ Are embedded before, during, and after lesson instruction
- ✔ Align to standards and to the instructional program
- ✔ Assess both skill acquisition and understanding
- ✔ Include meaningful rubrics to guide students
- ✔ Mirror the various formats of standardized tests

Prentice Hall *Science Explorer* now includes Success Tracker, an online tool to help teachers monitor and assess student progress with built-in remediation. Ask your sales rep about Success Tracker today!

Success Tracker™

Online at PHSchool.com

Assessment in *Science Explorer*

Science Explorer's remarkable range of strategies for checking progress will help teachers find the right opportunity for reaching all their students.

The assessment strategies in *Science Explorer* will help both students and teachers alike ensure student success in content mastery as well as high-stakes test performance. A wealth of opportunities built into the Student Edition helps students monitor their own progress. Teachers are supported with ongoing assessment opportunities in the Teacher's Edition and an easy-to-use, editable test generator linked to content objectives. These integrated, ongoing assessment tools assure success.

Especially to support state and national testing objectives, Prentice Hall has developed test preparation materials that model the NCLB approach.

- **Diagnostic Assessment** tools provide in-depth analysis of strengths and weaknesses, areas of difficulty, and probable underlying causes that can help teachers make instructional decisions and plan intervention strategies.

- **Progress Monitoring** tools aligned with content objectives and state tests provide ongoing, longitudinal records of student achievement detailing individual student progress toward meeting end-of-year and end-of-schooling grade level, district, or state standards.

- **Outcomes** tools that mimic state and national tests show whether individual students have met the expected standards and can help a school system judge whether it has made adequate progress in improving its performance year by year.

Caption Questions enhance critical thinking skills.

Reading Checkpoints reinforce students' understanding.

Scaffolded Section Assessment Questions model the way students think.

Comprehensive Chapter Reviews and Assessments provide opportunities for students to check their own understanding and practice valuable high-stakes test-taking skills.

ExamView® **Computer Test Bank CD-ROM** provides teachers access to thousands of modifiable test questions in English and Spanish.

Test Preparation Blackline Masters and Student Workbook include diagnostic and prescription tools, progress-monitoring aids, and practice tests that help teachers focus on improving test scores.

Section 3 Assessment

Target Reading Skill Sequencing Refer to your flowchart about seismographs as you answer Question 1.

Reviewing Key Concepts

1. a. Defining What is a seismogram?
   b. Explaining How can geologists tell apart the different types of seismic waves on a seismogram?
   c. Comparing and Contrasting Two identical seismographs are located 1,000 km and 1,200 km from an earthquake's epicenter. How would the two seismographs for the earthquake compare?

2. a. Reviewing What changes are measured by the instruments used to monitor faults?
   b. Describing How are satellites used to measure movements along a fault?
   c. Inferring A satellite that monitors a fault detects an increasing tilt in the land surface along the fault. What could this change in the land surface indicate?

3. a. Listing What are three ways in which geologists use seismographic data?
   b. Explaining How do geologists use seismographic data to make maps of faults?
   c. Making Generalizations Why is it difficult to predict earthquakes?

Writing in Science

Dialogue Geologists in Alaska have just detected an earthquake and located the earthquake's epicenter. Write a dialogue in which the geologists notify a disaster response team that will help people in the earthquake area.

Chapter 2 F ◆ 65

Standardized Test Prep

Test-Taking Tip
When answering questions about diagrams, read all parts of the diagram carefully, including title, captions, and labels. Make sure that you understand the meaning of arrows and other symbols. Determine exactly what the question asks. Then eliminate those answer choices that are not supported by the diagram.

Practice answering this question.
The diagram shows how stress affects a mass of rock in a process called
   A compression.
   B tension.
   C squeezing.
   D shearing.
The correct answer is D because the arrows show rock being pulled in opposite directions.

Choose the letter that best answers the question or completes the statement.

1. In a strike-slip fault, rock masses along the fault move
   A in the same direction.
   B down only.
   C together.
   D sideways past each other.

2. Stress will build until an earthquake occurs if friction along a fault is
   F decreasing.   G high.
   H low.   J changed to heat.

Use the information below and your knowledge of science to answer Questions 3 and 4.

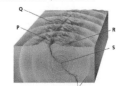

Seismic waves

3. When an earthquake occurs, seismic waves travel
   A from P in all directions.
   B from R to S.
   C from S in all directions.
   D from Q to P.

4. At point R, seismic waves from an earthquake would be
   F weaker than at P.
   G likely to cause little damage.
   H weaker than at Q.
   J likely to cause the most damage.

5. To estimate the total energy released by an earthquake, a geologist should use the
   A Mercalli scale.   B Richter scale.
   C epicenter scale.   D moment
                              magnitude scale.

Constructed Response

6. A geologist discovers a large fault beneath a major city. Why would this information be helpful in determining earthquake risk in the area? What three safety steps should the geologist recommend?

Chapter 2 F ◆ 79

Master Materials List

SCIENCE EXPLORER offers an abundance of activity options in the Student Edition so you can pick and choose those that suit your needs. Prentice Hall has worked with Science Kit to develop Consumable Kits and Nonconsumable Kits that precisely match the needs of the *SCIENCE EXPLORER* labs. Use this Master Materials List or contact your local Prentice Hall sales representative or Science Kit at 1-800-828-7777 or www.sciencekit.com/scienceexplorer.

SK Science Kit & Boreal Laboratories

Helping Teachers Make a World of Difference

Consumable Materials

Description	Textbook Section(s)	Quantity per class	Description	Textbook Section(s)	Quantity per class
Balloon, 9", round	3-1 (DIS)	5	*Paper, white, ream	3-4 (DIS), 4-3 (TT), 6-1 (DIS)	1
*Battery, D-cell	5-2 (DIS)	10	Paper clips, large, pkg/100	2-1 (Lab), 3-2 (TT)	1
*Bottle, empty	3-1 (DIS)	5	*Pencil	4-2 (TT), 4-3 (TT), 6-2 (Lab)	15
*Bottle, glass, clear, juice	6-1 (Lab)	5	Plate, paper, 9"	1-2 (DIS)	5
Bottle, plastic, 2-L, with cap	3-1 (DIS), 3-3 (DIS)	5	Rubber band, assorted, 1.5 oz	2-4 (DIS), 4-1 (DIS), 5-3 (DIS), 5-3 (Lab)	1
Bulb, 100-W	6-2 (TT)	5	Salt, 737 g	3-2 (Lab)	1
*Butter, frozen, pack	6-2 (DIS)	1	Sand, white, fine, 5.5 lb	4-1 (CP), 6-4 (TT)	1
*Can, soda, empty	3-1 (Lab), 6-1 (CP)	10	Spool, wooden	2-5 (DIS)	5
*Can, soup, 600 g	4-1 (CP)	5	Spoon, plastic	1-2 (DIS), 3-2 (DIS), 3-4 (TT), 6-2 (DIS)	10
Candle	6-3 (DIS)	5	Stirrer, wooden, pkg/25	5-4 (DIS)	5
Cardboard, piece, 12" x 12"	1-1 (Lab)		Straw, drinking, pkg/100	2-4 (DIS), 3-1 (DIS), 3-2 (DIS), 3-2 (TT), 5-3 (Lab), 6-1 (Lab)	1
Container, metal, with lid	6-4 (TT)	5	String, roll	2-3 (TT), 2-4 (Lab), 2-5 (DIS), 4-2 (TT), 5-3 (TT)	1
Cup, plastic, 9-oz	3-1 (TT)	5	Sugar, 454 g	3-2 (DIS)	1
Cup, styrofoam, 6-oz	6-2 (Lab)	20	Tape, masking, roll, 3/4" x 60 yd	1-1 (DIS), 1-1 (Lab), 1-2 (DIS), 1-3 (DIS), 2-1 (Lab), 2-2 (DIS), 2-3 (TT), 2-4 (TT), 2-4 (Lab), 4-2 (Lab), 5-3 (Lab)	1
Dropper, plastic, pkg/20	6-1 (Lab)	1			
Fishing line, spool	3-1 (Lab)	1			
Food coloring, red, 30 mL	6-1 (Lab)	1			
*Honey, small jar	1-2 (DIS)	1			
*Ice, bag	6-2 (Lab)	1	*Thread, spool	2-3	1
Index card, 3" x 5", blank, pkg/100	3-1 (TT), 5-3 (DIS)	10	*Tube, toilet paper, empty	5-3 (Lab)	5
*Marker, waterproof, fine-point	3-1 (Lab), 3-2 (DIS), 4-3 (Lab), 5-3 (Lab), 6-1 (DIS), 6-1 (Lab)	5	Wire, metal, 1 m, 22 gauge	6-3 (DIS)	1
Matches, box	5-4 (DIS), 6-3 (DIS)	1			
Modeling clay, white, 1 lb	3-2 (DIS), 6-1 (Lab)	1			
*Mug	4-1 (DIS)	5			
Oil, vegetable, 16 oz	6-1 (Lab)	1			
*Paper towel, roll	1-2 (DIS), 3-2 (Lab)	1			
Paper, graph, sheet	5-4 (SA)	25			

KEY: * = School Supplied; **CP:** Chapter Project; **DIS:** Discover; **SA:** Skills Activity; **TT:** Try This; **Lab:** Skills, Consumer, Design Your Own, or Technology

Quantities based on five groups of six students per class.

Master Materials List

Nonconsumable Materials

Description	Textbook Section(s)	Quantity per class	Description	Textbook Section(s)	Quantity per class
*Balance	2-1 (Lab), 2-2 (SA), 3-2 (Lab), 5-3 (Lab), 6-2 (Lab)	5	Meter stick, 1/2	1-1 (DIS), 1-1 (Lab), 1-3 (DIS), 2-4 (Lab), 4-2 (Lab), 5-1 (DIS), 5-2 (Lab), 5-3 (TT), 5-3 (Lab)	5
*Ball, soccer, deflated	6-4 (DIS)	5	Meter stick, wooden	1-3 (Lab)	5
Ball, table tennis, pkg/6	2-3 (TT)	1	Nail, 20 D, pkg/15	3-1 (Lab)	1
Ball, tennis	5-1 (DIS)	5	Nail, 1" wire, pkg/8	3-1 (Lab)	1
Basin, large	3-1 (Lab), 6-1 (DIS), 6-1 (Lab)	15	Nail, finishing, pkg/6	3-1 (Lab)	1
Beaker, 500-mL	6-1 (Lab)	5	*Object, 50-g mass	4-2 (Lab)	5
Beaker, 600-mL	3-2 (Lab)	5	*Objects, variety	2-2 (SA), 4-2 (DIS)	5
Beaker, polypropylene, 250-mL	3-1 (Lab), 6-2 (DIS), 6-2 (Lab)	5	*Oven mitt	6-3 (DIS)	5
*Block, wooden, 2" x 4" x 6"	4-3 (Lab)	5	Pan, aluminum, 22.5 cm	3-2 (Lab), 5-4 (DIS)	5
*Board, wooden, 1.5-m L	1-1 (Lab)	5	*Penny, minted after 1982	4-2 (Lab), 3-1 (CP)	250
*Board, wooden, 10 cm W, 50 cm L	4-3 (Lab)	5	*Pie plate, glass	2-2 (TT)	10
*Board, wooden, 2.5 x 30 x 120 cm	5-2 (Lab)	5	Pinwheel	4-1 (TT)	5
*Book	1-1 (Lab), 1-2 (DIS), 2-3 (DIS), 2-4 (DIS), 4-3 (Lab), 5-2 (Lab)	50	*Pot, cooking	4-2 (TT)	5
*Brick	2-4 (Lab)	15	Protractor	1-1 (Lab), 5-4 (SA)	5
*Broomstick	4-3 (DIS)	10	*Pump, bicycle	6-4 (DIS)	5
*Burner, lab	6-3 (SA)	5	*Quarter	2-2 (DIS)	20
*Calculator	5-2 (Lab)	5	*Ring stand	5-3 (TT), 5-4 (DIS), 6-3 (DIS)	5
Car, toy	2-3 (DIS), 2-4 (TT)	10	*Rope	4-3 (DIS)	1
*Clamp, utility	5-3 (TT), 5-4 (DIS), 6-3 (DIS)	10	Ruler, 15-cm	1-2 (DIS), 2-2 (DIS), 3-2 (DIS), 4-3 (Lab), 5-3 (Lab), 6-1 (Lab), 6-2 (TT)	5
Dowel, 10 cm L, 3-cm diameter	4-2 (Lab)	5	*Scissors	3-2 (DIS), 3-2 (TT), 4-3 (TT), 5-3 (DIS), 5-3 (Lab), 6-2 (Lab)	5
Eye-hook	4-3 (Lab)	5	*Skateboard	1-1 (Lab), 2-1 (DIS), 2-4 (Lab)	5
Flashlight	5-2 (DIS)	5	*Sneakers, variety	2-1 (Lab)	5
*Flask	5-4 (DIS)	5	Spring scale, 1–10-N	2-1 (DIS), 4-3 (Lab)	5
*Glass, drinking	3-2 (DIS)	5	Spring scale, 20-N	2-1 (Lab), 4-2 (TT)	5
*Goggles, safety	2-5 (DIS), 5-3 (DIS), 5-4 (DIS)	30	Spring scale, 5-N	2-1 (Lab), 2-4 (Lab)	5
*Hairdryer	4-1 (TT)	5	*Stopwatch	1-1 (DIS), 1-1 (Lab), 1-2 (DIS), 1-3 (DIS), 1-3 (Lab), 2-4 (Lab), 3-1 (Lab), 5-2 (Lab), 6-2 (TT)	10
Jar, plastic, 4-oz, with lid	3-2 (TT), 3-2 (Lab)	5	Tape measure, pkg/6	1-3 (Lab)	1
*Kettle, tea	6-3 (SA)	5	Thermometer, alcohol, 12", −10°C to 110°C	5-4 (DIS), 6-2 (Lab), 6-4 (TT)	10
*Lamp, without shade	6-2 (TT)	5	*Utensils, variety	6-2 (DIS)	15
Marbles, assorted	2-2 (TT), 2-4 (DIS)	2	Washer, metal, 1/2", pkg/30	2-3 (DIS), 5-3 (TT), 6-3 (DIS)	3
*Mass set	2-1 (Lab)	5			

KEY: * = School Supplied; **CP:** Chapter Project; **DIS:** Discover; **SA:** Skills Activity; **TT:** Try This; **Lab:** Skills, Consumer, Design Your Own, or Technology

Quantities based on five groups of six students per class.

Motion, Forces, and Energy

Book-Specific Resources

Student Edition
StudentExpress™ CD-ROM
Interactive Textbook Online
Teacher's Edition
All-in-One Teaching Resources
Color Transparencies
Guided Reading and Study Workbook
Student Edition in MP3 Audio
Discovery Channel School® Video
Consumable and Nonconsumable Materials Kits

Program Print Resources

Integrated Science Laboratory Manual
Computer Microscope Lab Manual
Inquiry Skills Activity Books
Progress Monitoring Assessments
Test Preparation Workbook
Test-Taking Tips With Transparencies
Teacher's ELL Handbook
Reading Strategies for Science Content

Differentiated Instruction Resources

Adapted Reading and Study Workbook
Adapted Tests
Differentiated Instruction Guide for Labs and Activities

Program Technology Resources

TeacherExpress™ CD-ROM
Interactive Textbooks Online
PresentationExpress™ CD-ROM
ExamView®, Test Generator CD-ROM
Lab zone™ Easy Planner CD-ROM
Probeware Lab Manual With CD-ROM
Computer Microscope and Lab Manual
Materials Ordering CD-ROM
Discovery Channel School® DVD Library
Lab Activity Video Library—DVD and VHS
Web Site at PearsonSchool.com

Spanish Print Resources

Spanish Student Edition
Spanish Guided Reading and Study Workbook
Spanish Teaching Guide With Tests

Acknowledgments appear on page 244, which constitutes an extension of this copyright page.

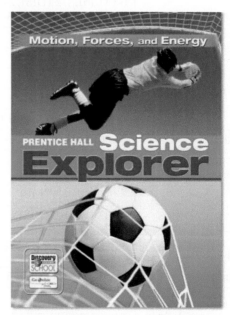

Cover
Both the goalie (top) and the goal net (bottom) change the motion of the soccer ball by exerting a force on it.

13-digit ISBN 978-0-13-365113-3
10-digit ISBN 0-13-365113-4
5 6 7 8 9 10   13 12 11 10 09

Program Authors

Michael J. Padilla, Ph.D.
Associate Dean and Director
Eugene T. Moore School of Education
Clemson University
Clemson, South Carolina

Michael Padilla is a leader in middle school science education. He has served as an author and elected officer for the National Science Teachers Association and as a writer of the National Science Education Standards. As lead author of Science Explorer, Mike has inspired the team in developing a program that meets the needs of middle grades students, promotes science inquiry, and is aligned with the National Science Education Standards.

Ioannis Miaoulis, Ph.D.
President
Museum of Science
Boston, Massachusetts

Originally trained as a mechanical engineer, Ioannis Miaoulis is in the forefront of the national movement to increase technological literacy. As dean of the Tufts University School of Engineering, Dr. Miaoulis spearheaded the introduction of engineering into the Massachusetts curriculum. Currently he is working with school systems across the country to engage students in engineering activities and to foster discussions on the impact of science and technology on society.

Martha Cyr, Ph.D.
Director of K–12 Outreach
Worcester Polytechnic Institute
Worcester, Massachusetts

Martha Cyr is a noted expert in engineering outreach. She has over nine years of experience with programs and activities that emphasize the use of engineering principles, through hands-on projects, to excite and motivate students and teachers of mathematics and science in grades K–12. Her goal is to stimulate a continued interest in science and mathematics through engineering.

Book Author

T. Griffith Jones, Ph.D.
Science Department Chair
P. K. Yonge Developmental Research School
College of Education—University of Florida
Gainesville, Florida

Contributing Writers

Mark Illingworth
Teacher
Hollis Public Schools
Hollis, New Hampshire

Thomas R. Wellnitz
Science Instructor
The Paideia School
Atlanta, Georgia

Consultants

Reading Consultant

Nancy Romance, Ph.D.
Professor of Science
    Education
Florida Atlantic University
Fort Lauderdale, Florida

Mathematics Consultant

William Tate, Ph.D.
Professor of Education and
    Applied Statistics and
    Computation
Washington University
St. Louis, Missouri

Reviewers

Teacher Reviewers

David R. Blakely
Arlington High School
Arlington, Massachusetts

Jane E. Callery
Two Rivers Magnet Middle
    School
East Hartford, Connecticut

Melissa Lynn Cook
Oakland Mills High School
Columbia, Maryland

James Fattic
Southside Middle School
Anderson, Indiana

Dan Gabel
Hoover Middle School
Rockville, Maryland

Wayne Goates
Eisenhower Middle School
Goddard, Kansas

Katherine Bobay Graser
Mint Hill Middle School
Charlotte, North Carolina

Darcy Hampton
Deal Junior High School
Washington, D.C.

Karen Kelly
Pierce Middle School
Waterford, Michigan

David Kelso
Manchester High School Central
Manchester, New Hampshire

Benigno Lopez, Jr.
Sleepy Hill Middle School
Lakeland, Florida

Angie L. Matamoros, Ph.D.
ALM Consulting, Inc.
Weston, Florida

Tim McCollum
Charleston Middle School
Charleston, Illinois

Bruce A. Mellin
Brooks School
North Andover, Massachusetts

Ella Jay Parfitt
Southeast Middle School
Baltimore, Maryland

Evelyn A. Pizzarello
Louis M. Klein Middle School
Harrison, New York

Kathleen M. Poe
Fletcher Middle School
Jacksonville, Florida

Shirley Rose
Lewis and Clark Middle School
Tulsa, Oklahoma

Linda Sandersen
Greenfield Middle School
Greenfield, Wisconsin

Mary E. Solan
Southwest Middle School
Charlotte, North Carolina

Mary Stewart
University of Tulsa
Tulsa, Oklahoma

Paul Swenson
Billings West High School
Billings, Montana

Thomas Vaughn
Arlington High School
Arlington, Massachusetts

Susan C. Zibell
Central Elementary
Simsbury, Connecticut

Safety Reviewers

W. H. Breazeale, Ph.D.
Department of Chemistry
College of Charleston
Charleston, South Carolina

Ruth Hathaway, Ph.D.
Hathaway Consulting
Cape Girardeau, Missouri

Douglas Mandt, M.S.
Science Education Consultant
Edgewood, Washington

Activity Field Testers

Nicki Bibbo
Witchcraft Heights School
Salem, Massachusetts

Rose-Marie Botting
Broward County Schools
Fort Lauderdale, Florida

Colleen Campos
Laredo Middle School
Aurora, Colorado

Elizabeth Chait
W. L. Chenery Middle School
Belmont, Massachusetts

Holly Estes
Hale Middle School
Stow, Massachusetts

Laura Hapgood
Plymouth Community
    Intermediate School
Plymouth, Massachusetts

Mary F. Lavin
Plymouth Community
    Intermediate School
Plymouth, Massachusetts

James MacNeil, Ph.D.
Cambridge, Massachusetts

Lauren Magruder
St. Michael's Country
    Day School
Newport, Rhode Island

Jeanne Maurand
Austin Preparatory School
Reading, Massachusetts

Joanne Jackson-Pelletier
Winman Junior High School
Warwick, Rhode Island

Warren Phillips
Plymouth Public Schools
Plymouth, Massachusetts

Carol Pirtle
Hale Middle School
Stow, Massachusetts

Kathleen M. Poe
Fletcher Middle School
Jacksonville, Florida

Cynthia B. Pope
Norfolk Public Schools
Norfolk, Virginia

Anne Scammell
Geneva Middle School
Geneva, New York

Karen Riley Sievers
Callanan Middle School
Des Moines, Iowa

David M. Smith
Eyer Middle School
Allentown, Pennsylvania

Gene Vitale
Parkland School
McHenry, Illinois

Contents

Motion, Forces, and Energy

Activities

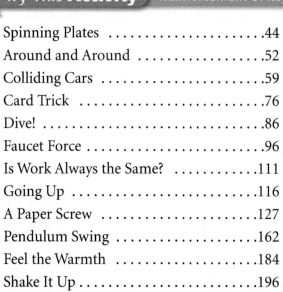

M • ix

active art ▶ Illustrations come alive online

Writing in Science

VIDEO

Web Links

Enhance understanding through dynamic video.

Preview Get motivated with this introduction to the chapter content.

Field Trip Explore a real-world story related to the chapter content.

Assessment Review content and take an assessment.

Get connected to exciting Web resources in every lesson.

SCiLINKS. Find Web links on topics relating to every section.

Active Art Interact with selected visuals from every chapter online.

Planet Diary® Explore news and natural phenomena through weekly reports.

Science News® Keep up to date with the latest science discoveries.

Experience the complete textbook online and on CD-ROM.

Activities Practice skills and learn content.

Videos Explore content and learn important lab skills.

Audio Support Hear key terms spoken and defined.

Self-Assessment Use instant feedback to help you track your progress.

M • xi

Understanding Nature's Designs

Inquiry and Biomechanics

Dr. Ioannis Miaoulis investigates engineering principles found in nature. This feature introduces the process of scientific inquiry and highlights similarities and differences between science and engineering. Students do not need any previous knowledge of forces or mechanics to understand and use this feature.

Build Background Knowledge
Observations About Nature

Encourage students to tell what they already know about designs in nature. To prompt student thinking, have them list techniques animals use to camouflage themselves. Another topic to brainstorm is ways in which animals change their body temperature. Point out that the animal behaviors they list are instinctive, not learned.

Introduce the Career

Before students read the feature, have them read the title and examine the pictures and captions. Ask: **What questions came into your mind as you looked at these pictures?** *(Sample answer: How did prairie dogs learn about air currents? How does the shape of a maple seed determine how it travels?)* Point out to students that just as they have questions about things they see, scientists too have questions about what they observe.

Careers in **Science**

Ioannis is at the steam-engine exhibit in Boston's Museum of Science.

Understanding Nature's Designs

"This is a biomechanics laboratory," says scientist and engineer Ioannis Miaoulis. "What we study is how animals and plants use energy, motion, and forces." Professor Miaoulis walks over to a network of earthen tunnels built between two panes of glass. The structure has a tube for blowing air over the top.

"This is a cross section of a prairie-dog burrow. There are two entrance holes. One hole is flat, while the other one is built up and rounded. Biologists were wondering why. They thought the prairie dogs wanted a good view, but then why not make both holes high and rounded and get a good view from both?"

Miaoulis and his students are learning the likely reason. Wind blowing over a flat surface moves more slowly, because it doesn't have to travel as far as the same breeze going over a rounded surface. "Slow air means high pressure across here" — Miaoulis points to the flat hole. "Fast air going over the rounded hole means low pressure. High pressure here, low pressure there. The holes' shape moves air through the burrow—in the flat hole and out the rounded one. It's prairie-dog air conditioning."

Career Path

Ioannis Miaoulis (YAHN is my OW lis) was born in Athens, Greece. He came to the United States to study engineering. He earned a master's degree in engineering at the Massachusetts Institute of Technology. He received a master's degree in economics and a Ph.D. in mechanical engineering at Tufts University in Massachusetts, where he later became the Dean of the School of Engineering. Now he is the president of Boston's Museum of Science.

Background

Engineering is the study of mathematical and natural sciences and their real-world application. Engineers specialize in various kinds of engineering such as automotive, aerospace, biomechanical, chemical, civil, industrial, mechanical, textile, and many others. Although engineers work in specialized fields, they usually have a basic knowledge of many of the other fields. Real-world engineering involves problems that are complex and draws from more than one field of engineering, so knowledge of a range of areas is essential.

Talking With
Dr. Ioannis Miaoulis

 How did you get started in science?

I grew up in Athens, Greece. It's a congested and polluted city, but my school was in the woods and I could do things outdoors. I got to love nature. I dug out anthills to see how they were inside. I found the places where turtles laid their eggs.

In the summers, we lived near the ocean and every day I'd go fishing and snorkeling. I got to know each rock underwater. I didn't even know what a scientist was then, but I was observing and thinking through things because I wanted to catch more fish. If the flow of water was in this direction, where would be a good place for the fish to hang out? I was observing flow patterns to see where, how, and why fish build their nests. I still do it, in part to catch them, because I still like fishing. But now I do it to observe them, to figure them out. I was always curious.

A prairie dog uses its paws to feed itself grass from the western prairie.

 **How is engineering different from science?**

Well, I enjoyed doing things with my hands, taking things apart and seeing how they worked, building things and making them work. I found that what I enjoyed about studying was learning science and then doing something with it. And that's engineering. I try to discover something about an animal that nobody ever understood before. Then I'll use that information to design something that will make people's lives easier.

Prairie-Dog Air Conditioning

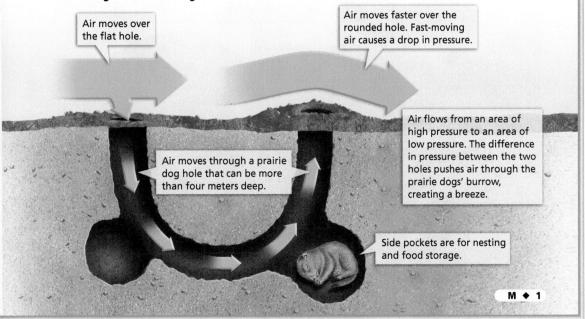

Air moves over the flat hole.

Air moves faster over the rounded hole. Fast-moving air causes a drop in pressure.

Air moves through a prairie dog hole that can be more than four meters deep.

Air flows from an area of high pressure to an area of low pressure. The difference in pressure between the two holes pushes air through the prairie dogs' burrow, creating a breeze.

Side pockets are for nesting and food storage.

M ◆ 1

Discuss Ask students to name items they have taken apart to see how they worked. Ask: **Have you ever changed the design of something so it would work better?** *(Sample answer: I modified the angle of my bicycle's handlebars so the bike is easier to turn.)* **What characteristics do you need to be able to take something apart and put it back together again?** *(Sample answer: Methodical, careful, organized, tidy)*

Demonstrate Bring to class a computer chip or a photograph of a chip for students who do not know what one looks like. Point out that computer chips do not make any noise as they operate. The sound a computer makes when it is turned on is the sound of the fan. Most computers have fans to keep the chips from overheating.

Discuss Ask: **Why did Dr. Miaoulis choose to study butterflies rather than lizards to solve the problem of chips heating unevenly?** *(Sample answer: Butterfly wings are made of thin films. Lizard skin is not.)* **How do we know that butterflies need heat?** *(Sample answer: They can be observed basking in sunlight.)*

? How do you use nature in your engineering designs?

Here's an example. I got interested in how heat travels in the chips that make computers work. They're made in very thin layers or films, thinner than one-hundredth the thickness of your hair. Sometimes, if chips don't heat evenly, they fall apart when you try to make them. I wondered if any plants or animals had solved that problem—using thin films to control how heat was absorbed or reflected. We looked for animals that bask or lie in the sun, or for animals and insects that depend on the warmth of the sun.

If you touch a butterfly, you get a dust on your fingers. When I was little I used to catch butterflies and didn't really understand what the dust was. If you slice those "dust" particles, you find that they are made of many layers. These thin films are little solar collectors. Butterflies can change the amount of heat they catch. They just change the angle at which they hold the thin films on their wings up to the sun. Large areas of butterfly wings heat evenly. So we're looking at the layers on butterfly wings to learn how to make computer chips that will transfer heat more evenly.

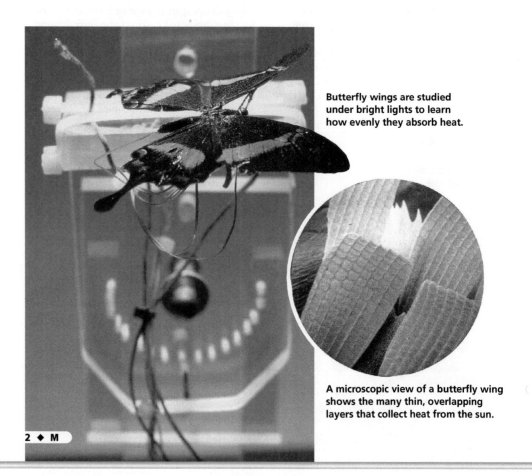

Butterfly wings are studied under bright lights to learn how evenly they absorb heat.

A microscopic view of a butterfly wing shows the many thin, overlapping layers that collect heat from the sun.

2 ◆ M

Background

Besides butterflies and prairie-dog tunnels, Dr. Miaoulis and his students studied other animals in the Comparative Biomechanics Laboratory. By studying sea anemones in a current, they worked to determine how the anemone's shape helps it filter food from sea water without being swept away by the current. Dr. Miaoulis hopes that understanding the design of these creatures will provide solutions to human design problems in the future.

A seed tends to detach when the wind is blowing.

Why is a maple seed shaped as it is?

Because of its winglike shape, the seed spirals slowly to the ground. So, in the wind, it travels away from the tree.

A seed that falls away from the roots and shade of the parent tree has a better chance to grow.

Maple seeds can fall to the ground anytime from May to early fall.

? How do you come up with the questions you ask?

It depends. Sometimes it's simply by observing things. If you see a maple seed with wings falling in a fancy way, you might not even think twice about it. But if you start observing and appreciating nature, you start asking questions about how things work. Why would it help the tree to have a seed that could be blown by the wind? I can combine my love of nature from when I was small with what I've learned of science and engineering.

Ioannis shows how water is lost through a plant's leaves.

Writing in Science

Career Link Scientist and engineer Ioannis carefully observes plants and animals and asks himself questions about them. Do you, too, have "a questioning eye"? Think about an animal that you observe often in your environment—a pet, insect, or bird. Write down four *how* or *why* questions about the movement and speed of the animal. In a paragraph, describe steps that you might take to collect data to find possible answers.

Go Online
PHSchool.com
For: More on this career
Visit: PHSchool.com
Web Code: cgb-3000

M ◆ 3

Demonstrate If possible, bring winged maple seeds to class or ask students to do so. Have students trace the seeds on paper and cut out their paper model of a seed. Have students drop their paper model from different heights to compare how the seed model travels. Ask: **Is the shape of the wing the only factor that affects how the seed travels? If not, what is another factor that affects the seed's motion?** (*Sample answer: No, the way the seed model travels is affected by the height from which it is dropped and the amount of breeze blowing as it falls.*)

Reading Resources

- Willis, Delta, *The Sand Dollar and the Slide Rule: Drawing Blueprints from Nature*, Perseus Press, 1996.

- Freedman, David H., "The Butterfly Solution," *Discover Magazine*, Vol. 18, Number 4, April 1997.

- Knight, Tim, *Magnificent Movers*, Heinemann, 2003.

- Vogel, Steven, and Davis, Kathryn K., *Cat's Paws and Catapults: Mechanical Worlds of Nature and People*, W.W. Norton & Company, 1998.

- National Society of Professional Engineers' Web site for high school students at www.nspe.org/students/home.asp

Writing in Science

Writing Mode Description
Scoring Rubric
4 Exceeds criteria; includes all required elements and extra, relevant material, for example, predictions of trends that might be found in the collected data
3 Meets criteria
2 Questions and descriptions are brief and inconclusive
1 Questions and descriptions are incomplete and/or very disconnected

Go Online
PHSchool.com
For: More on this career
Visit: PHSchool.com
Web Code: cgb-3000

Students can do further research on this career and others that are related to engineering.

Chapter at a Glance

 Chapter **Project** *Show Some Motion*

All in One Teaching Resources
- Chapter Project Teacher Notes, pp. 38–39
- Chapter Project Student Overview, pp. 40–41
- Chapter Project Student Worksheets 1–2, pp. 42–43
- Chapter Project Scoring Rubric, p. 44

Section 1

Describing and Measuring Motion
M.1.1.1 Determine when an object is in motion.
M.1.1.2 Calculate an object's speed and velocity.
M.1.1.3 Demonstrate how to graph motion.

4–5 periods
2–2 1/2 blocks

Section 2

Slow Motion on Planet Earth
M.1.2.1 Describe how the theory of plate tectonics explains the movement of Earth's landmasses.
M.1.2.2 Calculate the speed at which Earth's plates move.

1–2 periods
1/2–1 block

Section 3

Acceleration
M.1.3.1 Describe the motion of an object as it accelerates.
M.1.3.2 Calculate acceleration.
M.1.3.3 Describe what graphs are used to analyze the motion of an accelerating object.

3–4 periods
1 1/2–2 blocks

Review and Assessment

All in One Teaching Resources
- Key Terms Review, p. 72
- Transparency M10
- Performance Assessment Teacher Notes, p. 81
- Performance Assessment Scoring Rubric, p. 82
- Performance Assessment Student Worksheet, p. 83
- Chapter Test, pp. 84–87

Technology

Discovery CHANNEL SCHOOL
Video Preview

Discovery CHANNEL SCHOOL
Video Field Trip

Go Online
active art

Go Online
PHSchool.com

Go Online
active art

Go Online
SciLINKS NSTA

Discovery CHANNEL SCHOOL
Video Assessment

Go Online
PHSchool.com

PRENTICE HALL
TeacherEXPRESS™
Plan • Teach • Assess

Local Standards

Test Preparation

Test Preparation Blackline Masters

Chapter Activities Planner

Student Edition	Inquiry	Time	Materials	Skills	Resources
Chapter Project, p. 5	Open-Ended	2 weeks	**All in One Teaching Resources** p. 38	Measuring, calculating, communicating	**Lab zone Easy Planner** **All in One Teaching Resources** pp. 38–39
Section 1					
Discover Activity, p. 6	Guided	15 minutes	Meter stick, stopwatch, masking tape	Inferring	**Lab zone Easy Planner**
Skills Activity, p. 10	Directed	5 minutes		Calculating	**Lab zone Easy Planner**
Skills Lab pp. 16–17	Guided	40 minutes	Flat board about 1.5 m long, masking tape, meter stick, protractor, skateboard, small piece of sturdy cardboard, supports to prop up the board (books, boxes), two stopwatches	Measuring, calculating, graphing	**Lab zone Easy Planner** **Lab Activity Video** **All in One Teaching Resources** Skills Lab: *Inclined to Roll*, pp. 52–54
Section 2					
Discover Activity, p. 18	Guided	Prep: 1 hour; Class: 15 minutes	Spoon, plate, honey, books or blocks, masking tape, metric ruler, stopwatch or clock, damp cloths or paper towels	Forming operational definitions	**Lab zone Easy Planner**
At-Home Activity p. 21	Guided		Ruler	Measuring, applying concepts	**Lab zone Easy Planner**
Section 3					
Discover Activity, p. 22	Directed	15 minutes	Masking tape, meter stick, stopwatch	Inferring	**Lab zone Easy Planner**
Skills Lab, pp. 28–29	Guided	Prep: 15 minutes; Class: 40 minutes	2 stopwatches or watches with second hands, tape measure, wooden meter stick	Calculating, interpreting data	**Lab zone Easy Planner** **Lab Activity Video** **All in One Teaching Resources** Skills Lab: *Stopping on a Dime*, pp. 68–71

Section 1 Describing and Measuring Motion

 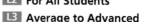
 4–5 periods, 2–2 1/2 blocks

Objectives

M.1.1.1 Determine when an object is in motion.
M.1.1.2 Calculate an object's speed and velocity.
M.1.1.3 Demonstrate how to graph motion.

Local Standards

Key Terms

• motion • reference point • International System of Units • meter • speed
• average speed • instantaneous speed • velocity • slope

Preteach

Build Background Knowledge

Ask leading questions for a discussion on recognizing motion.

 Discover Activity *How Fast and How Far*   L1

Targeted Print and Technology Resources

 **Teaching Resources**

L2 Reading Strategy Transparency
M1: Using Prior Knowledge

⊙ **PresentationExpress™ CD-ROM**

Instruct

Describing Motion Ask leading questions to clarify the need for a reference point to determine if an object is in motion.

Calculating Speed Use sample calculations to show how speed, distance, and time are related.

Describing Velocity Use a sample velocity to demonstrate that velocity describes both speed and direction of motion.

Graphing Motion Use figures in the text to demonstrate the use of a line graph to show how motion can be graphed.

 Skills Lab   *Inclined to Roll*   L2

Targeted Print and Technology Resources

 Teaching Resources

L2 Guided Reading, pp. 47–49
L2 Transparencies M2, M3
L2 Skills Lab: *Inclined to Roll*, pp. 52–54

📼 **Lab Activity Video/DVD**
Skills Lab: *Inclined to Roll*

PHSchool.com Web Code: cgp-3011

PHSchool.com Web Code: cgd-3012

DISCOVERY CHANNEL
SCHOOL
Video Field Trip

⊙ **Student Edition on Audio CD**

Assess

Section Assessment Questions

↻ Have students use their completed graphic organizers to answer the questions.

Reteach

Students work in pairs to review key terms.

Targeted Print and Technology Resources

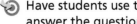 **Teaching Resources**

• Section Summary, p. 46
L1 Review and Reinforce, p. 50
L3 Enrich, p. 51

Section 2 Slow Motion on Planet Earth

 1–2 periods, 1/2–1 block

ABILITY LEVELS
- **L1** Basic to Average
- **L2** For All Students
- **L3** Average to Advanced

Objectives

M.1.2.1 Describe how the theory of plate tectonics explains the movement of Earth's landmasses.

M.1.2.2 Calculate the speed at which Earth's plates move.

Key Terms

- plate • theory of plate tectonics

Local Standards

Preteach

Build Background Knowledge

Use a map of the coastlines of North and South America, Europe, and Africa, to lead students to infer that the continents would fit together like puzzle pieces.

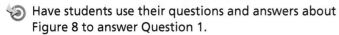 **Discover Activity** *How Slow Can It Flow?* **L1**

Targeted Print and Technology Resources

All in One Teaching Resources

L2 Reading Strategy Transparency M4: Previewing Visuals

PresentationExpress™ CD-ROM

Instruct

Earth's Plates Use Figure 8 to illustrate the changing positions of Earth's plates.

Plate Movement Reinforce the idea that Earth's plates move very slowly and lead a discussion about the information scientists need to predict the future location of Earth's plates

Targeted Print and Technology Resources

All in One Teaching Resources

Student Edition on Audio CD

L2 Guided Reading, pp. 57–58

L2 Transparency M5

PHSchool.com Web Code: cfp-1015

Student Edition on Audio CD

Assess

Section Assessment Questions

Have students use their questions and answers about Figure 8 to answer Question 1.

Reteach

Students use Figure 8 to review the motion of Earth's plates.

Targeted Print and Technology Resources

All in One Teaching Resources

- Section Summary, p. 56

L1 Review and Reinforce, p. 59

L3 Enrich, p. 60

Section 3 Acceleration

 3–4 periods, 1 1/2–2 blocks

ABILITY LEVELS
L1 Basic to Average
L2 For All Students
L3 Average to Advanced

Objectives

M.1.3.1 Describe the motion of an object as it accelerates.

M.1.3.2 Calculate acceleration.

M.1.3.3 Describe what graphs are used to analyze the motion of an accelerating object.

Key Terms
• acceleration

Local Standards

Preteach

Build Background Knowledge

Demonstrate changing speed and direction with a balloon.

 **Discover Activity** *Will You Hurry Up?*

Targeted Print and Technology Resources

All in One Teaching Resources

L2 Reading Strategy Transparency M6: Identifying Main Ideas

PresentationExpress™ CD-ROM

Instruct

What Is Acceleration? Challenge students to identify examples of increasing speed, decreasing speed, and changing direction.

Calculating Acceleration Lead students in interpreting the equation for calculating acceleration.

Graphing Acceleration Lead students in comparing two methods of graphing acceleration using examples shown in the text.

 Skills Lab *Stopping on a Dime* L2

Targeted Print and Technology Resources

All in One Teaching Resources

L2 Guided Reading, pp. 63–65
L2 Transparencies M7, M8, M9
L2 Skills Lab: *Stopping on a Dime*, pp. 68–71

Lab Activity Video/DVD
Skills Lab: *Stopping on a Dime*

www.SciLinks.org Web Code: scn-1313

Student Edition on Audio CD

Assess

Section Assessment Questions

 Have students use their graphic organizers to answer the questions.

Reteach

Students write sentences to review the three ways in which objects accelerate—speeding up, slowing down, or changing direction

Targeted Print and Technology Resources

All in One Teaching Resources

• Section Summary, p. 62
L1 Review and Reinforce, p. 66
L3 Enrich, p. 67

Chapter 1 Content Refresher

Section 1 Describing and Measuring Motion

Distance and Displacement Speed, velocity, and distance traveled can all be used to describe the motion of an object. Another useful measurement to describe an object's motion is the object's displacement. To find an object's displacement, a straight line is drawn from the point where an object begins its motion to the point where the object ends its motion. The distance and direction of the straight line is the object's displacement. Note that displacement, like velocity, is a vector quantity, that is, it has both a magnitude and a direction. For an object that travels in one straight line for the entire time it is in motion, the distance traveled and the displacement have the same magnitude. An object that moves in a complete circle may have traveled a large distance, but it will have zero displacement.

Address Misconceptions

Students might think that an object must be moving quickly to have speed. For a strategy for overcoming this misconception, see **Address Misconceptions** in the section, *Describing and Measuring Motion.*

Section 2 Slow Motion on Planet Earth

Plate Boundaries The locations where the edges of Earth's plates meet are called plate boundaries. Much of Earth's volcanic and earthquake activity occurs at these boundaries. Plate boundaries are commonly divided into three types: divergent, convergent, and transform (also called conservative).

The boundary between two plates that are moving away from each other is a divergent plate boundary. The most commonly used example of a divergent boundary is the mid-ocean ridge. As the plates move away from each other, molten material rises, cools, and forms new ocean floor.

At convergent boundaries, plates move toward each other. When the plates collide, one of the plates is pushed under the other plate, a process called subduction. Convergent plate boundaries are associated with the formation of mountains.

Transform, or conservative, plate boundaries are sites at which one plate slides past another. The San Andreas Fault is one example of a transform boundary.

Section 3 Acceleration

Acceleration Is Determined by Force and Mass In order for an object to accelerate, it must be acted upon by a net force. The size of the force and the object's mass determine the amount of acceleration that results. This is Newton's second law of motion, which can be written

$$\text{Acceleration} = \text{Force} \div \text{Mass}$$

So, a greater force results in increased acceleration if mass is held constant. A greater mass results in decreased acceleration if force is held constant.

When the mass of an object and the size of the force acting upon it are known, the resulting acceleration can be calculated. For example, if a 20-kg object is acted upon by a 100-N force, the resulting acceleration is 5 m/s^2.

Help Students Read

Outlining

Understanding Text Structure

Strategy Outlining is a good strategy to help students focus on the text. Outlining can be applied to an entire section using the headings as major divisions. Before you begin, choose a section for students to read and outline, such as Section 3, *Acceleration.*

Example
1. Before students read, have them preview the section's title and headings. Demonstrate how to make a skeleton outline, using the section title at the top level, the main headings as major divisions, and the subheadings at the next level.
2. Have students copy the skeleton outline as they read, filling in details under each heading and subheading.
3. After reading, have students review their outlines to be sure they have included all key terms and key concepts.
See Section 3, *Acceleration*, for a script using the Outlining strategy with students.

The BIG Idea

The Big Idea is the major scientific concept of the chapter. It is followed by the Essential Question. Read aloud the question to students. As students study the chapter, tell them to think about the Essential Question. Explain that they will discover the answer to the question as they read. The chapter Study Guide provides a sample answer.

The BIG Idea
Motion and Forces

Q How can an object's motion be described?
_____

Chapter Preview

❶ **Describing and Measuring Motion**
Discover How Fast and How Far?
Math Skills Converting Units
Skills Activity Calculating
Active Art Graphing Motion
Skills Lab Inclined to Roll

❷ **Slow Motion on Planet Earth**
Discover How Slow Can It Flow?
Active Art Continental Drift
At-Home Activity Fingernail Growth

❸ **Acceleration**
Discover Will You Hurry Up?
Skills Lab Stopping on a Dime

The wild horses running across this meadow are in motion. ▶

Lab zone Chapter *Project* L3

Objectives
This Chapter Project will allow students to identify and measure the motion of several objects. After completing this Chapter Project, students will be able to
- measure distance and time accurately
- record data in lists or tables
- calculate speed
- communicate results to the class

Skills Focus
Measuring, calculating, communicating

Project Time Line 2 weeks

All in One Teaching Resources
- Chapter Project Teacher Notes
- Chapter Project Overview
- Chapter Project Worksheet 1
- Chapter Project Worksheet 2
- Chapter Project Scoring Rubric

Developing a Plan
Students can begin measuring speeds the first week. Most measurements can be completed quickly, although some may take longer. Allow another week for students to prepare their display cards.

Possible Materials
Meter sticks, metric rulers, tape measures, timing devices such as a stopwatch or a clock with a second hand

Discovery
CHANNEL
SCHOOL

Motion
▶ Video Preview
Video Field Trip
Video Assessment

Discovery
CHANNEL
SCHOOL
Video Preview

Motion

Show the Video Preview to introduce the Chapter Project and provide an overview of chapter content. Discussion questions: **What is average speed? How is it calculated?** (*Average speed is the total distance traveled divided by the total time.*)

Lab zone™ Chapter **Project**

Show Some Motion

Your Goal To identify the motion of several common objects and calculate how fast each one moves

To complete this project, you must
- measure distance and time carefully
- calculate the speed of each object using your data
- prepare display cards of your data, diagrams, and calculations
- follow the safety guidelines in Appendix A

Plan It! With your classmates, brainstorm several examples of objects in motion, such as a feather falling, your friend riding a bicycle, or the minute hand moving on a clock. Choose your examples and have your teacher approve them. Create a data table for each example and record your measurements. For accuracy, repeat your measurements. Then calculate the speed of each object. Make display cards for each example that show data, diagrams, and calculations.

Chapter 1 M ◆ 5

Possible Shortcuts

Although the project is written to be completed by students individually at home, they may complete parts of the project in class.

Launching the Project

To stimulate interest, show students several toys that move, such as wind-up cars. Some should move in a straight line with constant speed; some can move in other ways. Ask: **How can we describe different types of motion?** (*Sample answer: You can describe motion by creating a map showing change in position over time.*)

Performance Assessment

The Chapter Project Scoring Rubric will help you evaluate how well students complete the Chapter Project. You may want to share the rubric with your students so that they will know what is expected. Students will be assessed on
- how carefully they measured and how thoroughly and accurately they recorded data
- their explanations of how they calculated speed
- their use of SI units
- thoroughness and organization of the display cards

Students can keep their notes and display cards in their portfolios.

Portfolio

Objectives

After this lesson, students will be able to

M.1.1.1 Determine when an object is in motion.

M.1.1.2 Calculate an object's speed and velocity.

M.1.1.3 Demonstrate how to graph motion.

Target Reading Skill

Using Prior Knowledge Explain that using prior knowledge helps students connect what they already know to what they are about to read.

Answers

Sample answers:

What You Know

1. A moving object changes position.

2. Objects move at different speeds.

What You Learned

1. Motion is compared to a reference point.

2. The SI unit of length is the meter.

All in One Teaching Resources

• Transparency M1

Preteach

Build Background Knowledge L2

Experience With Motion

Have students discuss motion. Ask: **How do you know an object is moving?** *(Sample answer: An object is moving when it is changing position.)* **How can you decide if an object is moving slowly or quickly?** *(Sample answer: An object is moving slowly if it moves a short distance in a long time.)*

Section 1
Describing and Measuring Motion

Reading Preview

Key Concepts

• When is an object in motion?
• How do you know an object's speed and velocity?
• How can you graph motion?

Key Terms

• motion • reference point
• International System of Units
• meter • speed • average speed
• instantaneous speed
• velocity • slope

Target Reading Skill

Using Prior Knowledge Before you read, write what you know about motion in a graphic organizer like the one below. As you read, write what you learn.

What You Know
1. A moving object changes position.
2.

What You Learned
1.
2.

Lab zone Discover Activity

How Fast and How Far?

1. Using a stopwatch, find out how long it takes you to walk 5 meters at a normal pace. Record your time.
2. Now find out how far you can walk in 5 seconds if you walk at a normal pace. Record your distance.
3. Repeat Steps 1 and 2, walking slower than your normal pace. Then repeat Steps 1 and 2 walking faster than your normal pace.

Think It Over

Inferring What is the relationship between the distance you walk, the time it takes you to walk, and your walking speed?

How do you know if you are moving? If you've ever traveled on a train, you know you cannot always tell if you are in motion. Looking at a building outside the window helps you decide. Although the building seems to move past the train, it's you and the train that are moving.

However, sometimes you may see another train that appears to be moving. Is the other train really moving, or is your train moving? How do you tell?

Lab zone Discover Activity

Skills Focus Inferring

Materials masking tape, meter stick, stopwatch

Time 15 minutes

Tips Use masking tape to mark the starting line, another line 5 meters from the starting line (for Step 1), and the distance walked after 5 seconds (for

L1 Step 2). Remind students to walk at a normal pace.

Think It Over The faster you walk, the less time it takes to move a certain distance. The faster you walk, the farther you will travel in a given time. If you walk a longer distance in a given amount of time, you are walking faster.

Describing Motion

Deciding if an object is moving isn't as easy as you might think. For example, you are probably sitting in a chair as you read this book. Are you moving? Well, parts of you may be. Your eyes blink and your chest moves up and down. But you would probably say that you are not moving. An object is in **motion** if its distance from another object is changing. Because your distance from your chair is not changing, you could say you are not in motion.

Reference Points To decide if you are moving, you use your chair as a reference point. A **reference point** is a place or object used for comparison to determine if something is in motion. **An object is in motion if it changes position relative to a reference point.**

Objects that we call stationary—such as a tree, a sign, or a building—make good reference points. From the point of view of the train passenger in Figure 1, such objects are not in motion. If the passenger is moving relative to a tree, he can conclude that the train is in motion.

You probably know what happens if your reference point is moving. Have you ever been in a school bus parked next to another bus? Suddenly, you think your bus is moving backward. But, when you look out a window on the other side, you find that your bus isn't moving at all—the other bus is moving forward! Your bus seems to be moving backward because you used the other bus as a reference point.

FIGURE 1
Reference Points
The passenger can use a tree as a reference point to decide if the train is moving. A tree makes a good reference point because it is stationary from the passenger's point of view.
Applying Concepts Why is it important to choose a stationary object as a reference point?

Describing Motion

Teach Key Concepts   L2

Changing Position and Reference Points

Focus Tell students that to determine if an object is in motion, they must compare it to another object, called a reference point. Remind students that distance is measured using SI units.

Teach Ask: **Are the passengers in a boat moving compared to a person standing on the shore? Why?** *(Yes, the distance between the passenger and the person on the shore is changing.)* **Are seated passengers in a boat moving compared to the boat? Why?** *(No, the distance between the boat and the passengers does not change.)*

Apply Ask: **Why do scientists need a consistent, accurate way to measure distance when they study motion?** *(Sample answer: So they can compare their work to the work of others)* **learning modality: logical/ mathematical**

Independent Practice   L2

All in One Teaching Resources

• Guided Reading and Study Worksheet: *Describing and Measuring Motion*

◉ Student Edition on Audio CD

Differentiated Instruction

Less Proficient Readers   L1
Interpreting Figures Have students listen while you read aloud the text under the heading Reference Points. After they have completed listening, have students use Figure 1 to help them verbally explain the concept of a reference point. **learning modality: verbal**

Special Needs   L1
Modeling Motion Ask pairs of students to model a moving object and a reference point. One student should serve as the reference point, and the other as the moving object. Ask: **How do you know which student in the pair is the reference point?** *(Reference points should not move, so the student who does not move must be the reference point.)* **learning modality: kinesthetic**

Monitor Progress   L2

Writing Have students write a paragraph that describes three examples of motion they observed on the way to school today.

Answer
Figure 1 If you choose a moving reference point, you may think that you are moving when you are not or that you are moving faster or slower than you really are.

Integrating Space Science [L2]

Most early astronomers used Earth as a reference point when they observed the sun, planets, and stars. Based on their observations, they developed a geocentric model of the universe in which Earth is stationary and the sun, planets, and stars revolve around it. A heliocentric model (a model in which Earth and the other planets revolve around the sun) was developed in ancient Greece. In the 1500's the heliocentric model was further developed by Copernicus. Ask: **Why might ancient astronomers have been convinced that the sun, planets, and stars revolve around Earth?** (*Sample answer: From the reference point of the moving Earth, the sun, planets, and stars appear to be moving around Earth.*) **learning modality: verbal**

Use Visuals: Figure 2 [L2]

Choosing Reference Points

Focus Have the students preview Figure 2 and read the inset captions.

Teach Ask: **Are the skydivers moving if your reference point is on the ground?** (*Sample answer: Yes. The distance between the skydivers and the ground is changing.*)

Apply Ask: **How is your choice of a reference point important when describing motion?** (*Sample answer: Objects that appear to be in motion when compared to one reference point might not be in motion when compared to a different reference point.*) **learning modality: visual**

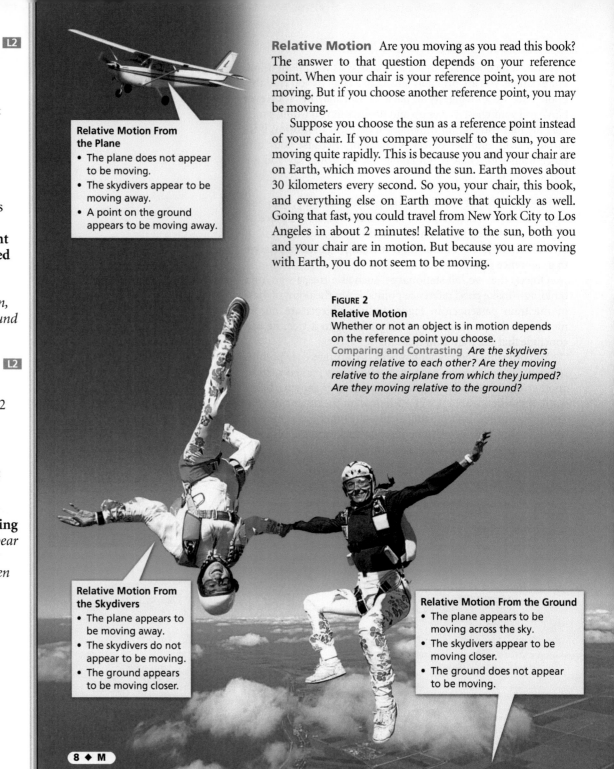

Relative Motion From the Plane
- The plane does not appear to be moving.
- The skydivers appear to be moving away.
- A point on the ground appears to be moving away.

Relative Motion From the Skydivers
- The plane appears to be moving away.
- The skydivers do not appear to be moving.
- The ground appears to be moving closer.

Relative Motion From the Ground
- The plane appears to be moving across the sky.
- The skydivers appear to be moving closer.
- The ground does not appear to be moving.

Relative Motion Are you moving as you read this book? The answer to that question depends on your reference point. When your chair is your reference point, you are not moving. But if you choose another reference point, you may be moving.

Suppose you choose the sun as a reference point instead of your chair. If you compare yourself to the sun, you are moving quite rapidly. This is because you and your chair are on Earth, which moves around the sun. Earth moves about 30 kilometers every second. So you, your chair, this book, and everything else on Earth move that quickly as well. Going that fast, you could travel from New York City to Los Angeles in about 2 minutes! Relative to the sun, both you and your chair are in motion. But because you are moving with Earth, you do not seem to be moving.

FIGURE 2
Relative Motion
Whether or not an object is in motion depends on the reference point you choose.
Comparing and Contrasting *Are the skydivers moving relative to each other? Are they moving relative to the airplane from which they jumped? Are they moving relative to the ground?*

FIGURE 3
Measuring Distance
You can measure distances shorter than 1 meter in centimeters. The wingspan of the butterfly is 7 cm.

Measuring Distance You can use units of measurement to describe motion precisely. You measure in units, or standard quantities of measurement, all the time. For example, you might measure 1 cup of milk for a recipe, run 2 miles after school, or buy 3 pounds of fruit at the store. Cups, miles, and pounds are all units of measurement.

Scientists all over the world use the same system of measurement so that they can communicate clearly. This system of measurement is called the **International System of Units** or, in French, *Système International* (SI).

When describing motion, scientists use SI units to describe the distance an object moves. When you measure distance, you measure length. The SI unit of length is the **meter** (m). A meter is a little longer than a yard. An Olympic-size swimming pool is 50 meters long. A football field is about 91 meters long.

The length of an object smaller than a meter often is measured in a unit called the centimeter (cm). The prefix *centi-* means "one hundredth." A centimeter is one hundredth of a meter, so there are 100 centimeters in a meter. The wingspan of the butterfly shown in Figure 3 can be measured in centimeters. For lengths smaller than a centimeter, the millimeter (mm) is used. The prefix *milli-* means "one thousandth," so there are 1,000 millimeters in a meter. Distances too long to be measured in meters often are measured in kilometers (km). The prefix *kilo-* means "one thousand." There are 1,000 meters in a kilometer.

Scientists also use SI units to describe quantities other than length. You can find more information about SI units in the Skills Handbook at the end of this book.

 Reading Checkpoint What system of measurement do scientists use?

Converting Units

Use a conversion factor to convert one metric unit to another. A conversion factor is a fraction in which the numerator and denominator represent equal amounts in different units. Multiply the number you want to convert by the conversion factor.

Suppose you want to know how many millimeters (mm) are in 14.5 meters (m). Since there are 1,000 millimeters in 1 meter, the conversion factor is

$$\frac{1,000 \text{ mm}}{1 \text{ m}}$$

Multiply 14.5 meters by the conversion factor to find millimeters.

$$14.5 \text{ m} \times \frac{1,000 \text{ mm}}{1 \text{ m}}$$

$$= 14.5 \times 1,000 \text{ mm}$$

$$= 14,500 \text{ mm}$$

Practice Problem How many centimeters are in 22.5 meters?

Calculating Speed

Teach Key Concepts

Distance and Time

Focus Tell the students that speed is the distance traveled by an object divided by the time it took to travel that distance.

Teach Write *Speed = Distance ÷ Time* on the board. Have students suggest a fictional distance and time. Use the suggested numbers to calculate a speed. Ask: **What are two ways to increase this speed?** *(Decrease the time or increase the distance traveled)* Show, by calculating, how each of these changes affects speed.

Apply Ask: **How can you compare the motion of two objects?** *(Sample answer: You can calculate the speed at which each object is moving, and compare the speeds.)* **learning modality: logical/mathematical**

Address Misconceptions

Differentiating Speed and Quickness

Focus Many students think that objects must move quickly to have speed.

Teach Explain that any object in motion has a speed, or rate of motion. Direct their attention to the clock. Explain that the hour hand has a speed even though it moves slowly. Point out that the word *speedy*, meaning quick, can be misleading.

Apply Ask: **How do you know that all objects in motion have a speed?** *(Sample answer: Because all objects in motion travel some distance, they all have a speed.)* **learning modality: visual**

Lab zone — Skills **Activity**

Calculating

Two families meet at the City Museum at 10:00 A.M. Each family uses a different means of transportation to get there. The Gonzalez family leaves at 9:00 A.M. and drives 90 km on a highway. The Browns leave at 9:30 A.M. and ride the train 30 km. What is the average speed for each family's trip? Which family travels at the faster speed?

FIGURE 4
Speed
The cyclists' speeds will vary throughout the cross-country race. However, the cyclist with the greatest average speed will win.

10 ◆ M

Calculating Speed

A measurement of distance can tell you how far an object travels. A cyclist, for example, might travel 30 kilometers. An ant might travel 2 centimeters. **If you know the distance an object travels in a certain amount of time, you can calculate the speed of the object.** Speed is a type of rate. A rate tells you the amount of something that occurs or changes in one unit of time. The **speed** of an object is the distance the object travels per unit of time.

The Speed Equation To calculate the speed of an object, divide the distance the object travels by the amount of time it takes to travel that distance. This relationship can be written as an equation.

$$\text{Speed} = \frac{\text{Distance}}{\text{Time}}$$

The speed equation consists of a unit of distance divided by a unit of time. If you measure distance in meters and time in seconds, you express speed in meters per second, or m/s. (The slash is read as "per.") If you measure distance in kilometers and time in hours, you express speed in kilometers per hour, or km/h. For example, a cyclist who travels 30 kilometers in 1 hour has a speed of 30 km/h. An ant that moves 2 centimeters in 1 second is moving at a speed of 2 centimeters per second, or 2 cm/s.

Lab zone — Skills **Activity**

Skills Focus Calculating

Time 5 minutes

Tips Pair students of differing ability levels for this activity.

Answer The Gonzalez family traveled at a speed of 90 km/h; the Browns traveled at 60 km/h. The Gonzalez family traveled at the faster speed.

Extend Ask: **At the same speed, how long would the Brown family need to ride the train to get to a destination 150 km from their home?** *(2.5 hours)* **learning modality: logical/mathematical**

Average Speed The speed of most moving objects is not constant. The cyclists shown in Figure 4, for example, change their speeds many times during the race. They might ride at a constant speed along flat ground but move more slowly as they climb hills. Then they might move more quickly as they come down hills. Occasionally, they may stop to fix their bikes.

Although a cyclist does not have a constant speed, the cyclist does have an average speed throughout a race. To calculate **average speed**, divide the total distance traveled by the total time. For example, suppose a cyclist travels 32 kilometers during the first 2 hours. Then the cyclist travels 13 kilometers during the next hour. The average speed of the cyclist is the total distance divided by the total time.

$$\text{Total distance} = \text{32 km} + \text{13 km} = \text{45 km}$$
$$\text{Total time} = \text{2 h} + \text{1 h} = \text{3 h}$$
$$\text{Average speed} = \frac{\text{45 km}}{\text{3 h}} = \text{15 km/h}$$

The cyclist's average speed is 15 kilometers per hour.

Instantaneous Speed Calculating the average speed of a cyclist during a race is important. However, it is also useful to know the cyclist's instantaneous speed. **Instantaneous speed** is the rate at which an object is moving at a given instant in time.

 Reading Checkpoint How do you calculate average speed?

FIGURE 5
Measuring Speed
Cyclists use an electronic device known as a cyclometer to track the distance and time that they travel. A cyclometer can calculate both average and instantaneous speed.
Comparing and Contrasting *Explain why the instantaneous speed and the average speed shown below are different.*

 **Build Inquiry** L2

Measuring Speed

Materials masking tape, metric rulers, stopwatches, two or three wind-up toys per group

Time 10 minutes

Focus Remind students that speed is the distance traveled in a period of time.

Teach Have students mark a measured distance on the floor with masking tape. Have students measure the time needed for each toy to travel the marked distance. Suggest that students perform three or more trials for each toy, and average the results. Students can use their results to calculate the speed of each toy.

Apply Ask: **For each trial, are you measuring instantaneous speed or average speed?** *(Average speed)* **learning modality: kinesthetic**

Differentiated Instruction

English Learners/Beginning L1
Vocabulary: Link to Visual Point out Figure 5, which shows the cyclist's instantaneous speed and average speed. Read the caption aloud for students. Ask: **What is this cyclist's average speed?** *(15 km/h)* **What is this cyclist's instantaneous speed?** *(22 km/h)* **learning modality: visual**

English Learners/Intermediate L2
Vocabulary: Link to Visual Have students examine Figure 5 and read the caption. Then have students write a sentence comparing the average and instantaneous speed of the cyclists. Ask for volunteers to read their sentences aloud. **learning modality: verbal**

Monitor Progress _____ L2

Skills Check Have students find the speed of an asteroid that travels 4,500 km in 60 s. *(4,500 km ÷ 60 s = 75 km/s)*

Answers
Figure 5 The instantaneous speed and the average speed are different because they are determined using different values of time. Instantaneous speed is calculated using a small instant in time. Average speed is calculated using a longer period of time.

 Reading Checkpoint Average speed = total distance ÷ total time

Describing Velocity

Teach Key Concepts L2

Speed and Direction

Focus Tell students that velocity is speed in a given direction.

Teach Write *25 km/h westward* on the board. Ask: **What is the speed of this object's motion?** *(25 km/h)* **What is the direction of this object's motion?** *(Westward)* Point out that a velocity has a speed and a direction.

Apply Ask: **Why is the phrase on the board a velocity?** *(Because it has both speed and direction)* **learning modality: visual**

DISCOVERY CHANNEL SCHOOL
Video Field Trip

Motion

Show the Video Field Trip to let students experience how average speed and acceleration are related. Discussion question: **What is acceleration?** *(Sample answer: The change in speed over time.)*

Lab zone Teacher **Demo** L2

Tracking Hurricanes

Materials hurricane-tracking charts from the local weather service

Time 10 minutes

Focus Discuss weather forecasts for the coming week that students may have seen in a newspaper or on TV.

Teach Show the hurricane charts. Have the students discuss the importance of both speed and direction in predicting the path of a hurricane.

Apply Ask: **Why is it important for weather forecasters to predict the velocity of a hurricane, rather than only its speed?** *(Sample answer: The path of a hurricane is determined by both its speed and direction.)* **learning modality: visual**

DISCOVERY CHANNEL SCHOOL

Motion

Video Preview
▶ Video Field Trip
Video Assessment

Describing Velocity

Knowing the speed at which something travels does not tell you everything about its motion. To describe an object's motion completely, you need to know the direction of its motion. For example, suppose you hear that a thunderstorm is traveling at a speed of 25 km/h. Should you prepare for the storm? That depends on the direction of the storm's motion. Because storms usually travel from west to east in the United States, you need not worry if you live to the west of the storm. But if you live to the east of the storm, take cover.

When you know both the speed and direction of an object's motion, you know the velocity of the object. Speed in a given direction is called **velocity.** You know the velocity of the storm when you know that it is moving 25 km/h eastward.

• Tech & Design in History •

The Speed of Transportation
The speed with which people can travel from one place to another has increased over the years.

**1908
Ford Model T
Mass-Produced**
Between 1908 and 1927, over 15 million of these automobiles were sold. The Model T had a top speed of 65 km/h.

**1818
National Road Constructed**
The speed of transportation has been limited largely by the quality of roadways. The U.S. government paid for the construction of a highway named the Cumberland Road. It ran from Cumberland, Maryland, to Wheeling, in present-day West Virginia. Travel by horse and carriage on the roadway was at a speed of about 11 km/h.

**1885
Benz Tricycle Car Introduced**
This odd-looking vehicle was the first internal combustion (gasoline-powered) automobile sold to the public. Although it is an ancestor of the modern automobile, its top speed was only about 15 km/h—not much faster than a horse-drawn carriage.

| 1800 | 1850 | 1900 |

Background

Facts and Figures Many people in America commute to work daily. Between 75% and 80% drive alone in an automobile, and about 10% use an automobile in a carpool. Slightly less than 5% of Americans use public transportation (buses, streetcars, subways, and elevated trains) for their commute to work. About 4% of Americans walk or ride a bicycle to get to their jobs. Slightly less than 3% of Americans work from their home and do not commute.

At times, describing the velocity of moving objects can be very important. For example, air traffic controllers must keep close track of the velocities of the aircraft under their control. These velocities continually change as airplanes move overhead and on the runways. An error in determining a velocity, either in speed or in direction, could lead to a collision.

Velocity is also important to airplane pilots. For example, stunt pilots make spectacular use of their control over the velocity of their aircrafts. To avoid colliding with other aircraft, these skilled pilots must have precise control of both their speed and direction. Stunt pilots use this control to stay in close formation while flying graceful maneuvers at high speed.

 Reading Checkpoint What is velocity?

Focus Review each item along the timeline with students.

Teach Point out the speeds at which each of the vehicles traveled. Ask: **How do you think improvements in transportation affected the lives of people at that time?** *(Sample answer: They were able to travel farther to find a job, get supplies, or visit relatives.)* **What do you think are some negative effects of widespread rapid transportation?** *(Sample answer: Increased pollution and accidents)*

Writing in Science

Writing Mode Research and write

Scoring Rubric

4 Exceeds criteria; includes a well-written advertisement with detailed information

3 Meet criteria

2 Advertisement is brief and/or not thoroughly researched

1 Advertisement is incomplete and/or includes numerous errors

Students can save their writing in their portfolio.

 Portfolio

Writing in Science

Research and Write What styles of automobile were most popular during the 1950s, 1960s, and 1970s? Were sedans, convertibles, station wagons, or sports cars the bestsellers? Choose an era and research automobiles of that time. Then write an advertisement for one particular style of car. Be sure to include information from your research.

1934 Zephyr Introduced

The first diesel passenger train in the United States was the *Zephyr*. The *Zephyr* set a long-distance record, traveling from Denver to Chicago at an average speed of 125 km/h for more than 1,600 km.

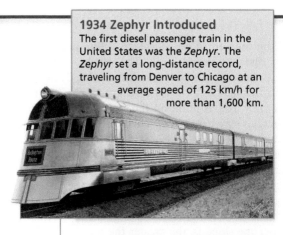

1956 Interstate Highway System Established

The passage of the Federal-Aid Highway Act established the Highway Trust Fund. This act allowed the construction of the Interstate and Defense Highways. Nonstop transcontinental auto travel became possible. Speed limits in many parts of the system were more than 100 km/h.

2003 Maglev in Motion

The first commercial application of high-speed maglev (magnetic levitation) was unveiled in Shanghai, China. During the 30-km trip from Pudong International Airport to Shanghaiës financial district, the train operates at a top speed of 430 km/h, reducing commuting time from 45 minutes to just 8 minutes.

1950   2000   2050

Chapter 1 M ◆ 13

Differentiated Instruction

Special Needs   **L1**

Classifying Organize students into small groups. Have students make a poster that includes pictures or drawings of various types of transportation. The pictures can be classified as "types of transportation used today" and "types of transportation used in the past." Have students indicate which group moves at a greater speed. **learning modality: visual**

Gifted and Talented   **L3**

Communicating Have students research the changes in highway speed limits that have occurred from the 1950's through the present. Students should relate changes in speed limits to changes in automotive technology. Students can report their findings to the class. **learning modality: verbal**

Monitor Progress _____ **L2**

Writing Have students compare the terms *speed* and *velocity*.

Answer

 Reading Checkpoint Velocity is speed in a given direction.

Graphing Motion

Teach Key Concepts
Distance Against Time

Focus Tell students that an object's motion can be shown on a line graph. Distance and time are the two variables shown on a motion graph.

Teach Direct students' attention to Figure 6. Ask: **In the first seven minutes of day 1, does the jogger move at a constant speed? How do you know?** *(Sample answer: Yes; because the graph is a straight line, I can tell that the jogger traveled the same distance in each time interval.)*

Apply Ask: **What would the graph look like if the jogger ran at a constant rate, but much slower than the jogger on Day 1?** *(The graph would be a straight line, but its slope would be less steep.)* **learning modality: logical/mathematical**

 **Teaching Resources**

• Transparencies M2, M3

Go Online
active art

For: Graphing Motion activity
Visit: PHSchool.com
Web Code: cgp-3011

Students can interact with the distance-versus-time graphs online.

Lab zone Build **Inquiry**

Motion Graphs

Materials graph paper, masking tape, measuring tape, pencils, stopwatch

Time 15 minutes

Focus Draw students' attention to the motion graphs in the text. Remind students that to graph motion, time and distance traveled are measured.

Teach Tell students they will be making a motion graph. Students can work in small groups or as a class. Have students mark a starting line in the hallway or outdoors. Then have a student start at the line and walk at a normal pace. Have another student mark with tape the distance traveled at 30-second intervals for a total of 2 minutes. Have students measure the distance traveled during each time period, and use their data to make a motion graph.

Go Online
active art

For: Graphing Motion activity
Visit: PHSchool.com
Web Code: cgp-3011

FIGURE 6
Graphing Motion

Distance-versus-time graphs can be used to analyze motion. On the jogger's first day of training, her speed is the same at every point. On the second day of training, her speed varies. Reading Graphs *On the first day, how far does the jogger run in 5 minutes?*

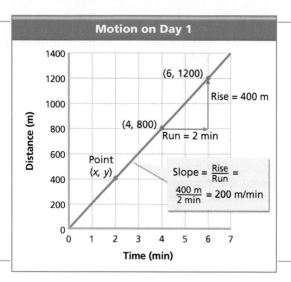

Motion on Day 1

Slope $= \dfrac{\text{Rise}}{\text{Run}} = \dfrac{400 \text{ m}}{2 \text{ min}} = 200$ m/min

Graphing Motion

You can show the motion of an object on a line graph in which you plot distance versus time. The graphs you see in Figure 6 are distance-versus-time motion graphs. Time is shown on the horizontal axis, or *x*-axis. Distance is shown on the vertical axis, or *y*-axis. A point on the line represents the distance an object has traveled at a particular time. The *x* value of the point is time, and the *y* value is distance.

The steepness of a line on a graph is called **slope.** The slope tells you how fast one variable changes in relation to the other variable in the graph. In other words, slope tells you the rate of change. Since speed is the rate that distance changes in relation to time, the slope of a distance-versus-time graph represents speed. The steeper the slope is, the greater the speed. A constant slope represents motion at constant speed.

Calculating Slope You can calculate the slope of a line by dividing the rise by the run. The rise is the vertical difference between any two points on the line. The run is the horizontal difference between the same two points.

$$\text{Slope} = \frac{\text{Rise}}{\text{Run}}$$

In Figure 6, using the points shown, the rise is 400 meters and the run is 2 minutes. To find the slope, you divide 400 meters by 2 minutes. The slope is 200 meters per minute.

Reading Checkpoint What is the slope of a graph?

14 ◆ M

Apply Ask: **On a motion graph, how can you tell if the student took a 30-second break?** *(The line for that time period would be flat.)* **learning modality: logical/ mathematical**

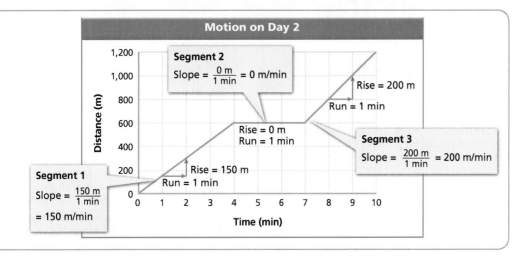

Motion on Day 2

Segment 2
$$\text{Slope} = \frac{0\ m}{1\ min} = 0\ m/min$$

Rise = 200 m
Run = 1 min

Rise = 0 m
Run = 1 min

Segment 3
$$\text{Slope} = \frac{200\ m}{1\ min} = 200\ m/min$$

Rise = 150 m
Run = 1 min

Segment 1
$$\text{Slope} = \frac{150\ m}{1\ min}$$
$$= 150\ m/min$$

Distance (m) (vertical axis): 0, 200, 400, 600, 800, 1,000, 1,200

Time (min) (horizontal axis): 0, 1, 2, 3, 4, 5, 6, 7, 8, 9, 10

Different Slopes Most moving objects do not travel at a constant speed. The graph above shows a jogger's motion on her second day. The line is divided into three segments. The slope of each segment is different. From the steepness of the slopes you can tell that the jogger ran the fastest during the third segment. The horizontal line in the second segment shows that the jogger's distance did not change at all.

Section 1 Assessment

↺ **Target Reading Skill**

Using Prior Knowledge Review your graphic organizer and revise it based on what you just learned about motion.

Reviewing Key Concepts

1. a. Reviewing How do you know if an object is moving?
   b. Explaining Why is it important to know if your reference point is moving?
   c. Applying Concepts Suppose you are riding in a car. Describe your motion relative to the car, the road, and the sun.

2. a. Defining What is speed?
   b. Describing What do you know about the motion of an object that has an average speed of 1 m/s?
   c. Comparing and Contrasting What is the difference between speed and velocity?

3. a. Identifying What does the slope of a distance-versus-time graph show you about the motion of an object?
   b. Calculating The rise of a line on a distance-versus-time graph is 600 m and the run is 3 minutes. What is the slope of the line?

Math Practice

This week at swim practice, Jamie swam a total of 1,500 m, while Ellie swam 1.6 km.

4. Converting Units Convert Ellie's distance to meters. Who swam the greater distance: Jamie or Ellie?

5. Converting Units How many kilometers did Jamie swim?

Chapter 1 M ◆ 15

Math Practice

Math Skill Converting units

Answers
4. Ellie's distance: 1.6 km × 1,000 m/1 km = 1,600 m; Ellie swam farther than Jamie.
5. 1.5 km

Lab zone Chapter **Project**

Keep Students on Track Provide a model for students of how to record the data from the project. You may want to model how to make the measurements, how to construct a data table, and how to perform the required calculations. Instruct students to choose the best units for each speed measurement.

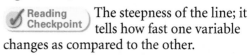
M ● 15

Inclined to Roll L2

Prepare for Inquiry

Key Concept
The steepness of a ramp affects the speed at which an object moves after rolling off of it.

Skills Objectives
After this lab, students will be able to
- calculate speed using time and distance
- measure the effect of an incline on speed
- graph average speed versus the angle of the ramp

 Prep Time 1 hour
Class Time 40 minutes

Advance Planning
Teach or review the skill of measuring, found in the Skills Handbook. Obtain 4 ft × 8 ft sheets of 1/2-in plywood or pegboard, and have them cut crosswise into six ramps, each 16 in. wide. This lab requires plenty of space, and may be done outside or in a gym.

Alternative Materials
Students can share skateboards or use other four-wheeled toys. Instead of using protractors, students can measure the height of the ramp. This measurement can be used instead of the angle to measure ramp incline.

Safety
Tell students to be careful when carrying boards. Tell students not to stand on the skateboards or roll them at other people. Review the safety guidelines in Appendix A.

All in One Teaching Resources
- Lab Worksheet: *Inclined to Roll*

Guide Inquiry

Invitation
Have students predict results. Ask: **Have you ever ridden a bicycle down a hill?** (*Most students will say yes.*) **How did the incline of the hill affect your average speed?** (*Sample answer: Speed is faster after a steeper hill.*)

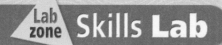
Inclined to Roll

Go Online
PHSchool.com

For: Data sharing
Visit: PHSchool.com
Web Code: cgd-3012

Problem
How does the steepness of a ramp affect how fast an object rolling off it moves across the floor?

Skills Focus
measuring, calculating, graphing

Materials
- skateboard • meter stick • protractor
- masking tape • flat board, about 1.5 m long
- small piece of sturdy cardboard
- supports to prop up the board (books, boxes)
- two stopwatches

Procedure
1. In your notebook, make a data table like the one below. Include space for five angles.
2. Lay the board flat on the floor. Using masking tape, mark a starting line in the middle of the board. Mark a finish line on the floor 1.5 m beyond one end of the board. Place a barrier after the finish line.
3. Prop up the other end of the board to make a slight incline. Use a protractor to measure the angle that the board makes with the ground. Record the angle in your data table.
4. Working in groups of three, have one person hold the skateboard so that its front wheels are even with the starting line. As the holder releases the skateboard, the other two students should start their stopwatches.
5. One timer should stop his or her stopwatch when the front wheels of the skateboard reach the end of the incline.
6. The second timer should stop his or her stopwatch when the front wheels reach the finish line. Record the times in your data table in the columns labeled Time 1 and Time 2.
7. Repeat Steps 4–6 two more times. If your results for the three times aren't within 0.2 second of one another, carry out more trials.

Data Table							
Angle (degrees)	Trial Number	Time 1 (to bottom) (s)	Time 2 (to finish) (s)	Avg Time 1 (s)	Avg Time 2 (s)	Avg Time 2 − Avg Time 1 (s)	Avg Speed (m/s)
	1						
	2						
	3						
	1						
	2						
	3						
	1						
	2						

Introduce the Procedure
Refer students to the photo illustrating the experimental setup. Show students how to use a stopwatch. Have students roll the skateboard down the ramp a few times to practice using the stopwatches.

Troubleshooting the Experiment
- Make sure the students begin with a very small incline.
- Make sure the skateboard rolls smoothly at the transition from the ramp to the ground.

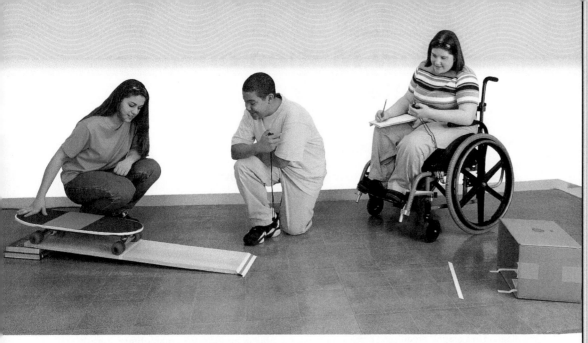

8. Repeat Steps 3–7 four more times, making the ramp gradually steeper each time.

9. For each angle of the incline, complete the following calculations and record them in your data table.
   a. Find the average time the skateboard takes to get to the bottom of the ramp (Time 1).
   b. Find the average time the skateboard takes to get to the finish line (Time 2).
   c. Subtract the average of Time 1 from the average of Time 2.

Analyze and Conclude

1. **Calculating** How can you find the average speed of the skateboard across the floor for each angle of the incline? Determine the average speed for each angle and record it in your data table.

2. **Classifying** Which is your manipulated variable and which is your responding variable in this experiment? Explain. (For a discussion of manipulated and responding variables, see the Skills Handbook.)

3. **Graphing** On a graph, plot the average speed of the skateboard (on the *y*-axis) against the angle of the ramp (on the *x*-axis).

4. **Drawing Conclusions** What does your graph show about the relationship between the skateboard's speed and the angle of the ramp?

5. **Measuring** If your measurements for distance, time, or angle were inaccurate, how would your results have been affected?

6. **Communicating** Do you think your method of timing was accurate? Did the timers start and stop their stopwatches exactly at the appropriate points? How could the accuracy of the timing be improved? Write a brief procedure for your method.

Design an Experiment

A truck driver transporting new cars needs to roll the cars off the truck. You offer to design a ramp to help with the task. What measurements would you make that might be useful? Design an experiment to test your ideas. *Obtain your teacher's permission before carrying out your investigation.*

Expected Outcome
As the ramp incline increases, Average Time 1 will decrease. As the ramp incline increases, the time taken to reach the finish line will decrease.

Analyze and Conclude
1. Average speed on floor is distance traveled on floor (from bottom of ramp to finish line, 1.5 m) divided by time on floor (Average time 2 − Average time 1).

2. Manipulated variable—ramp incline; responding variable—average speed. You vary the ramp incline to determine its relationship to the skateboard's average speed.

3. Graphs should show an increase in average speed when the angle of the ramp increases.

4. Speed increases as ramp incline angle increases.

5. Inaccurate measurements for distance, time, or angle would have caused average speeds to be inaccurate, too.

6. Sample answer: Yes, I think our method of measurement is accurate. To improve accuracy several students could time a particular run, and then the average time could be used. Alternatively, you could employ an electronic timing device, such as the ones used for downhill skiing and other athletic events.

Go Online
PHSchool.com

For: Data Sharing
Visit: PHSchool.com
Web Code: cgd-3012

Students can go online to pool and analyze their data with students nationwide.

Extend Inquiry

Design an Experiment To make the ramp wide enough and strong enough, students need to know the weights of the cars and the distances between the left and right wheels.

Objectives
After this lesson, students will be able to

M.1.2.1 Describe how the theory of plate tectonics explains the movement of Earth's landmasses.

M.1.2.2 Calculate the speed at which Earth's plates move.

Target Reading Skill

Previewing Visuals Explain that looking at the visuals before they read helps students activate prior knowledge and predict what they are about to read.

Answers
Sample questions and answers:
How have the positions of the continents changed over time? (*The distance between the continents has increased.*) **What causes Earth's plates to move?** (*Slow-moving currents beneath Earth's outer layer cause the plates to move.*)

All in One Teaching Resources

• Transparency M4

Preteach

Build Background Knowledge   L2
The Shape of Earth's Continents
Show students a map of the Atlantic Ocean that includes the coastlines of North and South America, Europe, and Africa. Ask: **What do you observe about the coastlines of South America and Africa?** (*Sample answer: They could fit together like puzzle pieces.*)

Reading Preview

Key Concepts
• How does the theory of plate tectonics explain the movement of Earth's landmasses?
• How fast do Earth's plates move?

Key Terms
• plate • theory of plate tectonics

Target Reading Skill
Previewing Visuals Before you read, preview Figure 8. Then write two questions that you have about the diagram in a graphic organizer like the one below. As you read, answer your questions.

Motion of the Continents

Q.	Why do the continents move over time?
A.	
Q.	

Lab zone Discover Activity

How Slow Can It Flow?
1. Put a spoonful of honey on a plate.
2. Place a piece of tape 4 cm from the bottom edge of the honey.
3. Lift one side of the plate just high enough that the honey starts to flow.
4. Reduce the plate's angle until the honey barely moves. Prop up the plate at this angle.
5. Time how long the honey takes to reach the tape. Calculate the speed of the honey.

Think It Over
Forming Operational Definitions When an object doesn't appear to be moving at first glance, how can you tell if it is?

Have you ever noticed that Earth's landmasses resemble pieces of a giant jigsaw puzzle? It's true. The east coast of South America, for example, would fit nicely into the west coast of Africa. The Arabian Peninsula would fit fairly well with the northeastern coast of Africa. Since the 1600s, people have wondered why Earth's landmasses look as if they would fit together. After all, land can't move. Or can it?

These landmasses would fit fairly well if they were pushed together like puzzle pieces. ▶

Lab zone Discover Activity

Skills Focus Forming operational definitions   L1

Materials books or blocks, damp cloths or paper towels, honey, masking tape, metric ruler, plate, spoon, stopwatch or a clock with a second hand

Time 15 minutes

Tips Refrigerate the honey if possible. Students can use books or blocks to prop up the plate. Use damp cloths or paper towels for spills. Write the equation for calculating speed on the board: *Speed = Distance ÷ Time.* Ask: **What distance will you use in the calculation?** (*4 cm*)

Think It Over You can tell an object is moving by observing that it changes position relative to a stationary reference point over a period of time.

Earth's Plates

Earth's rocky outer layer consists of pieces that fit together like a jigsaw puzzle. This outer layer is made of more than a dozen major pieces called **plates.** The boundaries between the plates are cracks in Earth's outer layer. As you can see in Figure 7, plate boundaries do not always lie along the edges of continents. The eastern boundary of the North American plate, for example, lies under the Atlantic Ocean. Many plates have both continents and oceans on them.

The Theory of Plate Tectonics Scientists use the concept of plates to explain how landmasses have changed over time. The **theory of plate tectonics** states that Earth's plates move slowly in various directions. Some plates slowly pull away from each other, some plates push toward each other, and some plates slide past each other. **According to the theory of plate tectonics, Earth's landmasses have changed position over time because they are part of plates that are slowly moving.**

Why Do Earth's Plates Move? Have you ever heated a pot of water and watched what happens? The liquid at the bottom gets hotter faster. The hotter liquid rises upward. At the surface it cools, and then hotter water moving upward pushes it aside. The same type of churning motion drives the movement of Earth's plates.

Underneath Earth's rigid plates is somewhat softer rock that moves similarly to boiling water. Scientists think that heat deep inside Earth causes material there to slowly rise upward. As more heated material rises, it pushes aside cooler material at the top of the layer. Eventually the cooler material sinks downward. The rising and sinking of material creates a slow-moving current beneath Earth's outer layer. It is this current that causes Earth's plates to move.

 What causes Earth's plates to move?

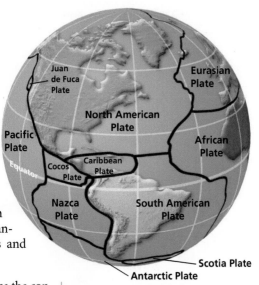

FIGURE 7
Earth's Plates
The black outlines show the boundaries of some of Earth's plates.
Interpreting Maps *Which plates border the Nazca plate?*

Earth's Plates

Teach Key Concepts L2
Earth's Plates in Motion

Focus Tell students to look at Figure 8. Have them note the change in position of the land masses over time.

Teach Point out the past movements of Earth's plates. Remind students that Earth's plates are moving now, and will continue to move in the future. Tell students that slow-moving currents below Earth's outer layer cause the plates to move.

Apply Ask: **Do you think the distance between South America and Africa will increase or decrease in the next 100 years? Why?** *(Sample answer: I think it will increase, because the distance between them has been increasing for millions of years.)* **learning modality: visual**

Independent Practice L2

 **Teaching Resources**
• Guided Reading and Study Worksheet: *Slow Motion on Planet Earth*

 **Student Edition on Audio CD**

Differentiated Instruction

Special Needs L1
Classifying Motion Have students listen to the **Student Edition on Audio CD** for this section. Remind them that Earth's plates move, even though they move too slowly for us to notice. Then have students prepare a poster that shows or lists objects in two categories: those that move quickly and those that move slowly. **learning modality: visual**

Gifted and Talented L3
Modeling Earth's Plates Challenge students to research the location of Earth's major plates. Then have students use materials of their choosing to make a three-dimensional model of Earth showing the location of Earth's major plates. Students can present their completed models to the class. **learning modality: visual**

Monitor Progress L2

Skills Check Have students calculate the distance that a plate will move in 8 million years if it moves at a speed of 4 cm/year. (*32,000,000 cm*)

Answers
Figure 7 The Cocos plate, the South American plate, the Antarctic plate, the Pacific plate, and the Caribbean plate

 A slow-moving current of material under Earth's outer layer causes Earth's plates to move.

M ● 19

Plate Movement

Teach Key Concepts L2

Rates of Plate Movement

Focus Remind students that Earth's plates usually move so slowly that they could not notice the motion.

Teach Point out the equation in the text. Remind student that many of Earth's plates move even more slowly than the rate shown in the text.

Apply Ask: In order for scientists to predict the future location of plates, what two things do they need to know about a plate's motion? *(Speed and direction)* **learning modality: logical/mathematical**

Go Online
active art

For: Continental Drift activity
Visit: PHSchool.com
Web Code: cfp-1015

Students can interact with art showing the movement of Earth's landmasses through time.

 **Teaching Resources**

• Transparency M5

Lab zone Build **Inquiry** L2

Modeling Plate Motion

Materials masking tape, meter stick

Time 10 minutes

Focus Tell students that Earth's plates move very slowly.

Teach For this activity, have students use the rate of 5 cm/year for plate movement. Have students work in pairs to use masking tape to mark on the floor the distance moved by a plate in one year *(5 cm)* and 100 years *(500 cm)*.

Apply Ask: Why are the changes in the location of Earth's plates shown over periods of millions of years? *(Sample: It takes many years for noticeable changes to occur.)* **learning modality: kinesthetic**

---

225 Million Years Ago

180-200 Million Years Ago

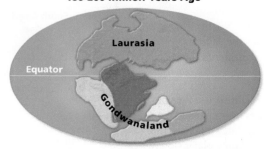

135 Million Years Ago

Present Day

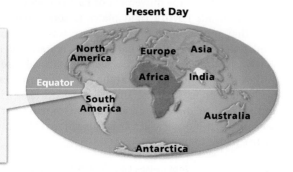

FIGURE 8
Motion of the Continents
The shapes and positions of Earth's continents have changed greatly over time and will continue to change in the future. *Interpreting Maps Locate Australia on the map. How does its position change over time?*

Go Online
active art

For: Continental Drift activity
Visit: PHSchool.com
Web Code: cfp-1015

Scientists have found that South America is moving 10 cm west per year. You can use this speed to predict how far the continent will move in 500 years.

Distance = Speed × Time

Distance = $\frac{10 \text{ cm}}{1 \text{ year}}$ × 500 years = 5,000 cm

South America will move 5,000 cm, or 50 m, in the next 500 years.

Plate Movement

Unless you have experienced an earthquake, you have probably never felt Earth's plates moving. Why not? After all, you live on one of Earth's plates. One reason may be that they move so slowly. **Some plates move at a rate of several centimeters each year. Others move only a few millimeters per year.**

Knowing the average speed of Earth's plates allows scientists to explain how Earth's surface has changed over time. It also helps them predict future changes. Figure 8 shows how scientists think the continents may have looked in the past.

Suppose you study the motion of a plate. You find that the plate moved a distance of 5 centimeters in one year. So, the speed of the plate is 5 cm/yr. You can use this speed to predict how far the plate will move in 1,000 years. Start by rearranging the speed formula to find the distance. Then calculate distance.

$$\text{Distance} = \text{Speed} \times \text{Time}$$

$$\text{Distance} = \frac{5 \text{ cm}}{1 \text{ yr}} \times 1{,}000 \text{ yr} = 5{,}000 \text{ cm}$$

In 1,000 years, the plate will move 5,000 centimeters. You could probably walk the same distance in 30 seconds!

Reading Checkpoint Why are scientists interested in the average speed of Earth's plates?

Section 2 Assessment

Target Reading Strategy Previewing Visuals
Refer to your questions and answers about Figure 8 to help you answer Question 1 below.

Reviewing Key Concepts

1. **a.** Defining What theory explains the movement of pieces of Earth's surface?
   b. Explaining Why do Earth's plates move?
   c. Interpreting Maps Use the map in Figure 7 to determine which plate contains most of the United States.
2. **a.** Reviewing In general, at what speed do Earth's plates move?
   b. Calculating A plate moves at a speed of 45 mm/yr. How far will the plate move in 100 years?
   c. Predicting Figure 8 shows that North America and Europe are moving apart from each other. In your lifetime, how will this affect the time it takes to travel between the two continents?

Lab zone **At-Home Activity**

Fingernail Growth Have a family member measure in millimeters the length of the white part of one fingernail. Record the result and which finger you used. In exactly three weeks, again measure the white part of the same fingernail. Then calculate the speed, in millimeters per day, at which the fingernail grew. Discuss with your family member how your results compare with the typical speed of Earth's plates.

Objectives

After the lesson, students will be able to

M.1.3.1 Describe the motion of an object as it accelerates.

M.1.3.2 Calculate acceleration.

M.1.3.3 Describe what graphs are used to analyze the motion of an accelerating object.

Target Reading Skill

Identifying Main Ideas Explain that identifying main ideas and details helps students sort the facts from the information into groups. Each group can have a main topic, subtopics, and details.

Answers

Sample answers:

Main Idea: In science acceleration refers to…

Detail: Increasing speed

Detail: Decreasing speed

Detail: Changing direction

All in One Teaching Resources

• Transparency M6

Preteach

Build Background Knowledge   L2

Experience With Acceleration

Ask a volunteer to blow up a balloon and hold the opening firmly shut. Ask: **How would you describe the motion of the balloon.** *(It is not moving.)* **What could you do to make the balloon move?** *(Release it)* Have the volunteer release the balloon away from other students. Ask: **Describe any changes in the speed or direction as the balloon moved.** *(Sample: It changed direction and speed constantly until it stopped.)* Tell students that this section explores changing speed and direction.

Section 3 Acceleration

Reading Preview

Key Concepts

• What kind of motion does acceleration refer to?
• How is acceleration calculated?
• What graphs can be used to analyze the motion of an accelerating object?

Key Term

• acceleration

Target Reading Skill

Identifying Main Ideas As you read the What Is Acceleration? section, write the main idea in a graphic organizer like the one below. Then write three supporting details that give examples of the main idea.

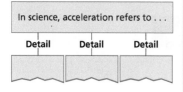

Main Idea

In science, acceleration refers to . . .

Detail	Detail	Detail

Lab zone Discover Activity

Will You Hurry Up?

1. Measure 10 meters in an open area. Mark the distance with masking tape.
2. Walk the 10 meters in such a way that you keep moving faster throughout the entire distance. Have a partner time you.
3. Repeat Step 2, walking the 10 meters in less time than you did before. Then try it again, this time walking the distance in twice the time as the first. Remember to keep speeding up throughout the entire 10 meters.

Think It Over

Inferring How is the change in your speed related to the time in which you walk the 10-meter course?

The pitcher throws. The ball speeds toward the batter. Off the bat it goes. It's going, going, gone! A home run!

Before landing, the ball went through several changes in motion. It sped up in the pitcher's hand, and lost speed as it traveled toward the batter. The ball stopped when it hit the bat, changed direction, sped up again, and eventually slowed down. Most examples of motion involve similar changes. In fact, rarely does any object's motion stay the same for very long.

What Is Acceleration?

Suppose you are a passenger in a car stopped at a red light. When the light changes to green, the driver steps on the accelerator. As a result, the car speeds up, or accelerates. In everyday language, *acceleration* means "the process of speeding up."

Acceleration has a more precise definition in science. Scientists define **acceleration** as the rate at which velocity changes. Recall that velocity describes both the speed and direction of an object. A change in velocity can involve a change in either speed or direction—or both. **In science, acceleration refers to increasing speed, decreasing speed, or changing direction.**

Lab zone Discover Activity

Skills Focus Inferring   L1

Materials masking tape, meter stick, stopwatch

Time 15 minutes

Tips This activity should be done in an open area. When students begin walking, suggest that they walk very slowly, then gradually increase their speed until they are moving as fast as they can without running. Students should not run during this activity.

Think About It The faster you speed up, the less time it takes to walk the course.

A softball accelerates when it is thrown.

A softball changes direction when it is hit.

A softball ▶ decelerates when it is caught.

Increasing Speed Whenever an object's speed increases, the object accelerates. A softball accelerates when the pitcher throws it, and again when a bat hits it. A car that begins to move from a stopped position or speeds up to pass another car is accelerating. People can accelerate too. For example, you accelerate when you coast down a hill on your bike.

Decreasing Speed Just as objects can speed up, they can also slow down. This change in speed is sometimes called deceleration, or negative acceleration. For example, a softball decelerates when it lands in a fielder's mitt. A car decelerates when it stops at a red light. A water skier decelerates when the boat stops pulling.

Changing Direction Even an object that is traveling at a constant speed can be accelerating. Recall that acceleration can be a change in direction as well as a change in speed. Therefore, a car accelerates as it follows a gentle curve in the road or changes lanes. Runners accelerate as they round the curve in a track. A softball accelerates when it changes direction as it is hit.

Many objects continuously change direction without changing speed. The simplest example of this type of motion is circular motion, or motion along a circular path. For example, the seats on a Ferris wheel accelerate because they move in a circle.

 Reading Checkpoint How can a car be accelerating if its speed is constant at 65 km/h?

FIGURE 9
Acceleration
A softball experiences acceleration when it is thrown, caught, and hit. Classifying *What change in motion occurs in each example?*

Differentiated Instruction

English Learners/Beginning Comprehension: Key Concept L1 Read aloud the boldface sentence about acceleration. Ask volunteers to model by walking one way in which acceleration can occur. Students should model acceleration by speeding up, slowing down, or changing direction while walking. **learning modality: kinesthetic**

English Learners/Intermediate Comprehension: Key Concepts L2 On the board rewrite the boldface sentence about acceleration into individual sentences that each tells one way an object can accelerate. Then have students construct a concept circle (cluster diagram) with "acceleration" in the center and the three ways an object can accelerate connected to the center by lines. **learning modality: visual**

What Is Acceleration?

Teach Key Concepts L2
Changing Velocity

Focus Tell students in science acceleration refers to increasing speed, decreasing speed, or changing direction.

Teach Write on the board: *Speeding up, Slowing down,* and *Changing direction.* Challenge students to give examples of each. Record students' responses on the board.

Apply Ask: **What do all of these objects have in common?** *(They are all accelerating.)* **learning modality: verbal**

Independent Practice L2

All in One Teaching Resources
• Guided Reading and Study Worksheet: *Acceleration*

◉ Student Edition on Audio CD

▪ Address Misconceptions L2
Defining Acceleration

Focus Many students think that acceleration means only speeding up. Explain that in science, acceleration also means slowing down or changing direction.

Teach Write these two sentences on the board: *When you step on the gas, the car accelerates. When you step on the brake, the car accelerates.* Ask: **According to the scientific meaning of acceleration, which of these sentences is true?** *(Both)*

Apply Ask: **What are three ways a car can accelerate.** *(Slow down, speed up, or change direction)* **learning modality: verbal**

Monitor Progress _____ L2

Drawing Have students sketch three ways an object can accelerate. *(Correct sketches will show speeding up, slowing down, and changing direction)*

Students can save their drawings in their portfolios. **Portfolio**

Answers
Figure 9 Thrown—ball accelerates as it is thrown. Hit—ball changes direction. Caught—ball decelerates

✔ **Reading Checkpoint** Even if a car's speed is steady, it can accelerate by changing direction.

Calculating Acceleration

Teach Key Concepts L2
The Formula for Acceleration

Focus Tell students that acceleration can be calculated. To find the acceleration of an object moving in a straight line, you need to know the final speed, initial speed, and the time.

Teach Explain that for an object moving in a straight line, the acceleration tells how the speed changes for each time period. Point out the formula for calculating acceleration in the text.

Apply Ask: **What number should you use for the initial speed if an object starts out at rest?** *(0 m/s)* **learning modality: logical/mathematical**

Help Students Read L1

Outlining Refer to the Content Refresher for this chapter, which provides the guidelines for the Outlining strategy. Have students read the section *Acceleration*. Have students create an outline for the section. Students can use the headings in the text as the major divisions in their outline. As they read, they can add the boldface sentences, key terms, and other details to their outline.

| 0.0s | 1.0s | | 2.0s | | 3.0s |

0 m/s   8 m/s   16 m/s   24 m/s

FIGURE 10
Analyzing Acceleration
The speed of the airplane above increases by the same amount each second. Interpreting Diagrams *How does the distance change in each second?*

Calculating Acceleration

Acceleration describes the rate at which velocity changes. If an object is not changing direction, you can describe its acceleration as the rate at which its speed changes. **To determine the acceleration of an object moving in a straight line, you must calculate the change in speed per unit of time.** This is summarized by the following formula.

$$\text{Acceleration} = \frac{\text{Final speed} - \text{Initial speed}}{\text{Time}}$$

If speed is measured in meters per second (m/s) and time is measured in seconds, the SI unit of acceleration is meters per second per second, or m/s^2. Suppose speed is measured in kilometers per hour and time is measured in hours. Then the unit for acceleration is kilometers per hour per hour, or km/h^2.

To understand acceleration, imagine a small airplane moving down a runway. Figure 10 shows the airplane's motion after each of the first five seconds of its acceleration. To calculate the average acceleration of the airplane, you must first subtract the initial speed of 0 m/s from the final speed of 40 m/s. Then divide the change in speed by the time, 5 seconds.

$$\text{Acceleration} = \frac{40 \text{ m/s} - 0 \text{ m/s}}{5 \text{ s}}$$

$$\text{Acceleration} = 8 \text{ m/s}^2$$

The airplane accelerates at a rate of 8 m/s^2. This means that the airplane's speed increases by 8 m/s every second. Notice in Figure 10 that, after each second of travel, the airplane's speed is 8 m/s greater than it was the previous second.

 **Reading Checkpoint** **What must you know about an object moving in a straight line to calculate its acceleration?**

Differentiated Instruction

English Learners/Beginning L1
Vocabulary: Science Glossary
Pronounce and define aloud the following key terms for students: *speed, velocity,* and *acceleration.* Write definitions of the terms on the board. Have the students then write the terms in their science glossaries. To help remember the terms they might define the terms in their own language. **learning modality: verbal**

English Learners/Intermediate L1
Vocabulary: Science Glossary Students can expand on the science glossary activity described in the Beginning strategy by writing sentences that use the key terms. Model this activity on the board. Call on volunteers to read their sentences aloud. **learning modality: verbal**

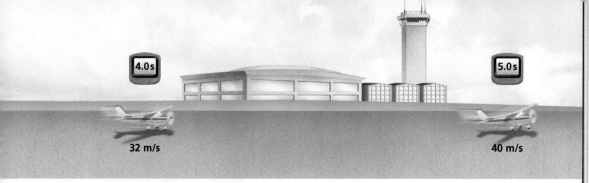

4.0 s   5.0 s

32 m/s   40 m/s

Math ▸ Sample Problem

Calculating Acceleration

As a roller coaster car starts down a slope, its speed is 4 m/s. But 3 seconds later, at the bottom, its speed is 22 m/s. What is its average acceleration?

1 **Read and Understand**
What information are you given?
  Initial speed = 4 m/s
  Final speed = 22 m/s
  Time = 3 s

2 **Plan and Solve**
What quantity are you trying to calculate?
  The average acceleration of the roller coaster car = ■

What formula contains the given quantities and the unknown quantity?

  $\text{Acceleration} = \dfrac{\text{Final speed} - \text{Initial speed}}{\text{Time}}$

Perform the calculation.

  $\text{Acceleration} = \dfrac{22 \text{ m/s} - 4 \text{ m/s}}{3 \text{ s}}$

  $\text{Acceleration} = \dfrac{18 \text{ m/s}}{3 \text{ s}}$

  $\text{Acceleration} = 6 \text{ m/s}^2$

  The roller coaster car's average acceleration is 6 m/s².

3 **Look Back and Check**
Does your answer make sense?
  The answer is reasonable. If the car's speed increases by 6 m/s each second, its speed will be 10 m/s after 1 second, 16 m/s after 2 seconds, and 22 m/s after 3 seconds.

Math ▸ Practice

1. **Calculating Acceleration** A falling raindrop accelerates from 10 m/s to 30 m/s in 2 seconds. What is the raindrop's average acceleration?
2. **Calculating Acceleration** A certain car can accelerate from rest to 27 m/s in 9 seconds. Find the car's average acceleration.

Math ▸ Sample Problem

Math Skill Calculating acceleration

Focus Tell students the formula shown in the text can be used to calculate the acceleration of an object moving in a straight line.

Teach Ask: **What happens to the speed of the car each second?** *(It increases by 6 m/s.)* **Does this make sense for a roller coaster going downhill?** *(Sample: Yes, roller coasters get faster as they go downhill.)*

Answers
1. $(30 \text{ m/s} - 10 \text{ m/s}) \div 2 \text{ seconds} = 10 \text{ m/s}^2$
2. $(27 \text{ m/s} - 0 \text{ m/s}) \div 9 \text{ s} = 27 \text{ m/s} \div 9 \text{ s} = 3 \text{ m/s}^2$

All in One Teaching Resources
• Transparency M7

Lab zone ▸ Build Inquiry   L2

Accelerating Marble

Materials marble, cardboard tubes, scissors, masking tape, books or blocks

Time 10 minutes

Safety ✂ Remind students that scissors can cut their skin. They should always direct a sharp edge away from themselves and others.

Focus Tell students they will construct a track that will allow a marble to accelerate.

Teach Have students use the cardboard tubes, tape, and books or blocks to build a track for a marble. Ask for volunteers to demonstrate how the marble will accelerate in their track.

Apply Remind students that accelerating means speeding up, slowing down, or changing direction. Ask for volunteers to demonstrate all three types of acceleration.
learning modality: kinesthetic

Monitor Progress _____ L2

Skills Check A badminton shuttlecock leaves the racquet traveling 30 m/s. It goes over the net 0.5 seconds later with a speed of 10 m/s. Calculate its average acceleration. *(−40 m/s²)*

Answers
Figure 10 The distance traveled in each second increases while the airplane is accelerating.

Reading Checkpoint If the object is moving in a straight line, you must know its change in speed over a period of time.

Graphing Acceleration

Teach Key Concepts L2

Analyzing Motion

Focus Direct the students' attention to Figures 11 and 12. Ask: **How are these graphs similar?** *(Sample answer: They both have time on the horizontal axis.)* **How are these graphs different?** *(Sample answer: One has speed on the vertical axis, the other has distance)*

Teach Direct students' attention to Figure 11. Ask: **How do you know this graph shows acceleration?** *(Sample answer: The speed changes each second.)* **How do you know the graph in Figure 12 shows acceleration?** *(Sample answer: The distance changes by a different amount over each time interval, so the object is not moving at a constant speed.)*

Apply Ask: **What would happen to the graph in Figure 11 if the acceleration were less?** *(Sample answer: The steepness, or slope, of the graph would be less.)* **learning modality: logical/mathematical**

All in One Teaching Resources

• Transparencies M8, M9

Address Misconceptions L2

Zero Acceleration

Focus Students may think that an object with zero acceleration is not moving.

Teach Explain that zero speed and zero acceleration are not the same. An object with zero speed is at rest. An object with zero acceleration is not speeding up, slowing down, or changing direction.

Apply Write on the board: Zero speed = no motion; Zero acceleration = no change in motion. Underline the word *change*. Ask: **Can an object have speed but not be accelerating?** *(Yes)* **learning modality: verbal**

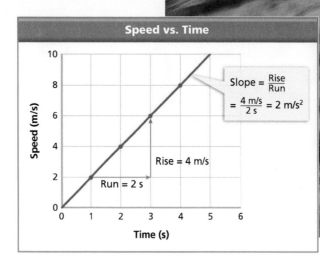

FIGURE 11
Speed-Versus-Time Graph
The slanted, straight line on this speed-versus-time graph tells you that the cyclist is accelerating at a constant rate. The slope of a speed-versus-time graph tells you the object's acceleration.
Predicting *How would the slope of the graph change if the cyclist were accelerating at a greater rate? At a lesser rate?*

Graphing Acceleration

Suppose you ride your bicycle down a long, steep hill. At the top of the hill your speed is 0 m/s. As you start down the hill, your speed increases. Each second, you move at a greater speed and travel a greater distance than the second before. During the five seconds it takes you to reach the bottom of the hill, you are an accelerating object. **You can use both a speed-versus-time graph and a distance-versus-time graph to analyze the motion of an accelerating object.**

Speed-Versus-Time Graph Figure 11 shows a speed-versus-time graph for your bicycle ride down the hill. What can you learn about your motion by analyzing this graph? First, since the line slants upward, the graph shows you that your speed was increasing. Next, since the line is straight, you can tell that your acceleration was constant. A slanted, straight line on a speed-versus-time graph means that the object is accelerating at a constant rate. You can find your acceleration by calculating the slope of the line. To calculate the slope, choose any two points on the line. Then, divide the rise by the run.

$$\text{Slope} = \frac{\text{Rise}}{\text{Run}} = \frac{8 \text{ m/s} - 4 \text{ m/s}}{4 \text{ s} - 2 \text{ s}} = \frac{4 \text{ m/s}}{2 \text{ s}}$$

$$\text{Slope} = 2 \text{ m/s}^2$$

During your bike ride, you accelerated down the hill at a constant rate of 2 m/s².

Distance-Versus-Time Graph You can represent the motion of an accelerating object with a distance-versus-time graph. Figure 12 shows a distance-versus-time graph for your bike ride. On this type of graph, a curved line means that the object is accelerating. The curved line in Figure 12 tells you that during each second, you traveled a greater distance than the second before. For example, you traveled a greater distance during the third second than you did during the first second.

The curved line in Figure 12 also tells you that during each second your speed is greater than the second before. Recall that the slope of a distance-versus-time graph is the speed of an object. From second to second, the slope of the line in Figure 12 gets steeper and steeper. Since the slope is increasing, you can conclude that the speed is also increasing. You are accelerating.

 Reading Checkpoint What does a curved line on a distance-versus-time graph tell you?

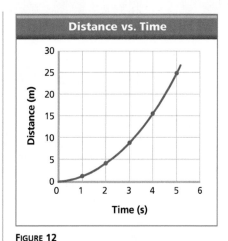

FIGURE 12
Distance-Versus-Time Graph
The curved line on this distance-versus-time graph tells you that the cyclist is accelerating.

Section 3 Assessment

Target Reading Skill Identifying Main Ideas Use information in your graphic organizer to answer Question 1 below.

Reviewing Key Concepts

1. **a. Describing** What are the three ways that an object can accelerate?
   b. Summarizing Describe how a baseball player accelerates as he runs around the bases after hitting a home run.
   c. Applying Concepts An ice skater glides around a rink at a constant speed of 2 m/s. Is the skater accelerating? Explain your answer.
2. **a. Identifying** What is the formula used to calculate the acceleration of an object moving in a straight line?
   b. Calculating A cyclist's speed changes from 0 m/s to 15 m/s in 10 seconds. What is the cyclist's average acceleration?
3. **a. Naming** What types of graphs can you use to analyze the acceleration of an object?
   b. Explaining How is an object moving if a slanted, straight line on a speed-versus-time graph represents its motion?
   c. Predicting What would a distance-versus-time graph look like for the moving object in part (b)?

Math Practice

4. **Calculating Acceleration** A downhill skier reaches the steepest part of a trail. Her speed increases from 9 m/s to 18 m/s in 3 seconds. What is her average acceleration?
5. **Calculating Acceleration** What is a race car's average acceleration if its speed changes from 0 m/s to 40 m/s in 4 seconds?

Technology Lab

Stopping on a Dime L2

Prepare for Inquiry

Key Concept
The measurement of reaction times, running speeds, and stopping distances are used to decide the location of a basketball court.

Skills Objectives
After this lab students will be able to
- calculate the total distance a student could travel after crossing an out-of-bounds line
- interpret data to determine the best location for a basketball court

 Prep Time 15 minutes
Class Time 40 minutes

Advance Planning
Reserve time and space on the school athletic field or in the gymnasium for Part 2 of the lab.

Safety
Instruct students to run in the same direction as other students. Review the safety guidelines in Appendix A.

All in One Teaching Resources
- Lab Worksheet: *Stopping on a Dime*

Guide Inquiry

Invitation
Have students think about the use of measurements and calculations to infer a safe location for a basketball court. Ask: **When you run out of bounds on a basketball court, what determines how long it takes you to stop?** (*Sample answer: Running speed*)

Introduce the Procedure
Tell students that three things determine how far past the out-of-bounds line a player will travel: maximum running speed, reaction time, and stopping distance. Tell students where running speed and stopping distance will be measured. Show where the timer will be placed. Show where the runner will begin and the direction the runner will travel. Perform a sample calculation on the board.

Troubleshooting the Procedure
Make sure students do not slow down before reaching the 25-meter mark. Be sure that the person dropping the meter stick does not inadvertently signal the person catching it.

Skills Lab

Stopping on a Dime

Problem
The school will put in a new basketball court in a small area between two buildings. Safety is an important consideration in the design of the court. What is the distance needed between an out-of-bounds line and a wall so that a player can stop before hitting the wall?

Skills Focus
calculating, interpreting data

Materials
- wooden meter stick • tape measure
- 2 stopwatches or watches with second hands

Procedure

PART 1 Reaction Time

1. Have your partner suspend a wooden meter stick, zero end down, between your thumb and index finger, as shown. Your thumb and index finger should be about 3 cm apart.
2. Your partner will drop the meter stick without giving you any warning. Try to grab it with your thumb and index finger.

Reaction Time			
Distance (cm)	Time (s)	Distance (cm)	Time (s)
15	0.175	25	0.226
16	0.181	26	0.230
17	0.186	27	0.235
18	0.192	28	0.239
19	0.197	29	0.243
20	0.202	30	0.247
21	0.207	31	0.252
22	0.212	32	0.256
23	0.217	33	0.260
24	0.221	34	0.263

3. Note the level at which you grabbed the meter stick and use the chart shown to determine your reaction time. Record the time in the class data table.
4. Reverse roles with your partner and repeat Steps 1–3.

PART 2 Stopping Distance

5. On the school field or in the gymnasium, mark off a distance of 25 m. **CAUTION:** *Be sure to remove any obstacles from the course.*
6. Have your partner time how long it takes you to run the course at full speed. After you pass the 25-m mark, come to a stop as quickly as possible and remain standing. You must not slow down before the mark.
7. Have your partner measure the distance from the 25-m mark to your final position. This is the distance you need to come to a complete stop. Enter your time and distance into the class data table.
8. Reverse roles with your partner. Enter your partner's time and distance into the class data table.

Class Data Table			
Student Name	Reaction Time (s)	Running Time (s)	Stopping Distance (m)

Analyze and Conclude

1. **Calculating** Calculate the average speed of the student who ran the 25-m course the fastest.

2. **Interpreting Data** Multiply the speed of the fastest student (calculated in Question 1) by the slowest reaction time listed in the class data table. Why would you be interested in this product?

3. **Interpreting Data** Add the distance calculated in Question 2 to the longest stopping distance in the class data table. What does this total distance represent?

4. **Drawing Conclusions** Explain why it is important to use the fastest speed, the slowest reaction time, and the longest stopping distance in your calculations.

5. **Controlling Variables** What other factors should you take into account to get results that apply to a real basketball court?

6. **Communicating** Suppose you calculate that the distance from the out-of-bounds line to the wall of the basketball court is too short for safety. Write a proposal to the school that describes the problem. In your proposal, suggest a strategy for making the court safer.

More to Explore

Visit a local playground and examine it from the viewpoint of safety. Use what you learned about stopping distance as one of your guidelines, but also try to identify other potentially unsafe conditions. Write a letter to the Department of Parks or to the officials of your town informing them of your findings.

M ◆ 29

Expected Outcome

Typical reactions time is about 0.2 s.
A typical running speed is about 5 m/s.
A typical stopping distance is about 3 m.
The safety margin should be about 4 m.

Analyze and Conclude

1. Find the student with the lowest time for running the course. Divide the distance (25 m) by their time to get the maximum running speed in m/s.

2. This calculation combines the fastest student with the slowest reaction time. In that way, multiplying the maximum running speed by the slowest reaction time gives the maximum out-of-bounds distance possible before any student tested would realize that he or she needed to stop.

3. Assuming the student in Question 2 also has the longest measured stopping distance, the total distance calculated here represents how far he or she would travel out of bounds before coming to a complete stop.

4. Sample answer: This answer represents the maximum distance it should take a student to stop, the so-called "worst-case scenario." It's highly unlikely that any one student will combine the fastest speed, the slowest reaction time, and the greatest stopping distance. In other words, all students should be able to stop in a distance that is shorter than the one calculated.

5. Sample answer: A player might go out of bounds running sideways, jumping, or stumbling. A player might not immediately realize that he or she is out of bounds. These factors might increase the distance the player travels out of bounds.

6. Sample answer: You could make the court safer by adding a wide yellow line to alert players when they are approaching the out-of-bounds line. You could also place cushions on the walls to reduce the risk of injury in collisions.

Extend Inquiry

More to Explore Students should check to make sure that there is enough distance between the out-of-bounds line and any obstructions. Students should note that basketball posts are close to the court and should be wrapped in foam. Students might also look for other unsafe conditions such as cracks in the playing surface.

The BIG Idea

Have students read the answer to the Essential Question. Encourage them to evaluate and revise their own answers as needed.

Help Students Read

Building Vocabulary

Paraphrasing Have students rewrite, in their own words, the paragraphs under the headings Average Speed and Instantaneous Speed. Students should rewrite the paragraphs to be more concise while still covering all of the main points. Students should be sure to define the key terms found in the sections in their own words.

Word/Part Analysis Explain that the word part *veloc-* is a Latin root meaning "swift" or "quick." Have students relate this to the meaning of the key term *velocity*. Ask: **What can you infer about the type of dinosaur named the velociraptor?** *(It could move quickly.)*

Connecting Concepts

Help students develop ways to show how the information in this chapter is related. The motion of an object can be described by measuring its speed, velocity, and acceleration and is measured using SI units; some objects move quickly, others, like Earth's plates, move very slowly. Have students brainstorm to identify the key concepts, key terms, details, and examples, then write each one on a self-sticking note and attach it at random on chart paper or on the board.

Tell students that this concept map will be organized in hierarchical order and to begin at the top with the key concepts. Ask students these questions to guide them to categorize the information on the self-sticking notes: **How is motion described and measured? How can the motion of Earth's plates be described? What is acceleration, and how is it calculated?**

Chapter 1 Study Guide

The BIG Idea **Motion and Forces** The motion of an object can be described by its position, speed, direction, and acceleration.

① Describing and Measuring Motion

Key Concepts

- An object is in motion if it changes position relative to a reference point.
- If you know the distance an object travels in a certain amount of time, you can calculate the speed of the object.
- Speed $= \dfrac{\text{Distance}}{\text{Time}}$
- When you know both the speed and direction of an object's motion, you know the velocity of the object.
- You can show the motion of an object on a line graph in which you plot distance versus time.
- Slope $= \dfrac{\text{Rise}}{\text{Run}}$

Key Terms

motion
reference point
International System of Units
meter
speed
average speed
instantaneous speed
velocity
slope

② Slow Motion on Planet Earth

Key Concepts

- According to the theory of plate tectonics, Earth's landmasses have changed position over time because they are part of plates that are slowly moving.
- Some plates move at a rate of several centimeters each year. Others move only a few millimeters per year.

Key Terms

• plate • theory of plate tectonics

③ Acceleration

Key Concepts

- In science, acceleration refers to increasing speed, decreasing speed, or changing direction.
- To determine the acceleration of an object moving in a straight line, you must calculate the change in speed per unit of time.
- Acceleration $= \dfrac{\text{Final speed} - \text{Initial speed}}{\text{Time}}$
- You can use both a speed-versus-time graph and a distance-versus-time graph to analyze the motion of an accelerating object.

Key Term

acceleration

Prompt students by using connecting words or phrases, such as "is described by" and "is measured using," to indicate the basis for the organization of the map. The phrases should form a sentence between or among a set of concepts.

Answer

Accept logical presentations by students.

All in One Teaching Resources

- Key Terms Review: *Motion*
- Connecting Concepts: *Motion*

Review and Assessment

Go Online
PHSchool.com
For: Self-Assessment
Visit: PHSchool.com
Web Code: cga-3010

Organizing Information

Concept Mapping Copy the concept map about motion onto a separate sheet of paper. Then complete it and add a title. (For more information on Concept Mapping, see the Skills Handbook.)

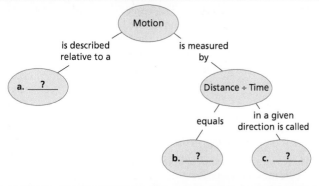

Motion

is described relative to a

is measured by

a. ?

Distance ÷ Time

equals

in a given direction is called

b. ?

c. ?

Reviewing Key Terms

Choose the letter of the best answer.

1. A change in position with respect to a reference point is
   a. acceleration.
   b. velocity.
   c. direction.
   d. motion.

2. You do not know an object's velocity until you know its
   a. speed.
   b. reference point.
   c. speed and direction.
   d. acceleration.

3. If you know a car travels 30 km in 20 minutes, you can find its
   a. acceleration.
   b. average speed.
   c. direction.
   d. instantaneous speed.

4. The parts of Earth's outer layer that move are called
   a. reference points.
   b. slopes.
   c. plates.
   d. boundaries.

5. The rate at which velocity changes is called
   a. acceleration.   b. constant speed.
   c. average speed.   d. velocity.

If the statement is true, write *true*. If it is false, change the underlined word or words to make the statement true.

6. The distance an object travels per unit of time is called <u>acceleration</u>.

7. The basic SI unit of length is the <u>meter</u>.

8. The <u>theory of plate tectonics</u> explains how Earth's landmasses have changed position over time.

9. The <u>slope</u> of a speed-versus-time graph represents acceleration.

10. Both <u>speed</u> and acceleration include the direction of an object's motion.

Writing in Science

News Report Two trucks have competed in a race. Write an article describing the race and who won. Explain the role the average speed of the trucks played. Tell how average speed can be calculated.

Discovery CHANNEL SCHOOL

Motion
Video Preview
Video Field Trip
▶ Video Assessment

Chapter 1 M ◆ 31

Go Online
PHSchool.com
For: Self-Assessment
Visit: PHSchool.com
Web Code: cga-3010

Students can take a practice test online that is automatically scored.

All in One Teaching Resources
- Transparency M10
- Chapter Test
- Performance Assessment Teacher Notes
- Performance Assessment Student Worksheet
- Performance Assessment Scoring Rubric

ExamView® **Computer Test Bank CD-ROM**

Review and Assessment

Organizing Information
a. Reference point
b. Speed
c. Velocity

Reviewing Key Terms
1. d **2.** c **3.** b **4.** c **5.** a
6. speed
7. true
8. true
9. true
10. velocity

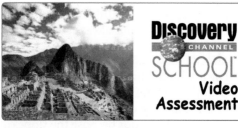

Discovery CHANNEL SCHOOL Video Assessment

Motion

Show the Video Assessment to review chapter content and as a prompt for the writing assignment. Discussion questions: **How do you calculate acceleration?** *(Subtract the starting speed from the maximum speed and divide by the amount of time it took to reach that speed.)* **What unit of measurement do you use for acceleration?** *(Meters per second squared)*

Writing in Science

Writing Mode Description
Scoring Rubric
4 Exceeds criteria; is well written and includes a thorough discussion of the calculation of average speed
3 Meets criteria
2 The news report is brief, lacks detail, and/or includes some incorrect information
1 The news report is poorly written and/or includes numerous errors

Checking Concepts

11. The passenger would appear to be moving backwards from a reference point on the train. From the ground, she would appear to be moving forward, because the train moves forward faster than she is walking backwards.

12. The duck, at 12 m/s, has a greater speed than the heron, which travels at 10 m/s.

13. The greater the slope, the greater the speed.

14. Sample answer: You could make a mark of where the object is today (a reference point), then come back after a certain period of time and make a mark to show where the object is at that time. If the object is still at the same reference point, the object is not moving.

15. The insect is accelerating because the direction of its motion is always changing.

Thinking Critically

16. The car is moving for the first 4 seconds, it stops for the next 4 seconds, and moves again for the last 4 seconds. It is moving fastest from 0–4 seconds because the slope of the graph is greatest during that time. It moves at 1 m/s. The car is moving slowest from 4–8 seconds because its slope is zero. The car is not moving.

17. Because the first driver drove the same distance in less time, the first driver had the greater average speed.

18. The family traveled 160 km in 3 hours, so their average speed is about 53 km/h.

Math Practice

19. 119 cm = 1.19 m

20. 22.4 km = 22,400 m

21. (35 m/s − 0 m/s) ÷ 0.5 s = 70 m/s^2

Applying Skills

22. Starting line to line B = 2.0 cm; line B to the finish line = 5.0 cm

23. 2 cm/s

24. 1.0 cm/s^2

Review and Assessment

Checking Concepts

11. A passenger walks toward the rear of a moving train. Describe her motion as seen from a reference point on the train. Then describe it from a reference point on the ground.

12. Which has a greater speed, a heron that travels 600 m in 60 seconds or a duck that travels 60 m in 5 seconds? Explain.

13. You have a motion graph for an object that shows distance and time. How does the slope of the graph relate to the object's speed?

14. How can you tell if an object is moving when its motion is too slow to see?

15. An insect lands on a compact disc that is put into a player. If the insect spins with the disc, is the insect accelerating? Why or why not?

Thinking Critically

16. Interpreting Graphs The graph below shows the motion of a remote-control car. During which segment is the car moving the fastest? The slowest? How do you know?

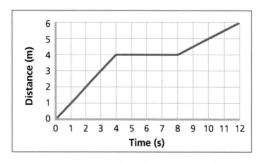

17. Problem Solving Two drivers make a 100-km trip. Driver 1 completes the trip in 2 hours. Driver 2 takes 3 hours but stops for an hour halfway. Which driver had a greater average speed? Explain.

18. Applying Concepts A family takes a car trip. They travel for an hour at 80 km/h and then for 2 hours at 40 km/h. Find their average speed during the trip.

Math Practice

19. Converting Units Convert 119 cm to meters.

20. Converting Units Convert 22.4 km to meters.

21. Calculating Acceleration During a slap shot, a hockey puck takes 0.5 second to reach the goal. It started from rest and reached a final speed of 35 m/s. What is the puck's average acceleration?

Applying Skills

Use the illustration of the motion of a ladybug to answer Questions 22–24.

Start   Finish

22. Measuring Measure the distance from the starting line to line B, and from line B to the finish line. Measure to the nearest tenth of a centimeter.

23. Calculating Starting at rest, the ladybug accelerated to line B and then moved at a constant speed until it reached the finish line. If the ladybug took 2.5 seconds to move from line B to the finish line, calculate its constant speed during that time.

24. Interpreting Data The speed you calculated in Question 21 is also the speed the ladybug had at the end of its acceleration at line B. If it took 2 seconds for the ladybug to accelerate from the start line to line B, what is its average acceleration during that time?

Lab zone Chapter **Project**

Performance Assessment Organize your display cards so that they are easy to follow. Remember to put a title on each card stating the speed that you measured. Place the cards in order from the slowest speed to the fastest. Then display them to your class. Compare your results with those of other students.

Lab zone Chapter **Project**

Performance Assessment Have students review each other's display cards. Prepare a table on which students can record and compare their different values.

Have individual students present their methods for calculating speed. Students should indicate how many trials they ran and whether or not they used average data. Students probably got slightly different answers when they measured the same speed more than once. Remind students that accurately measuring motion involves accurately measuring both time and distance.

Standardized Test Prep

Choose the letter of the best answer.

1. Members of the Fairview Track Club are running a 1.5 km race. What is the distance of the race in meters?
   A 0.15 m
   B 15 m
   C 150 m
   D 1,500 m

2. Your father is driving to the beach. He drives at one speed for two hours. He drives at a different speed for another two hours and a third speed for the final hour. How would you find his average speed for all five hours?
   F Divide the total driving time by the total distance.
   G Multiply the total driving time by the total distance.
   H Divide the total distance by the total driving time.
   J Subtract the total driving time from the total distance.

3. Two objects traveling at the same speed have different velocities if they
   A start at different times.
   B travel different distances.
   C have different masses.
   D move in different directions.

4. The graph below shows the distance versus time for a runner moving at a constant 200 m/min. What could the runner do to make the slope of the line rise?

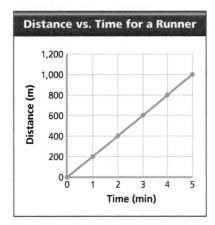

Distance vs. Time for a Runner

  F stop running
  G decrease speed
  H maintain the same speed
  J increase speed

5. An object used as a reference point to determine motion should be
   A accelerating.
   B stationary.
   C decelerating.
   D changing direction.

Constructed Response

6. Explain how speed, velocity, and acceleration are related.

Standardized Test Prep

1. D **2.** H **3.** D **4.** J **5.** B

6. Speed, velocity, and acceleration all are measures of motion. Speed measures how far an object moves in a given amount of time. Velocity not only measures an object's speed, but also the direction in which the object moves. Acceleration measures the rate at which velocity changes by considering an increase in speed, a decrease in speed, or a change in direction.

Chapter at a Glance

 PRENTICE HALL

TeacherEXPRESS™
Plan • Teach • Assess

 Lab zone **Chapter Project** — *Newton Scooters*

Technology

Local Standards

All in One Teaching Resources
- Chapter Project Teacher Notes, pp. 96–97
- Chapter Project Student Overview, pp. 98–99
- Chapter Project Student Worksheets, pp. 100–101
- Chapter Project Scoring Rubric, p. 102

 **DISCOVERY** CHANNEL SCHOOL
Video Preview

 Section 1

2–3 periods
1–1 1/2 blocks

The Nature of Force

M.2.1.1 Describe what a force is.

M.2.1.2 Explain how balanced and unbalanced forces are related to an object's motion.

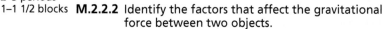 Go Online
SC*LINKS* NSTA

 Section 2

2–3 periods
1–1 1/2 blocks

Friction and Gravity

M.2.2.1 Describe friction, and identify factors that determine the friction force between two objects.

M.2.2.2 Identify the factors that affect the gravitational force between two objects.

M.2.2.3 Explain why objects accelerate during free fall.

 Go Online
SC*LINKS* NSTA

 Section 3

1–2 periods
1/2–1 block

Newton's First and Second Laws

M.2.3.1 State Newton's first law of motion.

M.2.3.2 State Newton's second law of motion.

 Go Online
PHSchool.com

 Section 4

3–4 periods
1 1/2–2 blocks

Newton's Third Law

M.2.4.1 State Newton's third law of motion.

M.2.4.2 Explain how an object's momentum is determined.

M.2.4.3 State the law of conservation of momentum.

 **DISCOVERY** CHANNEL SCHOOL
Video Field Trip

Go Online
active.art

Section 5

1–2 periods
1/2–1 block

Rockets and Satellites

M.2.5.1 Explain how a rocket lifts off the ground.

M.2.5.2 Describe the forces that keep a satellite in orbit.

Review and Assessment

All in One Teaching Resources
- Key Terms Review, p. 142
- Transparency M22
- Performance Assessment Teacher Notes, p. 150
- Performance Assessment Scoring Rubric, p. 151
- Performance Assessment Student Worksheet, p. 152
- Chapter Test, pp. 153–156

 DISCOVERY CHANNEL SCHOOL
Video Assessment

Go Online
PHSchool.com

Test Preparation

Test Preparation Blackline Masters

Chapter Activities Planner

For more activities

Student Edition	Inquiry	Time	Materials	Skills	Resources
Chapter Project, p. 35	Open-Ended	Ongoing (2–3 weeks)	**All in One** Teaching Resources p. 96	Controlling variables, making models, predicting	**Lab zone Easy Planner** **All in One** Teaching Resources pp. 96–97
Section 1					
Discover Activity, p. 36	Directed	15 minutes	Skateboard, two spring scales	Observing	**Lab zone Easy Planner**
At-Home Activity, p. 39	Guided	Home		Applying concepts	**Lab zone Easy Planner**
Consumer Lab, pp. 40–41	Directed	Prep: 30 minutes; Class: 40 minutes	Three or more different brands of sneakers, 2 spring scales (5-N and 20-N) or force sensors, mass set(s), tape, 3 large paper clips, balance	Controlling variables, interpreting data	**Lab zone Easy Planner** **Lab Activity Video** **All in One** Teaching Resources Consumer Lab: *Sticky Sneakers,* pp. 109–112
Section 2					
Discover Activity, p. 42	Directed	15 minutes	4 quarters, ruler, tape	Predicting	**Lab zone Easy Planner**
Try This Activity, p. 44	Guided	10 minutes	Marbles, two identical pie plates	Drawing conclusions	**Lab zone Easy Planner**
Skills Activity, p. 47	Directed	20 minutes	Balance, four distinct objects such as a book, a shoe, a spiral notebook, a pair of scissors	Calculating	**Lab zone Easy Planner**
Section 3					
Discover Activity, p. 51	Directed	10 minutes	Heavy book, metal washers, toy car	Observing	**Lab zone Easy Planner**
Try This Activity, p. 52	Guided	15 minutes	Masking or cellophane tape, table tennis ball, thread	Inferring	**Lab zone Easy Planner**
Section 4					
Discover Activity, p. 55	Directed	10 minutes	Hard cover book, rubber bands, marbles, plastic straw	Developing hypotheses	**Lab zone Easy Planner**
Try This Activity, p. 59	Guided	10 minutes	Masking tape, two toy cars with the same mass and low-friction wheels	Predicting	**Lab zone Easy Planner**
Skills Lab, pp. 62–63	Guided	Prep: 20 minutes; Class: 40 minutes	Skateboard, meter stick, string, stopwatch, masking tape, spring scale (5-N), several bricks or other large mass(es)	Calculating, graphing, interpreting data	**Lab zone Easy Planner** **Lab Activity Video** **All in One** Teaching Resources Skills Lab: *Forced to Accelerate,* pp. 133–135
Section 5					
Discover Activity, p. 64	Directed	10 minutes	Length of string no more than 1 m long, safety goggles, small object such as an empty thread spool	Forming operational definitions	**Lab zone Easy Planner**
At-Home Activity, p. 67	Guided	Home		Applying concepts	**Lab zone Easy Planner**

Section 1 The Nature of Force

 2–3 periods, 1–1 1/2 blocks

ABILITY LEVELS
L1 Basic to Average
L2 For All Students
L3 Average to Advanced

Objectives

M.2.1.1 Describe what a force is.

M.2.1.2 Explain how balanced and unbalanced forces are related to an object's motion.

Key Terms

• force • newton • net force • unbalanced forces • balanced forces

Local Standards

Preteach

Build Background Knowledge

Use a demonstration to show that force causes motion.

 **Discover Activity** *Is the Force With You?* L2

Targeted Print and Technology Resources

All in One **Teaching Resources**

L2 Reading Strategy Transparency M11: Asking Questions

 PresentationExpress™ CD-ROM

Instruct

What Is a Force? Guide students in creating a concept map describing forces.

Combining Forces Help students relate the concepts of net force, balanced forces, and unbalanced forces.

 **Consumer Lab** *Sticky Sneakers* L2

Targeted Print and Technology Resources

All in One **Teaching Resources**

L2 Guided Reading, pp. 105–106
L2 Transparency M12
L2 Consumer Lab: *Sticky Sneakers,* pp. 109–112

Lab Activity Video/DVD
Consumer Lab: *Sticky Sneakers*

www.SciLinks.org Web Code: scn-1321

 Student Edition on Audio CD

Assess

Section Assessment Questions

Have students use the answers to the questions they wrote about the headings to answer the questions.

Reteach

Students use Figure 2 to review key terms from the section.

Targeted Print and Technology Resources

All in One **Teaching Resources**

• Section Summary, p. 104
L1 Review and Reinforce, p. 107
L3 Enrich, p. 108

Section 2 **Friction and Gravity**

 2–3 periods, 1–1 1/2 blocks

ABILITY LEVELS
L1 Basic to Average
L2 For All Students
L3 Average to Advanced

Objectives

M.2.2.1 Describe friction, and identify factors that determine the friction force between two objects.

M.2.2.2 Identify the factors that affect the gravitational force between two objects.

M.2.2.3 Explain why objects accelerate during free fall.

Local Standards

Key Terms

• friction • static friction • sliding friction • rolling friction • fluid friction
• gravity • mass • weight • free fall • air resistance • terminal velocity
• projectile

Preteach

Build Background Knowledge

Use a demonstration to compare sliding friction and rolling friction.

 **Discover Activity** *Which Lands First?* L1

Targeted Print and Technology Resources

All in One Teaching Resources

L2 Reading Strategy Transparency M13: Comparing and Contrasting

◉ **PresentationExpress™ CD-ROM**

Instruct

Friction Ask leading questions to help students compare different types of friction.

Gravity Have students use the headings in the text to locate the main ideas about gravity.

Gravity and Motion Use an example of dropping a ball to introduce the concept of acceleration.

Targeted Print and Technology Resources

All in One Teaching Resources

L2 Guided Reading, pp. 115–118
L2 Transparency M14

www.SciLinks.org Web Code: scn-1322

◉ **Student Edition on Audio CD**

Assess

Section Assessment Questions

 Have students use their completed tables about friction and gravity to help them answer the questions.

Reteach

Students list examples of friction and gravity affecting motion.

Targeted Print and Technology Resources

All in One Teaching Resources

• Section Summary, p. 114
L1 Review and Reinforce, p. 119
L3 Enrich, p. 120

Section 3 Newton's First and Second Laws

ABILITY LEVELS
L1 Basic to Average
L2 For All Students
L3 Average to Advanced

1–2 periods, 1/2–1 block

Objectives

M.2.3.1 State Newton's first law of motion.
M.2.3.2 State Newton's second law of motion.

Key Terms

• inertia

Local Standards

Preteach

Build Background Knowledge

Use a demonstration to show the effect of force on an object's motion.

 **Discover Activity** *What Changes Motion?* L1

Targeted Print and Technology Resources

 **Teaching Resources**

L2 Reading Strategy Transparency
M15: Outlining

 PresentationExpress™ CD-ROM

Instruct

The First Law of Motion Ask leading questions to relate the concept of inertia to the motion of passengers in a car that stops quickly.

The Second Law of Motion Help students understand the relationship between force, mass, and acceleration by using an everyday example.

Targeted Print and Technology Resources

 **Teaching Resources**

L2 Guided Reading, pp. 123–124
L2 Transparency M16

PHSchool.com Web Code: cgd-3023

Student Edition on Audio CD

Assess

Section Assessment Questions

Have students use their completed outline to answer the questions.

Reteach

Students rewrite Newton's first and second laws in their own words.

Targeted Print and Technology Resources

 **Teaching Resources**

• Section Summary, p. 122
L1 Review and Reinforce, p. 125
L3 Enrich, p. 126

Section 4 Newton's Third Law

 3–4 periods, 1 1/2–2 blocks

ABILITY LEVELS
L1 Basic to Average
L2 For All Students
L3 Average to Advanced

Objectives

M.2.4.1 State Newton's third law of motion.
M.2.4.2 Explain how an object's momentum is determined.
M.2.4.3 State the law of conservation of momentum.

Key Terms

• momentum • law of conservation of momentum

Local Standards

Preteach

Build Background Knowledge

Use a demonstration to introduce the concept of action and reaction forces.

Lab zone Discover Activity *How Pushy Is a Straw?*   **L2**

Targeted Print and Technology Resources

All in One Teaching Resources
L2 Reading Strategy Transparency
M17: Previewing Visuals

 PresentationExpress™ CD-ROM

Instruct

Newton's Third Law of Motion Use an example to explain action and reaction forces.

Momentum Show the relationship between mass, velocity, and momentum using the equation: Momentum = Mass × Velocity.

Conservation of Momentum Use Figure 18 to help students visualize conservation of momentum.

Lab zone Skills Lab *Forced to Accelerate*   **L3**

Targeted Print and Technology Resources

All in One Teaching Resources
L2 Guided Reading, pp. 129–130
L2 Transparencies M18, M19
L3 Skills Lab: *Forced to Accelerate*, pp. 133–135

Lab Activity Video/DVD
Skills Lab: *Forced to Accelerate*

PHSchool.com Web Code: cgp-3024

DISCOVERY CHANNEL SCHOOL
Video Field Trip

 Student Edition on Audio CD

Assess

Section Assessment Questions

Have students use their questions and answers about Figure 18 to help them answer the questions.

Reteach

Students create a concept map about momentum and the law of conservation of momentum.

Targeted Print and Technology Resources

All in One Teaching Resources
• Section Summary, p. 128
L1 Review and Reinforce, p. 131
L3 Enrich, p. 132

Section 5 Rockets and Satellites

 1–2 periods, 1/2–1 block

ABILITY LEVELS
L1 Basic to Average
L2 For All Students
L3 Average to Advanced

Objectives

M.2.5.1 Explain how a rocket lifts off the ground.
M.2.5.2 Describe the forces that keep a satellite in orbit.

Local Standards

Key Terms

• satellite • centripetal force

Preteach

Build Background Knowledge

Have students describe a rocket launch in terms of the forces involved.

 **Discover Activity** *What Makes an Object Move in a Circle?* **L2**

Targeted Print and Technology Resources

All in One Teaching Resources

L2 Reading Strategy Transparency M20: Identifying Main Ideas

⊙ PresentationExpress™ CD-ROM

Instruct

How Do Rockets Lift Off? Use Figure 19 to help students relate Newton's third law to a space shuttle launch.

What Is a Satellite? Relate the curved path of a thrown object to the curved path of a satellite.

Targeted Print and Technology Resources

All in One Teaching Resources

L2 Guided Reading, pp. 138–139
L2 Transparency M21

⊙ Student Edition on Audio CD

Assess

Section Assessment Questions

Have students use their completed graphic organizer to help them answer the questions.

Reteach

Students review the boldface sentences and restate the main ideas in their own words.

Targeted Print and Technology Resources

All in One Teaching Resources

• Section Summary, p. 137
L1 Review and Reinforce, p. 140
L3 Enrich, p. 141

Chapter 2 Content Refresher

Go Online

NSTA-PDLINKS

For: Professional development support
Visit: www.SciLinks.org/PDLinks
Web Code: scf-1320

Professional Development

Section 1 The Nature of Force

Vector Quantities Quantities that are described by both a magnitude and a direction are vector quantities. Force is an example of a vector quantity. Other familiar vector quantities are velocity and displacement. Scalar quantities, like speed, have only a magnitude.

Arrows are used to represent vector quantities such as force. The arrow's length indicates the magnitude of the force. The direction the arrow points indicates the direction in which the force acts.

There is often more than one force acting on an object at any given time. The combination of forces acting on an object is called net force. In order to determine the magnitude and direction of the net force acting on an object, the vectors representing all of the forces acting (the component vectors) must be combined. Unlike scalar quantities that can be combined by simple addition or subtraction, forces must be combined using a process called vector addition. The vector representing the net force is called the resultant vector.

When combining forces act in the same direction, their magnitudes can simply be added. The resultant vector points in the same direction as the component vectors. When two forces act in opposite directions, the smaller magnitude is subtracted from the greater magnitude to find the resultant magnitude. The resultant vector points in the direction of the larger component vector.

> ⚑ **Address Misconceptions**
>
> *Some students might think that the terms* mass *and* weight *have the same meaning.* For a strategy for overcoming this misconception, see **Address Misconceptions** in the section *Friction and Gravity.*

Vector Subtraction

3N   6N   =   3N

Component Vectors   Resultant Vector

Component forces that do not act in either the same or opposite directions can also be combined. In this case the resultant force will always be less in magnitude than the sum of the magnitudes that are the two forces. An example is shown here.

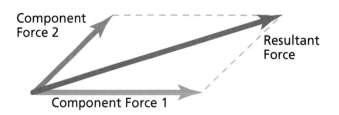

Component Force 2

Resultant Force

Component Force 1

Section 2 Friction and Gravity

Friction, Gravity, and Skydiving The sport of skydiving can be used to illustrate the concepts of gravity, free fall, terminal velocity, and air resistance. When a skydiver jumps from an airplane, the force of gravity causes the skydiver to accelerate toward Earth. Air resistance (the friction that results from moving through air) acts on the skydiver in an upward direction. When the forces of air resistance and gravity are equal in magnitude, the skydiver stops accelerating. The skydiver's velocity when acceleration stops is called terminal velocity.

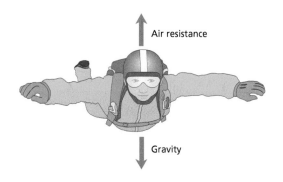

Air resistance

Gravity

Skydivers use this information to plan a safe jump and landing. After jumping, the skydiver accelerates to a terminal velocity of about 52 meters per second. The terminal velocity is affected by several things, including the size of the skydiver and the position of the skydiver's body during the fall. After the parachute is fully opened, the skydiver's velocity is reduced to about 4.5 meters per second. The reduction in velocity occurs because the parachute's large surface area greatly increases air resistance. At a velocity of 4.5 meters per second the skydiver can land safely.

Section 3 Newton's First and Second Laws

Seatbelts and Airbags Newton's first law of motion states that an object at rest will remain at rest, and an object in motion will continue in motion at a constant velocity unless acted upon by a net force. This law is sometimes referred to as the law of inertia. Inertia, a resistance to change in motion, is directly related to an object's mass. Therefore, an object with greater mass has a greater inertia than an object with a smaller mass.

Inertia is a prime consideration in the design of seatbelts and airbags for automobiles. Passengers in a moving car, like all objects and living things, have inertia. This resistance to change in motion can be hazardous if the car stops quickly. Passengers continue moving forward until acted upon by a force that stops their motion.

Seatbelts and airbags are designed to provide a force that stops the passengers' forward motion and keeps them from striking the dashboard, windshield, or steering wheel. The seatbelts used in cars today are called inertia-reel seatbelts. The seatbelts allow movement, but lock when a large force is applied. Today's inertia-reel seatbelts replaced the earlier technology. These fixed, or static seatbelts did not allow movement.

Airbags are a more recent innovation. Starting in the 1980s, airbags began to be a part of the design of some automobiles. They are now found in all new cars in the United States. Airbags work with seatbelts to increase driver and passenger safety. When an automobile rapidly decelerates, the airbag sensor deploys the airbag, causing it to inflate rapidly. Along with the passenger's seatbelt, the airbag greatly reduces the chance of serious injury due to an accident.

Section 4 Newton's Third Law

Momentum in Open and Closed Systems When the law of conservation of momentum is discussed in the text, the objects are assumed to be a part of a closed system. In a closed system, the only forces considered are those exerted by the objects themselves. So, objects in a closed system are not acted upon by outside forces. The total energy in a closed system remains constant. In a closed system, if one object gains momentum, another object must lose momentum so that the total momentum within the system remains constant.

In real life, however, systems are open. In an open system, forces such as friction and gravity act on objects, affecting their motion and momentum. In the case of colliding train cars, air resistance and friction with the tracks are outside forces that affect the motion of the cars. So, in an open system, the momentum of the two train cars, considered alone, will not be conserved—the cars will eventually come to a stop.

Section 5 Rockets and Satellites

Geostationary Satellites Satellites that circle Earth once every 24 hours remain at the same point above Earth as they orbit. These satellites, called geostationary or geosynchronous satellites, orbit at an elevation of about 36,000 km above Earth's surface. These satellites orbit in a position above the equator. The height of orbit is important, because the height at which a satellite orbits determines the amount of time required for the satellite to orbit Earth. At 36,000 km above Earth's surface, the satellite completes an orbit in the same amount of time that it takes Earth to complete one rotation.

One of the uses of geostationary satellites is producing images used in weather forecasting. The National Oceanic and Atmospheric Administration operates geostationary satellites (called GOES, short for geostationary operational environmental satellites) that provide continuous data about the world's weather. Each satellite is able to collect images from about one third of Earth's surface. A drawback of geostationary satellites is that due to their position above the equator, they cannot collect images of the North and South Poles. Data from geostationary satellites are supplemented by data from other satellites (that are not geostationary) that collect data about the weather at Earth's poles. Information from these satellites can be used to track weather patterns, predict weather, provide advance warning of severe weather, and estimate amounts of rainfall or snowfall in various locations.

Geostationary satellites are also used, along with satellites in lower orbits, for communications. One advantage of using a geostationary satellite for communications is that the dish antenna used to receive signals from the satellite can be aimed at one location in the sky, rather than having to be mobile. A disadvantage is that the relatively high orbit of geostationary satellites results in a time delay during signal transmission.

Help Students Read

Summarizing
Briefly Restate the Main Ideas

Strategy Help students understand the topics in the chapter by having them restate the main ideas using their own words. As students read a section of the text, have them note the main ideas found in the section. After they have completed their reading, have them write a sentence or two restating the main ideas. Summarizing is useful for short passages as well as large sections and entire chapters. Have students read about static friction in the section *Friction and Gravity*.

Example
1. Have students read the paragraph about static friction. Then have them review the paragraph to identify the main idea. Demonstrate this process for students by using the heading as an aid in determining the main idea of the passage. List the main idea on the board.

2. Students should then restate the main idea of the passage in their own words. Remind students to focus on the important concepts and to omit the details and examples. Students should review their statements to be sure they cover the terms mentioned in the bold heading.

3. Have students repeat this process with the remaining paragraphs on the page. Students should summarize the main ideas found in the text about sliding friction, rolling friction, and fluid friction.

4. Have students work in small groups to compare their summaries.

See the section *Friction and Gravity* for a script for using the Summarizing strategy with students.

The BIG Idea

The Big Idea is the major scientific concept of the chapter. It is followed by the Essential Question. Read aloud the question to students. As students study the chapter, tell them to think about the Essential Question. Explain that they will discover the answer to the question as they read. The chapter Study Guide provides a sample answer.

Lab zone Chapter **Project** L3

Objectives

This Chapter Project will allow students to explore applications of Newton's laws of motion. After completing this Chapter Project, students will be able to

- identify and manipulate variables that affect the performance of a vehicle
- make a model of a vehicle by drawing a diagram
- predict how the scooter will work based on the model
- communicate their results by demonstrating the vehicle

Skills Focus

Controlling variables, making models, predicting, communicating

Project Time Line 2–3 weeks

All in One **Teaching Resources**

- Chapter Project Teacher Notes
- Chapter Project Overview
- Chapter Project Worksheet 1
- Chapter Project Worksheet 2
- Chapter Project Scoring Rubric

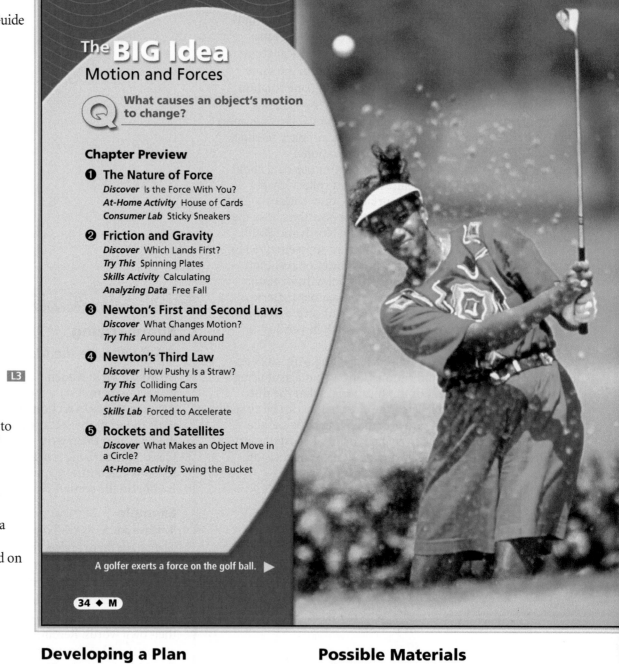

The BIG Idea
Motion and Forces

Q What causes an object's motion to change?
_____

Chapter Preview

❶ The Nature of Force
Discover Is the Force With You?
At-Home Activity House of Cards
Consumer Lab Sticky Sneakers

❷ Friction and Gravity
Discover Which Lands First?
Try This Spinning Plates
Skills Activity Calculating
Analyzing Data Free Fall

❸ Newton's First and Second Laws
Discover What Changes Motion?
Try This Around and Around

❹ Newton's Third Law
Discover How Pushy Is a Straw?
Try This Colliding Cars
Active Art Momentum
Skills Lab Forced to Accelerate

❺ Rockets and Satellites
Discover What Makes an Object Move in a Circle?
At-Home Activity Swing the Bucket

A golfer exerts a force on the golf ball. ▶

34 ◆ M

Developing a Plan

Allow students two or three days to brainstorm ideas for a vehicle. Identifying the forces acting on a vehicle requires that they have read most of the chapter. Students will need the remainder of the time to build and troubleshoot their vehicles.

Possible Materials

Provide a wide variety of materials for students to use, for example: toy vehicles, balloons, straws, fishing line, paper towel rolls, and basins of water. Encourage students to suggest and use other materials as well.

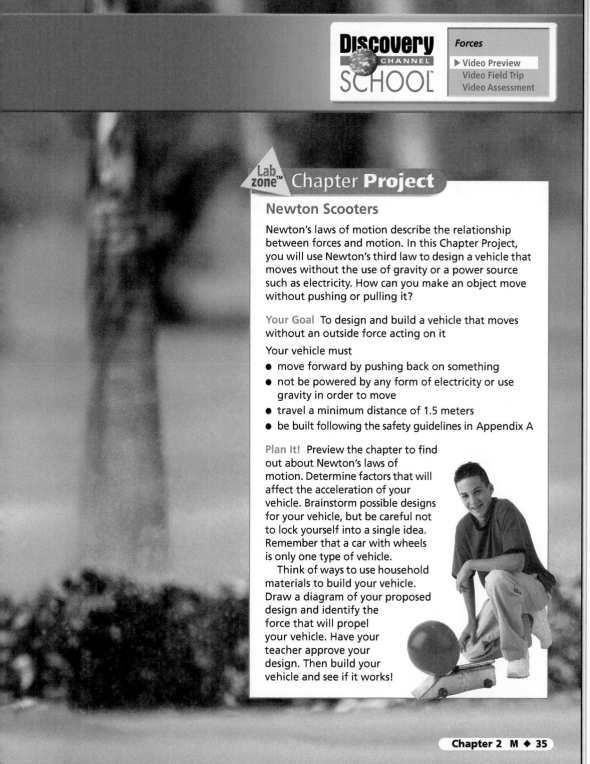

Video Preview

Forces

Show the Video Preview to introduce the chapter and provide an overview of chapter content. Discussion question: **In what way is a roller coaster similar to an aerobatic plane in flight?** *(Sample answer: Both subject their passengers to large acceleration forces.)*

Lab zone™ Chapter Project

Newton Scooters

Newton's laws of motion describe the relationship between forces and motion. In this Chapter Project, you will use Newton's third law to design a vehicle that moves without the use of gravity or a power source such as electricity. How can you make an object move without pushing or pulling it?

Your Goal To design and build a vehicle that moves without an outside force acting on it

Your vehicle must

- move forward by pushing back on something
- not be powered by any form of electricity or use gravity in order to move
- travel a minimum distance of 1.5 meters
- be built following the safety guidelines in Appendix A

Plan It! Preview the chapter to find out about Newton's laws of motion. Determine factors that will affect the acceleration of your vehicle. Brainstorm possible designs for your vehicle, but be careful not to lock yourself into a single idea. Remember that a car with wheels is only one type of vehicle.

Think of ways to use household materials to build your vehicle. Draw a diagram of your proposed design and identify the force that will propel your vehicle. Have your teacher approve your design. Then build your vehicle and see if it works!

Chapter 2 M ◆ 35

Launching the Project

Demonstrate Newton's third law of motion by releasing an inflated balloon into the air. Have the class discuss what makes the balloon move. Allow time for students to read the description of the project in the text. Have students work in small groups to brainstorm how they might power vehicles without using electricity or gravity. Tell students to apply the information about forces in the chapter to their designs. Once students have acceptable designs, they can begin to build and test their vehicles.

Performance Assessment

The Chapter Project Scoring Rubric will help you evaluate how well students complete the Chapter Project. You may want to share the scoring rubric with your students so they will know what is expected. Students will be assessed on

- the planning of their vehicle, including consideration of the forces acting on it
- the care with which the vehicle was built
- their ability to modify the design after testing
- thoroughness and organization of their presentation

Students can keep the designs and descriptions of their vehicles in their portfolios.

Portfolio

Objectives

After this lesson, students will be able to

M.2.1.1 Describe what a force is.
M.2.1.2 Explain how balanced and unbalanced forces are related to an object's motion.

Target Reading Skill

Asking Questions Explain that changing a head into a question helps students anticipate the ideas, facts, and events they are about to read.

Answers

Sample questions and answers:
What is a force? (*A force is a push or a pull.*)
What happens when forces combine?
(*Forces combine to produce a net force.*)

All In One Teaching Resources

• Transparency M11

Preteach

Build Background Knowledge L2

Demonstrating Force
Place a book in the middle of a table. Have students take turns moving the book, each using a different method. As each student moves the book, Ask: **Is the book moving because of a push or because of a pull?** (*Sample answer: Because of a push*) **Does the book move when there is no push or pull?** (*No*)

The Nature of Force

Reading Preview

Key Concepts
• How is a force described?
• How are unbalanced and balanced forces related to an object's motion?

Key Terms
• force
• newton
• net force
• unbalanced forces
• balanced forces

Target Reading Skill

Asking Questions Before you read, preview the red headings. In a graphic organizer like the one below, ask a *what* or *how* question for each heading. As you read, write the answers to your questions.

The Nature of Force

Question	Answer
What is a force?	A force is . . .

Lab zone Discover **Activity**

Is the Force With You?

1. Attach a spring scale to each end of a skateboard.
2.  Gently pull on one spring scale with a force of 4 N, while your partner pulls on the other with the same force. Observe the motion of the skateboard.
3. Now try to keep your partner's spring scale reading at 2 N while you pull with a force of 4 N. Observe the motion of the skateboard.

Think It Over
Observing Describe the motion of the skateboard when you and your partner pulled with the same force. How was the motion of the skateboard affected when you pulled with more force than your partner?

A hard kick sends a soccer ball shooting down the field toward the goal. Just in time, the goalie leaps forward, stops the ball, and quickly kicks it in the opposite direction. In a soccer game, the ball is rarely still. Its motion is constantly changing. Why? What causes an object to start moving, stop moving, or change direction? The answer is force.

What Is a Force?

In science, the word *force* has a simple and specific meaning. A **force** is a push or a pull. When one object pushes or pulls another object, you say that the first object exerts a force on the second object. You exert a force on a computer key when you push it and on a chair when you pull it away from a table.

Like velocity and acceleration, a force is described by its strength and by the direction in which it acts. If you push on a door, you exert a force in a different direction than if you pull on the door.

Lab zone Discover **Activity**

Skills Focus Observing L2

Materials skateboard, two spring scales

Time 15 minutes

Tips Both students should stop pulling on their spring scale before either student lets go of their spring scale. A third student can record the measurements on the spring scales.

Expected Outcome When one partner pulls with 3 N of force, the other partner's spring scale will also move to read 3 N.

Think It Over The reading on my partner's spring scale increased to 3 N also. Until the forces became equalized the skateboard moved slightly in the direction of the greater force.

The strength of a force is measured in the SI unit called the **newton** (N). This unit is named after the English scientist and mathematician Isaac Newton. You exert about one newton of force when you lift a small lemon.

The direction and strength of a force can be represented by an arrow. The arrow points in the direction of a force. The length of the arrow tells you the strength of a force—the longer the arrow, the greater the force.

 **Reading Checkpoint** What SI unit is used to measure the strength of a force?

Combining Forces

Often, more than a single force acts on an object at one time. The combination of all forces acting on an object is called the **net force.** The net force determines whether an object moves and also in which direction it moves.

When forces act in the same direction, the net force can be found by adding the strengths of the individual forces. In Figure 2, the lengths of the two arrows, which represent two forces, are added together to find the net force.

When forces act in opposite directions, they also combine to produce a net force. However, you must pay attention to the direction of each force. Adding a force acting in one direction to a force acting in the opposite direction is the same as adding a positive number to a negative number. So when two forces act in opposite directions, they combine by subtraction. The net force always acts in the direction of the greater force. If the opposing forces are of equal strength, there is no net force. There is no change in the object's motion.

FIGURE 2
Combining Forces
The strength and direction of the individual forces determine the net force. *Calculating How do you find the net force when two forces act in opposite directions?*

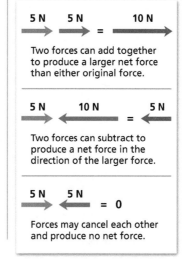

5 N   5 N   =   10 N

Two forces can add together to produce a larger net force than either original force.

5 N   10 N   5 N   =

Two forces can subtract to produce a net force in the direction of the larger force.

5 N   5 N   = 0

Forces may cancel each other and produce no net force.

Differentiated Instruction

English Learners/Beginning L1
Vocabulary: Prior Knowledge Explain that the word *net* has several different meanings in English. Explain that *net force* means overall, or total, force. Ask for volunteers to describe other meanings of the word *net* with which they are familiar. **learning modality: verbal**

English Learners/Intermediate L2
Vocabulary: Prior Knowledge Extend the Beginning activity by having students write sentences using different meanings of the word *net*. Model this activity for students before they begin. **learning modality: verbal**

What Is a Force?

Teach Key Concepts L2
Defining Force

Focus Remind students that the everyday meaning of the word *force* is different than its meaning in science.

Teach Write on the board: *Force is a push or a pull. Force is described by strength and direction. The SI unit for the strength of a force is newtons.* Have students use these facts to make a concept map describing forces.

Apply Ask: **When you kick a soccer ball, is the force a push or a pull?** *(A push)* **learning modality: verbal**

Combining Forces

Teach Key Concepts L2
Adding and Subtracting Forces

Focus Tell students that the combination of all the forces acting on an object is the net force.

Teach Explain that a net force of 0 means that the forces acting on an object are balanced. A net force of anything other than 0 indicates that the forces acting on the object are unbalanced.

Apply Ask: **If the net force on an object is 0, will the object's motion change? Why or why not?** *(No, because the forces acting on the object are balanced)* **learning modality: logical/mathematical**

All in One Teaching Resources
• Transparency M12

Independent Practice L2
All in One Teaching Resources
• Guided Reading and Study Worksheet: *The Nature of Force*

⊙ Student Edition on Audio CD

Monitor Progress _____ L2

Writing Have students describe two examples of forces acting on objects that they observed today.

Answers
Figure 2 Subtract the smaller force from the larger force. The net force will be in the direction of the larger force.

Reading Checkpoint The strength of a force is measured in newtons.

Modeling Unbalanced Forces

Materials rope about 4 meters long

Time 10 min

Focus Ask: **Has anyone ever played tug-of-war?** *(Some students will say yes.)* **How does a team win in tug-of-war?** *(Sample answer: One team pulls the other team over a line.)* **Why is one team able to pull the other over the line?** *(Sample answer: They are stronger.)* **If one team causes the other to move, what do you know about the forces of the teams?** *(They are unbalanced.)*

Teach Explain that you will be modeling forces using tug-of war teams. Remind students that it is not a competition, but a scientific demonstration. Caution the teams to pull only until one side moves. Ask four students to be on one team, and six students to be on the other team. The teams should pull until one side moves.

Apply Ask: **Did this activity model balanced forces or unbalanced forces?** *(Unbalanced forces)* **learning modality: kinesthetic**

Go Online

SciLINKS

For: Links on force
Visit: www.SciLinks.org
Web Code: scn-1321

Students can research force online.

Unbalanced Forces in the Same Direction
When two forces act in the same direction, the net force is the sum of the two individual forces. The box moves to the right.

Unbalanced Forces in the Opposite Direction
When two forces act in opposite directions, the net force is the difference between the two individual forces. The box moves to the right.

Unbalanced Forces Whenever there is a net force acting on an object, the forces are unbalanced. **Unbalanced forces** can cause an object to start moving, stop moving, or change direction. **Unbalanced forces acting on an object result in a net force and cause a change in the object's motion.**

Figure 3 shows two people exerting forces on a box. When they both push a box to the right, their individual forces add together to produce a net force in that direction. Since a net, or unbalanced, force acts on the box, the box moves to the right.

When the two people push the box in opposite directions, the net force on the box is the difference between their individual forces. Because the boy pushes with a greater force than the girl, their forces are unbalanced and a net force acts on the box to the right. As a result, the box moves to the right.

 Reading Checkpoint **What is the result of unbalanced forces acting on an object?**

Balanced Forces When forces are exerted on an object, the object's motion does not always change. In an arm wrestling contest, each person exerts a force on the other's arm, but the two forces are exerted in opposite directions. Even though both people push hard, their arm positions may not change.

Equal forces acting on one object in opposite directions are called **balanced forces.** Each force is balanced by the other.

Go Online

SciLINKS

For: Links on force
Visit: www.SciLinks.org
Web Code: scn-1321

Differentiated Instruction

English Learner/Beginning L1
Vocabulary: Word Analysis Contrast the meanings of the words *balanced* and *unbalanced.* Write the words on the board and underline the prefix *un-.* Point out that the prefix changes the meaning of the word. Ask students to supply examples of other words that have the prefix *un-.* *(Sample answer: untie, unavailable)* **learning modality: verbal**

English Learners/Intermediate L2
Vocabulary: Word Analysis Students can expand on the Beginning strategy by writing sentences using words that have the prefix *un-.* Model this activity for students before they begin. Ask for volunteers to read their sentences aloud. **learning modality: verbal**

Individual forces

No net force

FIGURE 3
Balanced and Unbalanced Forces
When the forces acting on an object are unbalanced, a net force acts on the object. The object will move. When balanced forces act on an object, no net force acts on the object. The object's motion remains unchanged.
Predicting If both girls pushed the box on the same side, would the motion of the box change? Why or why not?

Balanced Forces in Opposite Directions
When two equal forces act in opposite directions, they cancel each other out. The box doesn't move.

Balanced forces acting on an object do not change the object's motion. When equal forces are exerted in opposite directions, there is no net force. In Figure 3, when two people push on the box with equal force in opposite directions, the forces balance each other. The box does not move.

Section 1 Assessment

Target Reading Skill Asking Questions Use the answers to the questions you wrote about the headings to help you answer the questions below.

Reviewing Key Concepts
1. a. Defining What is a force?
   b. Explaining How is a force described?
   c. Interpreting Diagrams In a diagram, one force arrow is longer than the other arrow. What can you tell about the forces?
2. a. Reviewing How can you find the net force if two forces act in opposite directions?
   b. Comparing and Contrasting How do balanced forces acting on an object affect its motion? How do unbalanced forces acting on an object affect its motion?

   c. Calculating You exert a force of 120 N on a desk. Your friend exerts a force of 150 N in the same direction. What net force do you and your friend exert on the desk?

Lab zone At-Home Activity

House of Cards Carefully set two playing cards upright on a flat surface so that their top edges lean on each other. The cards should be able to stand by themselves. In terms of balanced forces, explain to a family member why the cards don't move. Then exert a force on one of the cards. Explain to a family member the role of unbalanced forces in what happens.

Answers
Figure 3 Yes. The two forces would act in the same direction and the box would move in that direction.

 Reading Checkpoint Unbalanced forces cause a change in an object's motion.

Assess

Reviewing Key Concepts
1. a. A force is a push or a pull. b. A force is described by the direction in which it acts and its strength, or magnitude. c. The longer force arrow represents a force with a greater strength, or magnitude.
2. a. To calculate the net force, you combine the opposing forces by subtraction.
b. Balanced forces cancel and do not change the object's motion. Unbalanced forces cause the object's motion to change. c. The net force is 270 N.

Reteach L1
Have students use Figure 3 to reinforce the definitions of *force*, *net force*, *balanced forces*, and *unbalanced forces*.

Performance Assessment L2
Drawing Have students sketch arm-wrestling matches in which balanced and unbalanced forces are demonstrated.
   Students can keep their drawings in their portfolio. **Portfolio**

All in One Teaching Resources
• Section Summary: *The Nature of Force*
• Review and Reinforce: *The Nature of Force*
• Enrich: *The Nature of Force*

Lab zone At-Home Activity

House of Cards L1 Students should explain that balanced forces do not cause a change in an object's motion. So, when the cards are not moving you know that the forces acting on them are balanced. When the student exerts a force on one of the cards, the forces are no longer balanced, and the position of the cards changes.

Sticky Sneakers L2

Prepare for Inquiry

Key Concept
Sneaker soles can be used to illustrate friction.

Skills Objectives
After this lab, students will be able to
- control variables in an investigation of friction
- interpret data to determine if the type of sneaker is related to the type of friction observed

 Prep Time 30 minutes
Class Time 40 minutes

Advance Planning
Assemble the spring scales, paper clips, tape, balance, and mass sets. Bring in an assortment of sneakers and ask students to volunteer their sneakers.

Safety
 Review the safety guidelines in Appendix A.

All in One Teaching Resources
- Lab Worksheet: *Sticky Sneakers*

Guide Inquiry

Invitation
Have a student wearing sneakers demonstrate three types of friction forces: stopping, starting, and sideways. Ask: **What does friction depend on?** (*Sample answer: Friction depends on the kinds of surfaces involved and how hard the surfaces push together.*) Have students discuss how different kinds of sneakers might have different kinds of friction.

Introduce the Procedure
Demonstrate how to zero and use a spring scale. Show students how to measure the force of sliding friction with a spring scale by pulling an object with a slow, constant motion. Tell students to pull an object forward to measure forward-stopping friction and sideways to measure sideways-stopping friction.

Sticky Sneakers

Problem
Friction is a force that acts in the opposite direction to motion. How does the amount of friction between a sneaker and a surface compare for different brands of sneakers?

Skills Focus
controlling variables, interpreting data

Materials
- three or more different brands of sneakers
- 2 spring scales, 5-N and 20-N, or force sensors
- mass set(s)
- tape
- 3 large paper clips
- balance

Procedure
1. Sneakers are designed to deal with various friction forces, including these:
   - starting friction, which is involved when you start from a stopped position
   - forward-stopping friction, which is involved when you come to a forward stop
   - sideways-stopping friction, which is involved when you come to a sideways stop
2. Prepare a data table in which you can record each type of friction for each sneaker.

3. Place each sneaker on a balance. Then put masses in each sneaker so that the total mass of the sneaker plus the masses is 1,000 g. Spread the masses out evenly inside the sneaker.

4. You will need to tape a paper clip to each sneaker and then attach a spring scale to the paper clip. (If you are using force sensors, see your teacher for instructions.) To measure
   - starting friction, attach the paper clip to the back of the sneaker
   - forward-stopping friction, attach the paper clip to the front of the sneaker
   - sideways-stopping friction, attach the paper clip to the side of the sneaker

Data Table			
Sneaker	Starting Friction (N)	Sideways-Stopping Friction (N)	Forward-Stopping Friction (N)
A			
B			

Troubleshooting the Experiment
- Students should zero the spring scale each time it is used. If the spring scale is calibrated in grams, multiply by 0.01 to obtain the approximate value in newtons.
- The spring scale should not be angled to the side or up and down while it is used, or the measurements will not be accurate.

5. To measure starting friction, pull the sneaker backward until it starts to move. Use the 20-N spring scale first. If the reading is less than 5 N, use a 5-N scale. The force necessary to make the sneaker start moving is equal to the friction force. Record the starting friction force in your data table.

6. To measure either type of stopping friction, use the spring scale to pull each sneaker at a slow, constant speed. Record the stopping friction force in your data table.

7. Repeat Steps 4–6 for the remaining sneakers.

Analyze and Conclude

1. Controlling Variables What are the manipulated and responding variables in this experiment? Explain. (See the Skills Handbook to read about experimental variables.)

2. Observing Why is the reading on the spring scale equal to the friction force in each case?

3. Interpreting Data Which sneaker had the most starting friction? Which had the most forward-stopping friction? Which had the most sideways-stopping friction?

4. Drawing Conclusions Do you think that using a sneaker with a small amount of mass in it is a fair test of the friction of the sneakers? Why or why not? (Hint: Consider that sneakers are used with people's feet inside them.)

5. Inferring Why did you pull the sneaker at a slow speed to test for stopping friction? Why did you pull a sneaker that wasn't moving to test starting friction?

6. Developing Hypotheses Can you identify a relationship between the brand of sneaker and the amount of friction you observed? If so, describe the relationship. What do you observe that might cause one sneaker to grip the floor better than another?

7. Communicating Draw a diagram for an advertising brochure that shows the forces acting on the sneaker for each type of motion.

Design an Experiment

Wear a pair of your own sneakers. Start running and notice how you press against the floor with your sneaker. How do you think this affects the friction between the sneaker and the floor? Design an experiment that will test for this variable. *Obtain your teacher's permission before carrying out your investigation.*

M ◆ 41

Objectives

After this lesson, students will be able to

M.2.2.1 Describe friction, and identify factors that determine the friction force between two objects.

M.2.2.2 Identify the factors that affect the gravitational force between two objects.

M.2.2.3 Explain why objects accelerate during free fall.

Target Reading Skill

Comparing and Contrasting Explain that comparing and contrasting information shows how ideas, facts, and events are similar and different. The results of the comparison can help students' understanding. Possible answers include the following:

Answers
Friction:
Effect on motion: opposes motion; Depends on: types of surfaces involved, how hard the surfaces push together; Measured in: newtons
Gravity:
Effect on motion: pulls objects toward one another; depends on: mass and distance; Measured in: newtons

All in One Teaching Resources

• Transparency M13

Preteach

Build Background Knowledge · L2

Demonstrating Friction

Stack two books on a table. Tie a string around the bottom book. Attach an elastic band to the string. Pull the elastic band to move the books. Now place several round pencils under the books, and pull the elastic band to move the books. Ask: **What do you observe about the elastic band when the books are pulled?** (*It stretches.*) **What difference do you observe when pencils are placed under the books?** (*The elastic band stretches less.*) **What causes this difference?** (*The books move more easily with pencils underneath.*)

Section 2
Friction and Gravity

Reading Preview

Key Concepts
• What factors determine the strength of the friction force between two surfaces?
• What factors affect the gravitational force between two objects?
• Why do objects accelerate during free fall?

Key Terms
• friction • static friction
• sliding friction
• rolling friction • fluid friction
• gravity • mass • weight
• free fall • air resistance
• terminal velocity • projectile

Target Reading Skill

Comparing and Contrasting As you read, compare and contrast friction and gravity by completing a table like the one below.

	Friction	Gravity
Effect on motion	Opposes motion	
Depends on		
Measured in		

Lab zone Discover Activity

Which Lands First?

1. Stack three quarters. Wrap tape around the quarters to hold them tightly together. Place the stack of quarters next to a single quarter near the edge of a desk.
2. Put a ruler flat on the desk behind the coins. Line it up parallel to the edge of the desk and just touching the coins.
3. Keeping the ruler parallel to the edge of the desk, push the coins over the edge at the same time. Observe how long the coins take to land.

Think It Over
Predicting Did you see a difference in the time the coins took to fall? Use what you observed to predict whether a golf ball will fall more quickly than a table tennis ball. Will a pencil fall more quickly than a book? How can you test your predictions?

What happens when you jump on a sled on the side of a snow-covered hill? You can predict that the sled will slide down the hill. Now think about what happens at the bottom of the hill. Does the sled keep sliding? You can predict that the sled will slow down and stop.

Why does the sled's motion change on the side of the hill and then again at the bottom? In each case, unbalanced forces act on the sled. The force of gravity causes the sled to accelerate down the hill. The force of friction eventually causes the sled to stop. These two forces affect many motions on Earth.

◀ Friction and gravity both act on the sled.

Lab zone Discover Activity

Skills Focus Predicting · L1

Materials 4 quarters, ruler, tape

Time 15 minutes

Tips Remind students to keep the ruler parallel to the edge of the desk.

Think It Over Students should observe that the single coin and the three-coin set took the same time to fall. They should predict that the soccer ball and the marble and the book and the pencil will all take the same time to fall. They can test their prediction by holding two of the objects at the same height, releasing them at the same time, and observing whether or not they land at the same time.

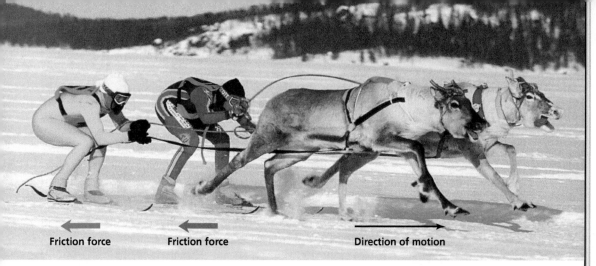

Friction force ←   Friction force ←   Direction of motion →

FIGURE 4
Friction and Smooth Surfaces The smooth surfaces of the skis make for a fast ride for these Finnish skiers.
Relating Diagrams and Photos *How does the direction of friction compare to the direction of motion?*

Friction

When a sled moves across snow, the bottom of the sled rubs against the surface of the snow. In the same way, the skin of a firefighter's hands rubs against the polished metal pole during the slide down the pole. The force that two surfaces exert on each other when they rub against each other is called **friction.**

The Causes of Friction In general, smooth surfaces produce less friction than rough surfaces. **The strength of the force of friction depends on two factors: how hard the surfaces push together and the types of surfaces involved.** The skiers in Figure 4 get a fast ride because there is very little friction between their skis and the snow. The reindeer would not be able to pull them easily over a rough surface such as sand. Friction also increases if surfaces push hard against each other. If you rub your hands together forcefully, there is more friction than if you rub your hands together lightly.

A snow-packed surface or a metal firehouse pole may seem quite smooth. But, as you can see in Figure 5, even the smoothest objects have irregular, bumpy surfaces. When the irregularities of one surface come into contact with those of another surface, friction occurs. Friction acts in a direction opposite to the direction of the object's motion. Without friction, a moving object might not stop until it strikes another object.

FIGURE 5
A Smooth Surface?
If you look at the polished surface of an aluminum alloy under a powerful microscope, you'll find that it is actually quite rough.

Chapter 2 M ◆ 43

Help Students Read

Summarizing Refer to the Content Refresher for this chapter, which provides the guidelines for the Summarizing strategy. Summarizing the information presented in the text will help students to focus on the main ideas and remember what they read. Have students read the paragraphs describing the four types of friction. Then have them summarize each paragraph by stating the main idea in their own words.

Go Online

SC*LINKS* NSTA

For: Links on friction
Visit: www.SciLinks.org
Web Code: scn-1322

Students can research friction online.

Lab zone Try This Activity

Spinning Plates

You can compare rolling friction to sliding friction.

1. Stack two identical pie plates together. Try to spin the top plate.
2. Now separate the plates and fill the bottom of one pie plate loosely with marbles.

3. Place the second plate in the plate with marbles.
4. Try to spin the top plate again. Observe the results.

Drawing Conclusions What applications can you think of for the rolling friction modeled in this activity?

Go Online

SC*LINKS* NSTA

For: Links on friction
Visit: www.SciLinks.org
Web Code: scn-1322

Static Friction Four types of friction are shown in Figure 6. The friction that acts on objects that are not moving is called **static friction.** Because of static friction, you must use extra force to start the motion of stationary objects. For example, think about what happens when you try to push a heavy desk across a floor. If you push on the desk with a force less than the force of static friction between the desk and the floor, the desk will not move. To make the desk move, you must exert a force greater than the force of static friction. Once the desk is moving, there is no longer any static friction. However, there is another type of friction—sliding friction.

Sliding Friction **Sliding friction** occurs when two solid surfaces slide over each other. Sliding friction can be useful. For example, you can spread sand on an icy path to improve your footing. Ballet dancers apply a sticky powder to the soles of their ballet slippers so they won't slip on the dance floor. And when you stop a bicycle with hand brakes, rubber pads slide against the tire surfaces, causing the wheels to slow and eventually stop. On the other hand, sliding friction is a problem if you fall off your bike and skin your knee!

Rolling Friction When an object rolls across a surface, **rolling friction** occurs. Rolling friction is easier to overcome than sliding friction for similar materials. This type of friction is important to engineers who design certain products. For example, skates, skateboards, and bicycles need wheels that move freely. So engineers use ball bearings to reduce the friction between the wheels and the rest of the product. These ball bearings are small, smooth steel balls that reduce friction by rolling between moving parts.

Fluid Friction Fluids, such as water, oil, or air, are materials that flow easily. **Fluid friction** occurs when a solid object moves through a fluid. Like rolling friction, fluid friction is easier to overcome than sliding friction. This is why the parts of machines that must slide over each other are often bathed in oil. In this way, the solid parts move through the fluid instead of sliding against each other. When you ride a bike, fluid friction occurs between you and the air. Cyclists often wear streamlined helmets and specially designed clothing to reduce fluid friction.

Reading Checkpoint What are two ways in which friction can be useful?

Lab zone Try This Activity

Skills Focus Drawing conclusions

Materials marbles, two identical pie plates

Time 10 minutes

Tips After Step 1, Ask: **What kind of friction occurred?** (*Sliding friction*) After Step 4, Ask: **What kind of friction occurred?** (*Rolling friction*)

Expected Outcome Students should note that the top plate spins more easily when the marbles are in place. Possible applications include wheels with ball bearings.

Extend Have students repeat the investigation, substituting water for the marbles in Step 3. Lead students to infer why lubrication is used in machinery.
learning modality: kinesthetic

FIGURE 6
Types of Friction

Types of friction include static, sliding, rolling, and fluid friction. **Making Generalizations** *In what direction does friction act compared to an object's motion?*

Static Friction ▼
To make the sled move, the athlete first has to overcome the force of static friction. Static friction acts in the opposite direction to the intended motion.

Sliding friction

Direction of motion

Sliding Friction ▲
Once the sled is moving, it slides over the floor. Sliding friction acts between the sled and the floor in the opposite direction to the sled's motion.

Static friction

Intended direction of motion

Rolling Friction ▼
Rolling friction occurs when an object rolls over a surface. For the skateboarder, rolling friction acts in the direction opposite to the skateboard's motion.

Direction of motion

Fluid friction

Fluid Friction ▲
When an object pushes fluid aside, friction occurs. The surfer must overcome the fluid friction of the water.

Direction of motion   Rolling friction

Chapter 2   M ◆ 45

Investigating Friction

Materials spring scale; wooden blocks; various materials such as sandpaper, carpeting, and aluminum foil

Time 15 min

Focus Ask: **How would you describe the texture of a surface that produces a lot of friction?** *(Sample answer: Rough or gritty)*

Teach Have students investigate the friction created by different surfaces. Use wooden blocks with hooks, or use elastic bands with paper clips to attach the spring scale to the wooden blocks. Students should drag the wooden block over various materials at a constant speed. The spring scale reading is equal to the friction force. Have students compare the friction created by different surfaces.

Apply Ask: **Which surface tested produced the least friction?** *(Sample answer: Aluminum foil)* **Which surface tested produced the most friction?** *(Sample answer: Sandpaper)* **learning modality: kinesthetic**

Monitor Progress _____ L2

Writing Have students write a sentence or two describing a situation in which friction is both a help and a hindrance. *(Sample answer: Friction slows a car when it is in motion, but allows the wheels to move forward without slipping.)*

Answers
Figure 6 Friction acts in the direction opposite the object's motion.

✓ **Reading Checkpoint** Static friction allows objects to remain in place. Sliding friction allows moving objects to stop to avoid colliding with other objects.

M ● 45

Gravity

Teach Key Skills

Key Ideas About Gravity

Focus Ask: **What would happen if I dropped my book?** *(Sample answer: It would fall to the floor.)*

Teach Write on the board: *Universal Gravitation, Factors Affecting Gravity,* and *Weight and Mass.* Have students locate these heads in the text. For each head, have students work as a class to write the main ideas found in the text under the head.

Apply Ask: **Why don't you notice the pull of gravity between most objects?** *(The forces of attraction are weak.)* **learning modality: logical/mathematical**

 **Teaching Resources**

- Transparency M14

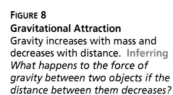

Measuring Mass and Weight

Materials spring scale, triple-beam balance or pan balance

Time 10 minutes

Focus Remind students that mass and weight are not the same. Mass is the amount of matter in an object; weight is the measure of the gravitational force on an object.

Teach Show students the scale and the balance. Ask: **Which of these is used to measure mass?** *(The balance)* **Which is used to measure weight?** *(The scale)* Point out that measurements made using the scale would be different on the moon, while measurements made using the balance would be the same on Earth and the moon.

Apply Ask: **What is measured by a bathroom scale?** *(Weight)* **learning modality: visual**

FIGURE 7
Gravity and Acceleration
Divers begin accelerating as soon as they leap from the platform.

FIGURE 8
Gravitational Attraction
Gravity increases with mass and decreases with distance. *Inferring What happens to the force of gravity between two objects if the distance between them decreases?*

Gravity

Would you be surprised if you let go of a pen you were holding and it did not fall? You are so used to objects falling that you may not have thought about why they fall. One person who thought about it was Isaac Newton. He concluded that a force acts to pull objects straight down toward the center of Earth. **Gravity** is a force that pulls objects toward each other.

Universal Gravitation Newton realized that gravity acts everywhere in the universe, not just on Earth. It is the force that makes an apple fall to the ground. It is the force that keeps the moon orbiting around Earth. It is the force that keeps all the planets in our solar system orbiting around the sun.

What Newton realized is now called the law of universal gravitation. The law of universal gravitation states that the force of gravity acts between all objects in the universe. This means that any two objects in the universe, without exception, attract each other. You are attracted not only to Earth but also to all the other objects around you. Earth and the objects around you are attracted to you as well. However, you do not notice the attraction among objects because these forces are small compared to the force of Earth's attraction.

Factors Affecting Gravity Two factors affect the gravitational attraction between objects: mass and distance. **Mass** is a measure of the amount of matter in an object. The SI unit of mass is the kilogram. One kilogram is the mass of about 400 modern pennies. Everything that has mass is made up of matter.

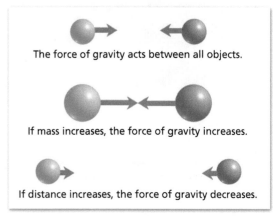

The force of gravity acts between all objects.

If mass increases, the force of gravity increases.

If distance increases, the force of gravity decreases.

The more mass an object has, the greater its gravitational force. Because the sun's mass is so great, it exerts a large gravitational force on the planets. That's one reason why the planets orbit the sun.

In addition to mass, gravitational force depends on the distance between the objects. The farther apart two objects are, the lesser the gravitational force between them. For a spacecraft traveling toward Mars, Earth's gravitational pull decreases as the spacecraft's distance from Earth increases. Eventually the gravitational pull of Mars becomes greater than Earth's, and the spacecraft is more attracted toward Mars.

Weight and Mass Mass is sometimes confused with weight. Mass is a measure of the amount of matter in an object; weight is a measure of the gravitational force exerted on an object. The force of gravity on a person or object at the surface of a planet is known as **weight.** So, when you step on a bathroom scale, you are determining the gravitational force Earth is exerting on you.

Weight varies with the strength of the gravitational force but mass does not. Suppose you weighed yourself on Earth to be 450 newtons. Then you traveled to the moon and weighed yourself again. You might be surprised to find out that you weigh only about 75 newtons—the weight of about 8 kilograms on Earth! You weigh less on the moon because the moon's mass is only a fraction of Earth's.

 Reading Checkpoint | **What is the difference between weight and mass?**

FIGURE 9
Mass and Weight This astronaut jumps easily on the moon. *Comparing and Contrasting How do his mass and weight on the moon compare to his mass and weight on Earth?*

Astronaut in Spacesuit	
Weight on Moon =	270 N
Weight on Earth =	1,617 N
Mass on Moon =	165 kg
Mass on Earth =	165 kg

M ◆ 47

Lab zone Skills Activity

Calculating
You can determine the weight of an object if you measure its mass.

1. Estimate the weight of four objects. (*Hint:* A small lemon weighs about 1 N.)
2. Use a balance to find the mass of each object. If the measurements are not in kilograms, convert them to kilograms.
3. Multiply each mass by 9.8 m/s^2 to find the weight in newtons.

How close to actual values were your estimates?

Lab zone Skills Activity

Skills Focus Calculating L2

Materials balance; four distinct objects, such as a book, a shoe, a spiral notebook, a pair of scissors

Time 15 minutes

Tips Have students create and use a data table.

Expected Outcome Students' estimates will vary. Students can check the reasonableness of their answers by mentally multiplying the mass by 10.

Extend Have students estimate the mass of an object, then measure its weight using a scale, then divide by 9.8 m/s^2 to find the actual mass. **learning modality: logical/ mathematical**

Address Misconceptions L2
Mass and Weight

Focus Most people use the term *weight* when they mean *mass.* Tell students you know of a revolutionary weight-loss plan.

Teach Explain that your weight-loss plan consists of a trip to the moon, where you will weigh one-sixth of what you do on Earth.

Apply Ask: **Why wouldn't this weight-loss plan have the effect most people want?** (*The amount of matter—or mass—in a person's body would not change.*) **learning modality: logical/mathematical**

Integrating Life Science L2
Ask: **In what direction do the roots of plants grow?** (*Downward*) **In what direction do the stems of plants grow?** (*Upward*) Tell students that plants' responses to gravity are called gravitropism. Negative gravitropism is the tendency to grow upward, away from the force of gravity. Positive gravitropism is the tendency to grow toward the pull of gravity. **learning modality: verbal**

Monitor Progress L2

Skills Check Ask students to describe in their own words the difference between mass and weight.

Answers
Figure 8 The force of gravity between the objects increases as the distance between the objects decreases.
Figure 9 The astronaut's mass is the same on Earth and the moon. The astronaut's weight is much less on the moon.

Reading Checkpoint | Mass is the amount of matter in an object; weight is the force of gravity on an object.

M ● 47

Gravity and Motion

Teach Key Skills L2
Gravity Causes Acceleration

Focus Ask: **What happens to a ball if you hold it out in front of you and then release it?** *(It falls to the ground.)* **Is the ball falling faster when it leaves your hand or when it is just about to hit the ground?** *(It falls faster when it is about to hit the ground.)*

Teach Explain that acceleration means speeding up, slowing down, or changing direction. Gravity causes objects to accelerate. When an object is dropped, gravity causes its velocity to increase. When an object is thrown horizontally, gravity causes a change in direction. Air resistance, a type of friction, also affects motion.

Apply Ask: **When you throw a baseball, how can you tell that the force of gravity is acting on it?** *(The ball eventually falls to the ground.)* **learning modality: verbal**

![Math Analyzing Data]

Math Skill Making and interpreting graphs

Focus Tell students that line graphs are useful for showing the relationship between two variables.

Teach Ask: **Why does a straight line represent the relationship between these two variables?** *(The speed increases by the same amount each second.)*

Answers
1. Time is on the horizontal axis, and speed is on the vertical axis.
2. The slope is 9.8. The speed increases by 9.8 m/s each second.
3. 58.8 m/s
4. The speed values would not change.

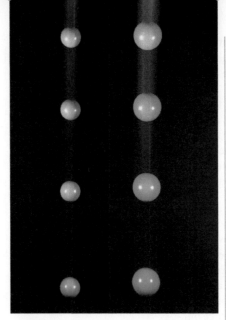

FIGURE 10
Free Fall
In the absence of air, two objects with different masses fall at exactly the same rate.

Gravity and Motion

On Earth, gravity is a downward force that affects all objects. When you hold a book, you exert a force that balances the force of gravity. When you let go of the book, gravity becomes an unbalanced force and the book falls.

Free Fall When the only force acting on an object is gravity, the object is said to be in **free fall.** An object in free fall is accelerating. Do you know why? **In free fall, the force of gravity is an unbalanced force, which causes an object to accelerate.**

How much do objects accelerate as they fall? Near the surface of Earth, the acceleration due to gravity is 9.8 m/s^2. This means that for every second an object is falling, its velocity increases by 9.8 m/s. For example, suppose an object is dropped from the top of a building. Its starting velocity is 0 m/s. After one second, its velocity has increased to 9.8 m/s. After two seconds, its velocity is 19.6 m/s (9.8 m/s + 9.8 m/s). The velocity continues to increase as the object falls.

While it may seem hard to believe at first, all objects in free fall accelerate at the same rate regardless of their masses. The two falling objects in Figure 10 demonstrate this principle.

![Math Analyzing Data]

Free Fall
Use the graph to answer the following questions.

1. **Interpreting Graphs** What variable is on the horizontal axis? The vertical axis?
2. **Calculating** Calculate the slope of the graph. What does the slope tell you about the object's motion?
3. **Predicting** What will be the speed of the object at 6 seconds?
4. **Drawing Conclusions** Suppose another object of the same size but with a greater mass was dropped instead. How would the speed values change?

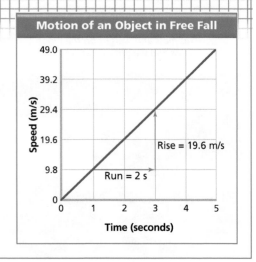

Motion of an Object in Free Fall

Rise = 19.6 m/s
Run = 2 s

Speed (m/s) — vertical axis: 0, 9.8, 19.6, 29.4, 39.2, 49.0
Time (seconds) — horizontal axis: 0, 1, 2, 3, 4, 5

Air Resistance

Despite the fact that all objects are supposed to fall at the same rate, you know that this is not always the case. For example, an oak leaf flutters slowly to the ground, while an acorn drops straight down. Objects falling through air experience a type of fluid friction called **air resistance.** Remember that friction is in the direction opposite to motion, so air resistance is an upward force exerted on falling objects. Air resistance is not the same for all objects. Falling objects with a greater surface area experience more air resistance. That is why a leaf falls more slowly than an acorn. In a vacuum, where there is no air, all objects fall with exactly the same rate of acceleration.

You can see the effect of air resistance if you drop a flat piece of paper and a crumpled piece of paper at the same time. Since the flat paper has a greater surface area, it experiences greater air resistance and falls more slowly. In a vacuum, both pieces of paper would fall at the same rate.

Air resistance increases with velocity. As a falling object speeds up, the force of air resistance becomes greater and greater. Eventually, a falling object will fall fast enough that the upward force of air resistance becomes equal to the downward force of gravity acting on the object. At this point the forces on the object are balanced. Remember that when forces are balanced, there is no acceleration. The object continues to fall, but its velocity remains constant. The greatest velocity a falling object reaches is called its **terminal velocity.** Terminal velocity is reached when the force of air resistance equals the weight of the object.

FIGURE 11
Air Resistance
Falling objects with a greater surface area experience more air resistance. If the leaf and the acorn fall from the tree at the same time, the acorn will hit first. Comparing and Contrasting *If the objects fall in a vacuum, which one will hit first? Why?*

Visualizing Air Resistance

Materials (for each group of students) stopwatch, two sheets of notebook paper

Time 10 minutes

Focus Ask: **Besides gravity, what force acts on falling objects?** (*Air resistance*)

Teach Students should work in small groups or pairs. Have one student hold a piece of notebook paper flat and release it. Have the other student measure the time it takes for the paper to fall to the ground. Have students repeat the procedure with a piece of notebook paper that has been crushed into a ball. Remind students to drop both objects from the same height.

Apply Ask: **Why did the flat sheet of notebook paper take longer to reach the ground?** (*It has a larger surface area, so the force of air resistance is greater.*) **learning modality: kinesthetic**

Differentiated Instruction

English Learners/Beginning L1
Vocabulary: Science Glossary
Pronounce and define aloud the following key terms for students: *free fall, air resistance, terminal velocity,* and *projectile.* Write definitions of the terms on the board. Have students copy the terms in their science glossaries. Students can add diagrams or pictures to help them remember the meaning of the terms. **learning modality: verbal**

English Learners/Intermediate L2
Vocabulary: Science Glossary Students can expand the Beginning activity by writing a sentence using each of the terms. Model this activity on the board before students begin. Call on volunteers to read their sentences aloud. **learning modality: verbal**

Monitor Progress ———— L2

Writing Have students write one or two sentences describing the forces acting on a falling object.

Answers
Figure 11 In a vacuum, the acorn and the leaf would both hit the bottom at the same time.

Monitor Progress

Answers

Figure 12 No, horizontal velocity does not affect how fast it will fall.

> **Reading Checkpoint** It pulls the objects toward the center of Earth in the same way it pulls a dropped object.

Assess

Reviewing Key Concepts

1. a. Static friction, sliding friction, rolling friction, fluid friction **b.** The strength of the friction force between two surfaces depends on the nature of the two surfaces and how hard they push together. **c.** rolling friction and fluid friction

2. a. The force of gravity acts between all objects in the universe. **b.** The more mass an object has, the greater the strength of its gravitational force; the greater the distance between two objects, the weaker the gravitational force between them. **c.** Your weight would be greater because the gravitational force would be greater.

3. a. Gravitational force causes the object to accelerate toward the center of Earth. **b.** An object's mass has no effect on its acceleration during free fall. **c.** Air resistance increases, but the force of gravity remains the same.

Reteach L1

Have students review the section to make lists of examples of friction and gravity affecting motion. Ask for volunteers to share items from their lists with the class.

Performance Assessment L2

Writing Have the students write a description of the motion of a brick and a feather dropped from a 50-meter tall building and the motion of the same objects dropped in a 50-meter tall tube from which the air has been removed.

All in One Teaching Resources

- Section Summary: *Friction and Gravity*
- Review and Reinforce: *Friction and Gravity*
- Enrich: *Friction and Gravity*

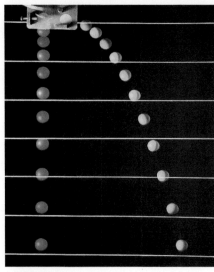

FIGURE 12
Projectile Motion
One ball is dropped vertically and a second ball is thrown horizontally at the same time.
Making Generalizations *Does the horizontal velocity of the ball affect how fast it falls?*

Projectile Motion Rather than dropping a ball straight down, what happens if you throw it horizontally? An object that is thrown is called a **projectile** (pruh JEK tul). Will a projectile that is thrown horizontally land on the ground at the same time as an object that is dropped?

Look at Figure 12. The yellow ball was given a horizontal push at the same time as the red ball was dropped. Even though the yellow ball moves horizontally, the force of gravity continues to act on it in the same way it acts on the red ball. The yellow ball falls at the same rate as the red ball. Thus, both balls will hit the ground at exactly the same time.

In a similar way, an arrow flying toward a target is a projectile. Because of the force of gravity, the arrow will fall as it flies toward the target. So if you try to hit the bull's-eye, you must aim above it to account for gravity's pull. When you throw a projectile at an upward angle, the force of gravity reduces its vertical velocity. Eventually, the upward motion of the projectile will stop, and gravity will pull it back toward the ground. From this point, the projectile will fall at the same rate as any dropped object.

> **Reading Checkpoint** How does gravity affect objects that are moving horizontally?

Section 2 Assessment

 Target Reading Skill

Comparing and Contrasting Use the information in your table about friction and gravity to help you answer the questions below.

Reviewing Key Concepts

1. a. Listing What are the four types of friction?
   b. Summarizing What factors affect the friction force between two surfaces?
   c. Classifying What types of friction occur when you ride a bike through a puddle?

2. a. Identifying What is the law of universal gravitation?
   b. Explaining How do mass and distance affect the gravitational attraction between objects?
   c. Predicting How would your weight change on the surface of an Earth-sized planet whose mass was greater than Earth's? Why?

3. a. Reviewing Why does an object accelerate when it falls toward Earth's surface?
   b. Describing How does the mass of an object affect its acceleration during free fall?
   c. Applying Concepts What force changes when a sky diver's parachute opens? What force stays the same?

Writing in Science

Cause-and-Effect Paragraph Suppose Earth's gravitational force were decreased by half. How would this change affect a game of basketball? Write a paragraph explaining how the motion of the players and the ball would be different.

Lab zone Chapter Project

Keep Students on Track Have students use the information they have learned about friction and gravity to assess how these forces will affect their vehicles. Have students draw a diagram that shows the direction in which gravity and friction will act on their vehicle. Have students brainstorm ways to reduce the friction forces that will affect their vehicle.

Writing in Science

Writing Mode Exposition/Cause-and-Effect

Scoring Rubric

4 Exceeds criteria

3 Meets criteria

2 Paragraph is not detailed and/or includes some incorrect information

1 Paragraph does not relate to the topic and/or includes numerous errors

Reading Preview

Key Concepts
- What is Newton's first law of motion?
- What is Newton's second law of motion?

Key Term
- inertia

Target Reading Skill
Outlining As you read, make an outline about Newton's first and second laws. Use the red headings for the main topics and the blue headings for the subtopics.

Newton's First and Second Laws
I. The First Law of Motion
A. Inertia
B.
II. The Second Law of Motion
A.

Isaac Newton ▼

Section
3
Newton's First and Second Laws

Lab zone — Discover Activity

What Changes Motion?

1. Stack several metal washers on top of a toy car.
2. Place a heavy book on the floor near the car.
3. Predict what will happen to both the car and the washers if you roll the car into the book. Test your prediction.

Think It Over

Observing What happened to the car when it hit the book? What happened to the washers? What might be the reason for any difference between the motions of the car and the washers?

How and why objects move as they do has fascinated scientists for thousands of years. In the early 1600s, the Italian astronomer Galileo Galilei suggested that, once an object is in motion, no force is needed to keep it moving. Force is needed only to change the motion of an object. Galileo's ideas paved the way for Isaac Newton. Newton proposed the three basic laws of motion in the late 1600s.

The First Law of Motion

Newton's first law restates Galileo's ideas about force and motion. **Newton's first law of motion states that an object at rest will remain at rest, and an object moving at a constant velocity will continue moving at a constant velocity, unless it is acted upon by an unbalanced force.**

If an object is not moving, it will not move until a force acts on it. Clothes on the floor of your room, for example, will stay there unless you pick them up. If an object is already moving, it will continue to move at a constant velocity until a force acts to change either its speed or direction. For example, a tennis ball flies through the air once you hit it with a racket. If your friend doesn't hit the ball back, the forces of gravity and friction will eventually stop the ball. On Earth, gravity and friction are unbalanced forces that often change an object's motion.

Chapter 2 M ♦ 51

Objectives

After this lesson, students will be able to

M.2.4.1 State Newton's first law of motion.
M.2.4.2 State Newton's second law of motion.

Target Reading Skill

Outlining Explain that using an outline format helps students organize information by main topic, subtopic, and details.

Answers
Newton's First and Second Laws
  I. The First Law of Motion
    A. Inertia
    B. Inertia Depends on Mass
  II. The Second Law of Motion
    A. Determining Acceleration
    B. Changes in Force and Mass

All in One Teaching Resources
- Transparency M15

Preteach

Build Background Knowledge [L2]

Force Affects Acceleration
Demonstrate the effect of force on acceleration by placing one end of a flexible ruler next to a golf ball, bending the ruler back slightly, and releasing it to exert a small force on the ball. Repeat the demonstration, but bend the ruler back further so it exerts a greater force against the ball. Have students compare the forces and the motion of the ball in each trial.

Lab zone — Discover Activity

Skills Focus Observing [L1]

Materials heavy book, metal washers, toy car

Time 10 minutes

Tips Students should be reminded not to fasten the washers to the top of the car.

Expected Outcome The car will stop or bounce backward when it hits the book.

The washers will continue to move forward.

Think It Over The car stopped or bounced back when it hit the book, while the washers kept moving forward. The book exerted a force on the car that caused it to stop, however the book did not exert a force on the washers, so they continued moving.

The First Law of Motion

Teach Key Concepts L2
Force and Motion

Focus Ask: **What happens to passengers when a car stops quickly?** *(Sample answer: They keep moving until the seatbelt stops them.)*

Teach Explain that an object's motion does not change unless it is acted upon by unbalanced forces. Resistance to a change in motion is called inertia.

Apply Ask: **How does Newton's first law explain what happens to passengers when a car stops quickly?** *(Sample answer: The passengers keep moving until acted upon by the unbalanced force exerted by the seatbelt.)*
learning modality: logical/mathematical

The Second Law of Motion

Teach Key Concepts L2
Force, Mass and Acceleration

Focus Have students recall experiences of pushing a grocery cart. Ask: **Would you need to exert more force to move a full cart or an empty cart?** *(A full cart)*

Teach Remind students that a full grocery cart has more mass than an empty cart. Newton's second law states the relationship between force, mass, and acceleration. The greater the mass, the more force that is required to produce a certain acceleration.

Apply Ask: **How could you make grocery carts with different masses have the same acceleration?** *(You would need to exert different forces on the carts.)* **learning modality: logical/mathematical**

Independent Practice L2

All in One Teaching Resources

- Guided Reading and Study Worksheet: *Newton's First and Second Laws*

⊙ Student Edition on Audio CD

FIGURE 13
Inertia The inertia of the objects on the table keeps them from moving.
Inferring Why should the girl use a slippery tablecloth?

 Try This Activity

Around and Around
An object moving in a circle has inertia.

1. Tape one end of a length of thread (about 1 m) to a table tennis ball.
2. Suspend the ball in front of you and swing it in a horizontal circle, keeping it 2–3 cm above the floor.
3. Let go of the thread and observe the direction in which the ball rolls.
4. Repeat this several times, letting go of the thread at different points.

Inferring At what point do you need to let go of the thread if you want the ball to roll directly away from you? Toward you? Draw a diagram as part of your answer.

52 ◆ M

Inertia Whether an object is moving or not, it resists any change to its motion. Galileo's concept of the resistance to a change in motion is called inertia. **Inertia** (in UR shuh) is the tendency of an object to resist a change in motion. Newton's first law of motion is also called the law of inertia.

Inertia explains many common events, such as why you move forward in your seat when a car stops suddenly. When the car stops, inertia keeps you moving forward. A force, such as the pull of a seat belt, is required to change your motion.

Inertia Depends on Mass Some objects have more inertia than other objects. For example, suppose you needed to move an empty aquarium and an aquarium full of water. Obviously, the full aquarium is harder to move than the empty one, because it has more mass. The greater the mass of an object is, the greater its inertia, and the greater the force required to change its motion. The full aquarium is more difficult to move because it has more inertia than the empty aquarium.

✓ Reading Checkpoint How is mass related to inertia?

The Second Law of Motion
Suppose you are baby-sitting two children who love wagon rides. Their favorite part is when you accelerate quickly. When you get tired and sit in the wagon, one of the children pulls you. He soon finds he cannot accelerate the wagon nearly as fast as you can. How is the wagon's acceleration related to the force pulling it? How is the acceleration related to the wagon's mass?

Try This Activity

Skills Focus Inferring L2
Materials masking or cellophane tape, table tennis ball, thread
Time 15 minutes

Expected Outcome The ball will continue to travel in the direction in which it was moving when it was released. Students' diagrams should show that the ball must be released when it is moving in the desired direction. **learning modality: kinesthetic**

Determining Acceleration **According to Newton's second law of motion, acceleration depends on the object's mass and on the net force acting on the object.** This relationship can be written as an equation.

$$\text{Acceleration} = \frac{\text{Net force}}{\text{Mass}}$$

Acceleration is measured in meters per second per second (m/s^2), and mass is measured in kilograms (kg). According to Newton's second law, then, force is measured in kilograms times meters per second per second ($kg \cdot m/s^2$). The short form for this unit of force is the newton (N). Recall that a newton is the SI unit of force. You can think of 1 newton as the force required to give a 1-kg mass an acceleration of $1\ m/s^2$.

Go Online
PHSchool.com

For: More on Newton's laws
Visit: PHSchool.com
Web Code: cgd-3023

 **Math** **Sample Problem**

Calculating Force

A speedboat pulls a 55-kg water-skier. The force causes the skier to accelerate at 2.0 m/s². Calculate the net force that causes this acceleration.

1 **Read and Understand**
What information are you given?
Mass of the water-skier (m) = 55 kg
Acceleration of the water-skier (a) = 2.0 m/s²

2 **Plan and Solve**
What quantity are you trying to calculate?
The net force (F_{net}) = ▨

What formula contains the given quantities and the unknown quantity?

$$a = \frac{F_{net}}{m} \quad \text{or} \quad F_{net} = m \times a$$

Perform the calculation.
$F_{net} = m \times a = 55\ kg \times 2.0\ m/s^2$
$F = 110\ kg \cdot m/s^2$
$F = 110\ N$

3 **Look Back and Check**
Does your answer make sense?
A net force of 110 N is required to accelerate the water-skier. This may not seem like enough force, but it does not include the force of the speedboat's pull that overcomes friction.

 **Math** **Practice**

1. **Calculating Force** What is the net force on a 1,000-kg object accelerating at 3 m/s²?
2. **Calculating Force** What net force is needed to accelerate a 25-kg cart at 14 m/s²?

Differentiated Instruction

Less Proficient Readers L1
Asking Questions Have students listen to the section on the **Student Edition on Audio CD.** Then have students locate the headings in the section. Have students phrase the headings in the form of a question, and share the answers verbally. **learning modality: verbal**

Lab zone **Teacher Demo**

Newton's Second Law L1

Materials 1-kg mass, spring scale
Time 10 minutes

Focus Remind students that 1 N equals the force needed to accelerate a 1-kg mass at a rate of $1\ m/s^2$.

Teach Demonstrate 1 N of force by attaching the spring scale to the 1-kg mass and dragging the mass along the table. You can minimize friction by pulling the mass over oil or beads.

Apply Ask: **How can you determine the amount of force it took to pull the mass?** (*Look at the measurement on the spring scale.*) **How could you make the mass accelerate at a greater rate?** (*Pull the mass with more force.*) **learning modality: visual**

Go Online
PHSchool.com

For: More on Newton's laws
Visit: PHSchool.com
Web Code: cgd-3023

Students can research Newton's laws online.

Math **Sample Problem**

Math Skill Calculating force

Focus Remind students that force equals mass multiplied by acceleration.

Teach Remind students to enter the known values into the provided formula. They can then solve for the unknown value. Remind students to perform the same operation on the units that they do on the numbers.

Answers
1. 3,000 N (1,000 kg × 3 m/s²)
2. 350 N (25 kg × 14 m/s²)

All in One **Teaching Resources**
• Transparency M16

Monitor Progress L2

Skills Check Have students calculate the force needed to accelerate a 25-kg crate of books at a rate of 3.0 m/s².
(*Force = 25 kg × 3.0 m/s² = 75 N*)

Answers
Figure 13 To reduce static and sliding friction

 Reading Checkpoint Mass is directly related to inertia. The greater the mass of an object, the greater is its inertia.

M ● 53

Answer

 Reading Checkpoint To increase acceleration you can decrease mass or increase force.

Assess

Reviewing Key Concepts

1. a. Unless acted upon by an unbalanced force, an object at rest will remain at rest and an object in motion at a constant velocity will continue moving at a constant velocity. **b.** Inertia is a measure of an object's tendency to resist a change in its motion, a statement that has the same meaning as Newton's first law of motion. **c.** Because of your inertia, your body tends to remain in place. The car seat causes you to accelerate, therefore, by exerting a force on your back.
2. a. Sample answer: When accelerating an object by applying a force, the greater the force, the greater the acceleration or the greater the object's mass, the lower the acceleration. **b.** You could double the object's mass. **c.** A greater force is required to accelerate a more massive car, therefore, more engine power is required and more fuel is needed to produce that power.

Reteach   L1

Have students write Newton's first and second laws in their own words. Ask volunteers to share their answers with the class.

Performance Assessment   L2

Oral Presentation Have students explain why the same force accelerates an empty wagon more than a wagon full of bricks. *(According to Newton's second law, if the mass is smaller, acceleration is larger for the same amount of force.)*

All in One Teaching Resources

- Section Summary: *Newton's First and Second Laws*
- Review and Reinforce: *Newton's First and Second Laws*
- Enrich: *Newton's First and Second Laws*

FIGURE 14
Force and Mass
The force of the boy's pull and the mass of the wagon determine the wagon's acceleration.

Changes in Force and Mass How can you increase the acceleration of the wagon? Look again at the equation. One way to increase acceleration is by changing the force. If the mass is constant, acceleration and force change in the same way. So to increase the acceleration of the wagon, you can increase the force used to pull it.

Another way to increase acceleration is to change the mass. According to the equation, acceleration and mass change in opposite ways. If the force is constant, an increase in mass causes a decrease in acceleration. The opposite is also true: A decrease in mass causes an increase in acceleration with a constant force. To increase the acceleration of the wagon, you can decrease its mass. So, instead of you, the children should ride in the wagon.

 Reading Checkpoint **What are two ways to increase the acceleration of an object?**

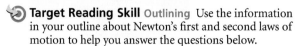
Section 3 Assessment

🎯 **Target Reading Skill** **Outlining** Use the information in your outline about Newton's first and second laws of motion to help you answer the questions below.

Reviewing Key Concepts

1. a. **Reviewing** What does Newton's first law of motion state?
   b. **Explaining** Why is Newton's first law of motion sometimes called the law of inertia?
   c. **Inferring** Use what you know about inertia to explain why you feel pressed back into the seat of a car when it accelerates.
2. a. **Defining** State Newton's second law of motion in your own words.
   b. **Problem Solving** How could you keep an object's acceleration the same if the force acting on the object were doubled?

   c. **Applying Concepts** Using what you know about Newton's second law, explain why a car with a large mass might use more fuel than a car with a smaller mass. Assume both cars drive the same distance.

Math Practice

3. **Calculating Force** Find the force it would take to accelerate an 800-kg car at a rate of 5 m/s^2.
4. **Calculating Force** What is the net force acting on a 0.15-kg hockey puck accelerating at a rate of 12 m/s^2?

Math Practice

Math Skill Calculating force

Answers
3. 4,000 N (800 kg $\times$ 5 m/s^2)
4. 1.8 N (0.15 kg $\times$ 12 m/s^2)

Lab zone Chapter Project

Keep Students on Track Remind students that their vehicles will need to accelerate from a resting position. From Newton's second law of motion, the students know that acceleration can be increased two ways: by decreasing the mass of the vehicle or by increasing the force acting on the vehicle. Have students work in small groups to brainstorm ways of increasing force or decreasing mass.

Reading Preview

Key Concepts
- What is Newton's third law of motion?
- How can you determine the momentum of an object?
- What is the law of conservation of momentum?

Key Terms
- momentum
- law of conservation of momentum

 Target Reading Skill
Previewing Visuals Before you read, preview Figure 18. Then write two questions that you have about the diagram in a graphic organizer like the one below. As you read, answer your questions.

Conservation of Momentum

Q.	What happens when two moving objects collide?
A.	
Q.	

Discover Activity

How Pushy Is a Straw?
1. Stretch a rubber band around the middle of the cover of a medium-size hardcover book.
2. Place four marbles in a small square on a table. Place the book on the marbles so that the cover with the rubber band is on top.
3. Hold the book steady by placing one index finger on the binding. Then, as shown, push a straw against the rubber band with your other index finger.
4. Push the straw until the rubber band stretches about 10 cm. Then let go of both the book and the straw at the same time.

Think It Over
Developing Hypotheses What did you observe about the motion of the book and the straw? Write a hypothesis to explain what happened in terms of the forces on the book and the straw.

Have you ever tried to teach a friend how to roller-skate? It's hard if you are both wearing skates. When your friend pushes against you to get started, you move too. And when your friend runs into you to stop, you both end up moving! To understand these movements you need to know Newton's third law of motion and the law of conservation of momentum.

Newton's Third Law of Motion

Newton proposed that whenever one object exerts a force on a second object, the second object exerts a force back on the first object. The force exerted by the second object is equal in strength and opposite in direction to the first force. Think of one force as the "action" and the other force as the "reaction." **Newton's third law of motion states that if one object exerts a force on another object, then the second object exerts a force of equal strength in the opposite direction on the first object.** Another way to state Newton's third law is that for every action there is an equal but opposite reaction.

Discover Activity

Skills Focus Developing hypotheses [L2]

Materials hardcover book, rubber band, marbles, plastic straw

Time 10 minutes

Tips Have students work in pairs. Make sure they do not use a twisting motion when they release the straw. Also be sure that they release the book and the straw at the same time.

Expected Outcome The book and the straw will move in opposite directions, and the straw will move faster than the book.

Think It Over Sample answer: The book and rubber band exerted a force on the straw while the straw exerted a force on the book and rubber band.

Objectives
After this lesson, students will be able to

M.2.4.1 State Newton's third law of motion.
M.2.4.2 Explain how an object's momentum is determined.
M.2.4.3 State the law of conservation of momentum.

Target Reading Skill

Previewing Visuals Explain that looking at the visuals before they read helps students activate prior knowledge and predict what they are about to read.

Answers
Sample questions and answers:
What happens when two moving objects collide? *(In the absence of friction, the total momentum is the same before and after the collision.)* **What is the momentum of an object?** *(Its mass multiplied by its velocity)*

All in One Teaching Resources
- Transparency M17

Preteach

Build Background Knowledge [L2]

Action and Reaction Forces
Ask a volunteer to sit facing forward on a skateboard and toss a basketball to you. Ask: **What happened when the student tossed the ball?** *(The student moved backward.)* **What made the ball move?** *(A force exerted by the student)* **What made the student move?** *(A force exerted by the ball)*

Instruct

Newton's Third Law of Motion

Teach Key Concepts   L2
Action and Reaction Forces

Focus Provide this example for students: When you hit a nail with a hammer, the hammer exerts a force on the nail. The nail exerts a reaction force on the hammer, causing the motion of the hammer to stop.

Teach Write on the board: For every action there is an equal and opposite reaction.

Apply Ask: **What are some examples of action and reaction forces?** (*Sample answer: You push on the ground with your foot when you walk; the ground pushes back on your foot so you move forward.*) **learning modality: verbal**

Help Students Read   L1

Using Prior Knowledge Before reading about action-reaction pairs, have students brainstorm lists of things they know about action-reaction pairs, using Figure 15 as a prompt. After reading the section, have students review their lists, replace any misconceptions with correct information, and add any new information that they learned while reading.

Independent Practice   L2

All In One Teaching Resources

- Guided Reading and Study Worksheet: *Newton's Third Law*

 **Student Edition on Audio CD**

When the gymnast does a flip, he pushes down on the vaulting horse. The reaction force of the vaulting horse pushes him up to complete the flip.

Action force

Reaction force

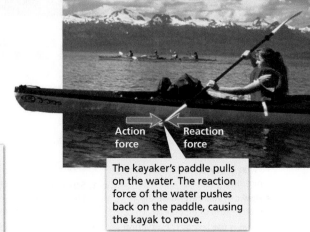

Action force   Reaction force

The kayaker's paddle pulls on the water. The reaction force of the water pushes back on the paddle, causing the kayak to move.

Action force

When the dog leaps, it pushes down on the ground. The reaction force of the ground pushes the dog into the air.

Reaction force

FIGURE 15
Action-Reaction Pairs
Action-reaction pairs explain how a gymnast can flip over a vaulting horse, how a kayaker can move through the water, and how a dog can leap off the ground. *Observing Name some other action-reaction pairs that you have observed.*

Action-Reaction Pairs You're probably familiar with many examples of Newton's third law. Pairs of action and reaction forces are all around you. When you jump, you push on the ground with your feet. This is an action force. The ground pushes back on your feet with an equal and opposite force. This is the reaction force. You move upward when you jump because the ground is pushing you! In a similar way, a kayaker moves forward by exerting an action force on the water with a paddle. The water pushes back on the paddle with an equal reaction force that propels the kayak forward.

Now you can understand what happens when you teach your friend to roller-skate. Your friend exerts an action force when he pushes against you to start. You exert a reaction force in the opposite direction. As a result, both of you move in opposite directions.

Detecting Motion Can you always detect motion when paired forces are in action? The answer is no. For example, when Earth's gravity pulls on an object, you cannot detect Earth's equal and opposite reaction. Suppose you drop your pencil. Gravity pulls the pencil downward. At the same time, the pencil pulls Earth upward with an equal and opposite reaction force. You don't see Earth accelerate toward the pencil because Earth's inertia is so great that its acceleration is too small to notice.

Do Action-Reaction Forces Cancel? Earlier you learned that if two equal forces act in opposite directions on an object, the forces are balanced. Because the two forces add up to zero, they cancel each other out and produce no change in motion. Why then don't the action and reaction forces in Newton's third law of motion cancel out as well? After all, they are equal and opposite.

The action and reaction forces do not cancel out because they are acting on different objects. Look at the volleyball player on the left in Figure 16. She exerts an upward action force on the ball. In return, the ball exerts an equal but opposite downward reaction force back on her wrists. The action and reaction forces act on different objects.

On the other hand, the volleyball players on the right are both exerting a force on the *same* object—the volleyball. When they hit the ball from opposite directions, each of their hands exerts a force on the ball equal in strength but opposite in direction. The forces on the volleyball are balanced and the ball does not move either to the left or to the right.

 Reading Checkpoint Why don't action and reaction forces cancel each other?

Forces

Video Preview
▶ Video Field Trip
Video Assessment

FIGURE 16
Action-Reaction Forces
In the photo on the left, the player's wrists exert the action force. In the photo below, the ball exerts reaction forces on both players.
Interpreting Diagrams In the photo below, which forces cancel each other out? What force is not cancelled? What will happen to the ball?

Lab zone Build Inquiry L1

Interpreting Illustrations

Materials magazines, glue, markers, poster board

Time 15 min

Focus Review with students the definition of action and reaction forces. Have students brainstorm everyday situations in which action and reaction forces occur.

Teach Ask students to use magazine clippings or drawings to illustrate action and reaction forces. Students should glue or draw their examples to the poster board and label the forces shown in each illustration.

Apply Ask: **What are some everyday activities that would not be possible without action and reaction forces?** *(Sample answer: Walking)* **learning modality: visual**

Forces

Show the Video Field Trip to let students experience how gravity, velocity, acceleration, and friction all are involved in roller coasters. Discussion question: **What are the main forces acting on passengers during a roller coaster ride?** *(Sample answer: Gravity and acceleration)*

Monitor Progress _____ L2

Skills Check Have students apply Newton's third law of motion to a pogo stick. Ask: **What are the action and reaction forces in a pogo stick jump?** *(Action force: person jumping on the pogo stick; reaction force: pogo stick pushing up on the person)*

Answers
Figure 15 Possible answers might include a hand and a ball, a swimmer and the water, and a horse and a cart.
Figure 16 Both the forces on the ball and the forces on the hands cancel each other out. The force of gravity is not cancelled out. The ball will fall to the gym floor.

✔ **Reading Checkpoint** Action-reaction forces do not cancel each other because they act on different objects.

Momentum

Teach Key Concepts
Relating Mass, Velocity, and Momentum

Focus Ask: **If a bicycle and a fire engine are both moving at a speed of 5 km/h, which would be easier to stop?** *(The bicycle)* **Why?** *(Sample answer: It has less mass, and therefore has less momentum.)*

Teach Tell students that the momentum of an object depends on its mass and velocity. Write Momentum = Mass × Velocity on the board. Ask: **How could an object with a large mass have the same momentum as an object with a small mass?** *(They could have the same momentum if they have different velocities.)*

Apply Ask: **When a car slows down, its velocity decreases and its mass stays the same. How does slowing down affect the car's momentum?** *(The momentum decreases.)* **learning modality: logical/ mathematical**

Math — Sample Problem

Math Skill Calculating momentum

Focus Remind students that formulas and equations can be used to find an unknown value.

Teach Check that students understand which values are known and which are unknown. Remind students to perform the same operations on the units that they do on the numbers.

Answers
1. Golf ball: 0.045 kg × 16 m/s = 0.72 kg·m/s
Baseball: 0.14 kg × 7 m/s = 0.98 kg·m/s
The baseball has greater momentum.
2. 0.27 kg·m/s (0.018 kg × 15 m/s = 0.27 kg·m/s)

All in One Teaching Resources
• Transparency M18

Momentum

All moving objects have what Newton called a "quantity of motion." What is this quantity of motion? Today we call it momentum. **Momentum** (moh MEN tum) is a characteristic of a moving object that is related to the mass and the velocity of the object. **The momentum of a moving object can be determined by multiplying the object's mass and velocity.**

> **Momentum = Mass × Velocity**

Since mass is measured in kilograms and velocity is measured in meters per second, the unit for momentum is kilogram-meters per second (kg·m/s). Like velocity, acceleration, and force, momentum is described by its direction as well as its quantity. The momentum of an object is in the same direction as its velocity.

Math — Sample Problem

Calculating Momentum
Which has more momentum: a 3.0-kg sledgehammer swung at 1.5 m/s, or a 4.0-kg sledgehammer swung at 0.9 m/s?

1 Read and Understand
What information are you given?
   Mass of smaller sledgehammer = 3.0 kg
   Velocity of smaller sledgehammer = 1.5 m/s
   Mass of larger sledgehammer = 4.0 kg
   Velocity of larger sledgehammer = 0.9 m/s

2 Plan and Solve
What quantities are you trying to calculate?
   The momentum of each sledgehammer = ▨

What formula contains the given quantities and the unknown quantity?
   Momentum = Mass × Velocity

Perform the calculations.
   Smaller sledgehammer: 3.0 kg × 1.5 m/s = 4.5 kg·m/s
   Larger sledgehammer: 4.0 kg × 0.9 m/s = 3.6 kg·m/s

3 Look Back and Check
Does your answer make sense?
   The 3.0-kg hammer has more momentum than the 4.0-kg one. This answer makes sense because it is swung at a greater velocity.

Math — Practice

1. **Calculating Momentum**
A golf ball travels at 16 m/s, while a baseball moves at 7 m/s. The mass of the golf ball is 0.045 kg and the mass of the baseball is 0.14 kg. Which has greater momentum?

2. **Calculating Momentum**
What is the momentum of a bird with a mass of 0.018 kg flying at 15 m/s?

FIGURE 17
Momentum
An object's momentum depends on velocity and mass.
Problem Solving *If both dogs have the same velocity, which one has the greater momentum?*

The more momentum a moving object has, the harder it is to stop. The mass of an object affects the amount of momentum the object has. For example, you can catch a baseball moving at 20 m/s, but you cannot stop a car moving at the same speed. The car has more momentum because it has a greater mass. The velocity of an object also affects the amount of momentum an object has. For example, an arrow shot from a bow has a large momentum because, although it has a small mass, it travels at a high velocity.

 **Reading Checkpoint** **What must you know to determine an object's momentum?**

Conservation of Momentum

In everyday language, conservation means saving resources. You might conserve water or fossil fuels, for example. The word *conservation* has a more specific meaning in physical science. In physical science, conservation refers to the conditions before and after some event. An amount that is conserved is the same amount after an event as it was before.

The total amount of momentum objects have is conserved when they collide. Momentum may be transferred from one object to another, but none is lost. This fact is called the law of conservation of momentum.

The **law of conservation of momentum** states that, in the absence of outside forces, the total momentum of objects that interact does not change. The amount of momentum is the same before and after they interact. **The total momentum of any group of objects remains the same, or is conserved, unless outside forces act on the objects.** Friction is an example of an outside force.

Lab zone Try This **Activity**

Colliding Cars
Momentum is always conserved—even by toys!

1. Find two nearly identical toy cars that roll easily.
2. Make two loops out of masking tape (sticky side out). Put one loop on the front of one of the cars and the other loop on the back of the other car.
3. Place on the floor the car that has tape on the back. Then gently roll the other car into the back of the stationary car. Was momentum conserved? How do you know?

Predicting What will happen if you put masking tape on the fronts of both cars and roll them at each other with equal speeds? Will momentum be conserved in this case? Test your prediction.

Teach Key Concepts   L2
Visualizing Conservation of Momentum

Focus Tell students that when objects collide, momentum is not lost if there is no friction.

Teach Direct students' attention to Figure 18. Point out the calculation of momentum found under each diagram. Ask: **In Part A, why does the blue car move more slowly after the collision?** (*Some of its momentum is transferred to the green car.*)

Extend Ask: **Describe an example of conservation of momentum you have observed during a sporting event.** (*Sample answer: One ice hockey player collides with another, and both players move forward.*)
learning modality: visual

Lab zone Try This **Activity**

Skills Focus Predicting   L2

Materials masking tape, two toy cars with the same mass and low-friction wheels

Time 10 minutes

Tips If the cars collide with too much force, friction, which is an external force, will affect the conservation of momentum.

Expected Outcome Sample answer: The cars will stick together and stop. Yes, momentum will be conserved. The cars had equal and opposite momentums before colliding, resulting in a total momentum of zero after the collision.

Extend Have students predict what would happen if the front of one car collided with the side of the other car. **learning modality: kinesthetic**

Monitor Progress _____ L2

Skills Check Ask students to determine the momentum of a 5.0 kg object moving at a velocity of 6.0 m/s? (*30 kg·m/s*)

Answers
Figure 17 The dog with the greater mass will have the greater momentum.

 Reading Checkpoint The object's velocity and mass

Modeling Conservation of Momentum L1

Materials plastic ruler with groove down the middle, two marbles of equal mass

Time 10 minutes

Focus Ask: **If a marble rolling in the groove of the ruler strikes an unmoving marble, what do you predict will happen?** (*Sample answer: The moving marble will stop, and the unmoving marble will start moving.*)

Teach Place a marble in the groove of the ruler. Roll another marble of equal mass so it strikes the unmoving marble. The moving marble will stop, and the stationary marble will start moving.

Apply Ask: **Which part of Figure 18 shows the same situation as this demonstration?** (*Part B—one moving object and one stationary object*) Use the ruler and marbles to demonstrate the other situations shown in Figure 18. **learning modality: visual**

Go Online *active art*

For: Momentum activity
Visit: PHSchool.com
Web Code: cgp-3024

Students can interact with conservation of momentum online.

All in One Teaching Resources
• Transparency M19

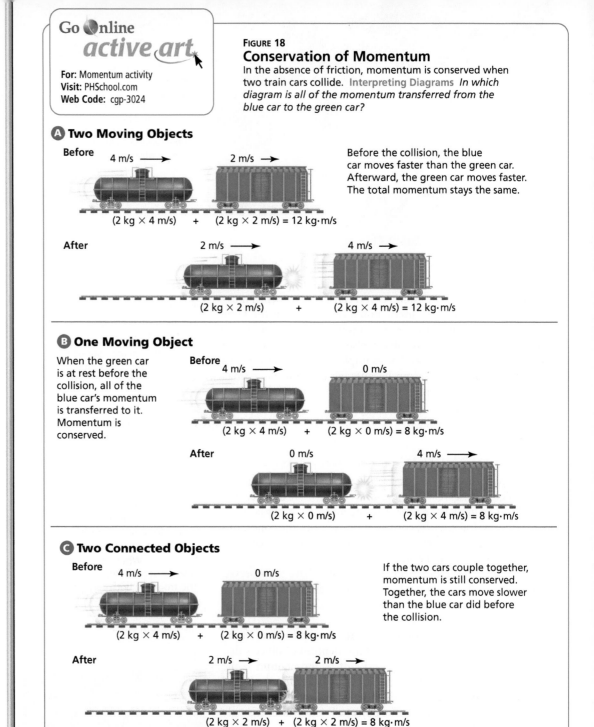

Go Online *active art*

For: Momentum activity
Visit: PHSchool.com
Web Code: cgp-3024

FIGURE 18
Conservation of Momentum
In the absence of friction, momentum is conserved when two train cars collide. **Interpreting Diagrams** *In which diagram is all of the momentum transferred from the blue car to the green car?*

A Two Moving Objects

Before   4 m/s →   2 m/s →

(2 kg × 4 m/s) + (2 kg × 2 m/s) = 12 kg·m/s

After   2 m/s →   4 m/s →

(2 kg × 2 m/s) + (2 kg × 4 m/s) = 12 kg·m/s

Before the collision, the blue car moves faster than the green car. Afterward, the green car moves faster. The total momentum stays the same.

B One Moving Object

When the green car is at rest before the collision, all of the blue car's momentum is transferred to it. Momentum is conserved.

Before   4 m/s →   0 m/s

(2 kg × 4 m/s) + (2 kg × 0 m/s) = 8 kg·m/s

After   0 m/s   4 m/s →

(2 kg × 0 m/s) + (2 kg × 4 m/s) = 8 kg·m/s

C Two Connected Objects

Before   4 m/s →   0 m/s

(2 kg × 4 m/s) + (2 kg × 0 m/s) = 8 kg·m/s

If the two cars couple together, momentum is still conserved. Together, the cars move slower than the blue car did before the collision.

After   2 m/s →   2 m/s →

(2 kg × 2 m/s) + (2 kg × 2 m/s) = 8 kg·m/s

60 ◆ M

Differentiated Instruction

English Learners/Beginning L1
Comprehension: Key Concept Have students locate the boldface sentence found under the head *Conservation of Momentum*. Read the sentence aloud for students. Have students point out the momentum in the *Before* and *After* sections of each part of Figure 18. Students should note that the *Before* and *After* momentums are equal in each section. **learning modality: visual**

English Learners/Intermediate L2
Comprehension: Key Concept Extend the Beginning activity by having students write the boldface sentence on a sheet of paper. Have students underline any words they can't define. Then, pair students with others who are proficient in English. Have the student teams look up the unfamiliar words in a dictionary. **learning modality: verbal**

Collisions With Two Moving Objects In Figure 18A, a train car travels at 4 m/s down the same track as another train car traveling at only 2 m/s. The two train cars have equal masses. The blue car catches up with the green car and bumps into it. During the collision, the speed of each car changes. The blue car slows down to 2 m/s, and the green car speeds up to 4 m/s. Momentum is conserved—the momentum of one train car decreases while the momentum of the other increases.

Collisions With One Moving Object In Figure 18B, the blue car travels at 4 m/s but the green car is not moving. Eventually the blue car hits the green car. After the collision, the blue car is no longer moving, but the green car travels at 4 m/s. Even though the situation has changed, momentum is conserved. All of the momentum has been transferred from the blue car to the green car.

Collisions With Connected Objects Suppose that, instead of bouncing off each other, the two train cars couple together when they hit. Is momentum still conserved in Figure 18C? After the collision, the coupled train cars make one object with twice the mass. The velocity of the coupled trains is 2 m/s—half the initial velocity of the blue car. Since the mass is doubled and the velocity is divided in half, the total momentum remains the same.

 Reading Checkpoint **What happens to the momentum of two objects after they collide?**

Section 4 Assessment

Target Reading Skill Previewing Visuals Refer to your questions and answers about Figure 18 to help you answer Question 3 below.

Reviewing Key Concepts

1. **a.** Reviewing State Newton's third law of motion.
   b. Summarizing According to Newton's third law of motion, how are action and reaction forces related?
   c. Applying Concepts What would happen if you tried to catch a ball when you were standing on roller skates?
2. **a.** Defining What is momentum?
   b. Predicting What is the momentum of a parked car?
   c. Relating Cause and Effect Why is it important for drivers to allow more distance between their cars when they travel at faster speeds?

3. **a.** Identifying What is conservation of momentum?
   b. Inferring The total momentum of two marbles before a collision is 0.06 kg·m/s. No outside forces act on the marbles. What is the total momentum of the marbles after the collision?

Math Practice

4. **Calculating Momentum** What is the momentum of a 920-kg car moving at a speed of 25 m/s?
5. **Calculating Momentum** Which has more momentum: a 250-kg dolphin swimming at 4 m/s, or a 350-kg manatee swimming at 2 m/s?

Lab zone Chapter Project

Keep Students on Track Have students construct their vehicles if they have not already done so. Have students add to their diagrams to reflect what they have learned about Newton's third law of motion. Have students explain their diagram to a partner. Working in pairs and explaining their diagram will allow students to practice for their class presentation.

Math Practice

Math Skill Calculating momentum
Answers
1. 23,000 kg·m/s
(920 kg × 25 m/s = 23,000 kg·m/s)
2. Dolphin: 1,000 kg·m/s
(250 kg × 4 m/s = 1,000 kg·m/s)
Manatee: 700 kg·m/s
(350 kg × 2 m/s = 700 kg·m/s)
The dolphin has more momentum.

Answers
Figure 18 All of the momentum is transferred to the green car in Part B.

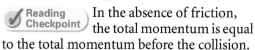 **Reading Checkpoint** In the absence of friction, the total momentum is equal to the total momentum before the collision.

Assess

Reviewing Key Concepts

1. **a.** If one object exerts a force on another object, the second object exerts an equal and opposite force on the first object. **b.** Action and reaction forces are equal in strength and opposite in direction. **c.** When you caught the ball, you (with the ball in your hand) would move in the direction of the ball's initial motion.
2. **a.** Momentum is a characteristic of a moving object equal to the product of its mass and its velocity. **b.** Because the velocity of a parked car is zero, its momentum is zero. **c.** Cars traveling at faster speeds have more momentum and are more difficult to stop than cars traveling at slower speeds.
3. **a.** Disregarding friction, the quantity of momentum is the same before and after objects interact. **b.** The total momentum stays the same: 0.06 kg·m/s.

Reteach L1

Have each student create a concept map that includes information about momentum and conservation of momentum. Challenge students to include as much information as possible.

Performance Assessment L2

Skills Check Have students write and solve a problem in which they must calculate the momentum of two objects before and after a collision.

All in One Teaching Resources

- Section Summary: *Newton's Third Law*
- Review and Reinforce: *Newton's Third Law*
- Enrich: *Newton's Third Law*

M ● 61

Forced to Accelerate L3

Prepare for Inquiry

Key Concept
Unbalanced forces cause acceleration.

Skills Objectives
After this lab, students will be able to
- calculate velocity and acceleration
- graph data of acceleration vs. force
- interpret data about the relationship between force and acceleration for a constant mass

🕐 **Prep Time** 20 minutes
🕐 **Class Time** 40 minutes

Advance Planning
Ask volunteers to bring skateboards from home. Check calibration of the spring scales. Practice the experiment.

Safety
Review the safety guidelines in Appendix A.

All in One Teaching Resources
- Lab Worksheet: *Forced to Accelerate*

Guide Inquiry

Invitation
Put a skateboard on the floor and put a brick on it. Have a student accelerate it for about 1 meter using a spring scale. Ask: **Why did the skateboard accelerate?** *(A force acted on it.)* Have students brainstorm ways they could investigate the effects of force on acceleration.

Introduce the Procedure
Demonstrate how to zero and use a spring scale. Review the concepts of average speed and acceleration. Ask: **What are the manipulated and responding variables in this experiment?** *(Manipulated variable: force with which the skateboard is pulled; responding variable: acceleration of the skateboard)* Have students look at the figure to clarify the procedure.

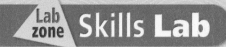
Forced to Accelerate

Problem
How is the acceleration of a skateboard related to the force that is pulling it?

Skills Focus
calculating, graphing, interpreting data

Materials
- skateboard • meter stick • string
- stopwatch • masking tape
- spring scale, 5-N
- several bricks or other large mass(es)

Procedure
1. Attach a loop of string to a skateboard. Place the bricks on the skateboard.
2. Using masking tape, mark off a one-meter distance on a level floor. Label one end "Start" and the other "Finish."
3. Attach a spring scale to the loop of string. Pull it so that you maintain a force of 2.0 N. Be sure to pull with the scale straight out in front. Practice applying a steady force to the skateboard as it moves.
4. Copy the data table into your notebook.

5. Find the smallest force needed to pull the skateboard at a slow, constant speed. Do not accelerate the skateboard. Record this force on the first line of the table.
6. Add 0.5 N to the force in Step 5. This will be enough to accelerate the skateboard. Record this force on the second line of the table.
7. Have one of your partners hold the front edge of the skateboard at the starting line. Then pull on the spring scale with the force you found in Step 6.
8. When your partner says "Go" and releases the skateboard, maintain a constant force until the skateboard reaches the finish line. A third partner should time how long it takes the skateboard to go from start to finish. Record the time in the column labeled Trial 1.
9. Repeat Steps 7 and 8 twice more. Record your results in the columns labeled Trial 2 and Trial 3.
10. Repeat Steps 7, 8, and 9 using a force 1.0 N greater than the force you found in Step 5.
11. Repeat Steps 7, 8, and 9 twice more. Use forces that are 1.5 N and 2.0 N greater than the force you found in Step 5.

Data Table							
Force (N)	Trial 1 Time (s)	Trial 2 Time (s)	Trial 3 Time (s)	Average Time (s)	Average Speed (m/s)	Final Speed (m/s)	Acceleration (m/s²)

Troubleshooting the Experiment
- Keep the mass on the skateboard constant throughout the experiment.
- The spring scale must be held horizontal, pulled straight, and zeroed before each use.

- If the spring scale is calibrated in grams, multiply by 0.01 to obtain newtons.
- Force should be measured after the skateboard starts moving.
- Final speed can be calculated using average speed because acceleration is constant.

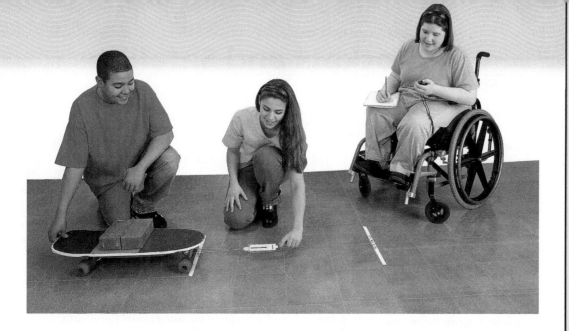

Analyze and Conclude

1. **Calculating** For each force, find the average of the three times that you measured. Record the average time in your data table.

2. **Calculating** For each force, find the average speed of the skateboard. Use this formula:

   Average speed = 1 m ÷ Average time

   Record this value for each force.

3. **Calculating** To obtain the final speed of the skateboard, multiply each average speed by 2. Record the result in your data table.

4. **Calculating** To obtain the acceleration, divide each final speed you found by the average time. Record the acceleration in your data table.

5. **Graphing** Make a line graph. Show the acceleration on the *y*-axis and the force on the *x*-axis. The *y*-axis scale should go from 0 m/s² to about 1 m/s². The *x*-axis should go from 0 N to 3.0 N. If your data points seem to form a straight line, draw a line through them.

6. **Interpreting Data** Your first data point is the force required for an acceleration of zero. How do you know the force for an acceleration of zero?

7. **Interpreting Data** According to your graph, how is the acceleration of the skateboard related to the pulling force?

8. **Communicating** Write a paragraph in which you identify the manipulated variable and the responding variable in this experiment. Describe other variables that might have affected the outcome of this experiment. (See the Skills Handbook to read about experimental variables.)

Design an Experiment

Design an experiment to test how the acceleration of the loaded skateboard depends on its mass. Think about how you would vary the mass of the skateboard. What quantity would you need to measure that you did not measure in this experiment? Do you have the equipment to make that measurement? If not, what other equipment would you need? *Obtain your teacher's permission before carrying out your investigation.*

Expected Outcome

Students' graphs should show that acceleration is proportional to force. Possible sources of error include improper use of the spring scale, errors during calculation, and failing to pull with constant force.

Analyze and Conclude

1. Sample answer: With a force of 2.2 N and a mass of 4.0 kg, the average time to accelerate for 1.0 m will be approximately 2 s.

2. Sample answer: For the same data, the average speed will be about 0.5 m/s.

3. Sample answer: For the same data, the final speed will be around 1 m/s.

4. Sample answer: For the same data, the acceleration will be around 0.5 to 0.6 m/s².

5. Students' graphs should show that force and acceleration are directly proportional.

6. The force for an acceleration of zero was measured in Step 5, when acceleration was zero.

7. Acceleration is proportional to pulling force.

8. Force is the manipulated variable; acceleration is the responding variable. Friction and errors in timing and pulling force might have affected the outcome.

Extend Inquiry

Design an Experiment Sample answer: Our experiment would be essentially the same, except we would vary the mass (using a different number of bricks) and keep the accelerating force constant. We would need to measure mass using a balance.

Objectives

After this lesson, students will be able to

M.2.5.1 Explain how a rocket lifts off the ground.

M.2.5.2 Describe the forces that keep a satellite in orbit.

⟲ Target Reading Skill

Identifying Main Ideas Explain that identifying main ideas and details helps students sort the facts from the information into groups. Each group can have a main topic, subtopic, and details.

Answers

Sample answers:

Main Idea: A satellite stays in orbit due to

Detail: its inertia

Detail: Earth's gravity

Detail: Earth's shape

All in One Teaching Resources

• Transparency M20

Preteach

Build Background Knowledge **L2**

Describing Forces in a Rocket Launch

Ask: **Have you ever seen a space shuttle launch on television?** *(Some students will say yes.)* Ask volunteers to describe the launch. Call students' attention to Figure 19, and have them describe the action-reaction force pair that produces lift.

Reading Preview

Key Concepts
• How does a rocket lift off the ground?
• What keeps a satellite in orbit?

Key Terms
• satellite
• centripetal force

⟲ Target Reading Skill

Identifying Main Ideas As you read the What Is a Satellite? section, write the main idea in a graphic organizer like the one below. Then write three supporting details that further explain the main idea.

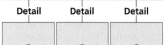

Main Idea

A satellite stays in orbit due to . . .

Detail	Detail	Detail

Lab zone Discover **Activity**

What Makes an Object Move in a Circle?

1. Tie a small mass, such as an empty thread spool, to the end of a string no more than one meter long.
2. Swing the object rapidly around in a circle that is perpendicular to the floor. Make sure no one is near the swinging object, and don't let it go!
3. Predict what will happen if you decrease the speed of the object. Test your prediction.
4. Predict how the length of the string affects the object's motion. Test your prediction.

Think It Over
Forming Operational Definitions Describe the object's motion. How do you know that the string exerts a force?

In October 1957, 14-year-old Homer Hickam looked upward and saw a speck of light move across the sky. It was the Russian satellite *Sputnik*, the first artificial satellite. It was propelled into space by a powerful rocket. This sight inspired Homer and his friends. They spent the next three years designing, building, and launching rockets in their hometown of Coalwood, West Virginia. Many of their first attempts failed, but they did not give up. Eventually, they built a rocket that soared to a height of almost ten kilometers. Their hard work paid off. In 1960, they won first place in the National Science Fair. Since then, rocket launches have become more familiar, but they are still an awesome sight.

◄ Homer Hickam holds a rocket that he and his friends designed.

Lab zone Discover **Activity**

Skills Focus Forming operational definitions **L2**

Materials length of string not more than 1 meter long, safety goggles, small object such as an empty thread spool

Time 10 minutes

Tips Caution students not to swing the object near another person. Have students wear safety goggles during the procedure.

Expected Outcome In Step 3 students might predict that the spool will move more slowly or that it won't make it over the top.

Think It Over The object moves in a circle; therefore it is constantly accelerating. What causes the acceleration is the pulling force, or tension, of the string.

How Do Rockets Lift Off?

A space shuttle like the one in Figure 19 has a mass of more than 2 million kilograms when loaded with fuel. To push the shuttle away from the pull of Earth's gravity and into space requires an incredible amount of force. How is this force generated? Rockets and space shuttles lift into space using Newton's third law of motion. As they lift off, they burn fuel and push the exhaust gases downward at a high velocity. In turn, the gases push upward on the rocket with an equal but opposite force. **A rocket can rise into the air because the gases it expels with a downward action force exert an equal but opposite reaction force on the rocket.** As long as this upward pushing force, called thrust, is greater than the downward pull of gravity, there is a net force in the upward direction. As a result, the rocket accelerates upward into space.

What Is a Satellite?

Rockets are often used to carry satellites into space. A **satellite** is any object that orbits another object in space. An artificial satellite is a device that is launched into orbit. Artificial satellites are designed for many purposes, such as communications, military intelligence, weather analysis, and geographical surveys. The International Space Station is an example of an artificial satellite. It was designed for scientific research.

Circular Motion Artificial satellites travel around Earth in an almost circular path. Recall that an object traveling in a circle is accelerating because it constantly changes direction. If an object is accelerating, a force must be acting on it. Any force that causes an object to move in a circular path is a **centripetal force** (sen TRIP ih tul). The word *centripetal* means "center-seeking."

In the Discovery Activity, the string supplies the centripetal force. The string acts to pull the object toward the center, and thereby keeps it moving in a circular path. For a satellite, the centripetal force is the gravitational force that pulls the satellite toward the center of Earth.

 Reading Checkpoint What type of force causes an object to move in a circular path?

Action force

Reaction force

FIGURE 19
A Rocket Launch
The action force pushes the rocket's exhaust gases downward. The reaction force of the gases sends the rocket into space. Predicting *As the rocket ascends, how will its mass change?*

Differentiated Instruction

Gifted and Talented L3
Researching Have students research the requirements for a rocket launch site and prepare a short report to share with the class. Have students find out why ideal launch sites are close to the equator. **learning modality: verbal**

Less Proficient Readers L1
Using Visuals Have students review the figures in Section 5. Help students read the caption of each figure. Then have students explain in their own words what is shown in each figure. **learning modality: visual**

How Do Rockets Lift Off?

Teach Key Concepts L2
Newton's Third Law and Rockets

Focus Remind students of Newton's third law: If one object exerts a force on another object, then the second object exerts an equal and opposite force on the first object.

Teach Direct students' attention to Figure 19. Remind students that during the launch, the upward force must be greater than the downward pull of gravity.

Apply Ask: **Is there a net force acting on the rocket in Figure 19?** *(Yes)* **How can you tell?** *(The rocket is accelerating.)* **learning modality: visual**

What Is a Satellite?

Teach Key Concepts L2
Gravity Affects Satellite Motion

Focus Ask: **What happens when you throw a baseball as hard as you can in an empty field?** *(It travels through the air and eventually falls to Earth.)* Point out that the baseball travels in a curved path. Tell students that satellites also travel in a curved path.

Teach Direct students' attention to Figure 20. Ask: **What force makes the ball fall toward Earth?** *(Gravity)* Explain that satellites stay in orbit due to inertia and the force of gravity.

Apply Ask: **Does a satellite require fuel once it is in orbit? Why?** *(No, inertia and the force of gravity keep the satellite in orbit.)* **learning modality: visual**

Independent Practice L2

All in One Teaching Resources

• Guided Reading and Study Worksheet: *Rockets and Satellites*

Student Edition on Audio CD

Monitor Progress L2

Answers
Figure 19 Its mass will decrease as the rocket burns fuel.

 Reading Checkpoint A centripetal force

Observing a Rocket Launch L1

Materials hand air pump, plastic water rocket, safety goggles

Time 15 minutes plus time for rocket assembly

Focus Ask: **What are some forces that affect a rocket launch?** (*Sample answer: Gravity, force of the gas expelled by the rocket*)

Teach This demonstration uses a plastic water rocket and must be done outdoors. Water rockets can be purchased from science supply companies. The rocket uses compressed air to expel a mixture of water and air from the rocket nozzle. **CAUTION:** *These water rockets are safe, but manufacturer's instructions must be followed exactly.* Students should wear goggles and stand at a safe distance. After the launch, challenge students to identify the action and reaction forces that acted as the rocket lifted off the ground.

Apply Ask: **As the rocket launches, are the forces acting on it balanced or unbalanced? How do you know?** (*Unbalanced, because the rocket is accelerating*) **learning modality: visual**

Help Students Read L1

Outlining Have students create an outline of the section, Rockets and Satellites. Outlines should use the headings in the section as main ideas. Check that students have included the key terms and boldface sentences under the appropriate headings.

All In One Teaching Resources

• Transparency M21

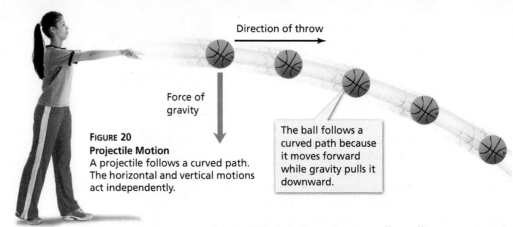

FIGURE 20
Projectile Motion
A projectile follows a curved path. The horizontal and vertical motions act independently.

Direction of throw

Force of gravity

The ball follows a curved path because it moves forward while gravity pulls it downward.

FIGURE 21
Satellite Motion
The faster a projectile is thrown, the farther it travels before it hits the ground. A projectile with enough velocity moves in a circular orbit. **Interpreting Diagrams** *How does the direction of gravity compare to the direction of the orbiting projectile's motion at any point?*

Satellite Motion Gravity pulls satellites toward Earth. So why don't satellites fall to the ground, as a ball thrown through the air would? The answer is that satellites have a greater horizontal velocity than a ball would have. Instead of falling to Earth, satellites fall around Earth.

If you throw a ball horizontally, as shown in Figure 20, the ball will move away from you at the same time that it is pulled to the ground because of gravity. The horizontal and vertical motions act independently, and the ball follows a curved path toward the ground. If you throw the ball faster, it will land even farther in front of you. The faster you throw a projectile, the farther it travels before it lands.

Now suppose, as Isaac Newton did, what would happen if you were on a high mountain and could throw a ball as fast as you wanted. The faster you threw it, the farther away it would land. But, at a certain speed, the path of the ball would match the curve of Earth. Although the ball would keep falling due to gravity, Earth's surface would curve away from the ball at the same rate. Thus the ball would fall around Earth in a circle, as shown in Figure 21.

Satellites in orbit around Earth continuously fall toward Earth, but because Earth is curved they travel around it. In other words, a satellite is a falling projectile that keeps missing the ground! It falls around Earth rather than into it. A satellite does not need fuel because it continues to move ahead due to its inertia. At the same time, gravity continuously changes the satellite's direction. The speed with which an object must be thrown in order to orbit Earth turns out to be about 7,900 m/s!

Satellite Location Some satellites, such as mapping and observation satellites, are put into low orbits of less than 1,000 kilometers. In a low orbit, satellites complete a trip around Earth in less than two hours. Other satellites are sent into higher orbits. At those distances, a satellite travels more slowly, taking longer to circle Earth. For example, communications satellites travel about 36,000 kilometers above Earth's surface. At that height, they circle Earth once every 24 hours. Because Earth rotates once every 24 hours, a satellite above the equator always stays at the same point above Earth as it orbits.

✓ Reading Checkpoint How does gravity help keep satellites in orbit?

FIGURE 22
Satellite Locations
Depending on their uses, artificial satellites orbit at different heights.

Communications satellite 35,800 km

Global Positioning System 20,000 km

Research satellite 6,000 km

Space shuttle 400 km

Section 5 Assessment

⟳ Target Reading Skill Identifying Main Ideas Use your graphic organizer to help you answer Question 2 below.

Reviewing Key Concepts

1. **a.** Identifying Which of Newton's three laws of motion explains how a rocket lifts off?
   b. Explaining How do action-reaction pairs explain how a rocket lifts off?
   c. Applying Concepts As a rocket travels upward from Earth, air resistance decreases along with the force of gravity. The rocket's mass also decreases as its fuel is used up. If thrust remains the same, how do these factors affect the rocket's acceleration?
2. **a.** Defining What is a satellite?
   b. Relating Cause and Effect What causes satellites to stay in orbit rather than falling toward Earth?

   c. Inferring In Figure 21, a projectile is thrown with enough velocity to orbit Earth. What would happen if the projectile were thrown with a greater velocity?

Lab zone **At-Home Activity**

Swing the Bucket Fill a small plastic bucket halfway with water and take it outdoors. Challenge a family member to swing the bucket in a vertical circle. Explain that the water won't fall out at the top if the bucket is moving fast enough. Tell your family member that if the bucket falls as fast as the water, the water will stay in the bucket. Relate this activity to a satellite that also falls due to gravity, yet remains in orbit.

Chapter 2 M ◆ 67

Lab zone **At-Home Activity**

Swing the Bucket L2 Review the concept of satellites so students will be prepared to discuss this with their families. Remind students that just as Earth's gravity causes the water to fall toward Earth as fast as the bucket, Earth's gravity causes the satellite to fall around Earth so that it remains in orbit.

Monitor Progress _____ L2

Answers
Figure 21 The direction of Earth's gravity is perpendicular to the direction of an orbiting projectile's motion.

✓ Reading Checkpoint Earth's gravity provides the entire centripetal force needed to keep satellites in orbit. Gravity also continuously changes the satellite's direction.

Assess

Reviewing Key Concepts

1. **a.** Newton's third law explains how a rocket lifts off. **b.** Action force—rocket exerts a downward force on exhaust gases; reaction force—exhaust gases exert an equal and opposite force on the rocket, propelling it upward. **c.** All three factors increase the rocket's acceleration. Decreased air resistance and decreased force of gravity allow the rocket to accelerate faster because both result in less force opposing the rocket's acceleration. Decreased rocket mass increases acceleration because the same force acting on a smaller mass causes greater acceleration.
2. **a.** A satellite is any object that travels around another object in space. **b.** Satellites stay in orbit because Earth's surface curves away as Earth's gravity causes them to fall toward Earth. **c.** If the projectile were thrown with a greater velocity, it would escape Earth's gravity and move off into space.

Reteach L1
Have students review the boldface sentences in the section. Challenge students to state the key concepts using their own words.

Performance Assessment L2
Writing Have students write a letter explaining the motion of a communications satellite and why these satellites do not require fuel to stay in orbit.

All in One Teaching Resources
- Section Summary: *Rockets and Satellites*
- Review and Reinforce: *Rockets and Satellites*
- Enrich: *Rockets and Satellites*

The BIG Idea · **Motion and Forces** An unbalanced force that acts on an object will cause a change in the object's motion.

The BIG Idea

Have students read the answer to the Essential Question. Encourage them to evaluate and revise their own answers as needed.

Help Students Read

Building Vocabulary

Words in Context Help students use context clues to learn and remember the meaning of unfamiliar words and phrases. Have students locate the term *terminal velocity* in the text. Ask: **What words in the surrounding text could help you remember the meaning of the term *terminal velocity*?** *(Greatest velocity of a falling object)*

Word/Part Analysis Tell students that the prefix *re-* is a Latin prefix meaning "again" or "against." Have students relate this to the term *reaction force*. Ask students to name other words that contain the prefix *re-*. Have students relate the meaning of the prefix to the meaning of the word. *(Sample answer: resealable—able to be sealed again)*

Connecting Concepts

Concept Maps Help students develop a concept map to show how the information in this chapter is related. Forces such as friction and gravity, can be balanced or unbalanced, act on objects, affect the motion of objects, and are explained by Newton's laws. Have students brainstorm to identify the key concepts, key terms, details, and examples. Then, write each one on a self-sticking note and attach it at random on chart paper or on the board.

Tell students that this concept map will be organized in hierarchical order and to begin at the top with the key concepts. Ask students these questions to guide them to categorize the information on the self-sticking notes: **What is force? How do friction and gravity affect the motion of objects? What are Newton's first and second laws? What is Newton's third law? What forces affect the motion of rockets and satellites?** Prompt students to use connecting words or phrases, such as "can

① The Nature of Force

Key Concepts
- A force is described by its strength and by the direction in which it acts.
- Unbalanced forces acting on an object result in a net force and a change in the object's motion.
- Balanced forces acting on an object do not change the object's motion.

Key Terms
- force • newton • net force
- unbalanced forces • balanced forces

② Friction and Gravity

Key Concepts
- The strength of the force of friction depends on two factors: how hard the surfaces push together and the types of surfaces involved.
- Two factors affect the gravitational attraction between objects: mass and distance.
- In free fall, the force of gravity is an unbalanced force, which causes an object to accelerate.

Key Terms

friction	mass
static friction	weight
sliding friction	free fall
rolling friction	air resistance
fluid friction	terminal velocity
gravity	projectile

68 ◆ M

③ Newton's First and Second Laws

Key Concepts
- An object at rest will remain at rest, and an object moving at a constant velocity will continue moving at a constant velocity, unless it is acted upon by an unbalanced force.
- Acceleration depends on the object's mass and on the net force acting on the object.
- $\text{Acceleration} = \dfrac{\text{Net force}}{\text{Mass}}$

Key Term
inertia

④ Newton's Third Law

Key Concepts
- If one object exerts a force on another object, then the second object exerts a force of equal strength in the opposite direction on the first object.
- The momentum of a moving object is equal to its mass times its velocity.
  $$\text{Momentum} = \text{Mass} \times \text{Velocity}$$
- The total momentum of any group of objects remains the same, or is conserved, unless outside forces act on the objects.

Key Terms
momentum
law of conservation of momentum

⑤ Rockets and Satellites

Key Concepts
- A rocket can rise into the air because the gases it expels with a downward action force exert an equal but opposite reaction force on the rocket.
- Satellites in orbit around Earth continuously fall toward Earth, but because Earth is curved they travel around it.

Key Terms

satellite	centripetal force

be," "affect," and "are explained by" to indicate the basis for the connections in the map. The phrases should form a sentence between or among a set of concepts.

Answer
Accept logical presentations by students.

All in One Teaching Resources
- Key Terms Review: *Forces*
- Connecting Concepts: *Forces*

Review and Assessment

Go Online
For: Self-Assessment
Visit: PHSchool.com
Web Code: cga-3020

Organizing Information

Contrasting Copy the table about the different types of friction onto a sheet of paper. Then complete it and add a title. (For more on Comparing and Contrasting, see the Skills Handbook.)

Type of Friction	Occurs When	Example
Static	An object is not moving	a. ___?
Sliding	b. ___?	c. ___?
Rolling	d. ___?	e. ___?
Fluid	f. ___?	g. ___?

Reviewing Key Terms

Choose the letter of the best answer.

1. When an unbalanced force acts on an object, the force
   a. changes the motion of the object.
   b. is canceled by another force.
   c. does not change the motion of the object.
   d. is equal to the weight of the object.

2. Air resistance is a type of
   a. rolling friction.
   b. sliding friction.
   c. centripetal force.
   d. fluid friction.

3. Which of the following is not a projectile?
   a. a satellite
   b. a thrown ball
   c. a ball on the ground
   d. a soaring arrow

4. The resistance of an object to any change in its motion is called
   a. inertia.
   b. friction.
   c. gravity.
   d. weight.

5. The product of an object's mass and its velocity is called the object's
   a. net force.
   b. weight.
   c. momentum.
   d. gravitation.

If the statement is true, write *true*. If it is false, change the underlined word or words to make the statement true.

6. <u>Balanced forces</u> are equal forces acting on an object in opposite directions.

7. <u>Rolling friction</u> occurs when two solid surfaces slide over each other.

8. The greatest velocity a falling object reaches is called its <u>momentum</u>.

9. The <u>law of universal gravitation</u> states that the total momentum of objects that interact does not change.

10. The type of force that causes a satellite to orbit Earth is a <u>centripetal force.</u>

Writing in Science

Descriptive Paragraph Suppose you have been asked to design a new amusement park ride. Write a description of how you will design it. Explain the role that friction and gravity will play in the ride's design.

Discovery CHANNEL SCHOOL

Forces
Video Preview
Video Field Trip
▶ Video Assessment

Chapter 2 M ◆ 69

All in One Teaching Resources
- Transparency M22
- Chapter Test
- Performance Assessment Teacher Notes
- Performance Assessment Student Worksheet
- Performance Assessment Scoring Rubric

ExamView® Computer Test Bank CD-ROM

Organizing Information
Sample answers:
a. Friction between an unmoving book and the desk on which it is sitting
b. Two solid surfaces slide over each other
c. Rubber pads on a bicycle's brakes rubbing against the tire
d. An object rolls across a surface
e. Ball bearings in skateboard wheels
f. A solid object moves through a fluid
g. Air resistance

Reviewing Key Terms
1. a 2. d 3. c 4. a 5. c
6. true
7. Sliding friction
8. terminal velocity
9. law of conservation of momentum
10. true

Discovery CHANNEL SCHOOL
Video Assessment

Forces

Show the Video Assessment to review chapter content and as a prompt for the writing assignment. Discussion questions: **What force accelerates a roller coaster train that is going downhill?** *(Gravity)* **What force helps a roller coaster to stop?** *(Friction)*

Writing in Science

Writing Mode Description
Scoring Rubric
4 Exceeds criteria; includes a detailed description of an amusement park ride with a thorough and correct explanation of the role of gravity and friction
3 Meets criteria
2 The paragraph lacks detail and/or includes information about only gravity or only friction
1 The paragraph does not relate gravity and friction to the amusement park ride and/or contains numerous errors

Checking Concepts

11. The forces the four children are exerting on the object balanced one another.

12. The fluids keep the surfaces from making direct contact and thus reduce friction.

13. No, a flat sheet of paper will accelerate more slowly due to increased air resistance.

14. Newton's second law states that force is equal to mass multiplied by acceleration.

15. You can throw your empty jet pack away from the space station. As a result, the reaction force exerted on you by the jet pack will accelerate you toward the space station.

16. Students' drawings should resemble the art in Figure 21, with Earth's gravitational force directed toward the center of Earth and perpendicular to the satellite's motion. Yes, the satellite is accelerating because it is changing direction.

Thinking Critically

17. Static friction allows you to walk without slipping.

18. The skateboard stops, but your inertia causes you to keep moving forward.

19. The net force is 90 N to the right. The acceleration is 6 m/s^2.

20. Yes, the pavement exerts a force on the ball.

Math Practice

21. 7.3 kg × 3.7 m/s^2 = 27.01 N

22. (240 + 75) kg × 16 m/s = 5,040 kg·m/s

Checking Concepts

11. Four children pull on the same toy at the same time, yet there is no net force on the toy. How is that possible?

12. Why do slippery fluids such as oil reduce sliding friction?

13. Will a flat sheet of paper dropped from a height of 2 m accelerate at the same rate as a piece of paper crumpled into a ball? Why or why not?

14. Explain how force, mass, and acceleration are related by Newton's second law of motion.

15. Suppose you are an astronaut making a space walk outside your space station when your jet pack runs out of fuel. How can you use your empty jet pack to get you back to the station?

16. Draw a diagram showing the motion of a satellite around Earth. Label the forces acting on the satellite. Is the satellite accelerating?

Thinking Critically

17. Classifying What kind of friction allows you to walk without slipping?

18. Applying Concepts You are moving fast on a skateboard when your wheel gets stuck in a crack on the sidewalk. Using the term *inertia*, explain what happens.

19. Problem Solving Look at the diagram below of two students pulling a bag of volleyball equipment. The friction force between the bag and the floor is 15 N. What is the net force acting on the bag? What is the acceleration of the bag?

45 N

60 N

10 kg

15 N

20. Relating Cause and Effect When you drop a golf ball to the pavement, it bounces up. Is a force needed to make it bounce up? If so, what exerts the force?

Math Practice

21. Calculating Force A 7.3-kg bowling ball accelerates at a rate of 3.7 m/s^2. What force acts on the bowling ball?

22. Calculating Momentum A 240-kg snowmobile travels at 16 m/s. The mass of the driver is 75 kg. What is the momentum of the snowmobile and driver?

Applying Skills

Use the illustration showing a collision between two balls to answer Questions 23–25.

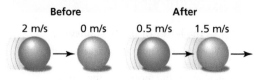

Before   After

2 m/s   0 m/s   0.5 m/s   1.5 m/s

23. Calculating Use the formula for momentum to find the momentum of each ball before and after the collision. Assume the mass of each ball is 0.4 kg.

24. Inferring Find the total momentum before and after collision. Is the law of conservation of momentum satisfied in this collision? Explain.

25. Designing Experiments Design an experiment in which you could show that momentum is not conserved between the balls when friction is strong.

Lab zone Chapter **Project**

Performance Assessment Test your vehicle to make sure it will work on the type of floor in your classroom. Will the vehicle stay within the bounds set by your teacher? Identify all the forces acting on the vehicle. What was the most significant source of friction for your vehicle? List at least three features you included in the design of the vehicle that led to an improvement in its performance. For example, did you give it a smooth shape for low air resistance?

Lab zone Chapter **Project** L3

Performance Assessment Provide time for students to test their vehicles. Remind students to include diagrams identifying forces on the vehicles. After all of the presentations are complete, have students discuss the source of friction for the different vehicles. Encourage students to incorporate Newton's laws of motion when they explain the features of their designs that improved performance. Also, encourage them to compare design features with their classmate's vehicles as they evaluate their own vehicles.

Standardized Test Prep

Test-Taking Tip
Interpreting Diagrams
On some tests, you may be asked questions about a diagram. Understanding the information in the diagram is the key to answering the question correctly. When you are shown a diagram, examine it carefully. Look at the objects and symbols in the diagram and read the labels.

Sample Question
What conclusion can you draw by looking at the diagram?

A Air resistance in front of the balloon pushes it backward.
B Gravity forces air out of the balloon's open end.
C The force of the air leaving the balloon propels it forward.
D Friction causes the balloon's acceleration to decrease.

Answer
The diagram shows a pair of action-reaction forces. The action force is caused by the balloon pushing out air. According to Newton's third law of motion, the reaction force of the air pushes on the balloon, propelling it forward. The answer is **C**.

Choose the letter of the best answer.

1. In the balloon diagram above, why don't the two forces cancel each other out?
  A They are not equal.
  B They both act on the air.
  C They both act on the balloon.
  D They act on different objects.

2. What force makes it less likely for a person to slip on a dry sidewalk as opposed to an icy sidewalk?
  F air resistance
  G friction
  H inertia
  J momentum

3. Which of the following is determined by the force of gravity?
  A weight
  B momentum
  C mass
  D distance

4. The table below shows the mass and velocity of four animals. Which animal has the greatest momentum?

Mass and Velocity of Animals		
Animal	Mass (kg)	Velocity (m/s)
Cheetah	45	20
Grizzly bear	200	13
Hyena	70	18
Wild turkey	11	7

  F cheetah
  G grizzly bear
  H hyena
  J wild turkey

5. A 50-car freight train and an 8-car passenger train are stopped on parallel tracks. It is more difficult to move the freight train than the passenger train. What accounts for this fact?
  A terminal velocity
  B inertia
  C centripetal force
  D speed

Constructed Response

6. Write a short paragraph explaining how a parachute works in terms of forces.

Applying Skills
23. Left ball before: 0.4 kg × 2 m/s = 0.8 kg·m/s; right ball before: 0.4 kg × 0 m/s = 0 kg·m/s; left ball after: 0.4 kg × 0.5 m/s = 0.2 kg·m/s; right ball after: 0.4 kg × 1.5 m/s = 0.6 kg·m/s

24. Total momentum before: 0.8 kg·m/s + 0 kg·m/s = 0.8 kg·m/s; total momentum after: 0.2 kg·m/s + 0.6 kg·m/s = 0.8 kg·m/s; Yes, the law of conservation is satisfied. The total momentum before the collision is equal to the total momentum after the collision.

25. Students' designs will vary, but should include a high-friction surface to demonstrate how friction will decrease momentum.

Standardized Test Prep

1. D **2.** G **3.** A **4.** G **5.** B
6. A parachute works by creating air resistance to act opposite the force of gravity. When a person jumps from a plane, gravity pulls that person toward the ground. Once the parachute opens, the air under the parachute canopy exerts an upward force. So while gravity continues to pull down on the person, air resistance pushes up on the parachute canopy and slows the rate of descent. The forces of gravity and air resistance are not balanced, however. The force of the air resistance is less than the force of gravity. If the forces were equal, the person would float in the air indefinitely and never make it to the ground.

Chapter at a Glance

 PRENTICE HALL

TeacherEXPRESS™
Plan • Teach • Assess

 Chapter **Project** *Staying Afloat*

All in One Teaching Resources
- Chapter Project Teacher Notes, pp. 168–169
- Chapter Project Student Overview, pp. 170–171
- Chapter Project Student Worksheets, pp. 172–173
- Chapter Project Scoring Rubric, p. 174

Technology

Local Standards

Video Preview

Section 1 **Pressure**

3–4 periods
1 1/2–2 blocks

M.3.1.1 Explain what pressure depends on.
M.3.1.2 Explain how fluids exert pressure.
M.3.1.3 Describe how fluid pressure changes with elevation and depth.

Section 2 **Floating and Sinking**

3–4 periods
1 1/2–2 blocks

M.3.2.1 Describe the effect of the buoyant force.
M.3.2.2 Explain how the density of an object determines whether it sinks or floats.

Video Field Trip

Section 3 **Pascal's Principle**

1–2 periods
1/2–1 block

M.3.3.1 State Pascal's principle, and recognize its applications.
M.3.3.2 Explain how a hydraulic system multiplies force.

Section 4 **Bernoulli's Principle**

1–2 periods
1/2–1 block

M.3.4.1 Use Bernoulli's principle to explain how fluid pressure is related to the motion of a fluid.
M.3.4.2 List some applications of Bernoulli's principle.

Review and Assessment

All in One Teaching Resources
- Key Terms Review, p. 208
- Transparency M34
- Performance Assessment Teacher Notes, p. 216
- Performance Assessment Scoring Rubric, p. 217
- Performance Assessment Student Worksheet, p. 218
- Chapter Test, pp. 219–222

Video Assessment

Go Online
PHSchool.com

Test Preparation

Test Preparation Blackline Masters

Lab zone Chapter Activities Planner

For more activities

LAB ZONE
Easy Planner
CD-ROM

Student Edition	Inquiry	Time	Materials	Skills	Resources
Chapter Project, p. 73	Open-Ended	2 weeks	**All in One Teaching Resources** p. 168	Applying concepts, making models, evaluating the design, redesigning, communicating	**All in One Teaching Resources** pp. 168–169 **Lab zone Easy Planner**
Section 1					
Discover Activity, p. 74	Guided	10 minutes	2-L plastic bottle, small balloon, straw	Developing hypotheses	**Lab zone Easy Planner**
Try This Activity, p. 76	Directed	10 minutes	Index card, small plastic cup, water	Inferring	**Lab zone Easy Planner**
Design Your Own Lab, p. 81	Open-Ended	Prep: 20 minutes; Class: 40 minutes	Empty soda can, fishing line (30 cm), waterproof marker, wide-mouth jar or beaker, stopwatch, nails of various sizes, large basin	Designing experiments, controlling variables	**Lab zone Easy Planner** **Lab Activity Video** **All in One Teaching Resources** Design Your Own Lab: *Spinning Sprinklers,* pp. 182–184
Section 2					
Discover Activity, p. 82	Guided	15 minutes	Drinking glass, metric ruler, plastic straw, scissors, spoon, sugar, waterproof clay, waterproof marker	Predicting	**Lab zone Easy Planner**
Try This Activity, p. 86	Directed	15 minutes	2-L plastic jar or bottle, paper clips, plastic straw, scissors	Drawing conclusions	**Lab zone Easy Planner**
At-Home Activity, p. 87	Guided	Home		Applying concepts	**Lab zone Easy Planner**
Skills Lab, pp. 88–89	Guided	Prep: 20 minutes; Class: 40 minutes	Paper towels, pie pan, triple-beam balance, 600-mL beaker, jar with watertight lid (about 30-mL), table salt	Controlling variables, interpreting data, drawing conclusions	**Lab zone Easy Planner** **Lab Activity Video** **All in One Teaching Resources** Skills Lab: *Sink and Spill,* pp. 192–194
Section 3					
Discover Activity, p. 90	Directed	10 minutes	2-L plastic bottle with cap, water	Observing	**Lab zone Easy Planner**
Section 4					
Discover Activity, p. 95	Directed	10 minutes	sheet of notebook paper	Inferring	**Lab zone Easy Planner**
Try This Activity, p. 96	Directed	10 minutes	Plastic spoon, faucet	Developing hypotheses	**Lab zone Easy Planner**
At-Home Activity, p. 99	Directed	Home		Applying concepts, communicating	**Lab zone Easy Planner**

Section 1 Pressure

 3-4 periods, 1 1/2-2 blocks

ABILITY LEVELS
L1 Basic to Average
L2 For All Students
L3 Average to Advanced

Objectives

M.3.1.1 Explain what pressure depends on.

M.3.1.2 Explain how fluids exert pressure.

M.3.1.3 Describe how fluid pressure changes with elevation and depth.

Key Terms

• pressure • pascal • fluid • barometer

Local Standards

Preteach

Build Background Knowledge.

Use a hands-on activity to introduce the concept of fluid pressure.

 **Discover Activity** *Can You Blow Up a Balloon in a Bottle?* L2

Targeted Print and Technology Resources

 **Teaching Resources**

L2 Reading Strategy Transparency M23: Previewing Visuals

⊙ **PresentationExpress™ CD-ROM**

Instruct

What Is Pressure? Relate pressure to force and area.

Fluid Pressure Use everyday examples to help students understand and create a concept map about fluid pressure.

Variations in Fluid Pressure Ask leading questions to relate variations in pressure to elevation and depth.

 **Design Your Own Lab** *Spinning Sprinklers* L3

Targeted Print and Technology Resources

 **Teaching Resources**

L2 Guided Reading, pp. 177–179
L2 Transparency M24
L3 Design Your Own Lab: *Spinning Sprinklers,* pp. 182–184

📼 **Lab Activity Video/DVD**
Design Your Own Lab: *Spinning Sprinklers*

www.SciLinks.org Web Code: scn-1331

⊙ **Student Edition on Audio CD**

Assess

Section Assessment Questions

Have students refer to their questions and answers about Figure 5 when answering Question 3.

Reteach

Have students work in pairs to review the objectives and key terms for the section.

Targeted Print and Technology Resources

 Teaching Resources

• Section Summary, p. 176
L1 Review and Reinforce, p. 180
L3 Enrich, p. 181

Section 2 **Floating and Sinking**

 3–4 periods, 1 1/2–2 blocks

ABILITY LEVELS
L1 Basic to Average
L2 For All Students
L3 Average to Advanced

Objectives

M.3.2.1 Describe the effect of the buoyant force.

M.3.2.2 Explain how the density of an object determines whether it sinks or floats.

Key Terms

• buoyant force • Archimedes' principle • density

Local Standards

 **Preteach**

Build Background Knowledge

Use a demonstration to introduce the concept of density as it relates to floating and sinking.

 Discover Activity   *What Can You Measure With a Straw?*   L2

 **Targeted Print and Technology Resources**

 Teaching Resources

L2   Reading Strategy Transparency
M25: Relating Cause and Effect

● **PresentationExpress™ CD-ROM**

Instruct

Buoyancy Explain to students how Archimedes' principle relates buoyant force to the weight of fluid an object displaces.

Density Explain that density relates an object's mass and volume.

 Skills Lab   *Sink and Spill*   L2

 **Targeted Print and Technology Resources**

Teaching Resources

L2   Guided Reading, pp. 187–189
L2   Transparencies M26, M27, M28
L2   Skills Lab: *Sink and Spill*, pp. 192–194

▭ **Lab Activity Video/DVD**
Skills Lab: *Sink and Spill*

● **Student Edition on Audio CD**

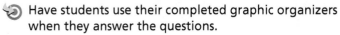 **Assess**

Section Assessment Questions

↺ Have students use their completed graphic organizers when they answer the questions.

Reteach

Students use Figure 10 to review the relationship between weight and buoyant force.

 **Targeted Print and Technology Resources**

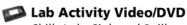 **Teaching Resources**

• Section Summary, p. 186
L1   Review and Reinforce, p. 190
L3   Enrich, p. 191

Section 3 Pascal's Principle

 1–2 periods, 1/2–1 block

Objectives

M.3.3.1 State Pascal's principle, and recognize its applications.

M.3.3.2 Explain how a hydraulic system multiplies force.

Key Terms

• Pascal's principle • hydraulic system

Local Standards

Preteach

Build Background Knowledge

Demonstrate how pressure is transmitted in fluids.

 Discover Activity *How Does Pressure Change?* L1

Targeted Print and Technology Resources

All in One Teaching Resources

L2 Reading Strategy Transparency
M29: Asking Questions

🔘 **PresentationExpress™ CD-ROM**

Instruct

Transmitting Pressure in a Fluid Explain Pascal's principle, and have students relate Pascal's principle to hydraulic systems.

Hydraulic Systems Explain that hydraulic systems have many everyday applications.

Targeted Print and Technology Resources

All in One Teaching Resources

L2 Guided Reading, pp. 197–198
L2 Transparencies M30, M31

PHSchool.com Web Code: cgp-3033

🔘 **Student Edition on Audio CD**

Assess

Section Assessment Questions

Have students use their questions and answers to help them answer the questions.

Reteach

Students work in pairs to review Pascal's principle and applications of hydraulic systems.

Targeted Print and Technology Resources

All in One Teaching Resources

• Section Summary, p. 196
L1 Review and Reinforce, p. 199
L3 Enrich, p. 200

Section 4 Bernoulli's Principle

 *1–2 periods, 1/2–1 block*

Objectives

M.3.4.1 Use Bernoulli's principle to explain how fluid pressure is related to the motion of a fluid.

M.3.4.2 List some applications of Bernoulli's principle.

Key Terms

• Bernoulli's principle • lift

Local Standards

Preteach

Build Background Knowledge

Use a paper airplane to introduce Bernoulli's principle.

 **Discover Activity** *Does the Movement of Air Affect Pressure?* **L1**

Targeted Print and Technology Resources

 Teaching Resources

L2 Reading Strategy Transparency M32: Identifying Main Ideas

 PresentationExpress™ CD-ROM

Instruct

Pressure and Moving Fluids Use Figure 17 to help students understand Bernoulli's principle.

Applying Bernoulli's Principle Challenge students to explain applications of Bernoulli's principle.

Targeted Print and Technology Resources

 **Teaching Resources**

L2 Guided Reading, pp. 203–205
L2 Transparency M33

www.SciLinks.org Web Code: scn-1334

PHSchool.com Web Code: cgh-3030

 Student Edition on Audio CD

Assess

Section Assessment Questions

 Have students use their graphic organizers to help them answer Question 1.

Reteach

Have students rewrite the main ideas of Section 4 in their own words.

Targeted Print and Technology Resources

 **Teaching Resources**

• Section Summary, p. 202
L1 Review and Reinforce, p. 206
L3 Enrich, p. 207

For: Professional development support
Visit: www.SciLinks.org/PDLinks
Web Code: scf-1330

Professional
Development

Section 1 Pressure

Atmospheric Pressure and Weather Atmospheric pressure is measured using a barometer. The first barometer was invented and used by the Italian physicist Evangelista Torricelli in 1643. Many different units are used to measure and report atmospheric pressure. Millimeters of mercury (the height of the column of mercury in a mercury barometer) is one common unit used to report atmospheric pressure. Typical air pressure at sea level at 0°C is 760 millimeters of mercury. Another term for 1 millimeter of mercury is a torr, named for Torricelli. The SI unit of pressure is the newton per square meter. This unit is commonly called the pascal.

Address Misconceptions

Some students may think the term fluid *refers only to liquids. Remind students that fluids are substances that can flow easily.* For a strategy for overcoming this misconception, see **Address Misconceptions** in the section *Pressure.*

Meteorologists often refer to areas of high and low pressure. These variations in atmospheric pressure have a major influence on weather. In areas of high pressure, also called anticyclones, air descends. High pressure is usually associated with good weather and clear skies. Low pressure areas, or cyclones, are areas in which air is rising. As air rises, it cools and moisture in the air condenses, forming clouds and causing precipitation.

Wind is caused by differences in air pressure. Air moves from areas of high pressure to areas of low pressure. Wind speed is determined by the size of the pressure difference between the two areas.

Because atmospheric pressure affects weather, weather maps often show isobars, which are lines that connect areas of equal atmospheric pressure. The lines on the weather map at the right illustrate isobars.

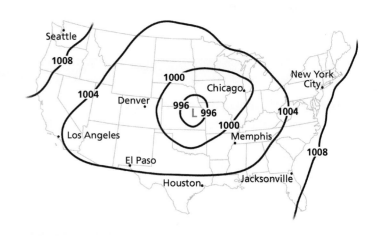

Help Students Read

Comparing and Contrasting
Identifying Similarities and Differences

Strategy Comparing and contrasting helps students understand how two or more related concepts are similar and how they are different. By using this strategy, students can link prior knowledge with new information. Model this strategy for students after they have read the section *Pressure.*

Example
1. After students have read the text, ask them to compare force and pressure. Tell students that comparing means looking for similarities between topics.
2. Next, have students contrast force and pressure. Remind students that contrasting means finding differences between topics.
3. Have students use a diagram or graphic organizer to present their information. Venn diagrams and compare/contrast tables are good choices for displaying this type of information.
See the section *Pressure* for guidelines for using the Comparing and Contrasting strategy with students.

Section 2 Floating and Sinking

Archimedes' Principle and Floating Objects An object that is floating or suspended in a fluid experiences both the downward force of gravity (its weight), and an upward force exerted by the fluid. This upward force is known as the buoyant force. Archimedes' principle states that the buoyant force acting on a submerged object is equal to the weight of the fluid the object displaces. This force does not depend on the weight of the object.

In some cases, objects float on the surface of the fluid. This indicates that the density of the object is less than the density of the fluid. Other objects float totally submerged. This indicates that the density of the object and the density of the fluid are about equal. Objects that sink to the bottom have a greater density than the fluid.

> **Address Misconceptions**
>
> *Many students may believe that whether an object sinks or floats depends on its weight, not its density.* For a strategy for overcoming this misconception, see **Address Misconceptions** in the section *Floating and Sinking.*

When an object floats, a portion of the object sinks below the surface of the fluid. A person floating on her back in the water does not rest on top of the surface of the fluid. The same is true of a ship in the ocean. The following mathematical relationship can be used to determine the portion of the object that will be submerged:

$$\frac{\text{Volume of fluid displaced}}{\text{Total volume of object}} = \frac{\text{Density of the object}}{\text{Density of the fluid}}$$

Consider a person floating in a freshwater lake compared to a person floating in the Great Salt Lake. The Great Salt Lake has a higher density than fresh water since it contains much more salt. So, a smaller volume of fluid is displaced. When a person displaces a smaller volume of water, he floats higher in the fluid. Therefore, a smaller percentage of a person's body is submerged when floating in the Great Salt Lake than when floating in fresh water.

Section 3 Pascal's Principle

Hydraulic Systems Pascal's principle is applied in hydraulic systems—fluid-filled tubes that connect two pistons. When the smaller of the two pistons is depressed, the larger piston rises. Pressure is transmitted through the fluid, and since the larger piston has a greater area, force is multiplied by the larger piston.

Hydraulic systems multiply force much like some types of simple machines. As with simple machines, the amount of work required to do a task is not changed. In other words, the hydraulic system multiplies force, but it does not multiply work. The equation for work, Work = Force × Distance, can be applied to hydraulic systems. In the absence of friction, the work put into the hydraulic system equals the work put out by the hydraulic system. This is a good illustration of the law of conservation of energy: although force is multiplied, you can't get more work out of a machine than you put in.

Section 4 Bernoulli's Principle

Bernoulli's Principle and the Flow of Liquids
Bernoulli's principle states that the faster a fluid flows, the lower the pressure within the fluid. Many common examples of applications of Bernoulli's principle, including airplane wings, chimneys, and atomizers, involve fluid pressure in gases. Bernoulli's principle also applies to the flow of liquids.

The flow of water in pipes is an example of Bernoulli's principle. When a pipe narrows, the speed at which water moves through the pipe increases and the pressure of the water in the narrow part of the pipe decreases.

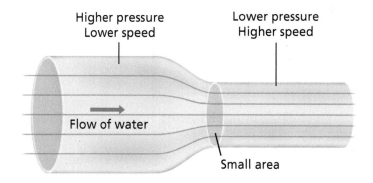

Higher pressure
Lower speed

Lower pressure
Higher speed

Flow of water

Small area

Bernoulli's principle is another good illustration of the law of conservation of energy. Flowing fluids have energy due to their motion (kinetic energy) and energy due to pressure. If the velocity of the water increases when the pipe narrows, how can this be accounted for in terms of energy? When the velocity of water increases, its kinetic energy increases. Since the total energy remains constant in the absence of friction, the pressure must decrease.

The **BIG Idea**

The Big Idea is the major scientific concept of the chapter. It is followed by the Essential Question. Read aloud the question to students. As students study the chapter, tell them to think about the Essential Question. Explain that they will discover the answer to the question as they read. The chapter Study Guide provides a sample answer.

 **Chapter Project** ⬛L3

Objectives

Students will use the principles of buoyancy to design, build, test, and modify a boat. After completing this Chapter Project, students will be able to
- design and build a boat using metal
- test and modify the boat so that it can hold 50 pennies for 10 seconds
- communicate the scientific principles used in their boat's design to the class

Skills Focus

Applying concepts, making models, evaluating the design, redesigning, communicating

Project Time Line 2 weeks

All in One Teaching Resources

- Chapter Project Teacher Notes
- Chapter Project Overview
- Chapter Project Worksheet 1
- Chapter Project Worksheet 2
- Chapter Project Scoring Rubric

Chapter **3**

Forces in Fluids

The **BIG Idea**
Science and Technology

Q How can you predict if an object will sink or float?

Chapter Preview

❶ **Pressure**
Discover Can You Blow Up a Balloon in a Bottle?
Math Skills Area
Try This Card Trick
Design Your Own Lab Spinning Sprinklers

❷ **Floating and Sinking**
Discover What Can You Measure With a Straw?
Try This Cartesian Diver
At-Home Activity Changing Balloon Density
Skills Lab Sink and Spill

❸ **Pascal's Principle**
Discover How Does Pressure Change?
Active Art Hydraulic Systems
Analyzing Data Comparing Hydraulic Lifts

❹ **Bernoulli's Principle**
Discover Does the Movement of Air Affect Pressure?
Try This Faucet Force
At-Home Activity Paper Chimney

▶ The force of air pushing on a hang glider's wing helps to keep the glider aloft.

Developing a Plan

Designing, building, and modifying the boats will take about 1 1/2 weeks. Set aside one or two class periods at the end of the project for students to present their boats to the class.

Possible Materials

Aluminum foil, cans, dishpan or tub, metal plates or bowls, meter stick, pennies, tin snips, sheet metal, string, wire

Discovery CHANNEL **SCHOOL**
Video Preview

Forces in Fluids

Show the Video Preview to introduce the Chapter Project and present an overview of the chapter content. Discussion question: **Why did the Titanic sink?** *(As the ship filled with water after striking an iceberg, its density increased, causing it to sink.)*

Lab zone™ Chapter Project

Staying Afloat

Whether an object sinks or floats depends on more than just its weight. In this Chapter Project, you will design and build a boat that can float in water and carry cargo. You will find out what forces in fluids make an object sink or float.

Your Goal To construct a boat that can float in water and carry cargo

Your boat must

• be made of metal only
• support a cargo of 50 pennies without allowing any water to enter for at least 10 seconds
• travel at least 1.5 meters
• be built following the safety guidelines in Appendix A

Plan It! Before you design your boat, think about the shape of real ships. Preview the chapter to find out what makes an object float. Then look for simple metal objects that you can form into a boat. Compare different materials and designs to build the most efficient boat you can. After your teacher approves your design, build your boat and test it.

Possible Shortcuts

This project can be completed in small groups. To save time, the choice of materials can be limited to aluminum foil and metal plates or bowls.

Launching the Project

To stimulate student interest, show students a cork and a small stone that have about the same mass. Fill a 500-mL beaker halfway with water. Ask: **What will happen when these are dropped in the water?** *(Many students will predict that the stone will sink and the cork will float.)* Drop both objects in the water. Explain to students that even objects that are heavy can float if they are shaped to hold a lot of air.

Performance Assessment

The Chapter Project Scoring Rubric will help you evaluate how well students complete the Chapter Project. You may want to share the rubric with your students so that they will know what is expected. Students will be assessed on

• how well the boat meets the size and material specifications
• how well they document the testing procedure and observations
• their ability to modify the device after testing
• how well the boat performs
• the clarity and organization of their presentation to the class

Students can save their plans and documentation in their portfolios. Portfolio

Objectives

After this lesson, students will be able to

M.3.1.1 Explain what pressure depends on.

M.3.1.2 Explain how fluids exert pressure.

M.3.1.3 Describe how fluid pressure changes with elevation and depth.

Target Reading Skill

Previewing Visuals Explain that looking at the visuals before they read helps students activate prior knowledge and predict what they are about to read.

Answers

Sample questions and answers:

Why does pressure change with elevation and depth? *(Air and water exert pressure, so pressure varies depending on how much air or water is above you.)* **How much greater is water pressure at a depth of 6,500 m than it is at sea level?** *(It is about 650 times greater.)*

All in One Teaching Resources

• Transparency M23

Preteach

Build Background Knowledge L2

Demonstrating Fluid Pressure

Have students take turns placing one arm (past the elbow) in a clean plastic bag, and submerging their arm into a container of water. Ask: **What did it feel like?** *(Most students will say that the water exerted pressure on their arm.)* **How did the plastic bag affect what you felt?** *(Sample answer: The bag allowed me to feel only the pressure of the water.)*

Section 1
Pressure

Reading Preview

Key Concepts
• What does pressure depend on?
• How do fluids exert pressure?
• How does fluid pressure change with elevation and depth?

Key Terms
• pressure • pascal • fluid
• barometer

Target Reading Skill

Previewing Visuals Before you read, preview Figure 5. Then write two questions that you have about the diagram in a graphic organizer like the one below. As you read, answer your questions.

Pressure Variations

Q.	Why does pressure change with elevation and depth?
A.	
Q.	

Lab zone Discover Activity

Can You Blow Up a Balloon in a Bottle?

1. Insert a balloon into the neck of an empty bottle. Try to blow up the balloon.
2. Now insert a straw into the bottle, next to the balloon. Keep one end of the straw sticking out of the bottle. Try again to blow up the balloon.

Think It Over
Developing Hypotheses Did using the straw make a difference? If it did, develop a hypothesis to explain why.

Outside, deep snow covers the ground. You put on your sneakers and head out, shovel in hand. When you step outside, your foot sinks deep into the snow. It's nearly up to your knees! Nearby, a sparrow hops across the surface of the snow. Unlike you, the bird does not sink. In fact, it barely leaves a mark! Why do you sink into the snow while the sparrow rests on the surface?

What Is Pressure?

The word *pressure* is related to the word *press*. It refers to a force exerted over an area on the surface of an object. You may recall that Earth's gravity pulls you downward with a force equal to your weight. Due to gravity, your feet exert a force on the surface of Earth over an area the size of your feet. In other words, your feet exert pressure on the ground.

Exerting pressure on snow ▶

Lab zone Discover Activity

Skills Focus Developing hypotheses L2

Materials 2-L plastic bottle, small balloon, straw

Time 10 minutes

Tips The mouth of the balloon must be outside the bottle. Caution students not to hold the straw near their eyes in Step 2.

Expected Outcome In Step 1, the balloon will inflate until it seals the neck of

the bottle. With the straw, the balloon will continue to inflate.

Think It Over Without the straw, blowing up the balloon compressed the air inside the bottle, making it difficult to blow up the balloon further. Holding the straw next to the balloon made blowing up the balloon easier because the straw allowed air inside the bottle to escape.

Area = 250 cm²

Area = 1,100 cm²

Pressure and Area

Pressure and Area Force and pressure are closely related, but they are not the same thing. **Pressure decreases as the area over which a force is distributed increases.** The larger the area over which the force is distributed, the less pressure is exerted. In order to stand on snow without sinking, you can't make yourself weigh the same as a bird. However, you can change the area over which you exert the force of your weight.

If you wear sneakers, like those shown in Figure 1, your weight is distributed over the soles of both shoes. You'll exert pressure over an area of about 500 cm² and sink into the snow. But if you wear snowshoes, you'll exert pressure over a much greater area—about 2,200 cm². Because the force of your weight is distributed over a greater area, the overall pressure exerted on the snow is much less. Like a sparrow, you can stand on the snow without sinking!

Calculating Pressure The relationship of force, area, and pressure is summarized by a formula.

$$\text{Pressure} = \frac{\text{Force}}{\text{Area}}$$

Pressure is equal to the force exerted on a surface divided by the total area over which the force is exerted. Force is measured in newtons (N). Area is measured in square meters (m²). Since force is divided by area, the SI unit of pressure is the newton per square meter (N/m²). This unit of pressure is also called the **pascal** (Pa): 1 N/m² = 1 Pa.

Reading Checkpoint What is the SI unit of pressure called?

FIGURE 1
Pressure and Area
Pressure depends on the area over which a force is distributed.
Inferring Which type of shoe would you use to keep from sinking into deep snow?

Math Skills

Area
The area of a surface is the number of square units that it covers. To find the area of a rectangle, multiply its length by its width. The area of the rectangle below is 2 cm × 3 cm, or 6 cm².

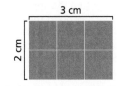
3 cm
2 cm

Practice Problem Which has a greater area: a rectangle that is 4 cm × 20 cm, or a square that is 10 cm × 10 cm?

Chapter 3 M ◆ 75

Math Skills

Math Skill Area

Answers
Both have the same area, 100 cm²:
5 cm × 20 cm = 100 cm²;
10 cm × 10 cm = 100 cm²

Fluid Pressure

Teach Key Concepts L2
Fluids Exerting Forces

Focus Ask: **Have you ever heard a meteorologist refer to areas of high pressure or low pressure?** *(Some students will say yes.)* **What is exerting the pressure they are referring to?** *(Air)*

Teach Ask for volunteers to write facts about fluid pressure on the board. Then use the facts to create a concept map about fluid pressure.

Apply Ask: **What is one type of fluid pressure that you experience at all times?** *(Sample answer: Air pressure, blood pressure)* **learning modality: visual**

 **Teaching Resources**

• Transparency M24

Lab zone Teacher Demo

Safety Buttons L1

Materials unopened jar with cap that says "Safety button will pop up if seal is broken."

Focus Show students the jar with the safety button.

Teach Explain that the pressure inside the jar is less than the pressure outside the jar. Before the seal is broken, the greater pressure outside pushes the button on the cap down. Have students listen closely as you open the jar. Ask: **Did air enter or leave the jar when the seal was broken?** *(Air entered the jar.)*

Apply Ask: **What happens to the inside pressure when the seal is broken?** *(The inside pressure becomes the same as the outside pressure.)* **learning modality: visual**

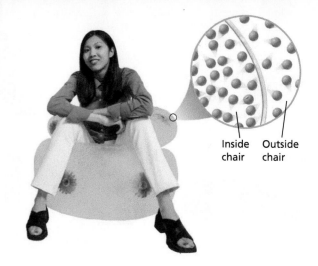

FIGURE 2
Fluid Particles
The particles that make up a fluid move constantly in all directions. When a particle collides with a surface, it exerts a force on the surface.
Relating Cause and Effect
What will happen to the force exerted by the particles in the chair when you add more air to the chair?

Inside chair   Outside chair

Fluid Pressure

Solids such as sneakers are not the only materials that exert pressure. Fluids also exert pressure. A **fluid** is a material that can easily flow. As a result, a fluid can change shape. Liquids such as water and oil and gases such as air and helium are examples of fluids.

What Causes Fluid Pressure? To understand how fluids exert forces that can result in pressure, think about the tiny particles that make up the fluid. Particles in a fluid constantly move in all directions, as shown in Figure 2. As they move, the particles collide with each other and with any surface that they meet.

As each particle in a fluid collides with a surface, it exerts a force on the surface. **All of the forces exerted by the individual particles in a fluid combine to make up the pressure exerted by the fluid.** Because the number of particles is large, you can consider the fluid as a whole. So, the fluid pressure is the total force exerted by the fluid divided by the area over which the force is exerted.

Air Pressure Did you know that you live at the bottom of 100 kilometers of fluid that surrounds Earth? This fluid, called air, is the mixture of gases that makes up Earth's atmosphere. These gases press down on everything on Earth's surface, all the time. Air exerts pressure because it has mass. You may forget that air has mass, but each cubic meter of air around you has a mass of about 1 kilogram. Because the force of gravity pulls down on this mass of air, the air has weight. The weight of the air is the force that produces air pressure, or atmospheric pressure.

Lab zone Try This Activity

Card Trick

1. Fill a small plastic cup to the brim with water. Gently place an index card over the top of the cup.
2. Hold the card in place and slowly turn the cup upside down. Let go of the card. What happens? Without touching the card, turn the container on its side.

Inferring Why does the water stay in the cup when you turn the cup upside down?

Lab zone Try This Activity

Skills Focus Inferring L1

Materials index card, small plastic cup, water

Time 10 minutes

Tips Make sure there are no air bubbles in the cup. The index card should be pressed down so it touches the entire rim.

Answer Air pressure holds the water in the cup.

Extend Have the students draw a diagram with labeled arrows indicating the fluid pressure exerted by the air and by the water in this activity. **learning modality: visual**

Balanced Pressure Hold out your hand, palm up. You are holding up air. At sea level, atmospheric pressure is about 10.13 N/cm^2. The surface area of your hand is about 100 cm^2. So, the weight supported by the surface area of your hand is about 1,000 newtons, or about the same weight as that of a large washing machine!

How could your hand possibly support that weight and not feel it? In a stationary fluid, pressure at a given point is exerted equally in all directions. The weight of the atmosphere does not just press down on your hand. It presses on your hand from every direction. The pressures balance each other.

Balanced pressures also explain why the tremendous air pressure pushing on you from all sides does not crush you. Your body contains fluids that exert outward pressure. For example, your lungs and sinus cavities contain air. Your cells and blood vessels contain liquids. So pressure from fluids inside your body balances the air pressure outside your body.

What happens when air pressure becomes unbalanced? Look at Figure 4. When the can is full of air, the air pressure inside the can balances the atmospheric pressure outside the can. When air is removed from the can, the unbalanced force of the outside air pressure crushes the can.

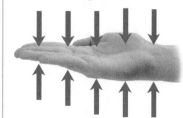

FIGURE 3
Atmospheric Pressure
The pressure of Earth's atmosphere is exerted over the entire surface of your hand.

 How is the pressure on your hand balanced?

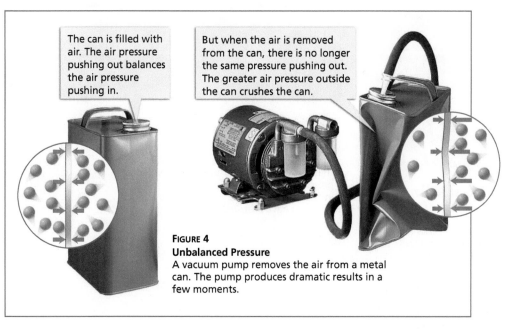

The can is filled with air. The air pressure pushing out balances the air pressure pushing in.

But when the air is removed from the can, there is no longer the same pressure pushing out. The greater air pressure outside the can crushes the can.

FIGURE 4
Unbalanced Pressure
A vacuum pump removes the air from a metal can. The pump produces dramatic results in a few moments.

Weather Forecasts

Materials weather maps from a local area

Time 10 minutes

Focus Point out the high- and low-pressure areas marked on the maps.

Teach Explain that air pressure is often measured in inches of mercury, which refers to how high the air can push a column of mercury. Have students analyze their maps to see what weather conditions are associated with high- and low-pressure areas.

Apply Have students monitor the local weather forecast for one week and note the high- and low-pressure systems mentioned in the forecasts. **learning modality: visual**

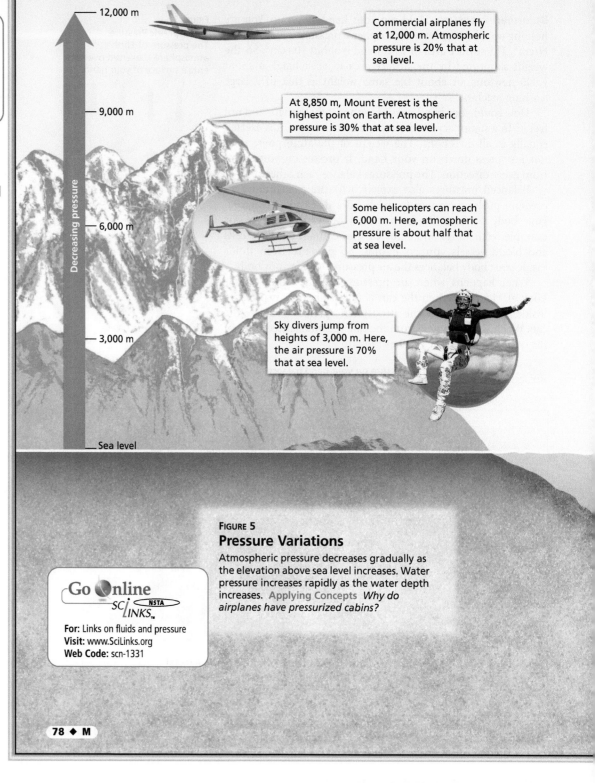

Commercial airplanes fly at 12,000 m. Atmospheric pressure is 20% that at sea level.

At 8,850 m, Mount Everest is the highest point on Earth. Atmospheric pressure is 30% that at sea level.

Some helicopters can reach 6,000 m. Here, atmospheric pressure is about half that at sea level.

Sky divers jump from heights of 3,000 m. Here, the air pressure is 70% that at sea level.

Decreasing pressure

12,000 m
9,000 m
6,000 m
3,000 m
Sea level

FIGURE 5
Pressure Variations
Atmospheric pressure decreases gradually as the elevation above sea level increases. Water pressure increases rapidly as the water depth increases. *Applying Concepts Why do airplanes have pressurized cabins?*

Variations in Fluid Pressure

Does the pressure of a fluid ever change? What happens to pressure as you climb to a higher elevation or sink to a lower depth within a fluid? Figure 5 shows how pressure changes depending on where you are.

Atmospheric Pressure and Elevation Have you ever felt your ears "pop" as you rode up in an elevator? The "popping" has to do with changing air pressure. At higher elevations, there is less air above you and therefore less air pressure. **As your elevation increases, atmospheric pressure decreases.**

The fact that air pressure decreases as you move up in elevation explains why your ears pop. When the air pressure outside your body changes, the air pressure inside adjusts, but more slowly. So, for a moment, the air pressure behind your eardrums is greater than it is in the air outside. Your body releases this pressure with a "pop," balancing the pressures.

Water Pressure and Depth Fluid pressure depends on depth. The pressure at one meter below the surface of a swimming pool is the same as the pressure one meter below the surface of a lake. But if you dive deeper into either body of water, pressure becomes greater as you descend. The deeper you swim, the greater the pressure you feel. **Water pressure increases as depth increases.**

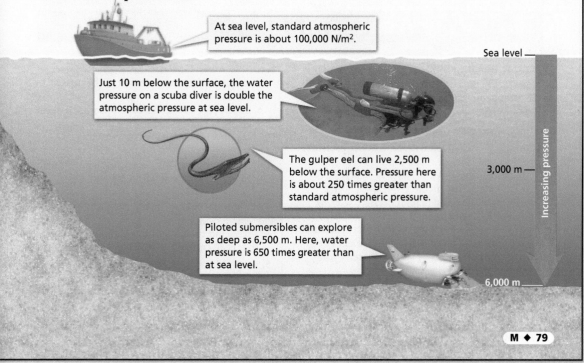

At sea level, standard atmospheric pressure is about 100,000 N/m².

Just 10 m below the surface, the water pressure on a scuba diver is double the atmospheric pressure at sea level.

The gulper eel can live 2,500 m below the surface. Pressure here is about 250 times greater than standard atmospheric pressure.

Piloted submersibles can explore as deep as 6,500 m. Here, water pressure is 650 times greater than at sea level.

Sea level

Increasing pressure

3,000 m

6,000 m

M ◆ 79

Monitor Progress

Answers

Figure 6 Rapidly decreasing atmospheric pressure usually means a storm is approaching.

Reading Checkpoint A barometer measures atmospheric pressure.

Assess

Reviewing Key Concepts

1. a. Pressure depends on force and the area over which the force is exerted. **b.** The woman standing in high heels exerts more pressure because the force is exerted over a smaller area.
2. a. Each particle in a fluid exerts a force when it collides with a surface. **b.** The pressure that Earth's atmosphere exerts on the body is equal in all directions. **c.** The body contains fluids, too, such as air in the lungs and blood in the veins and arteries.
3. a. Atmospheric pressure decreases as you move away from Earth's surface. **b.** Atmospheric pressure decreases with elevation, but water pressure increases with depth. **c.** In addition to providing oxygen, the pressurized suit balances the pressure outside and within the astronaut's body.

Reteach **L1**

Have students work in pairs to quiz one another on the section objectives and key terms.

Performance Assessment **L2**

Have students write and illustrate a story describing the changes in fluid pressure experienced by a diver as he or she rises from the ocean floor to the surface.

All in One Teaching Resources

• Section Summary: *Pressure*
• Review and Reinforce: *Pressure*
• Enrich: *Pressure*

FIGURE 6
Aneroid Barometer
An aneroid barometer measures atmospheric pressure.
Interpreting Photographs *What type of weather might be coming when atmospheric pressure decreases?*

As with air, you can think of water pressure as being due to the weight of the water above a particular point. At greater depths, there is more water above that point and therefore more weight to support. In addition, air in the atmosphere pushes down on the water. Therefore, the total pressure at a given point beneath the water results from the weight of the water plus the weight of the air above it. In the deepest parts of the ocean, the pressure is more than 1,000 times the air pressure you experience every day.

Measuring Pressure You can measure atmospheric pressure with an instrument called a **barometer.** There are two types of barometers: a mercury barometer and an aneroid barometer. The aneroid barometer is the barometer you usually see hanging on a wall. Weather forecasters use the pressure reading from a barometer to help forecast the weather. Rapidly decreasing atmospheric pressure usually means a storm is on its way. Increasing pressure is often a sign of fair weather. You may hear barometric pressure readings expressed in millimeters, inches, or another unit called a millibar. For example, the standard barometric pressure at sea level may be reported as 760 millimeters, 29.92 inches, or 1,013.2 millibars.

Reading Checkpoint What instrument measures atmospheric pressure?

Section 1 Assessment

Target Reading Skill
Previewing Visuals Refer to your questions and answers about Figure 5 to help you answer Question 3 below.

Reviewing Key Concepts

1. a. Reviewing What two factors does pressure depend on?
   b. Comparing and Contrasting Who exerts more pressure on the ground—a 50-kg woman standing in high heels, or a 50-kg woman standing in work boots?
2. a. Summarizing How do fluids exert pressure?
   b. Explaining Since most of the weight of the atmosphere is above you, why aren't you crushed by it?
   c. Inferring How is your body similar to the can containing air shown in Figure 4?

3. a. Describing How does atmospheric pressure change as you move away from the surface of Earth?
   b. Comparing and Contrasting Compare the change in atmospheric pressure with elevation to the change in water pressure with depth.
   c. Applying Concepts Why must an astronaut wear a pressurized suit in space?

Math Practice

4. Area Find the area of a rectangular photo that is 20 cm long and 15 cm wide.

5. Area Which has a greater area: a square table that measures 120 cm × 120 cm, or a rectangular table that measures 200 cm × 90 cm?

Math Practice

Math Skill Area

Answers

4. 20 cm × 15 cm = 300 cm^2
5. 120 cm × 120 cm = 14,400 cm^2; 200 cm × 90 cm = 18,000 cm^2; therefore the rectangular table has a greater area.

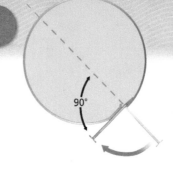

90°

Spinning Sprinklers

Problem
What factors affect the speed of rotation of a lawn sprinkler?

Skills Focus
designing experiments, controlling variables

Materials
- empty soda can
- fishing line, 30 cm
- waterproof marker
- wide-mouth jar or beaker
- stopwatch
- nails of various sizes
- large basin

Procedure

PART 1 Making a Sprinkler

1. Fill the jar with enough water to completely cover a soda can. Place the jar in the basin.

2. Bend up the tab of a can and tie the end of a length of fishing line to it. **CAUTION:** *The edge of the can opening can be sharp.*

3. Place a mark on the can to help you keep track of how many times the can spins.

4. Using the small nail, make a hole in the side of the can about 1 cm up from the bottom. Poke the nail straight in. Then twist the nail until it makes a right angle with the radius of the can as shown in the figure above. **CAUTION:** *Nails are sharp and should be used only to puncture the cans.*

5. Submerge the can in the jar and fill the can to the top with water.

6. Quickly lift the can with the fishing line so that it is 1–2 cm above the water level in the jar.

7. Practice counting how many spins the can completes in 15 seconds.

PART 2 What Factors Affect Spin?

8. How does the size of the hole affect the number of spins made by the can? Propose a hypothesis and then design an experiment to test the hypothesis. Obtain your teacher's approval before carrying out your experiment. Record all your data.

9. How does the number of holes affect the number of spins made by the can? Propose a hypothesis and then design an experiment to test the hypothesis. Obtain your teacher's approval before carrying out your experiment. Record all your data.

Analyze and Conclude

1. **Designing Experiments** How does the size of the hole affect the rate of spin of the can? How does the number of holes affect the rate of spin of the can?

2. **Controlling Variables** What other variables might affect the number of spins made by the can?

3. **Interpreting Data** Explain the motion of the can in terms of water pressure.

4. **Classifying** Which of Newton's three laws of motion could you use to explain the motion of the can? Explain.

5. **Communicating** Use the results of your experiment to write a paragraph that explains why a spinning lawn sprinkler spins.

More to Explore

Some sprinkler systems use water pressure to spin. Examine one of these sprinklers to see the size, direction of spin, and number of holes. What would happen if you connected a second sprinkler to the first with another length of hose? If possible, try it.

Extend Inquiry

More to Explore Sample answer: Water escaping from two sprinklers on the same hose may reduce the pressure in each. Because water from each sprinkler may interfere with water escaping from the other, I would need to consider how the distance between sprinklers and the directions of their rotations might affect their spins.

4. Newton's third law. The water escaping from the can exerts a force on the can that is equal and opposite to the force the can exerts on the escaping water, so the can spins in the direction opposite the escaping water.

5. Students should use Newton's third law of motion to explain why a spinning lawn sprinkler spins. Explanations may include how the number and size of the holes affect the speed of rotation.

Spinning Sprinklers L3

Prepare for Inquiry

Skills Objective
After this lab, students will be able to
- design an experiment to test factors affecting water pressure
- control variables in their experiment

 Prep Time 20 minutes
Class Time 40 minutes

Advance Planning
Gather materials. Obtain a sample sprinkler or make a diagram of one.

Safety
Make sure students avoid the sharp edges on the cans. Keep the floor dry so it doesn't get slippery. Review the safety guidelines in Appendix A.

All in One Teaching Resources
- Lab Worksheet: *Spinning Sprinklers*

Guide Inquiry

Introduce the Procedure
Have students read the procedure. Ask students to predict what factors will affect the can's rate of spinning. (*Amount of water in the can, size and number of nail holes*)

Troubleshooting the Experiment
- The angle of the holes must be the same for all trials.
- If the can drains in less than 15 seconds, have students use a proportion to find out how many spins would have occurred in 15 seconds.

Expected Outcome
The speed at which the can spins increases as the number and size of the holes increases.

Analyze and Conclude
1. The larger the hole, the faster the spin. The greater the number of holes, the faster the rate of spin.

2. Sample answer: The height of the hole in the can; the size and mass of the can

3. The water inside the can exerts pressure due to its weight. The force of the water escaping from the hole in the can causes the can to spin in the opposite direction.

Objectives

After this lesson, students will be able to
M.3.2.1 Describe the effect of the buoyant force.
M.3.2.2 Explain how the density of an object determines whether it sinks or floats.

Target Reading Skill 🎯

Relating Cause and Effect Explain that cause is the reason for what happens. The effect is what happens because of the cause. Relating cause and effect helps students relate the reason for what happens to what happens as a result.

Answers

Sample answers:
Cause: Weight is greater than buoyant force
Cause: Object is denser than fluid
Cause: Object takes on mass and becomes denser than fluid
Cause: Object is compressed and becomes denser than fluid
Effect: The object sinks.

All In One Teaching Resources

• Transparency M25

Preteach

Build Background Knowledge L2

Predicting Whether Objects Sink or Float

Fill a basin with water. Show students a variety of objects, such as soap, wood blocks, cans of diet and regular soda, and bathtub toys. Ask students to predict whether each object will sink or float. Test the predictions by putting each object into the water. Tell students that in this section they will learn why objects sink and float.

Reading Preview

Key Concepts
• What is the effect of the buoyant force?
• How can you use density to determine whether an object will float or sink in a fluid?

Key Terms
• buoyant force
• Archimedes' principle
• density

🎯 Target Reading Skill
Relating Cause and Effect
As you read, identify the reasons why an object sinks. Write the information in a graphic organizer like the one below.

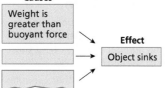

Causes

Weight is greater than buoyant force	→	**Effect**
	→	Object sinks
	→	

Lab zone Discover **Activity**

What Can You Measure With a Straw?

1. Cut a plastic straw to a 10-cm length.
2. Use a waterproof marker to make marks on the straw that are 1 cm apart.
3. Roll some modeling clay into a ball about 1.5 cm in diameter. Stick one end of the straw in the clay. You have built a device known as a hydrometer.
4. Place the hydrometer in a glass of water. About half of the straw should remain above water. If it sinks, remove some of the clay. Make sure no water gets into the straw.
5. Dissolve 10 spoonfuls of sugar in a glass of water. Try out your hydrometer in this liquid.

Think It Over
Predicting Compare your observations in Steps 4 and 5. Then predict what will happen if you use 20 spoonfuls of sugar in a glass of water. Test your prediction.

In April 1912, the *Titanic* departed from England on its first and only voyage. At the time, it was the largest ship afloat— nearly three football fields long. The *Titanic* was also the most technologically advanced ship in existence. Its hull was divided into compartments, and it was considered to be unsinkable.

Yet a few days into the voyage, the *Titanic* struck an iceberg. One compartment after another filled with water. Less than three hours later, the bow of the great ship slipped under the waves. As the stern rose high into the air, the ship broke in two. Both pieces sank to the bottom of the Atlantic Ocean. More than a thousand people died.

◄ **The bow section of the *Titanic* resting on the ocean floor**

Lab zone Discover **Activity**

Skills Focus Predicting L2

Materials drinking glass, metric ruler, plastic straw, scissors, spoon, sugar, waterproof clay, waterproof marker

Time 15 minutes

Tips Make sure students place the straw firmly in the clay so that water cannot leak into the straw. Help students realize they should count the marks above the water to take measurements.

Expected Outcome In plain water, the hydrometer will float lower. In sugar water, the hydrometer will float higher.

Think It Over Sample answer: The hydrometer will float higher when more sugar is dissolved in the water.

Buoyancy

Ships are designed to have buoyancy—the ability to float. How is it possible that a huge ship can float easily on the surface of water under certain conditions, and then in a few hours become a sunken wreck? To answer this question, you need to understand the buoyant force.

Gravity and the Buoyant Force You have probably experienced the buoyant force. If you have ever picked up an object under water, you know that it seems much lighter in water than in air. Water and other fluids exert an upward force called the **buoyant force** that acts on a submerged object. **The buoyant force acts in the direction opposite to the force of gravity, so it makes an object feel lighter.**

As you can see in Figure 7, a fluid exerts pressure on all surfaces of a submerged object. Since the pressure in a fluid increases with depth, the upward pressure on the bottom of the object is greater than the downward pressure on the top. The result is a net force acting upward on the submerged object. This is the buoyant force.

Remember that the weight of a submerged object is a downward force. If an object's weight is greater than the buoyant force, a net force acts downward on the object. The object will sink. If the weight of an object is equal to the buoyant force, no net force acts on the object. The object will not sink. A submerged object whose weight is equal to the buoyant force also has no net force acting on it. The object will not sink. For example, both the jellyfish and the turtle shown in Figure 8 have balanced forces acting on them. Neither animal will rise or sink.

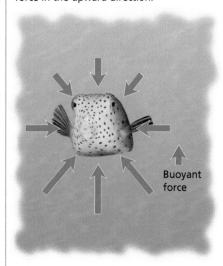

FIGURE 7
Buoyant Force
The pressure on the bottom of a submerged object is greater than the pressure on the top. The result is a net force in the upward direction.

Buoyant force

Weight

Buoyant force

Weight

Buoyant force

FIGURE 8
Buoyant Force and Weight
The weight of an object is a force that works opposite the buoyant force on the object. Comparing and Contrasting *Why does the lobster sink?*

Weight

Buoyant force

Instruct

Buoyancy

Teach Key Concepts [L2]
The Buoyant Force

Focus Tell students the buoyant force is a force that acts in the upward direction.

Teach Explain that Archimedes' principle states that the buoyant force acting on a submerged object is equal to the weight of the fluid the object displaces.

Apply Ask: **If a boat developed a leak and some water entered the ship, use Archimedes' principle to explain why the boat might sink.** *(The added water would increase the ship's weight. If the weight of the ship and the added water exceeds the buoyant force, the ship will sink.)* **learning modality: logical/mathematical**

Independent Practice [L2]

All in One Teaching Resources
• Guided Reading and Study Worksheet: *Floating and Sinking*

◉ Student Edition on Audio CD

All in One Teaching Resources
• Transparency M26

Monitor Progress [L2]

Skills Check Ask students to describe the relationship between the weight of the water an object displaces and the buoyant force.

Answer
Figure 8 If the creature's weight is greater than the buoyant force, it will sink.

Density

Teach Key Concepts L2
Floating and Sinking

Focus Tell students that comparing the densities of objects allows you to determine whether an object will float or sink.

Teach Tell students that density relates an object's mass to its volume. Ask for volunteers to state one fact about density and its application to floating and sinking. *(Sample answer: An object that is more dense than the fluid in which it is immersed will sink.)*

Apply Ask students to visualize a hot air balloon. Ask: **Using what you know about density, floating, and sinking, compare the densities of hot air and cool air.** *(The hot air balloon floats; therefore, hot air must be less dense than cool air.)* **learning modality: logical/mathematical**

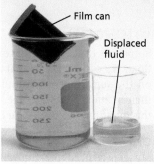

Teaching Resources
• Transparency M27

Forces in Fluids

Show the Video Field Trip to let students experience the relationship of forces in fluids and ships. Discussion question: **Given that steel is denser than water, why can a ship made of steel float?** *(Sample answer: The huge hull of the Titanic, which had 16 air-filled compartments, made the Titanic's density less than the density of water. Since its density was less than water, it floated.)*

FIGURE 9
Archimedes' Principle
Archimedes' principle applies to sinking and floating objects. **Predicting** *If you press down on the floating film can, what will happen to the volume of the displaced fluid in the small beaker?*

Forces in Fluids

Video Preview
▶ Video Field Trip
Video Assessment

Sinking
When the film can has film in it, it sinks. The volume of fluid displaced by the can is equal to the volume of the can.

Floating
When the film can is empty, it floats. The volume of displaced fluid is equal to the volume of the submerged portion of the can.

Archimedes' Principle You know that all objects take up space. A submerged object displaces, or takes the place of, a volume of fluid equal to its own volume. A partly submerged object, however, displaces a volume of fluid equal to the volume of its submerged portion only. You can see this in Figure 9.

Archimedes, a mathematician of ancient Greece, discovered a connection between the weight of a fluid displaced by an object and the buoyant force acting on it. This connection is known as Archimedes' principle. **Archimedes' principle** states that the buoyant force acting on a submerged object is equal to the weight of the fluid the object displaces. To understand what this means, think about swimming in a pool. Suppose your body displaces 50 liters of water. The buoyant force exerted on you will be equal to the weight of 50 liters of water, or about 500 N.

You can use Archimedes' principle to explain why a ship floats on the surface. Since the buoyant force equals the weight of the displaced fluid, the buoyant force will increase if more fluid is displaced. A large object displaces more fluid than a small object. A greater buoyant force acts on the larger object even if the large object has the same weight as the small object.

Look at Figure 10. The shape of a ship's hull causes the ship to displace a greater volume of water than a solid piece of steel with the same mass. A ship displaces a volume of water equal in weight to the submerged portion of the ship. According to Archimedes' principle, the weight of the displaced water is equal to the buoyant force. Since a ship displaces more water than a block of steel, a greater buoyant force acts on the ship. A ship floats on the surface as long as the buoyant force acting on it is equal to its weight.

 Reading Checkpoint **Does a greater buoyant force act on a large object or a small object?**

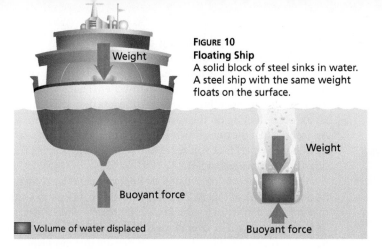

FIGURE 10
Floating Ship
A solid block of steel sinks in water. A steel ship with the same weight floats on the surface.

Weight

Weight

Buoyant force

Buoyant force

Volume of water displaced

Density

Exactly why do some objects float and others sink? To find the answer, you must relate an object's mass to its volume. In other words, you need to know the object's density.

What Is Density? The **density** of a substance is its mass per unit volume.

$$\text{Density} = \frac{\text{Mass}}{\text{Volume}}$$

For example, one cubic centimeter (cm^3) of lead has a mass of 11.3 grams, so its density is 11.3 g/cm^3. In contrast, one cubic centimeter of cork has a mass of only about 0.25 gram. So the density of cork is about 0.25 g/cm^3. Lead is more dense than cork. The density of water is 1.0 g/cm^3. So water is less dense than lead but more dense than cork.

Comparing Densities of Substances In Figure 11, several liquids and other materials are shown along with their densities. Notice that liquids can float on top of other liquids. (You may have seen salad oil floating on top of vinegar.) The liquids and materials with the greatest densities are near the bottom of the cylinder.

By comparing densities, you can predict whether an object will float or sink in a fluid. An object that is more dense than the fluid in which it is immersed sinks. An object that is less dense than the fluid in which it is immersed floats to the surface. And if the density of an object is equal to the density of the fluid in which it is immersed, the object neither rises nor sinks in the fluid. Instead, it floats at a constant depth.

FIGURE 11
Densities of Substances
You can use density to predict whether an object will sink or float when placed in a liquid. Interpreting Data *Will a rubber washer sink or float in corn oil?*

Substance	Density (g/cm^3)
Wood	0.7
Corn oil	0.925
Plastic	0.93
Water	1.00
Tar ball	1.02
Glycerin	1.26
Rubber washer	1.34
Corn syrup	1.38
Copper wire	8.8
Mercury	13.6

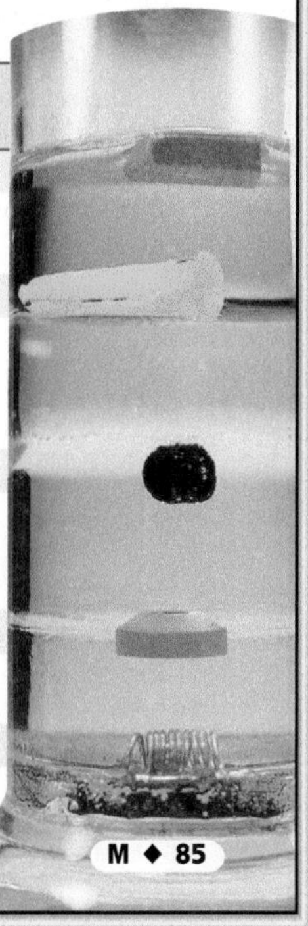

M ◆ 85

M ● 85

Layering Liquids

Materials corn syrup, food coloring, glycerin, rubbing alcohol, tall, clear container, vegetable oil, water

Time 15 minutes

Focus Remind students that whether an object sinks or floats depends on density.

Teach Pour a layer of corn syrup into the tall container. Then add a layer of glycerin. When the glycerin has settled, add liquids in this order—colored water, vegetable oil, and colored rubbing alcohol. Pour gently to avoid mixing. Ask: **Why do the different liquids float on top of each other?** (*The liquids have different densities, the liquid with the greatest density is at the bottom, and the densities decrease with each layer.*)

Apply Ask: **Which liquids used in this demonstration have a density greater than water?** (*Corn syrup and glycerin*) **learning modality: visual**

All in One **Teaching Resources**

• Transparency M28

Help Students Read   L1

Outlining Have students create an outline of the section *Floating and Sinking*. Have students use the headings as the major divisions in their outlines. Under each heading, have students include key concepts, key terms, and examples found in the text.

Lab zone **Try This Activity**

Dive!

1. Fill a plastic jar or bottle almost completely with water.

2. Bend a plastic straw into a U shape and cut the ends so that each side is 4 cm long. Attach the ends with a paper clip. Drop the straw in the jar, paper clip first.
3. Attach more paper clips to the first one until the straw floats with its top about 0.5 cm above the surface. This is the diver.
4. Put the lid on the jar. Observe what happens when you slowly squeeze and release the jar several times.

Drawing Conclusions
Explain the behavior of the diver.

FIGURE 12
Iceberg
An iceberg is dangerous to ships because most of it is under water.

Changing Density Changing density can explain why an object floats or sinks. For example, you can change the density of water by freezing it into ice. Since water expands when it freezes, ice occupies more space than water. That's why ice is less dense than water. But it's just a little less dense! So most of an ice cube floating on the surface is below the water's surface. An iceberg like the one shown in Figure 12 is really a very large ice cube. The part that you see above water is only a small fraction of the entire iceberg.

You can make an object sink or float in a fluid by changing its density. Look at Figure 13 to see how this happens to a submarine. The density of a submarine is increased when water fills its flotation tanks. The overall mass of the submarine increases. Since its volume remains the same, its density increases when its mass increases. So the submarine will dive. To make the submarine float to the surface, water is pumped out of it, decreasing its mass. Its density decreases, and it rises toward the surface.

You can also explain why a submarine dives and floats by means of the buoyant force. Since the buoyant force is equal to the weight of the displaced fluid, the buoyant force on the submerged submarine stays the same. Changing the water level in the flotation tanks changes the weight of the submarine. The submarine dives when its weight is greater than the buoyant force. It rises to the surface when its weight is less than the buoyant force.

Don't forget that air is also a fluid. If you decrease the density of an object, such as a balloon, the object will float and not sink in air. Instead of air, you can fill a balloon with helium gas. A helium balloon rises because helium is less dense than air. A balloon filled with air, however, is denser than the surrounding air because the air inside it is under pressure. The denser air inside, along with the weight of the balloon, make it fall to the ground.

 Reading Checkpoint **Why does a helium balloon float in air?**

Lab zone **Try This Activity**

Skills Focus Drawing conclusions   L2

Materials 2-L plastic jar or bottle, paper clips, plastic straw, scissors

Time 15 minutes

Tips Have students test the diver in the jar. If the diver is less than 0.5 cm above the water, it may sink in the jar.

Expected Outcome When the jar is squeezed, the pressure on the water increases, causing it to enter the straw. Students may conclude that the diver sinks because it has greater density.

Extend Challenge students to find a way to remove the diver from the jar without emptying the bottle. (*Fill the jar to the top, and the diver will rise to the surface.*)
learning modality: kinesthetic

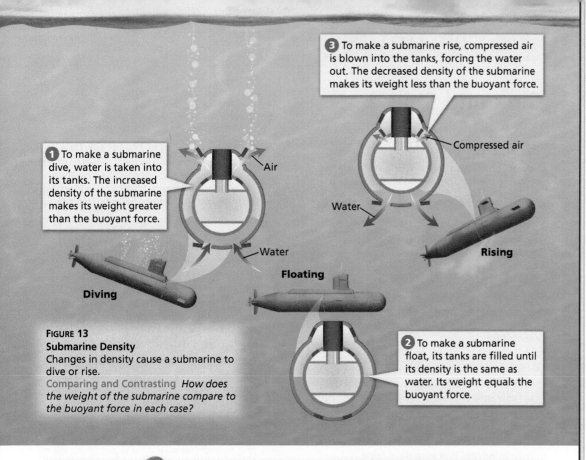

3 To make a submarine rise, compressed air is blown into the tanks, forcing the water out. The decreased density of the submarine makes its weight less than the buoyant force.

Compressed air

1 To make a submarine dive, water is taken into its tanks. The increased density of the submarine makes its weight greater than the buoyant force.

Air

Water

Diving

Water

Rising

Floating

FIGURE 13
Submarine Density
Changes in density cause a submarine to dive or rise.
Comparing and Contrasting How does the weight of the submarine compare to the buoyant force in each case?

2 To make a submarine float, its tanks are filled until its density is the same as water. Its weight equals the buoyant force.

Section 2 Assessment

Target Reading Skill

Relating Cause and Effect Refer to your graphic organizer to help you answer the questions below.

Reviewing Key Concepts

1. a. **Explaining** How does the buoyant force affect a submerged object?
   b. **Summarizing** How does Archimedes' principle relate the buoyant force acting on an object to the fluid displaced by the object?
   c. **Calculating** An object that weighs 340 N floats on a lake. What is the weight of the displaced water? What is the buoyant force?
2. a. **Defining** What is density?
   b. **Explaining** How can you use the density of an object to predict whether it will float or sink in water?

   c. **Applying Concepts** Some canoes have compartments on either end that are hollow and watertight. These canoes won't sink, even when they capsize. Explain why.

Lab zone At-Home Activity

Changing Balloon Density Attach paper clips to the string of a helium balloon. Ask a family member to predict how many paper clips you will need to attach to make the balloon sink to the floor. How many paper clips can you attach and still keep the helium balloon suspended in the air? Explain how adding paper clips changes the overall density of the balloon.

Answers
Figure 13 1—weight greater than the buoyant force; 2—weight equals the buoyant force; 3—weight less than the buoyant force

Reading Checkpoint Helium is less dense than air.

Assess

Reviewing Key Concepts

1. **a.** The buoyant force acts upward on a submerged object, making the object seem lighter. **b.** The buoyant force on the object equals the weight of the fluid displaced by the object. **c.** Because the object floats, the weight of the displaced water equals the weight of the object, 340 N. The buoyant force on the object equals its weight, 340 N.
2. **a.** Density equals mass per unit volume. **b.** If the object's density is greater than that of water, the object will sink; if the object's density is less than that of water, the object will float. **c.** Because water cannot enter these compartments, the air inside them gives the canoe a greater volume while adding only slightly to the canoe's mass. This makes the canoe less dense than water even if the material the canoe is made of is denser than water.

Reteach L1
Have students use Figure 10 to review the relationship between weight and buoyant force.

Performance Assessment L2
Writing Have students write a paragraph explaining how submarines use changing density to dive and rise.

All in One Teaching Resources

• Section Summary: *Floating and Sinking*
• Review and Reinforce: *Floating and Sinking*
• Enrich: *Floating and Sinking*

Lab zone At-Home Activity

Changing Balloon Density L1
Remind students of the relationship between mass, volume, and density so they are prepared to explain this to their families. Have students make notes of the number of paper clips that can be attached to the balloon before it sinks. Ask students how the actual number compared with their family member's prediction.

Lab zone Chapter Project

Keep Students on Track Have students keep a log as they experiment with various shapes and designs of boats. Encourage students to also record sketches of their designs in their logs. The students' logs should also include the materials used for each design and the results of each trial.

Sink and Spill

Prepare for Inquiry

Key Concept
The buoyant force on an object is equal to the weight of the fluid displaced by the object.

Skills Objectives
After this lab students will be able to
• control variables in their experiment
• interpret data from their experiment
• draw conclusions about the relationship between the weight of the fluid displaced and the buoyant force

Prep Time 20 minutes
Class Time 40 minutes

Advance Planning
Gather required materials. Prepare any solutions you will need if you plan to use liquids other than water.

Alternative Materials
Instead of water, part of the class can use sugar water, salt water, or vegetable oil. A denser material than salt, such as iron filings, could be used to fill the jar.

Safety
Caution students not to spill liquid on the floor. Remind students to be careful handling glass objects. Review the safety guidelines in Appendix A.

All in One Teaching Resources
• Lab Worksheet: *Sink and Spill*

Guide Inquiry

Invitation
Tell students that in this lab you will determine the relationship between buoyant force and the weight of fluid displaced, a comparison first made by Archimedes.

Introduce the Procedure
Discuss ways students might determine the weight of water displaced by an object. Explain the method used in the lab—subtracting the weight of the dry paper towel and the 250-mL beaker from its weight after the spill.

Sink and Spill

Problem
How is the buoyant force acting on a floating object related to the weight of the water it displaces?

Skills Focus
controlling variables, interpreting data, drawing conclusions

Materials
• paper towels • pie pan
• triple-beam balance • beaker, 600-mL
• jar with watertight lid, about 30-mL
• table salt

Procedure

1. Preview the procedure and copy the data table into your notebook.

2. Find the mass, in grams, of a dry paper towel and the pie pan together. Multiply the mass by 0.01. This gives you the weight in newtons. Record it in your data table.

3. Place the 600-mL beaker, with the dry paper towel under it, in the middle of the pie pan. Fill the beaker to the very top with water.

4. Fill the jar about halfway with salt. (The jar and salt must be able to float in water.) Then find the mass of the salt and the dry jar (with its cover on) in grams. Multiply the mass by 0.01. Record this weight in your data table.

5. Gently lower the jar into the 600-mL beaker. (If the jar sinks, take it out and remove some salt. Repeat Steps 2, 3, and 4.) Estimate the fraction of the jar that is underwater, and record it.

6. Once all of the displaced water has been spilled, find the total mass of the paper towel and pie pan containing the water. Multiply the mass by 0.01 and record the result in your data table.

7. Empty the pie pan. Dry off the pan and the jar.

8. Repeat Steps 3 through 7 several more times. Each time fill the jar with a different amount of salt, but make sure the jar still floats.

9. Calculate the buoyant force for each trial and record it in your data table. (*Hint*: When an object floats, the buoyant force is equal to the weight of the object.)

10. Calculate the weight of the displaced water in each case. Record it in your data table.

Data Table						
Jar	Weight of Empty Pie Pan and Dry Paper Towel (N)	Weight of Jar, Salt, and Cover (N)	Weight of Pie Pan With Displaced Water and Paper Towel (N)	Fraction of Jar Submerged in Water	Buoyant Force (N)	Weight of Displaced Water (N)
1						
2						
3						

Troubleshooting the Experiment
• Make sure students perform the lab on a level surface.
• Make sure students capture all of the displaced water.
• Tell students to use the same paper towel to wipe away any water that clings to the 600-mL beaker so it can be included in the mass.

Analyze and Conclude

1. **Controlling Variables** In each trial, the jar had a different weight. How did this affect the way that the jar floated?

2. **Interpreting Data** The jar had the same volume in every trial. Why did the volume of displaced water vary?

3. **Drawing Conclusions** What can you conclude about the relationship between the buoyant force and the weight of the displaced water?

4. **Drawing Conclusions** If you put too much salt in the jar, it will sink. What can you conclude about the buoyant force in this case? How can you determine the buoyant force for an object that sinks?

5. **Communicating** Write a paragraph suggesting places where errors may have been introduced into the experiment. Propose some ways to control the errors.

Design an Experiment

How do you think your results would change if you used a liquid that is more dense or less dense than water? Design an experiment to test your hypothesis. What liquid or liquids will you use? Will you need equipment other than what you used for this experiment? If so, what will you need? *Obtain your teacher's permission before carrying out your investigation.*

Expected Outcome

The weight of the displaced water will be equal to the buoyant force, which is equal to the weight of the jar, salt, and cover.

Analyze and Conclude

1. Because the jar's volume remained constant, the smaller its weight, the higher it floated.

2. The amount of displaced water depends only on the volume of the jar that is submerged. Because this varied each time, so did the amount of displaced water.

3. Because the jar floats, the buoyant force is the same as (or nearly the same as) the weight of the displaced water.

4. If the jar sinks, the buoyant force is less than the weight. The buoyant force will still be equal to the weight of the displaced water, which can be determined using the method from this lab.

5. Sample answer: If the jar was not dried completely between trials, some data for the total weight of the jar, salt, and cover would be incorrect. This error could be controlled by carefully drying the jar with a paper towel after each trial.

Extend Inquiry

Design an Experiment Sample answer: If a liquid denser than water is used, the same jar would float higher and a smaller volume of liquid would be displaced. To test this hypothesis, I could repeat the lab using a liquid denser than water, such as corn syrup or glycerin.

Objectives

After this lesson, students will be able to

M.3.3.1 State Pascal's principle, and recognize its applications.

M.3.3.2 Explain how a hydraulic system multiplies force.

Target Reading Skill

Asking Questions Explain that changing a head into a question helps students anticipate the ideas, facts, and events they are about to read.

Answer:
Sample questions and answers:
How is pressure transmitted in a fluid? *(Pressure is transmitted equally to all parts of the fluid.)* **What is a hydraulic system?** *(A hydraulic system uses a confined fluid to transmit pressure.)*

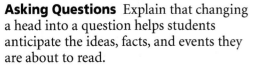 **Teaching Resources**

• Transparency M29

Preteach

Build Background Knowledge L2

Pressure in a Fluid

Show students a sealed bag of water. Ask:
What will happen if you squeeze one side of the bag? *(The water will move to the other side of the bag.)* Encourage students to describe what happens to the fluid in the bag when you push on one part of it. *(It all moves.)*

Pascal's Principle

Reading Preview

Key Concepts
• What does Pascal's principle say about change in fluid pressure?
• How does a hydraulic system work?

Key Terms
• Pascal's principle
• hydraulic system

Target Reading Skill

Asking Questions Before you read, preview the red headings. In a graphic organizer like the one below, ask a *what* or *how* question for each heading. As you read, write the answers to your questions.

Pascal's Principle

Question	Answer
How is pressure transmitted in a fluid?	Pressure is transmitted . . .

Discover Activity

How Does Pressure Change?

1. Fill an empty 2-liter plastic bottle with water. Then screw on the cap. There should be no bubbles in the bottle (or only very small bubbles).
2. Lay the bottle on its side. At one spot, push in the bottle with your left thumb.
3. With your right thumb, push in fairly hard on a spot at the other end, as shown. What does your left thumb feel?
4. Pick another spot on the bottle for your left thumb and repeat Step 3.

Think It Over
Observing When you push in with your right thumb, does the water pressure in the bottle increase, decrease, or remain the same? How do you know?

At first, you hesitate, but then you hold out your hand. The aquarium attendant places the sea star in your palm. You can feel motion on your skin. The many tiny "feet" on the animal's underside look something like suction cups, and they tickle just a bit! The attendant explains that the sea star has a system of tubes containing water in its body. As the water moves around in the tubes, it creates fluid pressure that allows the sea star to move. The sea star also uses this system to obtain its food.

A sea star uses fluid pressure to move. ▶

Discover Activity

Skills Focus Observing L1

Materials 2-L plastic bottle with cap, water

Time 10 minutes

Tips Remove the label from the plastic bottle. Remind students to maintain a constant, firm pressure with their left

thumbs. Encourage students to push in several different places on the bottle.

Think It Over Sample answer: The water pressure increases when you push in the bottle with your right thumb. You can tell because you can feel the increased pressure on your left thumb.

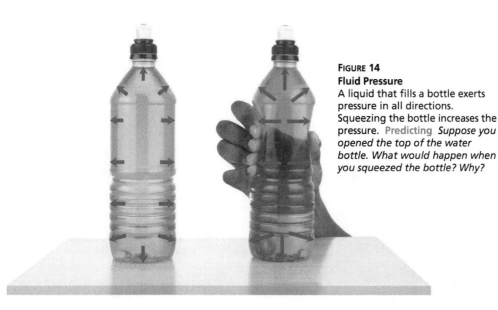

FIGURE 14
Fluid Pressure
A liquid that fills a bottle exerts pressure in all directions. Squeezing the bottle increases the pressure. *Predicting Suppose you opened the top of the water bottle. What would happen when you squeezed the bottle? Why?*

Transmitting Pressure in a Fluid

If you did the Discover Activity, you may be surprised to learn that a sea star's water-filled tube system is like the closed bottle you pushed your thumb against. Recall that the fluid pressure in the closed container increased when you pushed against its side. By changing the fluid pressure at any spot in the closed container, you transmitted pressure throughout the container. In the 1600s, a French mathematician named Blaise Pascal developed a principle to explain how pressure is transmitted in a fluid. Pascal's name is used for the unit of pressure.

What Is Pascal's Principle? As you may recall, fluid exerts pressure on any surface it touches. For example, the water in each bottle shown in Figure 14 exerts pressure on the entire surface of the bottle—up, down, and sideways.

What happens if you squeeze the bottle when its top is closed? The water has nowhere to go, so it presses harder on the inside surface of the bottle. The water pressure increases everywhere in the bottle. This is shown by the increased length of the arrows on the right in Figure 14.

Pascal discovered that pressure increases by the same amount throughout an enclosed or confined fluid. **When force is applied to a confined fluid, the change in pressure is transmitted equally to all parts of the fluid.** This relationship is known as **Pascal's principle.**

Transmitting Pressure in a Fluid

Teach Key Concepts   L2
Examples of Pascal's Principle

Focus Tell students that Pascal's principle states when force is applied to a confined fluid, the change in pressure is transmitted equally to all parts of the fluid.

Teach Ask: **How does Pascal's principle explain what you observe when you squeeze one side of a closed soda bottle that is full of water?** *(If you squeeze one side of a full, closed soda bottle, the pressure is transmitted to all parts of the soda bottle, as stated by Pascal's principle.)*

Extend Ask: **How does a hydraulic system apply Pascal's principle?** *(A hydraulic system is a device that uses pistons with different surface areas to multiply an input force that is transmitted through a fluid.)* **learning modality: verbal**

Independent Practice   L2

All in One Teaching Resources

• Guided Reading and Study Worksheet: *Pascal's Principle*

Differentiated Instruction

Less Proficient Readers   L1
Using Visuals Have students review the caption and labels for Figure 15. Then ask students to describe in their own words how the device shown in Figure 15 works. **learning modality: visual**

Gifted and Talented   L3
Making a Game Have students design and produce a board game that can be used to teach and review the chapter content. Students should use all the key concepts and key terms from the chapter in their game. Have the class use the game to review the chapter material. **learning modality: logical/mathematical**

Monitor Progress   L2

Oral Presentation Ask students to describe two everyday examples of pressure being transmitted in a fluid. *(Sample answer: Pressure applied to the bottom of a toothpaste tube forces toothpaste to come out the top of the tube.)*

Answer
Figure 14 Water would be forced from the bottle by the increase in pressure.

Modeling a Hydraulic System   **L3**

Materials two different sizes of plastic "air pistons" or similar devices, short piece of plastic tubing

Focus Tell students that you will build a working hydraulic system.

Teach Fill the smaller air piston with water. Fill the larger piston half way with water. Attach the plastic tubing to the end of the larger air piston. Squeeze a small amount of water into the tubing. Attach the other end of the tubing to the smaller air piston. Ask: **What will happen if I depress the larger air piston?** *(The smaller piston will move a greater distance.)* Demonstrate the system for students. Have the students note the effect of depressing the smaller piston and the effect of moving the larger piston.

Apply Ask: **When the smaller piston is depressed, what happens to the force?** *(The force is multiplied.)* **learning modality: visual**

Go Online
active art

For: Hydraulic Systems activity
Visit: PHSchool.com
Web Code: cgp-3033

Students can interact with art of the hydraulic systems online.

Integrating Life Science   **L2**

The Heimlich maneuver can be used when a person has food or a foreign object stuck in the trachea, or windpipe. When performed correctly, the Heimlich maneuver exerts a pressure on the diaphragm. In humans, the diaphragm is a muscle found under the lungs. Exerting a force on the diaphragm increases lung pressure. This, in turn, increases pressure on the narrower trachea, forcing air and the foreign object out of the trachea. **learning modality: verbal**

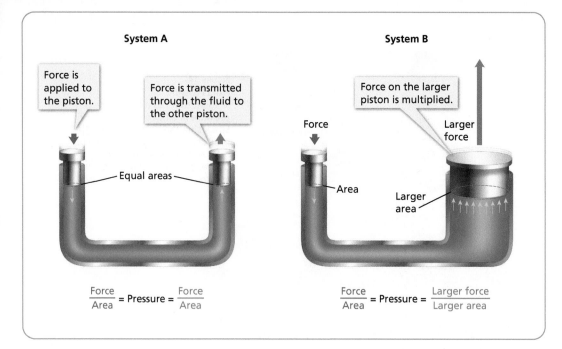

System A   System B

Force is applied to the piston.

Force is transmitted through the fluid to the other piston.

Force on the larger piston is multiplied.

Force   Larger force

Equal areas   Area   Larger area

$$\frac{Force}{Area} = Pressure = \frac{Force}{Area}$$

$$\frac{Force}{Area} = Pressure = \frac{Larger\ force}{Larger\ area}$$

FIGURE 15
Hydraulic Devices
In a hydraulic device, a force applied to one piston increases the fluid pressure equally throughout the fluid. By changing the area of the pistons, the force can be multiplied.
Problem Solving *To multiply the force applied to the left piston four times, how large must the area of the right piston be?*

Go Online
active art

For: Hydraulic Systems activity
Visit: PHSchool.com
Web Code: cgp-3033

Using Pascal's Principle You can see Pascal's principle at work in Figure 15, which shows a model of a hydraulic device. A hydraulic device works by applying a force to an enclosed fluid. The device consists of two pistons, one at each end of a U-shaped tube. A piston is like a stopper that slides up and down in a tube.

Suppose you fill System A with water and then push down on the left piston. The increase in fluid pressure will be transmitted to the right piston. According to Pascal's principle, both pistons experience the same fluid pressure. So, because both pistons have the same surface area, they will experience the same force.

Now look at System B. The right piston has a greater surface area than the left piston. Suppose the area of the small piston is 1 square centimeter and the area of the large piston is 9 square centimeters. The right piston has an area nine times greater than the area of the left piston. If you push down on the left piston, pressure is transmitted equally to the right piston. The force you exert on the left piston is multiplied nine times on the right piston. By changing the area of the pistons, you can multiply force by almost any amount you wish.

 Reading Checkpoint **How is force multiplied in System B?**

Hydraulic Systems

Hydraulic systems make use of hydraulic devices to perform a variety of functions. A **hydraulic system** uses liquids to transmit pressure in a confined fluid. **A hydraulic system multiplies force by applying the force to a small surface area. The increase in pressure is then transmitted to another part of the confined fluid, which pushes on a larger surface area.** You have probably seen a number of hydraulic systems at work, including lift systems and the brakes of a car. Because they use fluids to transmit pressure, hydraulic systems have few moving parts that can jam, break, or wear down.

Hydraulic Lifts Hydraulic lift systems are used to raise cars off the ground so mechanics can repair them with ease. You may be surprised to learn that hydraulic systems are also used to lift the heavy ladder on a fire truck to reach the upper windows of a burning building. In addition, hydraulic lifts are used to operate many pieces of heavy construction equipment such as dump trucks, backhoes, snowplows, and cranes. Next time you see a construction vehicle at work, see if you can spot the hydraulic pistons in action.

✓ Reading Checkpoint What are some uses of hydraulic systems?

Math — Analyzing Data

Comparing Hydraulic Lifts

In the hydraulic device in Figure 15, a force applied to the piston on the left produces a lifting force in the piston on the right. The graph shows the relationship between the applied force and the lifting force for two hydraulic lifts.

1. **Reading Graphs** Suppose a force of 1,000 N is applied to both lifts. Use the graph to determine the lifting force of each lift.

2. **Reading Graphs** For Lift A, how much force must be applied to lift a 12,000-N object?

3. **Interpreting Data** By how much is the applied force multiplied for each lift?

4. **Interpreting Data** What can you learn from the slope of the line for each lift?

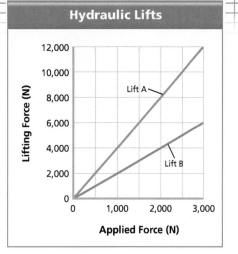

Hydraulic Lifts

5. **Drawing Conclusions** Which lift would you choose if you wanted to produce the greater lifting force?

Differentiated Instruction

English Learners/Beginning [L1]
Vocabulary: Word Analysis Write the word *hydraulic* on the board. Underline the root *hydr-*. Explain that this part of the words means *water*. Have students brainstorm other English words that include the word part *hydr* or *hydro*. Write correct responses on the board, and pronounce and define the words for students. **learning modality: verbal**

English Learners/Intermediate [L2]
Vocabulary: Word Analysis Students can expand on the activity described in Beginning by writing the list of words on a sheet of paper. Students should use a dictionary to find the definitions of the words, and use the words in a written or spoken sentence. **learning modality: verbal**

Hydraulic Systems

Teach Key Concepts [L2]
Uses of Hydraulic Systems

Focus Tell students that hydraulic systems have many applications.

Teach Ask: **What are some uses of hydraulic systems?** *(Hydraulic brakes and lift systems)*

Apply Ask: **Why is a leak in a hydraulic system a problem?** *(In order for pressure to be transmitted in a fluid, the fluid must be confined. If the hydraulic system is leaking, the fluid is not confined.)* **learning modality: logical/mathematical**

All in One Teaching Resources
• Transparency M30

Math — Analyzing Data

Math Skill Making and interpreting graphs

Focus This line graph shows the relationship between two variables: applied force and lifting force.

Teach Ask: **For both lifts, what happens as the applied force is increased?** *(The lifting force also increases.)* **Which lift provides a greater lifting force per newton of applied force?** *(Lift A)*

Answers
1. Lift A: 4,000 N; lift B: 2,000 N
2. 3,000 N
3. Lift A: applied force multiplied by four; lift B: applied force multiplied by two
4. The slope gives the ratio of the lifting force to the applied force. The greater the slope, the more the lift multiplies force.
5. Lift A, because it multiplies force more than lift B.

Monitor Progress [L2]

Drawing Ask students to make a diagram of a hydraulic system showing both the force applied and the resulting force.

Answers
Figure 15 Its surface area must be four times greater than that of the left piston.

✓ Reading Checkpoint The force applied to the left piston is multiplied on the right piston because the right piston has a larger surface area.

✓ Reading Checkpoint Uses include car brakes and lift systems for fire engines and construction equipment.

Monitor Progress — L2

Answer
Figure 16 It is smaller than a brake pad piston.

Assess

Reviewing Key Concepts

1. a. The pressure is transmitted equally throughout all parts of the fluid. **b.** When a force is applied to one part of the hydraulic device, a confined fluid transmits the increased pressure to a part of the device with a larger surface area. The increased pressure enables the part with the larger surface area to exert a force greater than the initial supplied force. **c.** The force will be multiplied ten times because the surface area of the larger piston is ten times greater. Therefore, the larger piston will apply a force of 100 N.

2. a. A hydraulic system is one that uses a confined fluid to transmit pressure and multiply force. **b.** When a force is applied to a small piston in contact with a confined fluid, the fluid transmits the increased pressure to a larger piston. Because the pressure on both pistons is the same and the larger piston has a greater surface area, the larger piston applies a greater force. **c.** The driver exerts a force on the brake pedal, which causes the brake pedal piston to exert increased pressure on the brake fluid. The confined brake fluid transmits the increased pressure to pistons that push on the brake pads in the car's wheels. When the brake pads rub against brake disks, the force of friction between pads and disks slows the car's wheels.

Reteach — L1
Have students work in pairs to review Pascal's principle and the applications of hydraulic systems.

All in One Teaching Resources
• Section Summary: *Pascal's Principle*
• Review and Reinforce: *Pascal's Principle*
• Enrich: *Pascal's Principle*

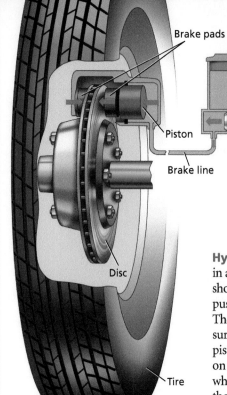

FIGURE 16
Hydraulic Brakes
The hydraulic brake system of a car multiplies the force exerted on the brake pedal.
Comparing and Contrasting *How does the size of the brake pedal piston compare with the size of a brake pad piston?*

(Labels: Brake pads, Brake fluid, Piston, Piston, Brake line, Brake pedal, Disc, Tire)

Hydraulic Brakes You rely on Pascal's principle when you ride in a car. The brake system of a car is a hydraulic system. Figure 16 shows a simplified brake system with disc brakes. When a driver pushes down on the brake pedal, he or she pushes a small piston. The piston exerts pressure on the brake fluid. The increased pressure is transmitted through the fluid in the brake lines to larger pistons within the wheels of the car. Each of these pistons pushes on a brake pad. The brake pads rub against the brake disc, and the wheel's motion is slowed down by the force of friction. Because the brake system multiplies force, a person can stop a large car with only a light push on the brake pedal.

Section 3 Assessment

🔄 **Target Reading Skill** Asking Questions Use the answers to the questions you wrote about the headings to help you answer the questions below.

Reviewing Key Concepts

1. a. Reviewing According to Pascal's principle, how is pressure transmitted in a fluid?
 b. Relating Cause and Effect How does a hydraulic device multiply force?
 c. Calculating Suppose you apply a 10-N force to a 10-cm^2 piston in a hydraulic device. If the force is transmitted to another piston with an area of 100 cm^2, by how much will the force be multiplied?
2. a. Defining What is a hydraulic system?
 b. Explaining How does a hydraulic system work?

 c. Sequencing Describe what happens in the brake system of a car from the time a driver steps on the brake pedal to the time the car stops.

Writing in Science

Cause-and-Effect Letter You are a mechanic who fixes hydraulic brakes. A customer asks you why his brakes do not work. When you examine the car, you notice a leak in the brake line and repair it. Write a letter to the customer explaining why a leak in the brake line caused his brakes to fail.

Lab zone Chapter Project

Keep Students on Track Make balances available as students evaluate their designs. Remind the students not to be content with the first design that floats. Challenge students to brainstorm ways to improve their designs. If a particular design sinks, have students determine whether it was too dense or if it capsized because it was unstable.

Writing in Science

Writing Mode Exposition/Cause-and-Effect

Scoring Rubric
4 Exceeds criteria; includes all required elements as well as extra information
3 Meets criteria
2 Includes some but not all required elements
1 Shows little effort and/or includes numerous errors

Bernoulli's Principle

Reading Preview

Key Concepts
- According to Bernoulli's principle, how is fluid pressure related to the motion of a fluid?
- What are some applications of Bernoulli's principle?

Key Terms
- Bernoulli's principle
- lift

Target Reading Skill

Identifying Main Ideas As you read the Applying Bernoulli's Principle section, write the main idea in a graphic organizer like the one below. Then write three supporting details that give examples of the main idea.

Main Idea

Bernoulli's principle is a factor that helps explain . . .

Detail	Detail	Detail

Lab zone Discover **Activity**

Does the Movement of Air Affect Pressure?

1. Use your thumb and forefinger to hold a sheet of paper by the corners.
2. Hold the paper just below your mouth, so that its edge is horizontal and the paper hangs down.
3. Blow across the top of the paper.
4. Repeat this several times, blowing harder each time.

Think It Over

Inferring On what side of the paper is the pressure lower? How do you know?

In December 1903, Wilbur and Orville Wright brought an odd-looking vehicle to a deserted beach in Kitty Hawk, North Carolina. People had flown in balloons for more than a hundred years, but the Wright brothers' goal was something no one had ever done before. They flew a plane that was heavier (denser) than air! They had spent years experimenting with different wing shapes and surfaces, and they had carefully studied the flight of birds. Their first flight at Kitty Hawk lasted just 12 seconds. The plane flew more than 36 meters and made history.

What did the Wright brothers know about flying that allowed them to construct the first airplane? And how can the principles they used explain how a jet can fly across the country? The answer has to do with fluid pressure and what happens when a fluid moves.

◄ On December 17, 1903, the Wright brothers' plane *Flyer* flew for the first time.

Chapter 3 M ◆ 95

Objectives
After this lesson, students will be able to

M.3.4.1 Use Bernoulli's principle to explain how fluid pressure is related to the motion of a fluid.

M.3.4.2 List some applications of Bernoulli's principle.

Target Reading Skill

Identifying Main Ideas Explain that identifying main ideas and details helps students sort the facts from the information into groups. Each group can have a main topic, subtopics, and details.

Answers
Sample answer:
Main Idea: Bernoulli's principle is a factor that helps explain…
Detail: how airplanes fly
Detail: why smoke rises up a chimney
Detail: how an atomizer works

All in One Teaching Resources
- Transparency M32

Preteach

Build Background Knowledge L2
Paper Airplanes
Fold a sheet of notebook paper to make a simple paper airplane. Launch the airplane away from students. Tell students that in this section they will learn how an object that weighs more than air can fly.

Lab zone Discover **Activity**

Skills Focus Inferring

Materials sheet of notebook paper

Time 10 minutes

Tips Be sure students hold only the corners of the paper.

L1 **Think It Over** Sample answer: The pressure is lower above the paper. Because the paper rises, the force on the bottom of the paper must be higher than the force on the top of the paper.

Pressure and Moving Fluids

Teach Key Concepts   L2

Observing Bernoulli's Principle

Focus Remind students that both liquids and gases are fluids. Tell students that Bernoulli's principle applies to any fluid in motion.

Teach Direct students' attention to Figure 17. Ask: **Is the fluid between the cans moving more quickly or more slowly than the air on the opposite sides of the cans?** *(More quickly)* **How does the movement of the air between the cans affect the pressure between the cans?** *(As the speed of the air increases, the pressure decreases)*

Apply Ask: **How does Bernoulli's principle explain how a drinking straw works?** *(When you sip on a straw, an area of low pressure forms above the liquid. The liquid rises because of the low pressure above it.)*
learning modality: logical/mathematical

Independent Practice   L2

All in One Teaching Resources

• Guided Reading and Study Worksheet: *Bernoulli's Principle*

◉ Student Edition on Audio CD

Lab zone Try This **Activity**

Faucet Force

1. Hold a plastic spoon loosely by the edges of its handle so it swings freely between your fingers.
2. Turn on a faucet to produce a steady stream of water. Predict what will happen if you touch the bottom of the spoon to the stream of water.
3. Test your prediction. Repeat the test several times.

Developing Hypotheses Use your observations to develop a hypothesis explaining why the spoon moved as it did.

FIGURE 17
Making Air Move
Blowing air quickly between two cans lowers the air pressure between them. Higher pressure exerted by the still air to either side pushes the cans toward each other.
Relating Cause and Effect How does the flowing air affect the air pressure around the two cans?

Pressure and Moving Fluids

So far in this chapter, you have learned about fluids that are not moving. What makes a fluid flow? And what happens to fluid pressure when a fluid moves?

Fluid Motion A fluid naturally flows from an area of high pressure to an area of low pressure. This happens, for example, when you sip a drink from a straw. When you start to sip, you remove the air from the straw. This creates an area of low pressure in the straw. The higher air pressure pushing down on the surface of your drink forces the drink up into the straw.

What Is Bernoulli's Principle? In the 1700s, Swiss scientist Daniel Bernoulli (bur NOO lee) discovered that the pressure of a moving fluid is different than the pressure of a fluid at rest. **Bernoulli's principle** states that the faster a fluid moves, the less pressure the fluid exerts.

If you did the Discover Activity, you saw that air moving over the paper caused the paper to rise. Bernoulli's principle explains the behavior of the paper. **Bernoulli's principle states that as the speed of a moving fluid increases, the pressure within the fluid decreases.** The air above the paper moves, but the air below the paper does not. The moving air exerts less pressure than the still air. As a result, the still air exerts greater pressure on the bottom of the paper, pushing the paper up.

✓ Reading Checkpoint   **What is Bernoulli's principle?**

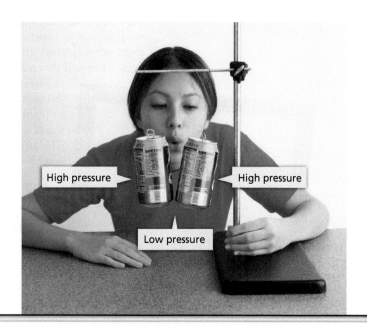

High pressure   High pressure

Low pressure

Lab zone Try This **Activity**

Skills Focus Developing hypotheses   L2

Materials plastic spoon, faucet

Time 10 minutes

Tips Have students write down their predictions before they begin. Remind students to hold the back of the spoon facing the stream of water.

Expected Outcome The spoon will move toward the stream of water. Sample answer: The spoon moved toward the stream of water because the moving water caused the pressure to be lower on the back of the spoon.

Extend Have students predict what would happen if they performed the experiment using a plastic fork rather than a spoon. Have students test their predictions.
learning modality: kinesthetic

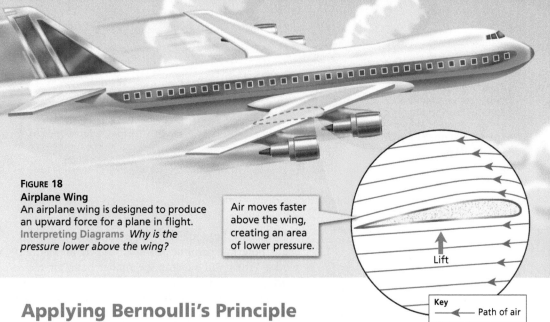

FIGURE 18
Airplane Wing
An airplane wing is designed to produce an upward force for a plane in flight. *Interpreting Diagrams* *Why is the pressure lower above the wing?*

Air moves faster above the wing, creating an area of lower pressure.

Lift

Key
← Path of air

Applying Bernoulli's Principle

The Wright brothers understood Bernoulli's principle. They used it when they designed and built their plane. **Bernoulli's principle helps explain how planes fly. It also helps explain why smoke rises up a chimney, how an atomizer works, and how a flying disk glides through the air.**

Objects in Flight Bernoulli's principle is one factor that helps explain flight—from a small kite to a huge airplane. Objects can be designed so that their shapes cause air to move at different speeds above and below them. If the air moves faster above the object, fluid pressure pushes the object upward. If the air moves faster below the object, fluid pressure pushes it downward.

The wing of an airplane is designed to produce **lift**, or an upward force. Look at Figure 18 to see the design of a wing. Both the slant and the shape of the wing are sources of lift. Because the wing is slanted, the air that hits it is forced downward as the plane moves. The air exerts an equal and opposite force on the wing and pushes it upward. This upward force helps an airplane to take off.

The curved shape of a wing also gives an airplane lift. Because the top of the wing is curved, air moving over the top has a greater speed than air moving under the bottom. As a result, the air moving over the top exerts less pressure than the air below. The difference in air pressure above and below the wing creates lift.

Go Online
SCi**LINKS** NSTA

For: Links on Bernoulli's principle
Visit: www.SciLinks.org
Web Code: scn-1334

Chapter 3 M ♦ 97

Applying Bernoulli's Principle

Teach Key Concepts   L2
Bernoulli's Principle at Work

Focus Ask for a volunteer to state Bernoulli's principle. Tell students that Bernoulli's principle explains many everyday occurrences.

Teach For each application of Bernoulli's principle shown in Figures 18–21 (airplane, atomizer, chimney, flying disk), have a volunteer explain, in his or her own words, how the object demonstrates Bernoulli's principle.

Apply The spoiler on the back of a race car is shaped like an upside-down wing. It is positioned above the rear tires. Ask: **What does the spoiler do to the pressure on the rear wheels?** *(It increases the pressure on the rear wheels.)* **learning modality: logical/mathematical**

Go Online
SCi**LINKS** NSTA

For: Links on Bernoulli's principle
Visit: www.SciLinks.org
Web Code: scn-1334

Download a worksheet that will guide students' review of Internet sources on Bernoulli's principle.

All in One Teaching Resources
• Transparency M33

Differentiated Instruction

English Learners/Beginning Comprehension: Ask Questions   L1
Distribute a rewritten, simplified version of the information under the heading Applying Bernoulli's Principle. Read the modified version of the information aloud while students follow along silently. Then ask questions that can be answered verbally. For example: Does air move more quickly over the top or the bottom of an airplane wing? *(Top)* **learning modality: verbal**

English Learners/Intermediate Comprehension: Ask Questions   L2
Have students independently read the modified text prepared for the Beginning activity. Then, have the students write the answers to the questions used in the Beginning activity. Call on students to read their answers aloud. **learning modality: verbal**

Monitor Progress   L2

Writing Have students write a paragraph that explains three examples of Bernoulli's principle.

Answers
Figure 17 Air pressure between the two cans is lowered.

Figure 18 Because the air moves faster above the wing than below it

Reading Checkpoint The faster a fluid moves, the less pressure the fluid exerts.

M ● 97

Objects in Flight

Materials craft sticks, masking tape, thin dowels, tissue paper, string

Time 20 minutes

Focus Have the students review the information about Bernoulli's principle and airplane wings.

Teach Have small groups design and build airplanes or gliders. Assign each student a task such as designer, assembler, and flight analyst. Allow students to test their designs outdoors. Challenge students to explain how the design of the plane or glider causes air to move more quickly over the top.

Apply After students have tested and designed their airplanes, Ask: **What design modifications did you make?** *(Sample answer: We changed the angle of the wing.)* **How did your modification affect the plane's flight?** *(Sample answer: It flew longer after the modification.)* **How did your design modification apply Bernoulli's principle?** *(The changed angle of the wing allowed air to flow more quickly over the top of the wing, increasing the lift.)* **learning modality: logical/mathematical**

Help Students Read
L1

Relating Cause and Effect Explain that cause is the reason for what happens. The effect is what happens because of the cause. Have students explain Bernoulli's principle in terms of cause and effect. *(Sample answer: Increased speed of a moving fluid is the cause; decreased pressure within the fluid is the effect.)*

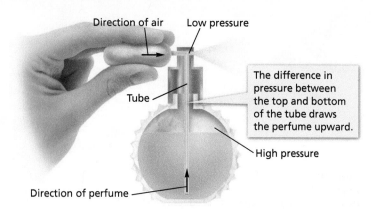

FIGURE 19
Perfume Atomizer
An atomizer is an application of Bernoulli's principle. *Applying Concepts Why is the perfume pushed up and out of the flask?*

Direction of air   Low pressure

The difference in pressure between the top and bottom of the tube draws the perfume upward.

Tube

High pressure

Direction of perfume

Atomizers Bernoulli's principle can help you understand how the perfume atomizer shown in Figure 19 works. When you squeeze the rubber bulb, air moves quickly past the top of the tube. The moving air lowers the pressure at the top of the tube. The greater pressure in the flask pushes the liquid up into the tube. The air stream breaks the liquid into small drops, and the liquid comes out as a fine mist. In a similar way, pressure differences in the carburetors of older gasoline engines push gasoline up a tube. There, the gasoline combines with air to create the mixture of air and fuel that runs the engine.

Chimneys You can sit next to a fireplace enjoying a cozy fire thanks in part to Bernoulli's principle. Smoke rises up the chimney partly because hot air rises, and partly because it is pushed. Wind blowing across the top of a chimney lowers the air pressure there. The higher pressure at the bottom pushes air and smoke up the chimney. Smoke will rise faster in a chimney on a windy day than on a calm day.

 Reading Checkpoint **How does an atomizer work?**

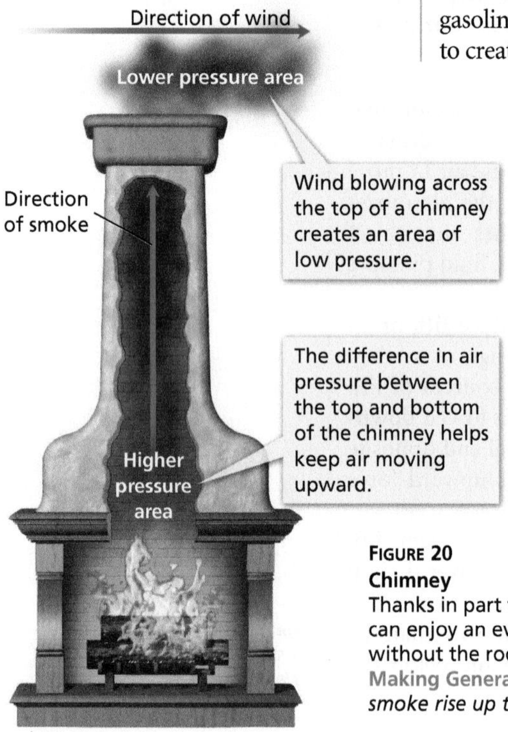

Direction of wind

Lower pressure area

Direction of smoke

Wind blowing across the top of a chimney creates an area of low pressure.

The difference in air pressure between the top and bottom of the chimney helps keep air moving upward.

Higher pressure area

FIGURE 20
Chimney
Thanks in part to Bernoulli's principle, you can enjoy an evening by a warm fireplace without the room filling up with smoke. *Making Generalizations Why does the smoke rise up the chimney?*

98 ◆ M

Differentiated Instruction

Less Proficient Readers **L1**
Using Visuals Have students review the figures in the section Bernoulli's Principle. As students look at each figure, ask the caption question aloud. Have students answer the caption question aloud.
learning modality: visual

Gifted and Talented **L3**
Demonstrating Bernoulli's Principle
Have students develop a lesson plan and demonstration that could be used to teach Bernoulli's principle to elementary school students. After students have completed their preparations, arrange for them to visit an elementary school to teach their prepared lessons. **learning modality: logical/mathematical**

Flying Disks Did you ever wonder what allows a flying disk to glide through the air? The upper surface of a flying disk is curved like an airplane wing. Bernoulli's principle explains that the faster-moving air following the disk's curved upper surface exerts less pressure than the slower-moving air beneath it. A net force acts upward on the flying disk, creating lift. Tilting the disk slightly toward you as you throw it also helps to keep it in the air. A tilted disk pushes air down. The air exerts an equal and opposite force on the disk, pushing it up. The spinning motion of a flying disk keeps it stable as it flies.

FIGURE 21
Flying Disk
Like an airplane wing, a flying disk uses a curved upper surface to create lift. *Comparing and Contrasting How does a flying disk differ from an airplane wing?*

Key
Path of air
Lift

Section 4 Assessment

Target Reading Skill Identifying Main Ideas Use your graphic organizer to help you answer Question 1 below.

Reviewing Key Concepts

1. a. Reviewing What makes fluids flow?
   b. Summarizing What does Bernoulli's principle say about the pressure exerted by a moving fluid?
   c. Applying Concepts You are riding in a car on a highway when a large truck speeds by you. Explain why your car is pushed toward the truck.

2. a. Listing List four applications of Bernoulli's principle.
   b. Explaining Why does the air pressure above an airplane wing differ from the pressure below it? How is this pressure difference involved in flight?
   c. Relating Cause and Effect How could strong winds from a hurricane blow the roof off a house?

Lab zone At-Home Activity

Paper Chimney With a family member, see how a chimney works by using a paper cup and a hair dryer. Cut up several small pieces of tissue and place them in the bottom of a paper cup. Hold on to the paper cup with one hand. With your other hand, use the hair dryer to blow cool air across the top of the cup. Explain to your family member how Bernoulli's principle explains how the chimney works.

Answers
Figure 19 Squeezing the bulb moves air through the top of the tube, lowering the pressure there. The higher pressure at the bottom of the tube pushes perfume up the tube and into the stream of air moving out of the tube.
Figure 20 Partly because hot air rises, and partly because wind lowers the pressure above the chimney, and higher air pressure at the bottom of the chimney pushes air and smoke upward
Figure 21 A flying disk spins as it moves through the air; an airplane wing does not.

Reading Checkpoint Squeezing an atomizer's bulb creates a difference in pressure between the top and bottom of its tube, which draws perfume upwards.

Assess

Reviewing Key Concepts

1. a. Unequal pressure makes fluids flow. b. The faster a fluid moves, the less pressure it exerts. c. The truck pulls air along with it, causing the air between the two vehicles to move faster than the air on the other side of the car. The greater pressure on the side of the car away from the truck pushes the car toward the truck.
2. a. Airplane wings, atomizers, chimneys, flying disks b. As the airplane travels through the air, the wing's shape causes air above the wing to move faster than air below the wing. The result is that air pressure above the wing is lower than air pressure below the wing. This causes a net upward force, or lift, that allows the plane to fly. c. Wind blowing over the roof exerts less pressure than the still air inside the house. The greater pressure inside the house pushes the roof upward.

Performance Assessment L2
Writing Native Americans of many different tribes have built dwellings that use a hole in the roof to allow smoke to escape. Have students write a paragraph using Bernoulli's principle to explain how this works. They should include a prediction of whether the smoke outlet works better with no wind or with wind.

Lab zone At-Home Activity

Paper Chimney L2 Students should base their explanations on Bernoulli's principle. They should describe how fast-moving air lowers the pressure above the cup just as moving air lowers the pressure above a chimney. Students also should point out that higher pressure inside the cup pushes pieces of tissue out of the cup the same way that higher pressure at the bottom of a chimney pushes smoke up the chimney.

All in One Teaching Resources
- Section Summary: *Bernoulli's Principle*
- Review and Reinforce: *Bernoulli's Principle*
- Enrich: *Bernoulli's Principle*

Technology and Society

Helicopters

Key Concept

Helicopters have some advantages and some disadvantages when compared to airplanes.

Build Background Knowledge

Applying Bernoulli's Principle

Remind students that Bernoulli's principle explains how airplane wings work. Ask: **How does Bernoulli's principle relate to the rotating blades of a helicopter?** *(Air flowing over the top of the rotating blades reduces the air pressure on top of the blades, producing lift.)*

Introduce the Debate

Explain that there are some differences between airplanes and helicopters. There are some applications for which helicopters are superior, and other applications for which airplanes are the best choice. Ask: **What are some benefits of helicopters?** *(Sample answer: Helicopters can hover and land almost anywhere, helicopters can fly forward, backward, and sideways)* **What are some constraints of the use of helicopters?** *(Sample answer: Helicopters must refuel more often than airplanes; helicopters cannot carry large numbers of people)*

Facilitate the Debate

- Have students read the feature and answer the Weigh the Impact questions using the information in the feature and the chapter. Allow students computer time to access information about the use of helicopters in national parks.

- After students have completed their research, divide the class into small groups. Have students discuss the information they located about helicopter missions in national parks.

- Divide the class into two groups. Have one group argue the positive aspects of using helicopters on national parks missions, and one group argue the negative aspects of using helicopters in national parks missions.

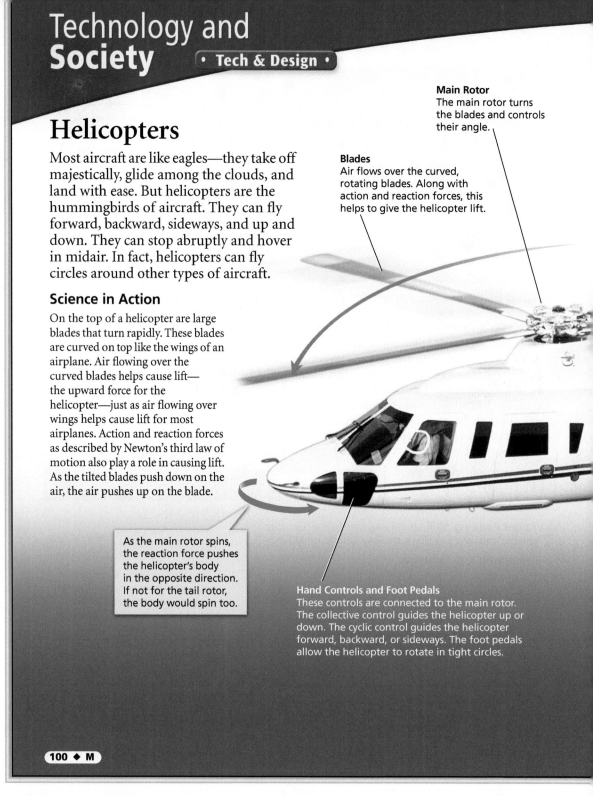

Helicopters

Most aircraft are like eagles—they take off majestically, glide among the clouds, and land with ease. But helicopters are the hummingbirds of aircraft. They can fly forward, backward, sideways, and up and down. They can stop abruptly and hover in midair. In fact, helicopters can fly circles around other types of aircraft.

Science in Action

On the top of a helicopter are large blades that turn rapidly. These blades are curved on top like the wings of an airplane. Air flowing over the curved blades helps cause lift— the upward force for the helicopter—just as air flowing over wings helps cause lift for most airplanes. Action and reaction forces as described by Newton's third law of motion also play a role in causing lift. As the tilted blades push down on the air, the air pushes up on the blade.

Main Rotor
The main rotor turns the blades and controls their angle.

Blades
Air flows over the curved, rotating blades. Along with action and reaction forces, this helps to give the helicopter lift.

As the main rotor spins, the reaction force pushes the helicopter's body in the opposite direction. If not for the tail rotor, the body would spin too.

Hand Controls and Foot Pedals
These controls are connected to the main rotor. The collective control guides the helicopter up or down. The cyclic control guides the helicopter forward, backward, or sideways. The foot pedals allow the helicopter to rotate in tight circles.

Background

History of Science The ideas behind helicopter technology have been developed and refined over thousands of years. Ancient Chinese toys that launch a propeller into flight use some of the same principles as today's helicopters. Leonardo Da Vinci drew up plans for a helicopter-like device in the late 1400's, but it wasn't until much later that the first helicopters were used. The technology of helicopters was the subject of intensive work in the 1920's. It was the 1930's before a truly functional and practical helicopter was developed.

The Aircraft of Choice—Or Not?

Helicopters can hover and land nearly anywhere. So they are often the aircraft of choice in emergency situations. They are used in search and rescue missions, in fighting forest fires, and in speeding injured people to the hospital. Construction companies also use helicopters to raise heavy equipment.

Despite these benefits, there are constraints to using helicopters. Compared to an airplane, a helicopter must refuel more often and can remain in the air for less time. Another constraint is that a helicopter cannot transport heavy equipment over long distances or carry large numbers of people.

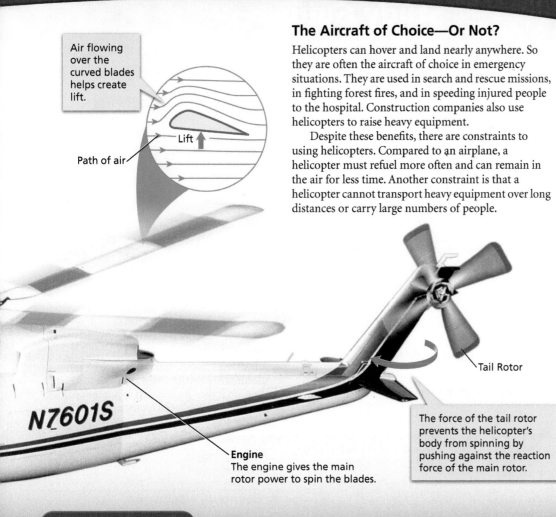

Air flowing over the curved blades helps create lift.

Lift

Path of air

N7601S

Tail Rotor

The force of the tail rotor prevents the helicopter's body from spinning by pushing against the reaction force of the main rotor.

Engine
The engine gives the main rotor power to spin the blades.

Weigh the Impact

1. Identify the Need
What advantages do helicopters have over airplanes?

2. Research
Using the Internet, research how helicopters are used in national parks, such as Yellowstone National Park. Choose one helicopter mission. Make notes on the mission's difficulty level, purpose, location, procedures, and outcome.

3. Write
Suppose you are a park ranger. Use your notes to write a report to your supervisor explaining why a helicopter was or was not the best technology to use for this mission.

For: More on helicopters
Visit: PHSchool.com
Web Code: cgh-3030

Weigh the Impact

1. Helicopters can hover and land at almost any location. Helicopters can fly forward, backward, sideways, and up and down.
2. Answers will vary depending on the chosen mission. Students' responses should include information about the helicopter missions including, but not limited to, the mission's difficulty, purpose, location, and outcome.
3. Students' reports should include information about the advantages or disadvantages of helicopters as a support for their opinion.

For: More on helicopters
Visit: PHSchool.com
Web Code: cgh-3030

Students can research this issue online.

Extend

Encourage interested students to investigate the use of helicopters for various applications in their home state or city. Possible areas of research include medical emergency flights, traffic reporting, use in law enforcement, and military applications. Students can research the type of helicopter used and the reasons a helicopter is a good choice for that particular application. Have students report their findings to the class.

The BIG Idea

Have students read the answer to the Essential Question. Encourage them to evaluate and revise their own answers as needed.

Help Students Read

Building Vocabulary

Words in Context Explain that the meaning of unfamiliar words and phrases can often be determined by examining context. Tell students that the words and phrases surrounding an unfamiliar term can be used to help determine the unfamiliar term's meaning. Have students examine the text surrounding the term *buoyant force*, found in the section Floating and Sinking. Point out that the words "upward force" are a good clue to the meaning of the term *buoyant force*.

Word/Part Analysis Explain that the word part *bar-* or *baro-* is a Greek root meaning heavy or pressure. The word part *-meter* is also from Greek, and means instrument or tool for measuring. Have students relate this information to the meaning of the term *barometer*.

Connecting Concepts

Help students develop a concept map to show how the information in this chapter is related. Fluids, such as water and air, exert pressure on objects; forces in fluids are explained by Archimedes principle, Pascal's principle, and Bernoulli's principle. Have students brainstorm to identify the key concepts, key terms, details, and examples, then write each one on a self-sticking note and attach it at random on chart paper or on the board.

Tell students that this concept map will be organized in hierarchical order and to begin at the top with the key concepts. Ask students these questions to guide them to categorize the information on the self-sticking notes: **What is pressure? How can you determine if an object will float or sink? What is Pascal's principle? What is Bernoulli's principle?**

The **BIG Idea** **Science and Technology** If an object is less dense than a fluid, it will float. If an object is denser than a fluid, it will sink.

① Pressure

Key Concepts

- Pressure decreases as the area over which a force is distributed increases.

- $\text{Pressure} = \dfrac{\text{Force}}{\text{Area}}$

- All of the forces exerted by the individual particles in a fluid combine to make up the pressure exerted by the fluid.

- As elevation increases, atmospheric pressure decreases.

- Water pressure increases as depth increases.

Key Terms

pressure	fluid
pascal	barometer

② Floating and Sinking

Key Concepts

- The buoyant force acts in the direction opposite to the force of gravity, so it makes an object feel lighter.

- By comparing densities, you can predict whether an object will float or sink in a fluid.

- $\text{Density} = \dfrac{\text{Mass}}{\text{Volume}}$

Key Terms
buoyant force
Archimedes' principle
density

③ Pascal's Principle

Key Concepts

- When force is applied to a confined fluid, the change in pressure is transmitted equally to all parts of the fluid.

- A hydraulic system multiplies force by applying the force to a small surface area. The increase in pressure is then transmitted to another part of the confined fluid, which pushes on a larger surface area.

Key Terms
Pascal's principle
hydraulic system

④ Bernoulli's Principle

Key Concepts

- Bernoulli's principle states that as the speed of a moving fluid increases, the pressure within the fluid decreases.

- Bernoulli's principle helps explain how planes fly. It also helps explain why smoke rises up a chimney, how an atomizer works, and how a flying disk glides through the air.

Key Terms
Bernoulli's principle
lift

Prompt students by using connecting words or phrases, such as "are explained by," and "such as," to indicate the basis for the organization of the map. The phrases should form a sentence between or among a set of concepts.

Answer
Accept logical presentations by students.

All in One **Teaching Resources**
- Key Terms Review: *Forces in Fluids*
- Connecting Concepts: *Forces in Fluids*

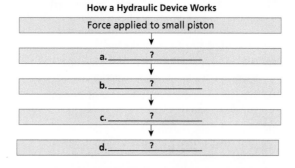

Go Online
PHSchool.com
For: Self-Assessment
Visit: PHSchool.com
Web Code: cga-3030

Organizing Information

Sequencing Create a flowchart that shows how a hydraulic device multiplies force. (For more on Sequencing, see the Skills Handbook.)

How a Hydraulic Device Works

Force applied to small piston
a. _____ ?
b. _____ ?
c. _____ ?
d. _____ ?

Reviewing Key Terms

Choose the letter of the best answer.

1. If you divide the force exerted on a surface by the total area of the surface, you will know
   a. density.   **b.** pressure.
   c. lift.   **d.** buoyant force.

2. If you know the weight of an object that floats, you know the
   a. object's density.
   b. object's mass.
   c. object's volume.
   d. buoyant force.

3. If you divide the mass of an object by its volume, you know the object's
   a. mass.   **b.** weight.
   c. density.   **d.** pressure.

4. The concept that an increase in pressure on a confined fluid is transmitted equally to all parts of the fluid is known as
   a. Pascal's principle.
   b. Bernoulli's principle.
   c. Archimedes' principle.
   d. Newton's third law.

5. The concept that the pressure in a fluid decreases as the speed of the fluid increases is known as
   a. Pascal's principle.
   b. Bernoulli's principle.
   c. Archimedes' principle.
   d. Newton's first law.

If the statement is true, write *true*. If it is false, change the underlined word or words to make the statement true.

6. Pressure is force per unit of <u>mass</u>.

7. A <u>fluid</u> is a material that can easily flow.

8. A factor that helps explain flight is <u>Archimedes' principle</u>.

9. A hydraulic system is designed to take advantage of <u>Pascal's principle</u>.

10. <u>Lift</u> is an upward force.

Writing in Science

News Report Suppose that you are a newspaper journalist on the day after the *Titanic* sank. Write a news report that tells what happened. Explain how the buoyancy of a ship is affected when it fills with water. Include information about the various fluid forces involved.

Discovery CHANNEL SCHOOL

Forces in Fluids
Video Preview
Video Field Trip
▶ Video Assessment

**Go Online**
PHSchool.com
For: Self-Assessment
Visit: PHSchool.com
Web Code: cga-3030

Students can take a practice test online that is automatically scored.

All in One Teaching Resources
- Transparency M34
- Chapter Test
- Performance Assessment Teacher Notes
- Performance Assessment Student Worksheet
- Performance Assessment Scoring Rubric

◉ ExamView® Computer Test Bank CD-ROM

Organizing Information
a. Pressure in a confined fluid is increased
b. The pressure is transmitted equally throughout the fluid
c. The confined fluid presses on a piston with a larger surface area
d. The original force is multiplied

Reviewing Key Terms
1. b **2.** d **3.** c **4.** a **5.** b
6. area
7. true
8. Bernoulli' principle
9. true
10. true

Discovery CHANNEL SCHOOL Video Assessment

Forces in Fluids

Show the video assessment to review chapter content and as a prompt for the writing assignment. Discussion questions: **Why did the front end of the Titanic begin to sink?** *(Water flooded into the front of the ship, increasing its density.)* **Why did the ship break in two?** *(When the front of the Titanic sank, the air-filled back was raised into the air. The uneven distribution of weight created a strain on the hull that caused the ship to break in two.)*

Writing in Science

Writing Mode Description
Scoring Rubric
4 Exceeds criteria; news report contains accurate and detailed information about fluid forces
3 Meets criteria
2 The news report is brief, lacks detail, and/or includes some incorrect information
1 The news report is poorly written and/or includes numerous errors

Checking Concepts

11. You exert less pressure lying down. When you lie down, you spread the force of your weight over a larger area, thus exerting less pressure.

12. The pressure of the fluids within the fish equals the pressure exerted by the water on the outside of the fish.

13. In water, a greater upward force (the buoyant force) acts in the opposite direction of your weight. The net downward force, then, is less than in air.

14. The pressure within a hydraulic system's confined fluid is equal throughout the fluid. Therefore, the larger piston experiences a greater force because it has a greater surface area than the smaller piston.

15. The braking system of a car and the hydraulic lift in an auto shop are examples of hydraulic systems that an auto mechanic would be familiar with.

16. Moving air above the chimney causes the pressure there to be lower than the pressure in the still air at the bottom of the chimney.

Thinking Critically

17. The pressure is higher at lower levels within the jug. The lowest hole has the greatest pressure. The fact that the stream of water leaving that hole travels farthest from the jug provides evidence for this conclusion.

18. The sphere may be hollow.

19. This method will increase the volume of displaced water, increasing the buoyant force. It will also decrease the ship's overall density.

20. Find an object that floats in both liquids or sinks in only one of the liquids. If it sinks in one liquid, the other liquid is denser. If it floats in both, the liquid in which it floats higher is denser.

Math Practice

21. about 620 cm^2

22. The dollar bill has an area of approximately 110 cm^2. The yuan note has an area of approximately 100 cm^2. Therefore, U.S. currency uses a larger bill.

Checking Concepts

11. How does the amount of pressure you exert on the floor when you are lying down compare with the amount of pressure you exert when you are standing up?

12. Why aren't deep-sea fish crushed by the tremendous pressure they experience?

13. Why do you seem to weigh more in air than you do in water?

14. In a hydraulic system, why is the force exerted on a small piston multiplied when it acts on a larger piston?

15. Name two hydraulic systems that an auto mechanic would know well.

16. Why is air pressure at the top of a chimney less than air pressure at the bottom?

Thinking Critically

17. **Making Generalizations** How does the water pressure change at each level in the jug below? How can you tell?

18. **Developing Hypotheses** A sphere made of steel is put in water and, surprisingly, it floats. Develop a possible explanation for this observation.

19. **Applying Concepts** One method of raising a sunken ship to the surface is to inflate large bags or balloons inside its hull. Explain why this procedure could work.

20. **Problem Solving** You have two fluids of unknown density. Suggest a method to determine which is denser, without mixing the two fluids.

Math Practice

21. **Area** The cover of your textbook measures about 28 cm × 22 cm. Find its area.

22. **Area** A dollar bill measures about 15.9 cm × 6.7 cm. The Chinese yuan note measures 14.5 cm × 7.0 cm. Which currency uses a larger bill?

Applying Skills

The illustration shows an object supported by a spring scale, both in and out of water. Use the illustration to answer Questions 23–25.

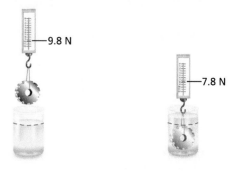

23. **Inferring** Why is there a difference between the weight of the object in air and its measured weight in water?

24. **Calculating** What is the buoyant force acting on the object?

25. **Drawing Conclusions** What can you conclude about the water above the dotted line?

Lab zone Chapter **Project**

Performance Assessment Test your boat to make sure it does not leak. Display the diagrams of different designs you tried and the observations and data you recorded for each design. Then demonstrate for the class how the boat floats. Point out to your classmates the features you used in your final design.

Lab zone Chapter **Project**

L3

Performance Assessment Encourage students to describe the design features of their boats and explain why they were included. Prepare a basin of water in which students can test their boats. Use a basin large enough to test two boats at one time. To test the boats, have students float them and add pennies gently so the momentum of the falling pennies doesn't push the lip of the boat under water. The number of pennies supported by the boat is one less than the number required to sink it. After students have tested their boats, collect the design logs.

Standardized Test Prep

Choose the letter of the best answer.

1. The upward force that acts on an airplane's wing is called
   A density.
   B inertia.
   C lift.
   D pressure.

2. Which of the following is an example of a hydraulic system?
   F a car's brakes
   G a barometer
   H an airplane's wing
   J a submarine's flotation tanks

3. A boat that weighs 28,800 N is loaded with 7,200 N of cargo. After it is loaded, what is the buoyant force acting on the boat?
   A 400 N
   B 22,000 N
   C 36,000 N
   D 360,000 N

4. Why doesn't air pressure crush human beings standing at sea level?
   F Air pressure at sea level is very low.
   G Clothing on our bodies shields us from air pressure.
   H Air is not as heavy as human beings.
   J Pressure from the fluids inside our bodies balances the air pressure outside.

5. You observe that a chunk of tar sinks in puddles of rainwater but floats on the ocean. An experiment to explain the behavior of the tar should measure
   A the difference between atmospheric pressure and water pressure.
   B the densities of fresh water, salt water, and tar.
   C the height from which the chunk of tar is dropped.
   D the depth of each type of water.

Constructed Response

Use the diagram below and your knowledge of science to help you answer Question 6.

6. Use Bernoulli's principle to explain why the fabric of a domed tent bulges outward on a windy day.

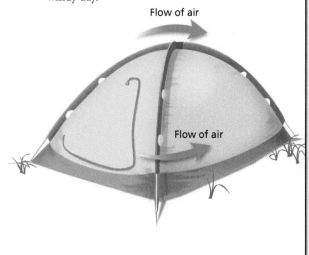

Flow of air

Flow of air

Applying Skills

23. The object weighs less in water because the buoyant force on it in water is opposite to the force of gravity.

24. The buoyant force is 2.0 N.

25. The volume of water above the dotted line is equal to the volume of the object. The weight of the volume of displaced water is equal to the buoyant force on the object, 2.0 N.

Standardized Test Practice

1. C **2.** F **3.** C **4.** J **5.** B
6. On a windy day, the air outside the tent is moving faster than the air inside the tent. According to Bernoulli's principle, the faster a stream of air moves, the less air pressure it exerts. Therefore, the air pressure outside the tent is less than the air pressure inside. The greater pressure inside the tent causes the fabric to bulge outward.

Chapter at a Glance

 Chapter **Project** *The Nifty Lifting Machine*

Technology

Local Standards

Video Preview

All in One Teaching Resources
- Chapter Project Teacher Notes, pp. 232–233
- Chapter Project Student Overview, pp. 234–235
- Chapter Project Student Worksheets, pp. 236–237
- Chapter Project Scoring Rubric, p. 238

 Section 1

What Is Work?

1–2 periods
1/2–1 block

M.4.1.1 Identify when work is done on an object.
M.4.1.2 Calculate the work done on an object.
M.4.1.3 Define and calculate power.

 Section 2

How Machines Do Work

3–4 periods
1 1/2–2 blocks

M.4.2.1 Explain how machines make work easier.
M.4.2.2 Calculate the mechanical advantage of a machine.
M.4.2.3 Calculate the efficiency of a machine.

Section 3

Simple Machines

4–5 periods
2–2 1/2 blocks

M.4.3.1 Describe the six kinds of simple machines and their uses.
M.4.3.2 Calculate the ideal mechanical advantage of each type of simple machine.
M.4.3.3 Describe compound machines.

Video Field Trip

active art

Go Online
PHSchool.com

Review and Assessment

Test Preparation

All in One Teaching Resources
- Key Terms Review, p. 269
- Transparency M45
- Performance Assessment Teacher Notes, p. 278
- Performance Assessment Scoring Rubric, p. 279
- Performance Assessment Student Worksheet, p. 280
- Chapter Test, pp. 281–284

Video Assessment

Go Online
PHSchool.com

Test Preparation Blackline Masters

Chapter Activities Planner

For more activities
LAB ZONE Easy Planner CD-ROM

Student Edition	Inquiry	Time	Materials	Skills	Resources
Chapter Project, p. 107	Open-Ended	2–3 weeks	**All in One Teaching Resources** p. 232	Designing, calculating, explaining	**All in One Teaching Resources** pp. 232–233 **Lab zone Easy Planner**
Section 1					
Discover Activity, p. 108	Guided	10 minutes	Mug, thin rubber band, water	Developing hypotheses	**Lab zone Easy Planner**
Try This Activity, p. 111	Directed	10 minutes	Hair dryer with at least two power settings, pinwheel	Inferring	**Lab zone Easy Planner**
Section 2					
Discover Activity, p. 114	Guided	20 minutes	Ball, book, can opener, corkscrew, eraser, paper, pencil, pliers, ruler, screwdriver	Forming operational definitions	**Lab zone Easy Planner**
Try This Activity, p. 116	Directed	15 minutes	Small cooking pot, 50-cm string or twine, 20-N spring scale, pencil	Developing hypotheses	**Lab zone Easy Planner**
Skills Lab pp. 122–123	Guided	Prep: 20 minutes; Class: 40 minutes	Meter stick; masking tape; 28 pennies, minted after 1982; small object with a mass of about 50 g; dowel or other cylindrical object, 10 cm long, 3 cm in diameter	Controlling variables, interpreting data	**Lab zone Easy Planner** **Lab Activity Video** **All in One Teaching Resources** Skills Lab: *Seesaw Science*, pp. 253–256
Section 3					
Discover Activity, p. 124	Guided	10 minutes	2 broomsticks or dowels, long rope	Predicting	**Lab zone Easy Planner**
Try This Activity, p. 127	Directed	10 minutes	Sheet of paper, pencil, scissors	Making models	**Lab zone Easy Planner**
Skills Activity, p. 132	Directed	20 minutes	Pencil, paper	Communicating	**Lab zone Easy Planner**
At-Home Activity, p. 135	Guided	Home		Classifying	**Lab zone Easy Planner**
Skills Lab pp. 136–137	Guided	Prep: 20 minutes; Class: 40 minutes	4 books, about 2-cm thick, metric ruler; wooden block with eye-hook; marker; board, at least 10 cm wide and 50 cm long; spring scale, 0–10 N; or force sensor	Controlling variables, calculating	**Lab zone Easy Planner** **Lab Activity Video** **All in One Teaching Resources** Skills Lab: *Angling for Access*, pp. 266–268

Section 1 What Is Work?

 1–2 periods, 1/2–1 block

Objectives

M.4.1.1 Identify when work is done on an object.
M.4.1.2 Calculate the work done on an object.
M.4.1.3 Define and calculate power.

Key Terms

• work • joule • power

Local Standards

Preteach

Build Background Knowledge

Students determine when work is being done on a book by viewing a demonstration.

 **Discover Activity** *What Happens When You Pull at an Angle?* L1

Targeted Print and Technology Resources

 Teaching Resources

L2 Reading Strategy Transparency M35: Asking Questions

PresentationExpress™ CD-ROM

Instruct

The Meaning of Work Ask students to list examples of everyday situations in which work is done. Help students differentiate the everyday meaning of work from the scientific meaning of work.

Calculating Work Use examples to show students that the amount of work done is dependent on the force required and the distance over which the force acts.

Power Use the mathematical formula for power to demonstrate that power is a rate.

Targeted Print and Technology Resources

 **Teaching Resources**

L2 Guided Reading, pp. 241–243
L2 Transparency M36

www.SciLinks.org Web Code: scn-1341

Student Edition on Audio CD

Assess

Section Assessment Questions

Have students use their completed graphic organizers with their questions and answers to help answer the questions.

Reteach

Students review the units and formulas for work and power.

Targeted Print and Technology Resources

Teaching Resources

• Section Summary, p. 240
L1 Review and Reinforce, p. 244
L3 Enrich, p. 245

Section 2 How Machines Do Work

3–4 periods, 1 1/2–2 blocks

ABILITY LEVELS
L1 Basic to Average
L2 For All Students
L3 Average to Advanced

Objectives

M.4.2.1 Explain how machines make work easier.
M.4.2.2 Calculate the mechanical advantage of a machine.
M.4.2.3 Calculate the efficiency of a machine.

Key Terms

• machine • input force • output force • input work • output work
• mechanical advantage • efficiency

Local Standards

Preteach

Build Background Knowledge

Students compare everyday tools and determine which would make work easier.

 Discover Activity *Is It a Machine?* L1

Targeted Print and Technology Resources

 **Teaching Resources**

L2 Reading Strategy Transparency
M37: *Identifying Main Ideas*

⊙ **PresentationExpress™ CD-ROM**

Instruct

What Is a Machine? Challenge students to think of times they have used a machine to make work easier, and to describe the three ways in which machines make work easier.

Mechanical Advantage Ask leading questions to show that machines can have an ideal mechanical advantage of greater than 1, exactly 1, or less than 1.

Efficiency of Machines Ask leading questions to help students understand why no real machine has an efficiency of 100%.

 Skills Lab *Seesaw Science* L2

Targeted Print and Technology Resources

 **Teaching Resources**

L2 Guided Reading, pp. 248–250
L2 Transparencies M38, M39
L2 Skills Lab: *Seesaw Science*, pp. 253–256

🎞 **Lab Activity Video/DVD**
Skills Lab: *Seesaw Science*

www.SciLinks.org Web Code: scn-1342

⊙ **Student Edition on Audio CD**

Assess

Section Assessment Questions

🔄 Have students use their completed graphic organizers with their outline to help answer the questions.

Reteach

Have students work in pairs to review the key terms for Section 2.

Targeted Print and Technology Resources

Teaching Resources

• Section Summary, p. 247
L1 Review and Reinforce, p. 251
L3 Enrich, p. 252

Section 3 Simple Machines

 4–5 periods, 2–2 1/2 blocks

ABILITY LEVELS
L1 Basic to Average
L2 For All Students
L3 Average to Advanced

Objectives

M.4.3.1 Describe the six kinds of simple machines and their uses.

M.4.3.2 Calculate the ideal mechanical advantage of each type of simple machine.

M.4.3.3 Describe compound machines.

Local Standards

Key Terms

• inclined plane • wedge • screw • lever • fulcrum • wheel and axle • pulley
• compound machine

Preteach

Build Background Knowledge

Have students compare and contrast examples of simple machines.

 Discover Activity *How Can You Increase Force?* L2

Targeted Print and Technology Resources

 **Teaching Resources**

L2 Reading Strategy Transparency M40: *Previewing Visuals*

 PresentationExpress™ CD-ROM

Instruct

Inclined Plane Ask students to generate facts about inclined planes and use the facts to make a concept map.

Wedge Challenge students to make a list of everyday examples of wedges.

Screws Use the formula for mechanical advantage of a screw to generate ideas about ways to increase the mechanical advantage.

Levers Ask students to generate a list of levers and classify the examples as first-, second-, or third-class levers.

Wheel and Axle Use Figures 18 and 19 to discuss various uses of wheel and axles.

Pulley Ask students to use facts about pulleys to create a concept map about pulleys.

Simple Machines in the Body Have students bend their arms at the elbow to show one example of a simple machine in the human body. Then have students brainstorm other examples of simple machines in the body.

Compound Machines Challenge students to generate a list of compound machines they encounter over several days.

 Skills Lab *Angling for Access* L2

Targeted Print and Technology Resources

 **Teaching Resources**

L2 Guided Reading, pp. 259–263
L2 Transparencies M41, M42, M43, M44
L2 Skills Lab: *Angling for Access,* pp. 266–268

Lab Activity Video/DVD
Skills Lab: *Angling for Access*

DISCOVERY CHANNEL SCHOOL
Video Field Trip

PHSchool.com Web Code cgp-2031

 **Student Edition on Audio CD**

Assess

Section Assessment Questions

 Have students use their graphic organizers to answer the questions.

Reteach

Have students work in pairs to list the six types of simple machines and an example of each.

Targeted Print and Technology Resources

Teaching Resources

• Section Summary, p. 258
L1 Review and Reinforce, p. 264
L3 Enrich, p. 265

Chapter 4 **Content Refresher**

Section 1 **What Is Work?**

Work and Energy Work and energy are closely related concepts. The SI unit of measure for both work and energy is the joule. Work is done on an object only when the object moves at least partly in the direction of the force applied on it. For example, if you lift a book upward from the floor, work is done on the book. Work is a transfer, or change, of energy. In this example, energy is transferred to the book, causing its potential energy to change. The relationship between work and energy is expressed by the work-energy theorem:

$$W = \Delta E$$

This principle states that the work done on an object is equal to the change in the object's energy. So, if an object's kinetic or potential energy increases, work has been done on the object. Consider what happens if you do work that slows an object's motion. In that case, work is done because the object's kinetic energy decreases.

Section 2 **How Machines Do Work**

Increasing the Efficiency of Real Machines The efficiency of a machine is the percentage of input work that is converted to output work. All real machines have an efficiency of less than 100%, due mainly to the effects of friction. Friction occurs whenever two surfaces are in contact and is classified into four categories: sliding friction, static friction, rolling friction, and fluid friction.

When considering the design of a machine, there are several ways to reduce the friction between the machine's parts and increase the machine's efficiency. Fluid friction is more easily overcome than sliding friction. So, lubrication between moving parts reduces overall friction by replacing sliding friction with fluid friction. Rolling friction is more easily overcome than sliding friction, so adding ball bearings or wheels also reduces overall friction.

Automobiles are subject to friction within the engine, as moving parts rub against one another. The friction in the engine can be reduced, but not eliminated, by the lubrication provided by motor oil. When an automobile is moving, it is subject to air resistance, a type of fluid friction. Automobile designers can change the amount of air resistance encountered by an automobile by changing the shape of the automobile's body.

Section 3 **Simple Machines**

Levers and Torque Levers are simple machines consisting of a rigid object that rotates around a fixed point, called the fulcrum. To use a lever, an input force is applied to the object,

causing the object to rotate. When the force applied is multiplied by the distance from the force to the fulcrum (this distance is called the lever arm), the result is torque.

Torque may be an unfamiliar term, but the concept of torque is familiar. Imagine selecting a paint-can opener to open a stubborn can of paint. You know, without performing calculations, that a longer paint-can opener will be more useful than a shorter paint-can opener. Applying the mathematics of torque, you can see that the longer the lever arm, the greater the output force is for any given input force. Another example is a wrench. The longer the wrench handle, the greater the output force that can be generated with a given input force.

Help Students Read

Think Aloud
Verbalize Thought Processes

Strategy Model processes that students can use to build understanding of the chapter content. Develop comments and questions to use as models as you show students how to think aloud.

Example
1. Read several paragraphs aloud and have your students follow along silently. Then, pause to check your own comprehension. You might model some of these strategies for students:
- Make a prediction, and then revise or verify it.
- Describe mental pictures from the text.
- Connect new information to prior knowledge.
- Talk through confusing points and plan steps to clarify them.

2. After you have modeled the technique for one section, have students read the next section silently and apply these strategies internally. Ask students to share the strategies they used.

3. Encourage students to repeat the process individually or with a partner.

See the section *What Is Work?* for a script using the think-aloud strategy with students.

Address Misconceptions

Students may think machines with mechanical advantages of less than 1 aren't useful. For a strategy for overcoming this misconception, see **Address Misconceptions** in Section 2, *How Machines Do Work.*

106F

The BIG Idea

The Big Idea is the major scientific concept of the chapter. It is followed by the Essential Question. Read aloud the question to students. As students study the chapter, tell them to think about the Essential Question. Explain that they will discover the answer to the question as they read. The chapter Study Guide provides a sample answer.

 **Chapter Project** L3

Objectives

Students will demonstrate their understanding of simple machines by designing and building a device to reduce the input force required to lift a 600-gram soup can 5 centimeters. After completing this Chapter Project, students will be able to

- design and build a compound machine able to lift a 600-gram load using less than a 600-gram mass as an input force.
- calculate actual and ideal mechanical advantage.
- communicate to others how their device incorporates simple machines in its construction.

Skills Focus

Designing, building, calculating, communicating

Project Time Line 2–3 weeks

All in One Teaching Resources
- Chapter Project Teacher Notes
- Chapter Project Overview
- Chapter Project Worksheet 1
- Chapter Project Worksheet 2
- Chapter Project Scoring Rubric

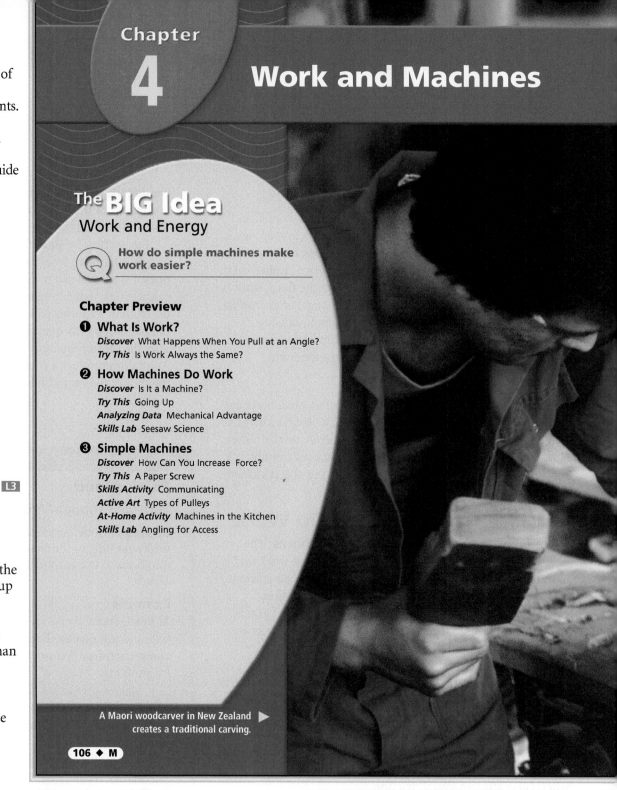

Chapter 4

Work and Machines

The BIG Idea
Work and Energy

Q How do simple machines make work easier?

Chapter Preview

❶ What Is Work?
Discover What Happens When You Pull at an Angle?
Try This Is Work Always the Same?

❷ How Machines Do Work
Discover Is It a Machine?
Try This Going Up
Analyzing Data Mechanical Advantage
Skills Lab Seesaw Science

❸ Simple Machines
Discover How Can You Increase Force?
Try This A Paper Screw
Skills Activity Communicating
Active Art Types of Pulleys
At-Home Activity Machines in the Kitchen
Skills Lab Angling for Access

▶ A Maori woodcarver in New Zealand creates a traditional carving.

Developing a Plan

Have students design their devices in the first week of the project. Week 2 should be spent building and modifying the devices. During the third week, the students can write a description of their devices and demonstrate them to the class.

Possible Materials

Provide a wide variety of materials for the project including wood scraps, cardboard and plastic tubes, nails and screws, coat hangers, straws, toy wheels, string, paper clips, and cardboard. Encourage students to use other materials as well. Also provide sanding paper and light lubricating oil. Sand will be needed to fill soup cans to 600 grams for the load and to fill soup cans for the input force.

Chapter **Project**

The Nifty Lifting Machine

In this Chapter Project, you will design and build a lifting machine and then demonstrate it to the class.

Your Goal To design, build, and test a complex machine that can lift a 600-gram soup can 5 centimeters

Your machine must

- be made of materials that are approved by your teacher
- consist of at least two simple machines working in combination
- be able to lift the soup can to a height of at least 5 centimeters
- be built following the safety guidelines in Appendix A

Plan It! Preview the chapter to find out what simple machines you can use and how to use them. Determine the amount of work your machine must do. Brainstorm different machine designs and materials with your classmates. Analyze factors affecting efficiency and mechanical advantage, and then construct your machine. When your teacher has approved your design, build and test your machine.

Chapter 4 M ◆ 107

Work and Machines

Show the Video Preview to introduce the chapter and provide an overview of the chapter content. Discussion question: **Why would moving more than 20,000 tons of stone be a major challenge to builders working back in 447 BCE?** *(These workers had only simple machines and no power equipment to use to move the stone over a difficult route.)*

Performance Assessment

The Chapter Project Scoring Rubric will help you evaluate how well students complete the Chapter Project. You may want to share the rubric with your students so that they will know what is expected. Students will be assessed on

- the clarity, simplicity, and completeness of their designs
- the construction of the device
- ability to modify the device after testing
- clarity and completeness of the written explanation
- how well the device performs during the demonstration
- students can keep their plans for a compound machine in their portfolios.

Portfolio

Possible Shortcuts

Have students work alone during the first phase of the project, then have students work in small groups to build and modify a device selected from the group members' plans.

Launching the Project

To stimulate student interest, load an empty soup can with sand to a mass of 600 grams. Demonstrate how the input force required to lift the mass can be reduced using a meter stick as a lever and an eraser as a fulcrum. Have students read the description of the project in the text. Encourage students to discuss simple machines and how simple machines can be combined to form compound machines.

Section 1
What Is Work?

Objectives

After this lesson, students will be able to
M.4.1.1 Identify when work is done on an object.
M.4.1.2 Calculate the work done on an object.
M.4.1.3 Define and calculate power.

Target Reading Skill

Asking Questions Explain that changing a head into a question helps students anticipate the ideas, facts, and events they are about to read.

Answers

Sample graphic organizer:

Questions

What is work?
How can I calculate work?
What is power?

Answers

Work is done when an object moves in the same direction in which the force is exerted.
Work = Force × Distance
Power is the rate at which work is done.

All in One Teaching Resources

• Transparency M35

Preteach

Build Background Knowledge   L2

Doing Work

Ask a volunteer to hold a book while standing perfectly still. Ask another volunteer to lift a book from the floor and place it on a table. Ask: **Which student is exerting force?** *(Both)* **Which student is doing work?** *(Only the student lifting the book.)*

Reading Preview

Key Concepts

• When is work done on an object?
• How do you determine the work done on an object?
• What is power?

Key Terms

• work • joule • power

Target Reading Skill

Asking Questions Before you read, preview the red headings. In a graphic organizer like the one below, ask a *what* or *how* question for each heading. As you read, write the answers to your questions.

Question	Answer
What is work?	Work is . . .

Lab zone Discover **Activity**

What Happens When You Pull at an Angle?

1. Fill a mug half full with water.
2. Cut a medium-weight rubber band to make a strand of elastic. Thread the elastic through a mug handle. By pulling on the elastic, you can move the mug across a table.
3. You can hold the two halves of elastic parallel to each other or at an angle to each other, as shown. Predict which way will be more effective in moving the mug.
4. Pull on the elastic both ways. Describe any differences you observe.

Think It Over
Developing Hypotheses Which of the two pulls was more effective in moving the mug? Explain why.

This morning you probably woke up and went to school with your backpack of books. You lifted the backpack and then carried it with you. If you had a lot of books to bring home, carrying your backpack might have felt like a lot of work. But in the scientific definition of work, after you lifted the backpack, you did no work to carry it at all!

The Meaning of Work

In scientific terms, you do **work** when you exert a force on an object that causes the object to move some distance. **Work is done on an object when the object moves in the same direction in which the force is exerted.** If you push a child on a swing, for example, you are doing work on the child. If you pull your books out of your backpack, you do work on the books. If you lift a bag of groceries out of a shopping cart, you do work on the bag of groceries.

FIGURE 1
Doing Work
Lifting books out of a backpack is work, but carrying them to class is not.

108 ◆ M

Lab zone Discover **Activity**

Skills Focus Developing hypotheses   L1

Materials mug, thin rubber band, water

Time 10 minutes

Tips Students should fill the mug halfway with water so it will not turn over when pulled. Provide paper towels to clean up any spills.

Expected Outcome Students will find that it is more effective to pull with the two halves of the elastic band held parallel.

Think It Over Pulling with the two halves of elastic held parallel was more effective. When held parallel, both forces were exerted in the same direction. When held at an angle, however, the forces partially opposed each other.

No Work Without Motion To do work on an object, the object must move some distance as a result of your force. If the object does not move, no work is done, no matter how much force is exerted.

There are many situations in which you exert a force but don't do any work. Suppose, for example, you are pushing a car that is stuck in the snow. You certainly exert a force on the car, so it might seem as if you do work. But if the force you exert does not make the car move, you are not doing any work on it.

Force in the Same Direction So why didn't you do any work when you carried your books to school? To do work on an object, the force you exert must be in the same direction as the object's motion. When you carry an object at constant velocity, you exert an upward force to hold the object so that it doesn't fall to the ground. The motion of the object, however, is in the horizontal direction. Since the force is vertical and the motion is horizontal, you don't do any work on the object as you carry it.

How much work do you do when you pull a suitcase with wheels? When you pull a suitcase, you pull on the handle at an angle to the ground. As you can see in Figure 2, your force has both a horizontal part and a vertical part. When you pull this way, only part of your force does work—the part in the same direction as the motion of the suitcase. The rest of your force does not help pull the suitcase forward.

 Reading Checkpoint If you pull an object horizontally, what part of your force does work?

FIGURE 2
Force, Motion, and Work
Whether the girl does work on the suitcase depends on the direction of her force and the suitcase's motion. *Drawing Conclusions Why doesn't the girl do work when she carries her suitcase rather than pulling it?*

A The lifting force is not in the direction of the suitcase's motion, so no work is done.

B The force acts in the same direction as the suitcase's motion, so the maximum work is done.

C Only the horizontal part of the force does work to move the suitcase.

Part of the force that does no work

Force

Part of the force that does work

Force

Force

Direction of motion

Direction of motion

Direction of motion

Chapter 4 M ◆ 109

Calculating Work

Teach Key Concepts L2
How Work Is Calculated

Focus Ask: **Which involves more work—lifting a full backpack 1 meter from the ground, or lifting an empty backpack 1 meter from the ground?** *(Lifting the full backpack)* **Which involves more work—lifting the full backpack 1 centimeter from the ground or lifting the same backpack 1 meter from the ground?** *(Lifting the full backpack 1 meter)*

Teach Tell students the work done on an object is the amount of force exerted multiplied by the distance the object moves. Write on the board: Work = Force × Distance. Point out that moving a full backpack involves more work than moving an empty backpack, because it requires more force. Point out that lifting a full backpack 1 meter involves more work than lifting the same backpack 1 centimeter, because it moves a greater distance. Remind students that the SI unit for work is the newton–meter, which is also called a joule.

Apply Ask: **What are the two factors that determine how much work is involved in moving an object?** *(The force required and the distance the object is moved)* **learning modality: logical/mathematical**

Go Online
SCI LINKS NSTA

For: Links on work
Visit: www.SciLinks.org
Web Code: scn-1341

Download a worksheet that will guide students' review of Internet resources on work.

Help Students Read L1
Think Aloud Refer to the Content Refresher in this chapter for guidelines for applying the Think Aloud reading strategy.

Set the example for this strategy by verbalizing your own thought processes while reading aloud the first paragraph of *Calculating Work*. Encourage student volunteers to continue reading the text while quietly verbalizing their own thought processes. Then have a class discussion about the advantages students found in staying focused on a logical thought process while reading in this manner.

FIGURE 3
Amount of Work
When you lift a plant, you do work. You do more work when you lift a heavier plant the same distance.
Relating Cause and Effect
Why does it take more work to lift the heavier plant?

Go Online
SCI LINKS NSTA

For: Links on work
Visit: www.SciLinks.org
Web Code: scn-1341

Calculating Work

Which do you think involves more work: lifting a 50-newton potted plant 0.5 meter off the ground onto a table, or lifting a 100-newton plant onto the same table? Your common sense may suggest that lifting a heavier object requires more work than lifting a lighter object. This is true. Is it more work to lift a plant onto a table or up to the top story of a building? As you might guess, moving an object a greater distance requires more work than moving the same object a shorter distance.

The amount of work you do depends on both the amount of force you exert and the distance the object moves. **The amount of work done on an object can be determined by multiplying force times distance.**

$$\text{Work} = \text{Force} \times \text{Distance}$$

You can use the work formula to calculate the amount of work you do to lift a plant. When you lift an object, the upward force you exert must be at least equal to the object's weight. So, to lift the lighter plant, you would have to exert a force of 50 newtons. The distance you lift the plant is 0.5 meter. The amount of work you do on the plant can be calculated using the work formula.

$$\text{Work} = \text{Force} \times \text{Distance}$$
$$\text{Work} = 50 \text{ N} \times 0.5 \text{ m} = 25 \text{ N·m}$$

To lift the heavier plant, you would have to exert a force of 100 newtons. So the amount of work you do would be 100 newtons × 0.5 meter, or 50 N·m. As you can see, you do more work to lift the heavier object.

Differentiated Instruction

Special Needs L1
Practicing Calculations Review the formula for calculating work. Write some forces and some distances on cards and place the cards in separate piles. Pair students with those who are more able. Have student pairs draw a force and a distance from the piles and use the numbers to calculate work. **learning modality: logical/mathematical**

Less Proficient Readers L2
Restating Ideas Have students listen to the **Student Edition on Audio CD** for *What Is Work?* After students have completed listening, have them restate the key concepts in their own words. **learning modality: verbal**

When force is measured in newtons and distance in meters, the SI unit of work is the newton × meter (N·m). This unit is also called a joule (JOOL) in honor of James Prescott Joule, a physicist who studied work in the mid-1800s. One **joule** (J) is the amount of work you do when you exert a force of 1 newton to move an object a distance of 1 meter. You would have to exert 25 joules of work to lift the lighter plant and 50 joules of work to lift the heavier plant.

 Reading Checkpoint What is the SI unit for work?

Power

The amount of work you do on an object is not affected by the time it takes to do the work. For example, if you carry a backpack up a flight of stairs, the work you do is the weight of the backpack times the height of the stairs. Whether you walk or run up the stairs, you do the same amount of work because time is not part of the definition of work.

But time is important when you talk about power. **Power** is the rate at which work is done. **Power equals the amount of work done on an object in a unit of time.** You need more power to run up the stairs with your backpack than to walk because it takes you less time to do the same work.

You can think of power in another way. An object that has more power than another object does more work in the same time. It can also mean doing the same amount of work in less time.

For example, a car's engine does work to accelerate the car from its rest position. The greater a car engine's power, the faster the engine can accelerate the car.

Lab zone Try This **Activity**

Is Work Always the Same?

1. Obtain a pinwheel along with a hair dryer that has at least two power settings.
2. Set the dryer on its lowest setting. Use it to blow the pinwheel. Observe the pinwheel's motion.
3. Set the dryer on its highest setting. Again, blow the pinwheel and observe its motion.

Inferring Explain why work is done on the pinwheel. How are the two situations different? Is the amount of work done greater for the high or low setting? Why?

FIGURE 4
Work and Power
Whether you use a rake or a blower, the same amount of work is done to gather leaves. However, the blower has more power.
Inferring Will the blower or the rake do the same amount of work in less time?

M ◆ 111

Lab zone Try This **Activity**

Skills Focus Inferring [L1]

Materials hair dryer with at least two power settings, pinwheel

Time 10 minutes

Tips CAUTION: *All work areas must be dry.* This activity can be a demonstration.

Expected Outcome Wheel spins faster when blown by dryer at highest setting.

Work is done because pinwheel moves in the direction in which force is exerted. The dryer has more power on the highest setting. More work is done in the same amount of time on the high setting.

Extend Have students infer the best locations for windmills used to produce electricity. **learning modality: kinesthetic**

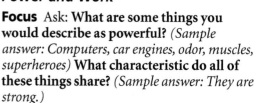

Power

Teach Key Concepts [L2]
Power and Work

Focus Ask: **What are some things you would describe as powerful?** *(Sample answer: Computers, car engines, odor, muscles, superheroes)* **What characteristic do all of these things share?** *(Sample answer: They are strong.)*

Teach Explain that the term *power* has a different meaning in science than it does in everyday use. In science, power is the rate at which work is done. Ask: **What is a rate?** *(It describes how much of something happens in a certain time period.)* Write on the board: Power = Work/Time. Tell students that the unit of power is the J/s, which is also called a watt.

Apply Ask: **How does the amount of time it takes to lift a stack of books affect the amount of work involved?** *(It doesn't affect the amount of work.)* **How does the time it takes to lift a stack of books affect the power involved?** *(It can increase or decrease the amount of power.)* **learning modality: logical/mathematical**

Monitor Progress [L2]

Skills Check Ask students what quantities they must measure to find the power of an elevator that travels to the top of a tall building. *(Force, distance, time)*

Answers
Figure 3 You perform more work because you have to exert more force to lift the heavier plant.
Figure 4 The blower is more powerful than the rake. It will do the same amount of work in less time.

Reading Checkpoint The SI unit for work is the joule.

Lab zone Build **Inquiry**

Investigating Power

Materials various objects that can be comfortably lifted, such as paint cans, small barbells

Time 20 minutes

Focus Remind students that power is the rate at which work is done.

Teach Tell the students to conduct two trials. First, have students lift the object several times slowly. For the second trial, have the students lift the same object the same number of times, but quickly.

Apply Ask: **Did you do more work on the object when you lifted it slowly or when you lifted it quickly?** *(It was the same amount of work.)* Ask: **What was different?** *(Sample answer: The rate at which work was done, or the power)* **learning modality: kinesthetic**

Math Sample Problem

Math Skill Calculating power

Focus Remind students that power equals the amount of work done on an object in a unit of time.

Teach Walk students through the steps in the sample problem. Remind them to substitute known values into the equation so they can solve for the unknown value. Tell students to perform the same operations on the units that they do on the numbers. Point out that power is a rate, so their answer should be expressed in joules/second, which are also called watts.

Answers

1. 16,000 W or 16 kW
2. 20,000 W or 20 kW

All in One **Teaching Resources**

Transparency M36

Calculating Power Whenever you know how fast work is done, you can calculate power. Power is calculated by dividing the amount of work done by the amount of time it takes to do the work. This can be written as the following formula.

$$\text{Power} = \frac{\text{Work}}{\text{Time}}$$

Since work is equal to force times distance, you can rewrite the equation for power as follows.

$$\text{Power} = \frac{\text{Force} \times \text{Distance}}{\text{Time}}$$

Full Serve

Math Practice

1. **Calculating Power** A motor exerts a force of 12,000 N to lift an elevator 8.0 m in 6.0 seconds. What is the power of the motor?

2. **Calculating Power** A crane lifts an 8,000-N beam 75 m to the top of a building in 30 seconds. What is the crane's power?

Math Sample Problem

Calculating Power

A tow truck exerts a force of 11,000 N to pull a car out of a ditch. It moves the car a distance of 5 m in 25 seconds. What is the power of the tow truck?

1 **Read and Understand**
What information are you given?
Force of the tow truck (F) = 11,000 N
Distance (d) = 5.0 m
Time (t) = 25 s

2 **Plan and Solve**
What quantity are you trying to calculate?
The power (P) of the tow truck = ■

What formula contains the given quantities and the unknown quantity?

$$\text{Power} = \frac{\text{Force} \times \text{Distance}}{\text{Time}}$$

Perform the calculation.

$$\text{Power} = \frac{11,000 \text{ N} \times 5.0 \text{ m}}{25 \text{ s}}$$

$$\text{Power} = \frac{55,000 \text{ N·m}}{25 \text{ s}} \text{ or } \frac{55,000 \text{ J}}{25 \text{ s}}$$

$$\text{Power} = 2,200 \text{ J/s} = 2,200 \text{ W}$$

3 **Look Back and Check**
Does your answer make sense?
The answer tells you that the tow truck pulls the car with a power of 2,200 W. This value is about the same power of three horses, so the answer is reasonable.

Power Units When work is measured in joules and time in seconds, the SI unit of power is the joule per second (J/s). This unit is also known as the watt (W), in honor of James Watt, who made great improvements to the steam engine. One joule of work done in one second is one watt of power. In other words, 1 J/s = 1 W.

A watt is a relatively small unit of power. Because a watt is so small, power is often measured in larger units. One kilowatt (kW) equals 1,000 watts.

When people talk about engines for vehicles, they use another power unit instead of the watt. This unit is the horsepower. One horsepower equals 746 watts. (The horsepower is not an SI unit.)

 Reading Checkpoint What is a kilowatt?

FIGURE 5
Horsepower
James Watt used the word *horsepower* to advertise the advantages of his improved steam engine (next to the chimney) of 1769.

Section 1 Assessment

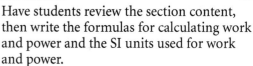 **Target Reading Skill** Asking Questions Use the answers to the questions you wrote about the headings to help you answer the questions below.

Reviewing Key Concepts

1. a. Reviewing What is work?
   b. Describing In order for work to be done on an object, what must happen to the object?
   c. Applying Concepts In which of the following situations is work being done: rolling a bowling ball, pushing on a tree for ten minutes, kicking a football?
2. a. Identifying What is a joule?
   b. Explaining How can you determine the amount of work done on an object?
   c. Problem Solving Is more work done when a force of 2 N moves an object 3 m or when a force of 3 N moves an object 2 m? Explain.

3. a. Defining What is power?
   b. Summarizing How are power and work related?

Math Practice

4. **Calculating Power** Your laundry basket weighs 22 N and your room is 3.0 m above you on the second floor. It takes you 6.0 seconds to carry the laundry basket up. What is your power?

5. **Calculating Power** If you take only 4.4 seconds to carry the basket upstairs, what is your power?

Chapter 4 M ◆ 113

Math Practice

Math Skill Calculating power

Answers

4. 11 W
5. 15 W

Lab zone Chapter **Project**

Keep Students on Track Students should determine the amount of work a machine must do to lift a 600-gram soup can 5 centimeters. Show students how to convert 600 g to newtons and 5 cm to meters. Have students use these numbers to calculate work. Help students brainstorm ways in which their machine could lift the soup can.

Objectives

After this lesson students will be able to

M.4.2.1 Explain how machines make work easier.

M.4.2.2 Calculate the mechanical advantage of a machine.

M.4.2.3 Calculate the efficiency of a machine.

Target Reading Skill ⟳

Identifying Main Ideas Explain that identifying main ideas and details helps students sort the facts from the information into groups. Each group can have a main topic, subtopics, and details.

Answers

Sample graphic organizer:

Main Idea: The mechanical advantage of a machine helps by…

Detail: Changing the amount of force you exert

Detail: Changing the distance over which you exert your force

Detail: Changing the direction of the force

All In One Teaching Resources

• Transparency M37

Preteach

Build Background Knowledge   L2

Comparing Tools

Show the class a kitchen spoon, a whisk, and an egg beater. Ask: **Which tool do you think is the best one to use to mix cake batter? Why?** (*Any of the tools can be used, but the egg beater will make the work easier.*)

How Machines Do Work

Reading Preview

Key Concepts

• How do machines make work easier?

• What is a machine's mechanical advantage?

• How can you calculate the efficiency of a machine?

Key Terms

• machine • input force
• output force • input work
• output work
• mechanical advantage
• efficiency

⟳ Target Reading Skill

Identifying Main Ideas As you read the What Is a Machine? section, write the main idea in a graphic organizer like the one below. Then write three supporting details.

Main Idea

The mechanical advantage of a machine helps by . . .

Detail	Detail	Detail

Lab zone Discover Activity

Is It a Machine?

1. Examine the objects that your teacher gives you.

2. Sort the objects into those that are machines and those that are not machines.

3. Determine how each object that you classified as a machine functions. Explain each object to another student.

Think It Over
Forming Operational Definitions Why did you decide certain objects were machines while other objects were not?

A load of soil for your school garden has been dumped 10 meters from the garden. How can you move the soil easily and quickly? You could move the soil by handfuls, but that would take a long time. Using a shovel would make the job easier. If you had a wheelbarrow, that would make the job easier still! But be careful what you think. Using a machine may make work go faster, but it doesn't mean you do less work.

FIGURE 6
Using Machines
Shovels and rakes make the work of these students easier.

Lab zone Discover Activity

Skills Focus Forming operational definitions   L1

Materials Objects that are machines—can opener, corkscrew, pliers, screwdriver; objects that are not machines—ball, book, chalk, eraser, paper, pencil, ruler

Time 20 minutes

Tips Assign students to small groups, and give each group a few objects to examine.

Once a group has classified an object, the students should pass it along to another group. Allow students to classify machines based on their own criteria.

Think It Over Sample answer: Machines are objects that can help you apply more force or perform work more easily or effectively.

What Is a Machine?

Shovels and wheelbarrows are two examples of machines. A **machine** is a device that allows you to do work in a way that is easier. You may think of machines as complex gadgets with motors, but a machine can be quite simple. For example, think about using a shovel. A shovel makes the work of moving soil easier, so a shovel is a machine.

Moving a pile of soil will involve the same amount of work whether you use your hands or a shovel. What a shovel or any other machine does is change the way in which work is done. **A machine makes work easier by changing at least one of three factors. A machine may change the amount of force you exert, the distance over which you exert your force, or the direction in which you exert your force.** In other words, a machine makes work easier by changing either force, distance, or direction.

Input and Output Forces When you use a machine to do work, you exert a force over some distance. For example, you exert a force on the shovel when you use it to lift soil. The force you exert on the machine is called the **input force.** The input force moves the machine a certain distance, called the input distance. The machine does work by exerting a force over another distance, called the output distance. The force the machine exerts on an object is called the **output force.**

Input and Output Work The input force times the input distance is called the **input work.** The output force times the output distance is called the **output work.** When you use a machine, the amount of output work can never be greater than the amount of input work.

FIGURE 7
Input and Output Work
The output work done by the shovel can never be greater than the input work done by the gardener.
Inferring When are you doing more work—using a shovel or using your hands?

Input Work
The gardener exerts an input force over an input distance.

Output Work
The shovel exerts an output force over an output distance.

M ◆ 115

Differentiated Instruction

Special Needs L1
Making a Display Have students make a poster with two sections—*Objects that are machines* and *Objects that are not machines.* Students can make drawings or attach pictures clipped from newspapers and magazines on the appropriate side of the poster. **learning modality: visual**

Gifted and Talented L3
Researching and Reporting A perpetual motion machine runs continuously with no input work. Have students research the history of such machines and prepare a short report describing their findings. The report should explain why perpetual motion machines do not work. **learning modality: verbal**

Instruct

What Is a Machine?

Teach Key Concepts L2
Machines Make Work Easier

Focus Direct students' attention to Figures 7 and 8. Ask: **Describe a time when you have seen a machine used to make work easier.** *(Sample answer: I have seen a ramp used to move furniture onto a moving van.)*

Teach Tell students there are three ways in which machines can make work easier—by changing the amount of force exerted, by changing the distance over which the force is exerted, or by changing the direction in which the force is exerted. Challenge students to think of examples of each. List correct examples on the board.

Apply Ask: **What is one way a pulley makes work easier?** *(Some pulleys change the direction of a force; others require less force.)* **learning modality: logical/mathematical**

Independent Practice L2

All in One Teaching Resources
- Guided Reading and Study Worksheet: *How Machines Do Work*

◉ Student Edition on Audio CD

Monitor Progress L2

Oral Presentation Ask students to give a short report describing how a snow shovel makes clearing a sidewalk easier. Students' explanations should include the terms *input force* and *output force*. *(A snow shovel multiplies the input force, and the shovel exerts an output force on the snow.)*

Answer
Figure 7 The same amount of work is involved. The shovel makes the work easier.

M ● 115

Build Inquiry

Interpreting Illustrations

Materials For each group of students: five pictures of machines taken from magazines and newspapers

Time 15 minutes

Focus Ask: **What are the three ways in which machines can make work easier?** *(Changing force, changing distance, or changing direction)*

Teach Have students examine the five pictures of machines. Then challenge students to use a marker to identify the machine, the input force, and the output force. Also have students infer whether each machine changes the force, the distance, or the direction of the force.

Apply Ask: **Does a machine change the amount of work required to do a task?** *(No)* **What does a machine do?** *(It makes work easier by changing the amount of force applied, changing the direction of the applied force, or changing the distance over which the force is exerted)* **learning modality: visual**

Help Students Read   L1

Summarize Have students read the text on this page about the three ways machines make work easier. Then have students summarize how machines change force, change distance, or change direction. Call on students to share their summaries with the class.

Lab zone Try This Activity

Going Up

Does a rope simply turn your force upside down? Find out!

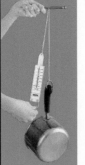

1. Tie a piece of string about 50 cm long to an object, such as an empty cooking pot. Make a small loop on the other end of the string.

2. Using a spring scale, slowly lift the pot 20 cm. Note the reading on the scale.

3. Now loop the string over a pencil and pull down on the spring scale to lift the pot 20 cm. Note the reading on the scale.

Developing Hypotheses
How did the readings on the spring scale compare? If the readings were different, suggest a reason why. What might be an advantage to using this system?

Changing Force In some machines, the output force is greater than the input force. How can this happen? Recall the formula for work: Work = Force × Distance. If the amount of work stays the same, a decrease in force must mean an increase in distance. So if a machine allows you to use less input force to do the same amount of work, you must apply that input force over a greater distance.

What kind of machine allows you to exert a smaller input force? Think about a ramp. Suppose you have to lift a heavy box onto a stage. Instead of lifting the box, you could push it up a ramp. Because the length of the ramp is greater than the height of the stage, you exert your input force over a greater distance. However, when you use the ramp, the work is easier because you can exert a smaller input force. The faucet knob in Figure 8 changes force in the same way.

Changing Distance In some machines, the output force is less than the input force. Why would you want to use a machine like this? This kind of machine allows you to exert your input force over a shorter distance. In order to apply a force over a shorter distance, you need to apply a greater input force.

When do you use this kind of machine? Think about taking a shot with a hockey stick. You move your hands a short distance, but the other end of the stick moves a greater distance to hit the puck. When you use chopsticks to eat your food, you move the hand holding the chopsticks a short distance. The other end of the chopsticks moves a greater distance, allowing you to pick up and eat food. When you ride a bicycle in high gear, you apply a force to the pedals over a short distance. The bicycle, meanwhile, travels a much longer distance.

Changing Direction Some machines don't change either force or distance. What could be the advantage of these machines? Well, think about a weight machine. You could stand and lift the weights. But it is much easier to sit on the machine and pull down than to lift up. By running a steel cable over a small wheel at the top of the machine, as shown in Figure 8, you can raise the weights by pulling down on the cable. This cable system is a machine that makes your job easier by changing the direction in which you exert your force.

 Reading Checkpoint How does the cable system on a weight machine make raising the weights easier?

Lab zone Try This Activity

Skills Focus Developing hypotheses   L2

Materials small cooking pot, 50-cm string or twine, 20-N spring scale, pencil

Time 15 minutes

Tips Help students analyze results by asking them to compare the amount of friction on the string in Steps 2 and 3.

Expected Outcome The reading was higher with the string looped over the pencil. Sliding friction between the string and the pencil caused the higher reading. It might be more convenient to pull the string down than to lift it up.

Extend Have the students find the force needed to raise another pot with a pulley and compare their results to the first activity. **learning modality: kinesthetic**

FIGURE 8
Making Work Easier

A machine can make work easier in one of three ways.

Input force

Output force

When a machine increases force, you must exert the input force over a greater distance.

Input Work = **Output Work**

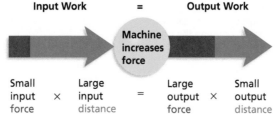

Machine increases force

| Small input force | × | Large input distance | = | Large output force | × | Small output distance |

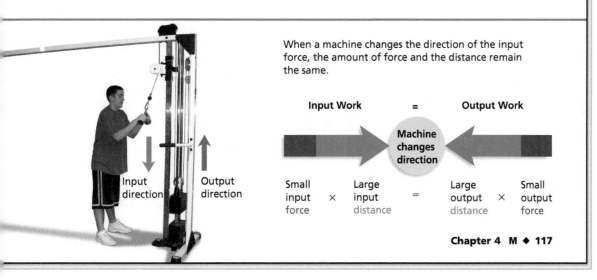

Input distance

Output distance

When a machine increases distance, you must apply a greater input force.

Input Work = **Output Work**

Machine increases distance

| Large input force | × | Small input distance | = | Small output force | × | Large output distance |

Input direction

Output direction

When a machine changes the direction of the input force, the amount of force and the distance remain the same.

Input Work = **Output Work**

Machine changes direction

| Small input force | × | Large input distance | = | Large output distance | × | Small output force |

Chapter 4   M ◆ 117

Use Visuals
Chopsticks

Focus Direct the students' attention to the arrows indicating input work and output work in Figure 8. Ask: **Do any of the machines shown here produce more output work than input work?** (*No, the arrows indicate that the amounts of output work and input work are the same.*)

Teach Repeat the observation that no machine produces more work than is input. Ask: **If machines don't decrease the work required to do a task, how can they be helpful?** (*Machines make work easier by increasing the force, increasing the distance, or changing the direction of the input force.*)

Apply Ask: **Which machine shown here makes work easier by changing the direction of the input force?** (*The weight machine changes the direction of the input force.*) **learning modality: visual**

All in One Teaching Resources

• Transparency M38

Monitor Progress _____ L2

Drawing Have students make three diagrams showing how machines change force, change distance, or change direction to make work easier.

Answer

 Reading Checkpoint   The cable system enables you to raise the weights more conveniently by changing the direction in which you exert force.

M ● 117

Mechanical Advantage

FIGURE 9
Mechanical Advantage
Without the mechanical advantage of the can opener, opening the can would be very difficult.

Mechanical Advantage

If you compare the input force to the output force, you can find the advantage of using a machine. **A machine's mechanical advantage is the number of times a machine increases a force exerted on it.** Finding the ratio of output force to input force gives you the **mechanical advantage** of a machine.

$$\text{Mechanical advantage} = \frac{\text{Output force}}{\text{Input force}}$$

Increasing Force When the output force is greater than the input force, the mechanical advantage of a machine is greater than 1. Suppose you exert an input force of 10 newtons on a hand-held can opener, and the opener exerts an output force of 30 newtons on a can. The mechanical advantage of the can opener is

$$\frac{\text{Output force}}{\text{Input force}} = \frac{30 \text{ N}}{10 \text{ N}} = 3$$

The can opener triples your input force!

Increasing Distance For a machine that increases distance, the output force is less than the input force. So in this case, the mechanical advantage is less than 1. For example, suppose your input force is 20 newtons and the machine's output force is 10 newtons. The mechanical advantage is

$$\frac{\text{Output force}}{\text{Input force}} = \frac{10 \text{ N}}{20 \text{ N}} = 0.5$$

The output force of the machine is half your input force, but the machine exerts that force over a longer distance.

Mechanical Advantage

The input force and output force for three different ramps are shown in the graph.

1. **Reading Graphs** What variable is plotted on the horizontal axis?

2. **Interpreting Data** If an 80-N input force is exerted on Ramp 2, what is the output force?

3. **Interpreting Data** Find the slope of the line for each ramp.

4. **Drawing Conclusions** Why does the slope represent each ramp's mechanical advantage? Which ramp has the greatest mechanical advantage?

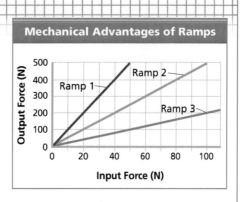

Mechanical Advantages of Ramps

Graph: Output Force (N) on vertical axis (0–500), Input Force (N) on horizontal axis (0–100). Ramp 1, Ramp 2, Ramp 3 shown as lines.

Changing Direction What can you predict about the mechanical advantage of a machine that changes the direction of the force? If only the direction changes, the input force will be the same as the output force. The mechanical advantage will always be 1.

Efficiency of Machines

So far, you have learned that the work you put into a machine is exactly equal to the work done by the machine. In an ideal situation, this equation is true. In real situations, however, the output work is always less than the input work.

Friction and Efficiency If you have ever tried to cut something with scissors that barely open and close, you know that a large part of your work is wasted overcoming the tightness, or friction, between the parts of the scissors.

In every machine, some work is wasted overcoming the force of friction. The less friction there is, the closer the output work is to the input work. The **efficiency** of a machine compares the output work to the input work. Efficiency is expressed as a percent. The higher the percent, the more efficient the machine is. If you know the input work and output work for a machine, you can calculate a machine's efficiency.

 **Reading Checkpoint** Why is output work always less than input work in real situations?

FIGURE 10
Efficiency
A rusty pair of shears is less efficient than a new pair of shears.
Applying Concepts What force reduces the efficiency of the shears?

Chapter 4   M ◆ 119

Math Skill Making and interpreting graphs

Focus A graph shows how two variables are related. In this graph, the relationship between input force and mechanical advantage of a ramp is shown.

Teach Ask: **Which variable is on the y-axis?** *(Mechanical advantage)* **What happens as mechanical advantage increases?** *(Input force decreases.)*

Answers

1. Input force
2. 400 N
3. Ramp 1: 10; Ramp 2: 5; Ramp 3: 2
4. The slope of each ramp's graph equals the change in output force divided by the change in input force. This is the formula for mechanical advantage. Ramp 1 has the greatest mechanical advantage.

Efficiency of Machines

Teach Key Concepts L2
Defining and Calculating Efficiency

Focus Ask: **A person is described as an efficient worker. What other phrases could describe this person?** *(Sample answer: Doesn't waste time, works effectively)*

Teach Remind students that friction is a force that opposes motion. Ask: **If friction in a machine increases, what happens to the machine's efficiency?** *(It decreases.)* **Is any machine 100% efficient?** *(No, all machines waste some work overcoming friction.)*

Apply Ask: **Why is it important to maintain machines?** *(To maintain as high an efficiency as possible)* **learning modality: logical/mathematical**

Monitor Progress _____ L2

Skills Check Have students find the mechanical advantage of a lever if they exert 10 N to push it down and it exerts a force of 30 N to raise a box. *(3)*

Answers
Figure 10 Friction

 Reading Checkpoint Because friction exists in every machine and reduces the machine's efficiency.

Differentiated Instruction

English Learners/Beginning L1
Comprehension: Modified Cloze
Distribute a simplified paragraph about machines, but leave some words blank. Model how to fill in the blank, using a sample sentence on the board. Provide students with the correct answers as choices. **learning modality: verbal**

English Learners/Intermediate L2
Comprehension: Modified Cloze
Distribute the same paragraph, but include some additional terms as incorrect choices. After students complete the paragraph, have them work together to write definitions for the answer choices that were not used. Model this activity on the board before students begin. **learning modality: verbal**

Math Skill Calculating efficiency

Focus Remind students that efficiency is expressed as a percentage. Tell students that it is important to divide output work by input work (rather than the reverse).

Teach Ask: **If your calculations result in an efficiency greater than 100%, is your answer reasonable? Why?** *(No; no machine has an efficiency greater than 100%.)*

Answers

1. 90%
2. 40%

 **Teaching Resources**

- Transparency M39

 Build **Inquiry** L1

Friction and Efficiency

Materials scissors with adjustable tension, one pair for each student

Time 10 minutes

Safety Scissors can cut students' skin. Students should always direct a sharp edge or point away from themselves and others.

Focus Ask: **What happens to the force required to cut paper if the friction in a pair of scissors is increased?** *(It increases.)*

Teach Students should work in small groups. Give each group several pairs of scissors with varying tension. Ask students to cut paper with each of the scissors. After each student has used each pair of scissors, have the students work in a group to place the scissors in order from most efficient to least efficient.

Apply Ask: **Why do you want to use scissors with a greater efficiency when you cut paper?** *(It takes less input force.)*
learning modality: kinesthetic

Go Online
SciLINKS
For: Links on mechanical efficiency
Visit: www.SciLinks.org
Web Code: scn-1342

Download a worksheet that will guide students' review of Internet sources on mechanical efficiency.

For: Links on mechanical efficiency
Visit: www.SciLinks.org
Web Code: scn-1342

Calculating Efficiency To calculate the efficiency of a machine, divide the output work by the input work and multiply the result by 100 percent. This is summarized by the following formula.

$$\text{Efficiency} = \frac{\text{Output work}}{\text{Input work}} \times 100\%$$

If the tight scissors described above have an efficiency of 60%, only a little more than half of the work you do goes into cutting the paper. The rest is wasted overcoming the friction in the scissors.

Math Sample Problem

Calculating Efficiency

You do 250,000 J of work to cut a lawn with a hand mower. If the work done by the mower is 200,000 J, what is the efficiency of the lawn mower?

1 Read and Understand.
What information are you given?

Input work (W_{input}) = 250,000 J

Output work (W_{output}) = 200,000 J

2 Plan and Solve
What quantity are you trying to calculate?

The efficiency of the lawn mower = ■

What formula contains the given quantities and the unknown quantity?

$$\text{Efficiency} = \frac{\text{Output work}}{\text{Input work}} \times 100\%$$

Perform the calculation.

$$\text{Efficiency} = \frac{200,000 \text{ J}}{250,000 \text{ J}} \times 100\%$$

$$\text{Efficiency} = 0.8 \times 100\% = 80\%$$

The efficiency of the lawn mower is 80%.

3 Look Back and Check
Does your answer make sense?

An efficiency of 80% means that 80 out of every 100 J of work went into cutting the lawn. This answer makes sense because most of the input work is converted to output work.

Math Practice

1. **Calculating Efficiency** You do 20 J of work while using a hammer. The hammer does 18 J of work on a nail. What is the efficiency of the hammer?

2. **Calculating Efficiency** Suppose you left your lawn mower outdoors all winter. Now it's rusty. Of your 250,000 J of work, only 100,000 J go to cutting the lawn. What is the efficiency of the lawn mower now?

FIGURE 11
An Ideal Machine?
The balls of this Newton's cradle may swing for a long time, but friction will eventually bring them to rest.

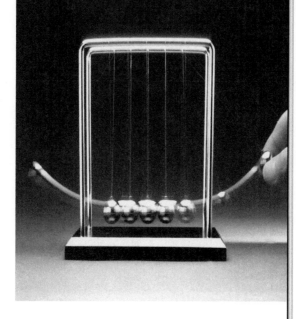

Real and Ideal Machines If you could find a machine with an efficiency of 100%, it would be an ideal machine. Unfortunately, such a machine does not exist. In all machines, some work is wasted due to friction. Even the balls in Figure 11 will eventually come to rest. All machines have an efficiency of less than 100%. The machines you use every day, such as scissors, screwdrivers, and rakes, lose some work due to friction.

A machine's ideal mechanical advantage is its mechanical advantage with 100% efficiency. However, if you measure a machine's input force and output force, you will find the efficiency is always less than 100%. A machine's measured mechanical advantage is called actual mechanical advantage.

✓ Reading Checkpoint | **What is a machine's ideal mechanical advantage?**

Section 2 Assessment

 Target Reading Skill
Identifying Main Ideas Use your graphic organizer to help you answer Question 1 below.

Reviewing Key Concepts
1. a. Defining What is a machine?
   b. Describing In what three ways can machines make work easier?
   c. Applying Concepts How does a screwdriver make work easier?
2. a. Reviewing What is the mechanical advantage of a machine?
   b. Making Generalizations What is the mechanical advantage of a machine that changes only the direction of the applied force?
   c. Calculating If a machine has an input force of 40 N and an output force of 80 N, what is its mechanical advantage?

3. a. Reviewing What must you know in order to calculate a machine's efficiency?
   b. Explaining What is an ideal machine?
   c. Comparing and Contrasting How is a real machine like an ideal machine, and how is it different?

Math Practice

4. Calculating Efficiency The input work you do on a can opener is 12 J. The output work the can opener does is 6 J. What is the efficiency of the can opener?

5. Calculating Efficiency Suppose the efficiency of a manual pencil sharpener is 58%. If the output work needed to sharpen a pencil is 4.8 J, how much input work must you do to sharpen the pencil?

Chapter 4 M ◆ 121

Monitor Progress _____ L2
Answer
✓ Reading Checkpoint) A machine's ideal mechanical advantage is its mechanical advantage when it operates at 100% efficiency.

Assess

Reviewing Key Concepts
1. a. A machine is a device that allows work to be done in a way that is easier or more effective. **b.** Machines can make work easier by changing the amount of force you exert, the distance over which you exert force, or the direction in which you exert force. **c.** A screwdriver multiplies force because you exert an input force on the handle over a greater distance than the output force is exerted on the tip of the screwdriver.
2. a. A machine's mechanical advantage is its output force divided by its input force. **b.** If only direction changes, the mechanical advantage is 1. **c.** The mechanical advantage is 2.
3. a. To calculate a machine's efficiency, you must know its output work and input work. **b.** An ideal machine is one with an efficiency of 100%. **c.** Both ideal machines and real machines perform work. Because of friction, however, real machines operate at less than the 100% efficiency of ideal machines.

Reteach L1
Have students work in pairs to review the key terms found in the section.

Performance Assessment L2
Writing Have students imagine that they are engineering consultants for a lawn-mower manufacturer. They must explain why the actual mechanical advantage of their latest lawn mower is only 80% of its ideal mechanical advantage.

All in One Teaching Resources
- Section Summary: *How Machines Do Work*
- Review and Reinforce: *How Machines Do Work*
- Enrich: *How Machines Do Work*

Math Practice
Math Skill Formulas and equations
Answers
4. 50%
5. about 8.3 J

Lab zone Chapter Project
Keep Students on Track Have students think about whether force or distance is multiplied by each simple machine in their design. Students should finalize their plans and build their machines. Inform students that the ideal mechanical advantage of a compound machine is the product of the ideal mechanical advantages of its components.

Seesaw Science

Prepare for Inquiry

Key Concept
Distance from the pivot point and the amount of input force play equal roles in determining the effect of the force on each side of a seesaw.

Skills Objectives
After this lab students will be able to
- control variables to determine the effect of a particular variable.
- interpret data about how various factors affect a seesaw.

Prep Time 20 minutes
Class Time 40 minutes

Advance Planning
Gather required materials.

Alternative Materials
Washers, hex nuts, or other standard-sized items can be used in place of pennies.

All in One Teaching Resources
- Lab Worksheet: *Seesaw Science*

Guide Inquiry

Invitation
Ask: **What happens when an adult gets on one end of a seesaw and a child on the other?** (*The side with the adult sinks to the ground, and the side with the child rises.*) Model this for students using a meter stick. Place a dowel at 50 cm for the pivot point. Put 10 pennies at one end of the meter stick, and five pennies at the other end. Ask: **What can we do to make the meter stick balance?** (*Move the ten pennies closer to the pivot point, or move the dowel closer to the ten pennies*)

Introduce the Procedure
Have the students read the procedure. Ask: **What variables are changed in this investigation? What variables are held constant?** (*Changed: number of pennies; held constant: pivot point, position of eight pennies*)

Troubleshooting the Experiment
- The meter stick will move as it is used and should be readjusted before each trial.
- Students should measure the position of the center of the stack of pennies to the nearest tenth of a centimeter.

Seesaw Science

Problem
What is the relationship between distance and weight for a balanced seesaw?

Skills Focus
controlling variables, interpreting data

Materials
- meter stick • masking tape
- 28 pennies, minted after 1982
- small object with a mass of about 50 g
- dowel or other cylindrical object for pivot point, about 10 cm long and 3 cm in diameter

Procedure
1. Begin by using the dowel and meter stick to build a seesaw. Tape the dowel firmly to the table so that it does not roll.

2. Choose the meter stick mark that will rest on the dowel from the following: 55 cm or 65 cm. Record your choice. Position your meter stick so that it is on your chosen pivot point with the 100-cm mark on your right.

3. Slide the 50-g mass along the shorter end of the meter stick until the meter stick is balanced, with both sides in the air. (This is called "zeroing" your meter stick.)

4. Copy the data table into your notebook.

5. Place a stack of 8 pennies exactly over the 80-cm mark. Determine the distance, in centimeters, from the pivot point to the pennies. Record this distance in the "Distance to Pivot" column for the right side of the seesaw.

6. Predict where you must place a stack of 5 pennies in order to balance the meter stick. Test your prediction and record the actual position in the "Position of Pennies" column for the left side of the seesaw.

Data Table

Your group's pivot point position: _____ cm

Trial Number	Side of Seesaw	Number of Pennies or Weight of Pennies (pw)	Position of Pennies (cm)	Distance to Pivot (cm)	Weight of Pennies × Distance
1	Right				
	Left				
2	Right				
	Left				
3	Right				

7. Determine the distance, in centimeters, from the pivot point to the left stack of pennies. Record this distance in the "Distance to Pivot" column for the left side of the seesaw.

8. If you use an imaginary unit of weight, the pennyweight (pw), then one penny weighs 1 pw. Multiply the weight of each stack of pennies by the distance to the pivot point. Record the result in the last column of the data table.

9. Predict how the position of the pennies in Step 6 would change if you used 7, 12, 16, and 20 pennies instead of 5 pennies. Test your predictions.

Analyze and Conclude

1. **Controlling Variables** In this experiment, what is the manipulated variable? The responding variable? How do you know which is which?

2. **Interpreting Data** As you increase the number of pennies on the left, what happens to the distance at which you must place the stack in order to balance the meter stick?

3. **Drawing Conclusions** What conclusion can you draw about the relationship between distances and weights needed to balance a seesaw?

4. **Controlling Variables** Why was it important to zero the meter stick with the 50-g mass?

5. **Interpreting Data** Compare your results with those of the other groups. How do different pivot point positions affect the results?

6. **Communicating** Write a dialogue that occurs when two friends try to balance themselves on opposite sides of a seesaw. One friend has a mass of 54 kg and the other friend has a mass of 42 kg.

Design an Experiment

Suppose you have a seesaw with a movable pivot. You want to use it with a younger friend who weighs half what you weigh. If you and your friend sit on the ends of the seesaw, where should you position the pivot point? Develop a hypothesis and then design an experiment to test it. *Obtain your teacher's permission before carrying out your investigation.*

Expected Outcome

Students' data should show that a large weight close to the pivot point can be compensated by a small weight far from the pivot point.

Analyze and Conclude

1. Manipulated variable: weight on left side of pivot, because it is the variable that is being changed in each trial; responding variable: distance between that weight and the pivot point needed to achieve balance, because it changes as a result of the change in weight

2. As you increase the number of pennies on the left, you must decrease the distance between the pivot and the pennies to achieve balance.

3. For a balanced seesaw, the product of weight and distance from the pivot point on the left is equal to the product of weight and distance from the pivot point on the right ($w_1 d_1 = w_2 d_2$). Weight and distance have equal importance in achieving balance.

4. To ensure that the meter stick was balanced before you began.

5. For all groups, $w_1 d_1 = w_2 d_2$. So, different positions of the pivot point do not affect the results.

6. Students' dialogues should reflect the fact that the 42-kg friend must be farther from the seesaw pivot than the 54-kg friend to achieve balance.

Extend Inquiry

Design an Experiment Sample answer: We should position the pivot point so that the distance between the pivot point and my lighter friend is twice the distance between the pivot point and me. We could test the hypothesis by placing 5 weights at 95 cm, 10 weights at 5 cm, and the pivot point at 35 cm. If the meter stick balances, the hypothesis is correct.

Objectives
After this lesson students will be able to
M.4.3.1 Describe the six kinds of simple machines and their uses.
M.4.3.2 Calculate the ideal mechanical advantage of each type of simple machine.
M.4.3.3 Describe compound machines.

Target Reading Skill ⤺

Previewing Visuals Explain that looking at the visuals before they read helps students activate prior knowledge and predict what they are about to read.

Answers
Sample graphic organizer:

Three Classes of Levers
What are the three classes of levers? *(The three classes of levers are first-class levers, second-class levers, and third-class levers.)*
How do the three classes of levers differ? *(They differ in the position of the fulcrum, input force, and output force.)*

All In One Teaching Resources
• Transparency M40

Preteach

Build Background Knowledge L2
Simple Machines
Using a variety of ordinary household objects, such as chopsticks and screwdrivers, show students examples of each kind of simple machine. Have students compare and contrast the different machines and how they are used.

Reading Preview

Key Concepts
• What are the six kinds of simple machines, and how are they used?
• What is the ideal mechanical advantage of each simple machine?
• What is a compound machine?

Key Terms
• inclined plane • wedge
• screw • lever • fulcrum
• wheel and axle • pulley
• compound machine

⤺ **Target Reading Skill**
Previewing Visuals Before you read, preview Figure 17. Then write two questions that you have about the diagram in a graphic organizer like the one below. As you read, answer your questions.

Three Classes of Levers

Q.	What are the three classes of levers?
A.	
Q.	

Lab zone Discover **Activity**

How Can You Increase Force?
1. Working with two partners, wrap a rope around two broomsticks as shown.
2. Your two partners should try to hold the brooms apart with the same amount of force throughout the activity. For safety, they should hold firmly, but not with all their strength.
3. Try to pull the two students together by pulling on the broomsticks. Can you do it?
4. Can you pull them together by pulling on the rope?

Think It Over
Predicting What do you think will be the effect of wrapping the rope around the broomsticks several more times?

Look at the objects shown on these pages. Which of them would you call machines? Would it surprise you to find out that each is made up of one or more simple machines? As you learned in the last section, a machine helps you do work by changing the amount or direction of the force you apply.

There are six basic kinds of simple machines: the inclined plane, the wedge, the screw, the lever, the wheel and axle, and the pulley. In this section, you will learn how the different types of simple machines help you do work.

◀ An eggbeater, a bolt, and a fishing pole all make use of simple machines.

Lab zone Discover **Activity**

Skills Focus Predicting L2
Materials 2 broomsticks or dowels, long rope
Time 10 minutes
Tips After students have pulled the broomsticks together using the rope, Ask: **What did the rope do to the force?** (It multiplied the force.)

Expected Outcome Students will find it difficult to bring the students together by pulling the broomstick. They will be able to bring the broomsticks together by pulling on the rope.

Think It Over Sample answer: You will be able to increase your force even more with several more wraps around the broomsticks. At some point the increased

friction will offset that effect. You could reduce friction by using nylon rope or lubricating the broomsticks with vegetable oil.

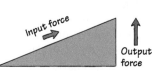

Inclined Plane

Have you ever had to lift something from a lower level to a higher level? The job is much easier if you have a ramp. For example, a ramp makes it much easier to push a grocery cart over a curb. A ramp is an example of a simple machine called an inclined plane. An **inclined plane** is a flat, sloped surface.

How It Works An inclined plane allows you to exert your input force over a longer distance. As a result, the input force needed is less than the output force. The input force that you use on an inclined plane is the force with which you push or pull an object. The output force is the force that you would need to lift the object without the inclined plane. Recall that this force is equal to the weight of the object.

Mechanical Advantage You can determine the ideal mechanical advantage of an inclined plane by dividing the length of the incline by its height.

$$\text{Ideal mechanical advantage} = \frac{\text{Length of incline}}{\text{Height of incline}}$$

For example, if you are loading a truck that is 1 meter high using a ramp that is 3 meters long, the ideal mechanical advantage of the ramp is 3 meters ÷ 1 meter, or 3. The inclined plane increases the force you exerted three times. If the height of the incline does not change, increasing the length of the incline will increase the mechanical advantage. The longer the incline, the less input force you need to push or pull an object.

FIGURE 12
Inclined Plane
Although the amount of work is the same whether you lift the boxes or push them up the ramp to the truck, you need less force when you use an inclined plane. Relating Cause and Effect *When you use a ramp, what happens to the distance over which you exert your force?*

Wedge

Teach Key Concepts
L2

Everyday Examples of Wedges

Focus Tell students that many of the tools they use each day are wedges or contain wedges as a part of a compound machine.

Teach Ask: **Other than the examples of wedges shown in your book, what are other examples of wedges?** *(Sample answers: Knives, shovels)* Write correct answers on the board under the heading *Wedges*.

Apply Ask: **What other simple machine are wedges most similar to?** *(Inclined planes)* **learning modality: visual**

Lab zone Teacher **Demo**

Modeling Use of a Wedge
L1

Materials butter knife, claw hammer, simple can opener, nail

Focus Show students the items listed above.

Teach Ask: **Which of these tools are wedges?** *(All are wedges or contain wedges.)* If students do not recognize each of the objects as a wedge, ask for volunteers to explain why each is a wedge.

Apply Ask: **Which tool would be best to open a juice can?** *(Can opener)* **How does the wedge on the can opener use input force to open a can?** *(The input force exerted on the handle of the can opener is multiplied by the wedge. The larger output force of the thin edge can puncture the juice can.)* **learning modality: visual**

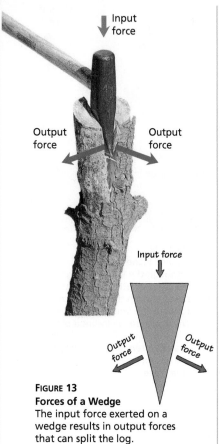

Input force

Output force   Output force

Input force

Output force   Output force

FIGURE 13
Forces of a Wedge
The input force exerted on a wedge results in output forces that can split the log.

Wedge

If you've ever sliced an apple with a knife, pulled up a zipper, or seen someone chop wood with an ax, you are familiar with another simple machine known as a wedge. A **wedge** is a device that is thick at one end and tapers to a thin edge at the other end. It might be helpful to think of a wedge, like the one shown in Figure 13, as an inclined plane (or sometimes two inclined planes back to back) that can move.

How It Works When you use a wedge, instead of moving an object along the inclined plane, you move the inclined plane itself. For example, when an ax is used to split wood, the ax handle exerts a force on the blade of the ax, which is the wedge. That force pushes the wedge down into the wood. The wedge in turn exerts an output force at a 90° angle to its slope, splitting the wood in two.

Wedges are a part of your everyday life. For example, a zipper depends on wedges to close and open. A pencil sharpener, a cheese grater, and a shovel all make use of wedges.

Mechanical Advantage The mechanical advantage of the wedge and the inclined plane are similar. **The ideal mechanical advantage of a wedge is determined by dividing the length of the wedge by its width.** The longer and thinner a wedge is, the greater its mechanical advantage. For example, the cutting edge of a steel carving knife is a wedge. When you sharpen a knife, you make the wedge thinner and increase its mechanical advantage. That is why sharp knives cut better than dull knives.

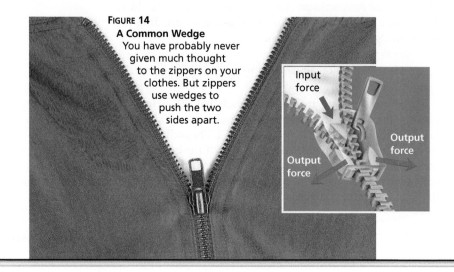

FIGURE 14
A Common Wedge
You have probably never given much thought to the zippers on your clothes. But zippers use wedges to push the two sides apart.

Input force

Output force

Output force

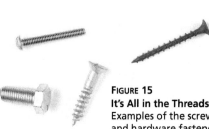

FIGURE 15
It's All in the Threads
Examples of the screw are found in jars and hardware fasteners.
Relating Cause and Effect How does the distance between the threads of a screw affect its mechanical advantage?

Screws

Like a wedge, a screw is a simple machine that is related to the inclined plane. A **screw** can be thought of as an inclined plane wrapped around a cylinder. This spiral inclined plane forms the threads of the screw.

How It Works When you twist a screw into a piece of wood, you exert an input force on the screw. The threads of a screw act like an inclined plane to increase the distance over which you exert the input force. As the threads of the screw turn, they exert an output force on the wood, pulling the screw into the wood. Friction between the screw and the wood holds the screw in place.

Many devices act like screws. Examples include bolts, light bulbs, and jar lids. Look at the jar lid in Figure 15. When you turn the lid, your small input force is greatly increased because of the screw threads on the lid. The threads on the lid are pulled against the matching threads on the jar with a strong enough force to make a tight seal.

Mechanical Advantage The closer together the threads of a screw are, the greater the mechanical advantage. This is because the closer the threads are, the more times you must turn the screw to fasten it into a piece of wood. Your input force is applied over a longer distance. The longer input distance results in an increased output force. Think of the length around the threads as the length of the inclined plane, and the length of the screw as the height of the inclined plane. **The ideal mechanical advantage of a screw is the length around the threads divided by the length of the screw.**

 Reading Checkpoint How is a screw like an inclined plane?

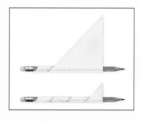
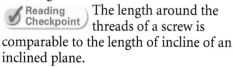

Levers

Teach Key Concepts L2
Comparing Levers

Focus Ask: **What are some everyday examples of levers?** *(Sample answer: Paint can opener, seesaw, wheelbarrow)*

Teach Write on the board three headings: First-class levers, Second-class levers, and Third-class levers. Have students give examples of each, and list the examples under the appropriate headings. After students have named examples of each class of lever, have them brainstorm other facts that could be included under each heading. The facts could include the location of the fulcrum in relation to the input and output forces and the direction of the output force in comparison to the direction of the input force.

Apply Ask: **In which class of lever is the fulcrum located between the input force and the output force?** *(First-class lever)* **learning modality: logical/mathematical**

Help Students Read L1
Using Prior Knowledge Before reading about levers, have students brainstorm lists of things they know about levers. After reading the selection, have students review their lists, replace any misconceptions with correct understandings of the topic, and add new information from the text.

Work and Machines

Show the Video Field Trip to let students experience the restoration of the Parthenon and understand how machines were important to its construction. Discussion question: **Name some of the simple machines used by the builders of the Parthenon.** *(Pulley, wheel and axle, lever, wedge, inclined plane)*

Work and Machines

Video Preview
▶ Video Field Trip
Video Assessment

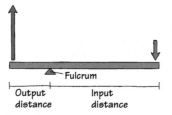

Fulcrum

Output distance   Input distance

FIGURE 16
Mechanical Advantage of a Lever
A lever's input distance and output distance determine its ideal mechanical advantage.

Levers

Have you ever ridden on a seesaw or pried open a paint can with an opener? If so, then you are already familiar with another simple machine called a lever. A **lever** is a rigid bar that is free to pivot, or rotate, on a fixed point. The fixed point that a lever pivots around is called the **fulcrum.**

How It Works To understand how levers work, think about using a paint-can opener. The opener rests against the edge of the can, which acts as the fulcrum. The tip of the opener is under the lid of the can. When you push down, you exert an input force on the handle, and the opener pivots on the fulcrum. As a result, the tip of the opener pushes up, thereby exerting an output force on the lid.

Mechanical Advantage A lever like the paint-can opener helps you in two ways. It increases your input force and it changes the direction of your input force. When you use the paint-can opener, you push the handle a long distance down in order to move the lid a short distance up. However, you are able to apply a smaller force than you would have without the opener.

The ideal mechanical advantage of a lever is determined by dividing the distance from the fulcrum to the input force by the distance from the fulcrum to the output force.

$$\text{Ideal mechanical advantage} = \frac{\text{Distance from fulcrum to input force}}{\text{Distance from fulcrum to output force}}$$

In the case of the paint-can opener, the distance from the fulcrum to the input force is greater than the distance from the fulcrum to the output force. This means that the mechanical advantage is greater than 1.

Different Types of Levers When a paint-can opener is used as a lever, the fulcrum is located between the input and output forces. But this is not always the case. As shown in Figure 17, there are three different types of levers. Levers are classified according to the location of the fulcrum relative to the input and output forces.

 Reading Checkpoint   What point on a lever does not move?

FIGURE 17

Three Classes of Levers

The three classes of levers differ in the positions of the fulcrum, input force, and output force. *Applying Concepts Which type of lever always has an ideal mechanical advantage less than 1?*

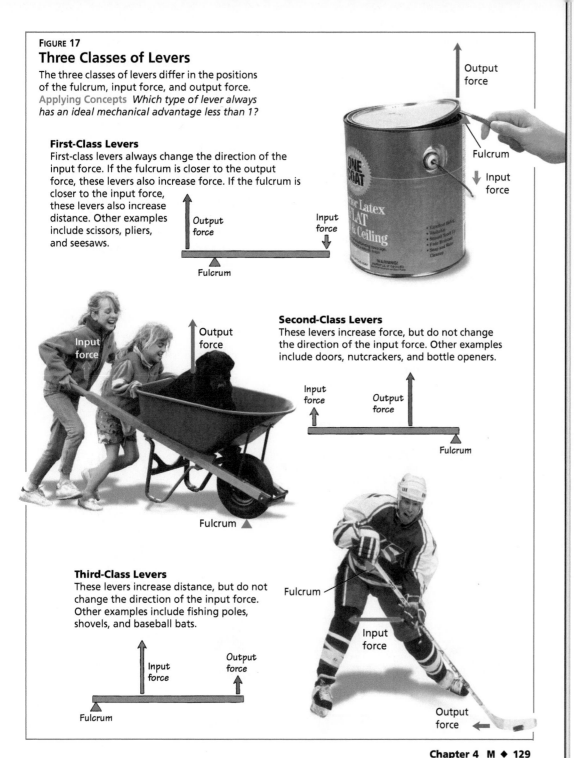

First-Class Levers
First-class levers always change the direction of the input force. If the fulcrum is closer to the output force, these levers also increase force. If the fulcrum is closer to the input force, these levers also increase distance. Other examples include scissors, pliers, and seesaws.

Output force
Input force
Fulcrum

Output force
Fulcrum
Input force

Second-Class Levers
These levers increase force, but do not change the direction of the input force. Other examples include doors, nutcrackers, and bottle openers.

Input force
Output force

Input force
Output force
Fulcrum

Fulcrum

Third-Class Levers
These levers increase distance, but do not change the direction of the input force. Other examples include fishing poles, shovels, and baseball bats.

Fulcrum

Input force
Output force
Fulcrum

Input force
Output force

Chapter 4 M ◆ 129

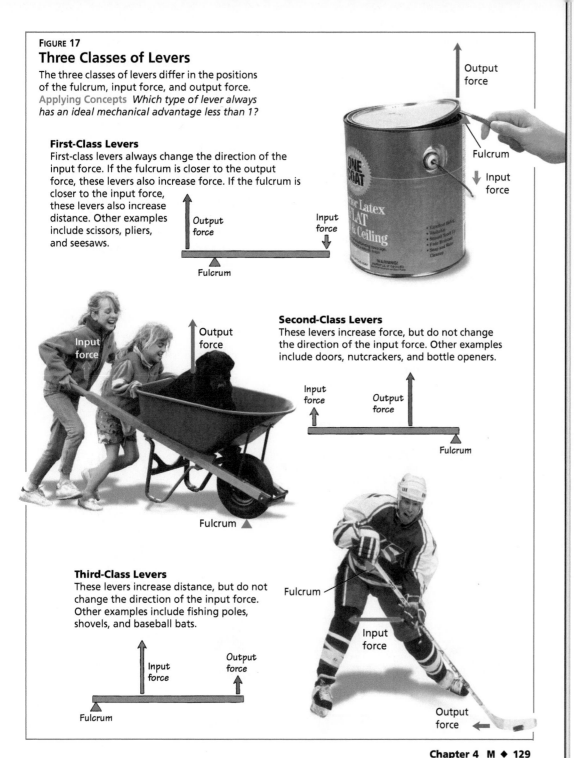 **Lab zone** **Build Inquiry** L3

Modeling Levers

Materials plastic spoons, dried beans
Time 10 minutes

Focus Review the definition of the three classes of levers.

Teach Pair students. Have one student place his or her index finger flat on a table and balance the spoon on the finger. The other student can place a bean in the bowl of the spoon and demonstrate how pressing the spoon handle allows them to lift the bean. Make certain each group can identify the input force, output force, and fulcrum. Ask: **What class of lever did this activity model?** (*First-class lever*) Next, have one group member place the bowl of the spoon on the table, and balance a bean on the middle of the spoon's handle. The other student can carefully lift the edge of the handle. Ask: **What class of lever did this activity model?** (*Second-class lever*) Finally, challenge students to use these materials to model a third-class lever. Ask: **Where are the input force, output force, and fulcrum located in your model of a third-class lever?** (*Input force is in the center of the spoon handle; output force is at the bowl of the spoon; fulcrum is at the top of the spoon's handle.*)

Apply Ask: **What other materials could you use to model the three different classes of levers?** (*Sample answer: Ruler, pencil, and coin*) **learning modality: kinesthetic**

All in One Teaching Resources
• Transparency M41

Differentiated Instruction

English Learners/Beginning Vocabulary: Science Glossary L1
Pronounce and define aloud for students the key terms from the section. Students can write each key term on the front of an index card and draw a picture or diagram of the object represented by the term on the back of the index card. Model this activity before students begin. **learning modality: visual**

English Learners/Intermediate Vocabulary: Science Glossary L2
Students can expand on the activity described in Beginning by writing the definition of the key term on the back of the index card. Model this activity before students begin. Students can use the index cards for individual review or to quiz one another. **learning modality: verbal**

Monitor Progress L2

Skills Check Have students prepare a compare/contrast table that analyzes the three classes of levers.

Answers
Figure 17 Third-class levers have an ideal mechanical advantage of less than 1.

Reading Checkpoint The point on a lever in contact with the fulcrum does not move.

Wheel and Axle

Teach Key Concepts L2
Using a Wheel and Axle

Focus Direct student's attention to Figure 18. Explain that a screwdriver is an example of a wheel and axle.

Teach Tell students that when the input force is applied to the wheel, the wheel and axle increases your force. When the input force is applied to the axle, the wheel and axle increase the distance over which the output force is applied, as illustrated in Figure 19.

Apply Ask: **When using a screwdriver, do you apply the input force to the wheel or the axle?** (*To the wheel*) **learning modality: visual**

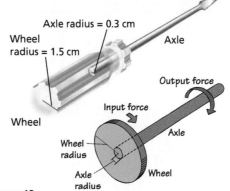

FIGURE 18
Wheel and Axle
A screwdriver increases force by exerting the output force over a shorter distance.
Observing *Which has a larger radius, the wheel or the axle?*

Wheel and Axle

It's almost impossible to insert a screw into a piece of wood with your fingers. But with a screwdriver, you can turn the screw easily. A screwdriver makes use of a simple machine known as the **wheel and axle.** A wheel and axle is a simple machine made of two circular or cylindrical objects fastened together that rotate about a common axis. The object with the larger radius is called the wheel and the object with the smaller radius is called the axle. In a screwdriver, the handle is the wheel and the shaft is the axle. A doorknob and a car's steering wheel are also examples of a wheel and axle.

Science and **History**

Engineering Marvels
Simple machines have been used to create some of the most beautiful and useful structures in the world.

2550 B.C.
Great Pyramid, Giza, Egypt
Workers used wedges to cut 2.3 million blocks of stone to build the pyramid. At the quarry, the wedges were driven into cracks in the rock. The rock split into pieces. Workers hauled the massive blocks up inclined planes to the tops of pyramid walls.

500 B.C.
Theater at Epidaurus, Greece
Instead of ramps, the Greeks relied on a crane powered by pulleys to lift the stone blocks to build this theater. The crane was also used to lower actors to the stage during performances.

3000 B.C.	2000 B.C.	1000 B.C.

Background

Facts and Figures
• The wheel was most likely invented in Mesopotamia during the Bronze Age, around 3500 B.C.
• The spinning wheel was probably invented in India, but reached Europe in the Middle Ages.
• The first practical four-wheeled roller skates were designed in 1863 by James Plimpton, who lived in Massachusetts.

• The kinetoscope, the predecessor to the motion-picture projector, was invented in 1891 by Thomas Edison and William Dickson.
• The world's first true automobile, a steam-powered tricycle, was invented in France in 1869 by Nicholas-Joseph Cugnot.

How It Works How does a screwdriver make use of a wheel and axle to do work? Look at Figure 18. When you use a screwdriver, you apply an input force to turn the handle, or wheel. Because the wheel is larger than the shaft, or axle, the axle rotates and exerts a large output force. The wheel and axle increases your force, but you must exert your force over a long distance.

What would happen if the input force were applied to the axle rather than the wheel? For the riverboat in Figure 19 on the next page, the force of the engine is applied to the axle of the large paddle wheel. The large paddle wheel in turn pushes against the water. In this case, the input force is exerted over a short distance. So when the input force is applied to the axle, a wheel and axle multiplies distance.

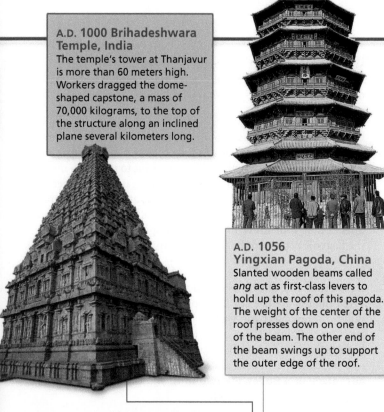

A.D. 1000 Brihadeshwara Temple, India
The temple's tower at Thanjavur is more than 60 meters high. Workers dragged the dome-shaped capstone, a mass of 70,000 kilograms, to the top of the structure along an inclined plane several kilometers long.

A.D. 1056 Yingxian Pagoda, China
Slanted wooden beams called *ang* act as first-class levers to hold up the roof of this pagoda. The weight of the center of the roof presses down on one end of the beam. The other end of the beam swings up to support the outer edge of the roof.

A.D. 1994 The Chunnel, United Kingdom to France
Special drilling equipment was built to tunnel under the English Channel. Opened in May of 1994, the tunnel is 50 kilometers long. It carries only railway traffic.

0	A.D. 1000	A.D. 2000

Chapter 4 **M ◆ 131**

Writing in Science

Research and Write
Suppose that you are the person who first thought of using a simple machine at one of the construction sites in the timeline. Write out your proposal. You'll need to research the time and place. Explain to the people in charge why the simple machine you suggest will give workers a mechanical advantage.

Writing in Science

Writing Mode Research
Scoring Rubric
4 Exceeds criteria; proposal illustrates in-depth research and is written clearly and logically
3 Meets criteria
2 Proposal needs more research and/or is not written clearly and logically
1 Proposal shows minimal research and/or is poorly written or incomplete

Lab zone **Build Inquiry** L2

Measuring Wheels and Axles

Materials long pencil, marker, scissors, measuring tape, piece of cardboard or poster board, plastic lid from coffee can, white paper

Time 15 minutes

Focus Remind students that when using a wheel and axle, the input force can be applied to either the wheel or the axle.

Teach Have students trace the coffee can lid onto the cardboard, cut out the circle, make a hole in the center of the circle, and insert the pencil into the hole. Have students measure the circumference of the wheel (cardboard) and the axle (pencil) with the measuring tape. These equal the distance traveled during one rotation. Ask: **How does the distance traveled by the wheel compare to the distance traveled by the axle?** *(It is greater.)*

Apply Ask: **Based on your measurements, what will happen to an input force exerted on the wheel?** *(An input force exerted on the wheel will cause the output force to be greater.)* Ask: **What will happen to an input force exerted on the axle?** *(An input force exerted on the axle will cause the distance that the force travels to be increased.)* **learning modality: kinesthetic**

Science and History

Focus List the six types of simple machines on the board. Then ask student volunteers to read the description of each engineering marvel shown in the time line. After each is read, Ask: **What simple machines were likely used in the construction of the structure?** *(Sample answer: Wedges, inclined planes)* Write the name of the structure under the correct machine on the board.

Teach Ask: **What tools might be used to build similar structures today?** *(Sample answer: Most tools used today are probably compound machines.)*

Monitor Progress L2

Drawing Have students draw a diagram of a commonly used wheel and axle. The diagram should include labels for the wheel, axle, input force, and output force.

Answer
Figure 18 The wheel has a larger radius.

M ● 131

Diameter, Radius, and Circumference

Focus Some students may confuse the radius of a circle with its diameter or circumference. While any of these may be used to calculate mechanical advantage of a wheel and axle, using the radius assures consistency.

Teach Draw a large circle on the board. Invite volunteers to draw and label the radius, circumference, and diameter. Ask: **What is the relationship between radius and diameter?** *(The radius is one half the diameter.)* Remind students that of the words *radius* and *diameter*, *diameter* is the longer word. When measuring radius and diameter, the diameter is the longer line.

Apply Draw a wheel and axle on the board. Have a volunteer measure the radius of the wheel and the axle with a meter stick. Ask: **What is the ideal mechanical advantage of this wheel and axle?** *(Answers will vary, students should use the following formula to find their answer: Ideal mechanical advantage = Radius of the wheel/Radius of the axle.)* **learning modality: logical/ mathematical**

Pulley

Teach Key Concepts L2

How Pulleys Work

Focus Ask: **What is a pulley?** *(A grooved wheel with a rope or cable wrapped around it)*

Teach Tell students to preview the material under the headings *How It Works* and *Types of Pulleys*. Have volunteers write facts from these two paragraphs on the board. Then have students use this information to create a concept map describing pulleys.

Apply Ask: **How can a pulley make work easier?** *(Sample answer: By changing the direction of the input force or by multiplying the strength of the input force.)*

Extend The Active Art will show students how the three types of pulleys make work easier. **learning modality: visual**

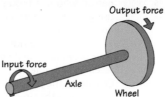

FIGURE 19
Increasing Distance
In a riverboat paddle wheel, the axle turns the wheel. The output force is less than the input force, but it is exerted over a longer distance.

Lab zone Skills **Activity**

Communicating

Write a packaging label for a machine that uses a wheel and axle. On your label, describe the advantages of using this simple machine. Include a drawing of the forces that act on the machine.

Mechanical Advantage You can find the ideal mechanical advantage of a wheel and axle by dividing the radius of the wheel by the radius of the axle. (A radius is the distance from the outer edge of a circle to the circle's center.) The greater the ratio between the radius of the wheel and the radius of the axle, the greater the mechanical advantage.

$$\text{Mechanical advantage} = \frac{\text{Radius of wheel}}{\text{Radius of axle}}$$

Suppose the radius of a screwdriver's wheel is 1.5 cm and its axle radius is 0.3 cm. The screwdriver's ideal mechanical advantage would be 1.5 centimeters ÷ 0.3 centimeter, or 5.

 Reading Checkpoint **What is a radius?**

Pulley

When you raise a flag on a flagpole or when you open and close window blinds, you are using a pulley. A **pulley** is a simple machine made of a grooved wheel with a rope or cable wrapped around it.

How It Works You use a pulley by pulling on one end of the rope. This is the input force. At the other end of the rope, the output force pulls up on the object you want to move. To move a heavy object over a distance, a pulley can make work easier in two ways. First, it can decrease the amount of input force needed to lift the object. Second, the pulley can change the direction of your input force. For example, you pull down on the flagpole rope, and the flag moves up.

Types of Pulleys There are two basic types of pulleys. A pulley that you attach to a structure is called a fixed pulley. Fixed pulleys are used at the tops of flagpoles. If you attach a pulley to the object you wish to move, you use a movable pulley. Construction cranes often use movable pulleys. By combining fixed and movable pulleys, you can make a pulley system called a block and tackle. **The ideal mechanical advantage of a pulley is equal to the number of sections of rope that support the object.**

Reading Checkpoint **A pulley is attached to the object that is being moved. What kind of pulley is it?**

Lab zone Skills **Activity**

Skills Focus Communicating L2

Time 20 minutes

Tip Encourage students to review the text on pulleys before starting the activity.

Expected Outcome The students' packaging label should include a description of how a wheel and axle makes work easier. The drawing of the wheel and axle should have the forces properly labeled. The label should be clear, correct, and persuasive. **learning modality: verbal**

FIGURE 20

Types of Pulleys

A fixed pulley and a movable pulley are the two basic types of pulleys. A block and tackle combines a fixed and movable pulley.
Comparing and Contrasting Which type of pulley has the greatest mechanical advantage?

Go Online
active art

For: Types of Pulleys activity
Visit: PHSchool.com
Web Code: cgp-3043

Fixed Pulley
A fixed pulley does not change the amount of force applied. It does change the direction of the force.

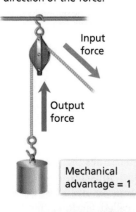

Input force

Output force

Mechanical advantage = 1

Movable Pulley
A movable pulley decreases the amount of input force needed. It does not change the direction of the force.

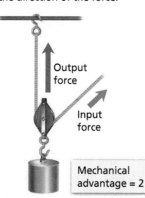

Output force

Input force

Mechanical advantage = 2

Block and Tackle
A block and tackle is a pulley system made up of fixed and movable pulleys.

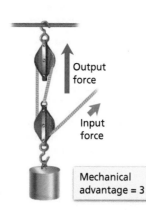

Output force

Input force

Mechanical advantage = 3

Cranes use block-and-tackle systems to lift heavy loads.

Chapter 4 M ◆ 133

Lab zone **Build Inquiry**   L2

Interpreting Diagrams

Materials for each group: 1-kg mass, 2 pulleys, rope, spring scale

Time 15 minutes

Focus Review Figure 20 with students, pointing out the location of the pulley in each type of pulley system.

Teach Challenge students to assemble each type of pulley shown in Figure 20. You may wish to provide a clothesline, wire, or wooden dowel between two chairs for students to hang their pulleys. For each pulley constructed, have students record the force needed to lift the mass and the ideal mechanical advantage.

Apply Ask: **In which setups did you change the direction of the force?** *(In the fixed-pulley setup)* **learning modality: kinesthetic**

Go Online
active art

For: Types of Pulleys activity
Visit: PHSchool.com
Web Code: cgp-3043

Students can interact with the art describing types of pulleys online.

All in One Teaching Resources
• Transparency M43

Monitor Progress _____ L2

Oral Presentation Have students compare and contrast a fixed pulley with a movable pulley and a block and tackle.

Answers
Figure 20 A block and tackle has the greatest mechanical advantage.

✓ **Reading Checkpoint** A radius is the distance between the outer edge of a circle and the circle's center.

✓ **Reading Checkpoint** A movable pulley

Simple Machines in the Body

Human Anatomy and Simple Machines

Focus Have students bend their arms at the elbow.

Teach Ask: **What kind of simple machine is your lower arm?** *(It is a third-class lever.)* Use Figure 21 to point out the input force, output force, and fulcrum in the arm, neck, and foot.

Apply Challenge students to identify other types of levers in the human body. *(The lower leg is also a third-class lever, with the fulcrum at the knee.)* **learning modality: visual**

All In One **Teaching Resources**

• Transparency M44

Compound Machines

Describing and Identifying Compound Machines

Focus List the six types of simple machines on the board.

Teach Ask students to brainstorm ways in which the simple machines are combined in everyday objects. Write examples on the board. Challenge students to add to the list over several days as they find more examples of compound machines.

Apply Ask: **What is one compound machine you have used today?** *(Sample answer: a bicycle)* **learning modality: verbal**

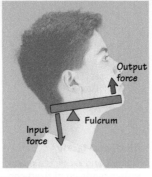
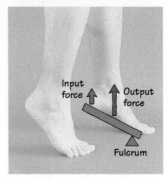
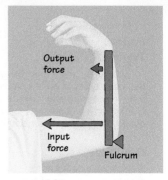

First-Class Lever The joint at the top of your neck is the fulcrum of a first-class lever. The muscles in the back of your neck provide the input force. The output force is used to tilt your head back.

Second-Class Lever The ball of your foot is the fulcrum of a second-class lever. The muscle in the calf of your leg provides the input force. The output force is used to raise your body.

Third-Class Lever Your elbow is the fulcrum of a third-class lever. Your biceps muscle provides the input force. The output force is used to lift your arm.

FIGURE 21
Levers in the Body
You don't need to look further than your own body to find simple machines. Three different types of levers are responsible for many of your movements.

Simple Machines in the Body

You probably don't think of the human body as being made up of machines. Believe it or not, machines are involved in much of the work that your body does.

Living Levers Most of the machines in your body are levers that consist of bones and muscles. Every time you move, you use a muscle. Your muscles are attached to your bones by connecting structures called tendons. Tendons and muscles pull on bones, making them work as levers. The joint, near where the tendon is attached to the bone, acts as the fulcrum. The muscles produce the input force. The output force is used for doing work, such as lifting your hand.

Working Wedges When you bite into an apple, you use your sharp front teeth, called incisors. Your incisors are shaped like wedges to enable you to bite off pieces of food. When you bite down on something, the wedge shape of your front teeth produces enough force to break it into pieces, just as an ax splits a log. The next time you take a bite of a crunchy apple, think about the machines in your mouth!

 Reading Checkpoint   **What type of simple machine do your front teeth resemble?**

FIGURE 22
Wedges to Help You Eat
Your front teeth, known as incisors, are shaped like wedges.

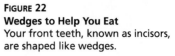

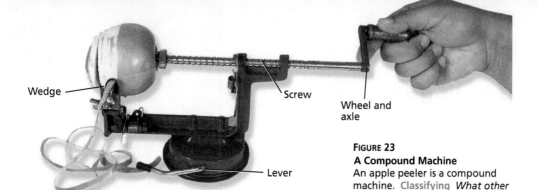

Wedge

Screw

Wheel and axle

Lever

FIGURE 23
A Compound Machine
An apple peeler is a compound machine. **Classifying** *What other compound machines can you think of? What simple machines make them up?*

Compound Machines

Many machines do not resemble the six simple machines you just read about. That's because many machines consist of combinations of simple machines.

A **compound machine** is a machine that utilizes two or more simple machines. **The ideal mechanical advantage of a compound machine is the product of the individual ideal mechanical advantages of the simple machines that make it up.**

An apple peeler like the one shown in Figure 23 is a compound machine. Four different simple machines make it up. The handle is a wheel and axle. The axle is also a screw that turns the apple. A wedge peels the apple's skin. To hold the machine in place, a lever can be switched to engage a suction cup.

Section 3 Assessment

Target Reading Skill Previewing Visuals Refer to your questions and answers about Figure 17 to help you answer Question 1 below.

Reviewing Key Concepts

1. **a.** Listing List the six kinds of simple machines.
   b. Classifying What type of simple machine is a door stopper? A rake? A windmill? A slide?
   c. Developing Hypotheses Can you consider your thumb to be a lever? Why or why not?
2. **a.** Identifying What is the ideal mechanical advantage of each type of simple machine?
   b. Inferring How can you increase a pulley's mechanical advantage?
   c. Drawing Conclusions How is calculating the ideal mechanical advantage of an inclined plane similar to calculating that of a screw?

3. **a.** Reviewing How many simple machines are needed to make a compound machine?
   b. Describing How do you find the mechanical advantage of a compound machine?

Lab zone **At-Home Activity**

Machines in the Kitchen Look around your kitchen with a family member. Identify at least five machines. Classify each as a simple machine or a compound machine. Explain to your family member how each machine makes work easier.

Lab zone **At-Home Activity**

Machines in the Kitchen L1 Students should correctly identify and classify the machines based on what they learned in *Simple Machines*. Explanations should focus on how the machines make work easier or more convenient.

Answers
Figure 23 Sample answer: A bicycle is a compound machine made up of wheels and axles and levers.

✓ Reading Checkpoint Human front teeth resemble a wedge.

Assess

Reviewing Key Concepts

1. **a.** The six simple machines are the inclined plane, the wedge, the screw, the lever, the wheel and axle, and the pulley.
b. Door stopper—wedge; rake—lever; windmill—wheel and axle; slide—inclined plane **c.** Yes, because the muscles in your hand provide the input force and the output force is used to move your thumb.
2. **a.** Ideal mechanical advantage: inclined plane—length of incline ÷ height of incline; wedge—length of wedge ÷ width of wedge; screw—length around threads ÷ length of screw; lever—distance from fulcrum to input force ÷ distance from fulcrum to output force; wheel and axle—radius of wheel ÷ radius of axle; pulley—number of sections of rope that support object. **b.** You can increase a pulley's mechanical advantage by combining fixed and movable pulleys to increase the number of sections of rope that support the object. **c.** The length of incline of an inclined plane is similar to the length around the threads of a screw.
3. **a.** A compound machine is made up of two or more simple machines. **b.** multiply the ideal mechanical advantages of the simple machines that make up the compound machine.

Reteach L1
Have students work in pairs to list the six types of simple machines and name examples of each.

Performance Assessment L2
Drawing Have students draw blueprints for a design of a compound machine that allows them to open their bedroom door while still lying in bed.

All in One **Teaching Resources**
• Section Summary: *Simple Machines*
• Review and Reinforce: *Simple Machines*
• Enrich: *Simple Machines*

Angling for Access L2

Prepare for Inquiry

Key Concept
The actual and ideal mechanical advantage of an inclined plane vary with steepness.

Skills Objectives
After this lab students will be able to
- model a wheelchair ramp.
- calculate ideal and actual mechanical advantages.

 Prep Time 20 minutes
Class Time 40 minutes

Advance Planning
Gather listed materials.

Alternative Materials
A ballistic cart, which you may be able to borrow from the physics department, can be substituted for the wooden block.

All in One Teaching Resources
- Lab Worksheet: *Angling for Access*

Guide Inquiry

Invitation
Have the boards, spring scales, and blocks or carts in the front of the room. Ask: **Have you ever seen or used a wheelchair ramp?** (*Some students may say yes.*) Have students brainstorm ways in which they could model a ramp using the displayed materials. Ask: **What variables can you manipulate?** (*Weight of block, steepness of ramp, type of material ramp is made of, length of ramp*) **What are some responding variables?** (*Force needed to pull the block up the ramp, amount of friction*)

Introduce the Procedure
Show students how to use and zero a spring scale. Remind students to pull the spring scale parallel to the inclined plane to prevent inaccurate readings.

Lab zone Skills Lab

Angling for Access

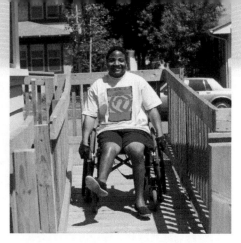

Problem
How does the steepness of a wheelchair-access ramp affect its usefulness?

Skills Focus
making models, calculating

Materials
- 4 books, about 2 cm thick • metric ruler
- wooden block with eye-hook • marker
- board, at least 10 cm wide and 50 cm long
- spring scale, 0–10 N, or force sensor

Procedure
1. Preview the following steps that describe how you can construct and use a ramp. Then copy the data table into your notebook.

2. The output force with an inclined plane is equal to the weight of the object. Lift the block with the spring scale to measure its weight. Record this value in the data table. If you are using a force sensor, see your teacher for instructions.

3. Make a mark on the side of the board about 3 cm from one end. Measure the length from the other end of the board to the mark and record it in the data table.

4. Place one end of the board on top of a book. The mark you made on the board should be even with the edge of the book.

5. Measure the vertical distance in centimeters from the top of the table to where the underside of the incline touches the book. Record this value in the data table as "Height of Incline."

6. Lay the block on its largest side and use the spring scale to pull the block straight up the incline at a slow, steady speed. Be sure to hold the spring scale parallel to the incline, as shown in the photograph. Measure the force needed and record it in the data table.

7. Predict how your results will change if you repeat the investigation using two, three, and four books. Test your predictions.

8. For each trial, determine the ideal mechanical advantage and the actual mechanical advantage. Record the calculations in your data table.

Data Table						
Number of Books	Output Force (N)	Length of Incline (cm)	Height of Incline (cm)	Input Force (N)	Ideal Mechanical Advantage	Actual Mechanical Advantage
1						
2						
3						
4						

Troubleshooting the Experiment
- If the spring scale is calibrated in grams, the students can multiply by 0.01 to obtain an approximate reading in newtons.
- The block or cart should be pulled at a slow, constant speed to measure the pulling force. The force needed to get the block or cart moving will be more than this and should not be used.

Analyze and Conclude

1. **Interpreting Data** How did the ideal mechanical advantage and the actual mechanical advantage compare each time you repeated the experiment? Explain your answer.

2. **Making Models** How did the model help you in determining the ramp's usefulness? What kind of limitations does your model have?

3. **Making Models** What happens to the actual mechanical advantage as the inclined plane gets steeper? On the basis of this fact alone, which of the four inclined planes models the best steepness for a wheelchair-access ramp? Explain your answer.

4. **Drawing Conclusions** What other factors, besides mechanical advantage, should you consider when deciding on the steepness of the ramp?

5. **Calculating** Suppose the door of the local public library is 2.0 m above the ground and the distance from the door to the parking lot is 15 m. What is the ideal mechanical advantage of a ramp built from the door to the parking lot?

6. **Communicating** Write a letter to a local business explaining how a ramp could help the employees and customers. Give some examples of work that could be made easier using a ramp. Explain how the steepness of a ramp affects its mechanical advantage.

More to Explore

Find actual ramps that provide access for people with disabilities. Measure the heights and lengths of these ramps and calculate their ideal mechanical advantages. Find out what the requirements are for access ramps in your area. Should your ramp be made of a particular material? Should it level off before it reaches the door? How wide should it be? How does it provide water drainage?

Expected Outcome

The actual mechanical advantage will always be less than the ideal mechanical advantage. The actual advantage decreases with increased height. If both cart and block are used, the actual mechanical advantage for the cart will be much higher than for the block.

Analyze and Conclude

1. The ideal mechanical advantage was always more than the actual mechanical advantage because of friction between the block and the incline.

2. Sample answer: I found that making the ramp longer decreased the input force; however, making the ramp longer caused a greater difference between the ideal mechanical advantage and the actual mechanical advantage. The model had sliding friction, which is greater than the rolling friction between wheelchair wheels and a ramp.

3. The mechanical advantage decreases as the ramp gets steeper. On this basis alone, one would choose the least steep ramp because it has the highest mechanical advantage.

4. Sample answer: If the ramp is too gradual, it may be too long to be feasible. If the ramp is too steep, it will be dangerous.

5. The ideal mechanical advantage is $15/2.0 = 7.5$.

6. Students' letters may be creative and should point out the advantages of ramps in businesses. Possible examples include ease of moving heavy loads into and out of the building and providing access to people in wheelchairs.

Extend Inquiry

More to Explore Students may have difficulty measuring the lengths and heights of the ramps chosen. Explain that only the ratio of length to height determines the ideal mechanical advantage and that the ratio is the same for all or part of the ramp. Therefore, students can work with only part of a ramp if that is more feasible. If students plan to interview people who use access ramps, they should prepare a series of questions in advance. Students should explain what they are doing and why, so that people will be more inclined to respond to their requests for interviews.

M ● 137

Science and Society

Automation in the Workplace—Lost Jobs or New Jobs?

Key Concept
Machines used in industry can replace some jobs, but they can also create jobs.

Build Background Knowledge
Recalling Science Concepts
Ask: **What are some everyday machines that make work easier?** *(Sample answer: Can opener, pizza cutter, bicycle)* **What are some examples of machines used in workplaces?** *(Sample answer: Cranes, forklifts)*

Introduce the Debate
Set the context for the debate by having students read the text and study the figures in the feature. Then begin a discussion by asking students if they know anyone who has had to change jobs as a result of automation in the workplace. Work through an example of automation-induced changes with students. For example, in the automobile industry, robots now do most of the body welding formerly done by individual workers.

Facilitate the Debate
- Explain to students that they will be debating the proposition that "It is the responsibility of the local, state, or federal government to fund retraining for workers displaced by automation."
- Remind students that a debate is not an argument. In a debate, two groups discuss a proposition by presenting reasons that support their position.
- Separate the class into two groups: one to support the proposition, the other to oppose it. Have groups investigate the issue from their respective points of view.

Automation in the Workplace—Lost Jobs or New Jobs?

In the 1800s, the first makers of baseball bats spent long days carving bats by hand. In a modern American factory, bat-making machines can produce a much larger number of bats in a shorter time. Since ancient times, people have invented machines to help with their work. Today, factories can use automated machines to perform jobs that are difficult, dangerous, or even just boring. Like science-fiction robots, these machines can do a whole series of different tasks.

But if a machine does work instead of a person, then someone loses a job. How can society use machines to make work easier and more productive without some people losing their chance to work?

The Issues

What Are the Effects of Automation?
New machines replace some jobs, but they also can create jobs. Suppose an automobile factory starts using machines instead of people to paint cars. At first, some workers may lose their jobs. But the factory may be able to produce more cars. Then it may need to hire more workers—to handle old tasks as well as some new ones. New jobs are created for people who are educated and skilled in operating and taking care of the new machines.

Still, some workers whose skills are no longer needed lose their jobs. Some may find work in different jobs for less money. Others may be unable to find new jobs. Can society provide people who are out of work with the skills they need to start a new career?

Carving a single bat with a lathe can take several hours.

Background

History of Science The number of jobs in many fields of employment has declined due to automation. Students may be unaware that at one time telephone operators were required to place every call. Today most telephone calls are direct dialed, requiring no operator assistance. Another profession affected by automation is banking, where many jobs have been lost due to ATMs. Sewing machine operators are being replaced by machines in many factories. In many offices typists have been replaced by computers with word processing programs. Due to the increased capabilities of desktop publishing, many jobs in the printing industry have been lost.

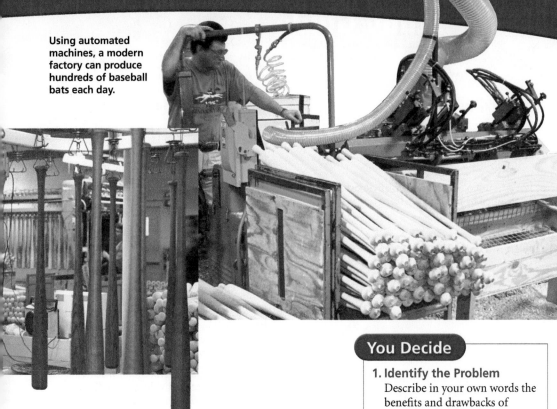

Using automated machines, a modern factory can produce hundreds of baseball bats each day.

What Can People Do?

Education programs can train young people for new jobs and teach older workers new skills. Those who learn how to use computers and other new technologies can take on new tasks. Learning how to sell or design a product can also prepare workers for new careers. Workers who have lost jobs can train for different types of work that cannot be done by machines. For example, a machine cannot replace human skill in day care or medical care.

Who Should Pay?

Teaching young people how to work in new kinds of jobs costs money. So do training programs for adult workers who have lost jobs. How could society pay for these costs? Businesses might share some of the costs. Some businesses give workers full pay until they are retrained or find new work. Also, the government might provide unemployment pay or training for jobless workers. Then all taxpayers would share the costs.

You Decide

1. Identify the Problem
Describe in your own words the benefits and drawbacks of workplace automation.

2. Analyze the Options
List ways society could deal with the effects of automation. For each plan, give the benefits and drawbacks and tell how it would be paid for.

3. Find a Solution
The owner of the pizza shop in your neighborhood has bought an automated pizza-making system. Make a plan for the shop to use the system without having to fire workers.

For: More on automation in the workplace
Visit: PHSchool.com
Web Code: cgh-3040

You Decide

1. Student answers should name at least one benefit and one drawback of workplace automation, phrased in the students' own words.
2. Sample answer: States could offer free retraining for displaced workers. A benefit of this would be that the workers could find new jobs. A drawback of this plan is that the cost might be reflected in higher taxes.
3. Sample answer: Workers could be trained to perform the jobs that the automated pizza-maker cannot perform, for example, customer service or marketing.

For: More on automation in the workplace
Visit: PHSchool.com
Web Code: cgh-3040

Students can research this issue online.

Extend

Have students review newspapers and news magazines to find articles about automation in the workplace. As students find articles have them write a short summary of the article and present their findings to the class. Copies of relevant articles can be posted in the classroom.

The BIG Idea

Have students read the answer to the Essential Question. Encourage them to evaluate and revise their own answers as needed.

Help Students Read

Building Vocabulary

Words in Context Remind students to use context clues to help determine the meaning of unfamiliar words and phrases. Have the students look for familiar words and phrases that surround the unfamiliar term. For example, in sentences describing the mechanical advantage of a machine, students will often find the terms input force and output force. Students can use this information to infer that mechanical advantage is a term related to the input and output forces of a machine.

Compare/Contrast Table Have students make a table comparing and contrasting groups of terms from the chapter. Students should look for similarities and differences among the words before they develop their tables. For example the terms, *pulley*, *lever*, and *screw* are similar in that they refer to a type of simple machine. These machines differ in how they make work easier. (A pulley changes direction of a force, a lever changes the force, and a screw changes the distance over which a force acts.)

Connecting Concepts

Concept Maps Help students develop a concept map to show how the information in this chapter is related. Work is done on an object when a force results in movement in the same direction. Machines are used to make work easier by changing force, distance, or direction. Have students brainstorm to identify the key concepts, key terms, details, and examples, then write each one on a self-sticking note and attach it at random on chart paper or on the board.

Tell students that this concept map will be organized in hierarchical order and to begin at the top with the key concepts. Ask students these questions to guide them to

---

The BIG Idea **Work and Energy** Simple machines make work easier by changing the amount of force needed, the distance over which a force is exerted, or the direction in which a force is exerted.

1 What Is Work?

Key Concepts

- Work is done on an object when the object moves in the same direction in which the force is exerted.
- The amount of work done on an object can be determined by multiplying force times distance.

$$\text{Work} = \text{Force} \times \text{Distance}$$

- Power equals the amount of work done on an object in a unit of time.

$$\text{Power} = \frac{\text{Work}}{\text{Time}}$$

Key Terms

work   joule   power

2 How Machines Do Work

Key Concepts

- A machine makes work easier by changing at least one of three factors. A machine may change the amount of force you exert, the distance over which you exert your force, or the direction in which you exert your force.
- A machine's mechanical advantage is the number of times a machine increases a force exerted on it.

$$\text{Mechanical advantage} = \frac{\text{Output force}}{\text{Input force}}$$

- To calculate the efficiency of a machine, divide the output work by the input work and multiply the result by 100 percent.

$$\text{Efficiency} = \frac{\text{Output work}}{\text{Input work}} \times 100\%$$

Key Terms

machine	output work
input force	mechanical advantage
output force	efficiency
input work	

3 Simple Machines

Key Concepts

- There are six basic kinds of simple machines: the inclined plane, the wedge, the screw, the lever, the wheel and axle, and the pulley.
- You can determine the ideal mechanical advantage of an inclined plane by dividing the length of the incline by its height.
- The ideal mechanical advantage of a wedge is determined by dividing its length by its width.
- The ideal mechanical advantage of a screw is the length around the threads divided by the length of the screw.
- The ideal mechanical advantage of a lever is determined by dividing the distance from the fulcrum to the input force by the distance from the fulcrum to the output force.
- You can find the ideal mechanical advantage of a wheel and axle by dividing the radius of the wheel by the radius of the axle.
- The ideal mechanical advantage of a pulley is equal to the number of sections of rope that support the object.
- Most of the machines in your body are levers that consist of bones and muscles.
- The ideal mechanical advantage of a compound machine is the product of the individual ideal mechanical advantages of the simple machines that make it up.

Key Terms
- inclined plane • wedge • screw • lever
- fulcrum • wheel and axle • pulley
- compound machine

---

categorize the information on the self-sticking notes: **What are some examples of work being done on objects? How do machines make work easier? What are some examples and uses of simple machines?**

Prompt students by using connecting words or phrases, such as "are used to" or "results in," to indicate the basis for the organization of the map. The phrases should form a sentence between or among a set of concepts.

Answer
Accept logical presentations by students.

All in One Teaching Resources
- Key Terms Review: *Work and Machines*
- Connecting Concepts: *Work and Machines*

Review and Assessment

Organizing Information

Comparing and Contrasting Copy the compare/contrast table about simple machines onto a separate sheet of paper. Then complete it for each type of simple machine and add a title. (For more on Comparing and Contrasting, see the Skills Handbook.)

Simple Machine	Ideal Mechanical Advantage	Example
Inclined plane	Length of incline ÷ Height of incline	Ramp
a. ___?___	b. ___?___	c. ___?___

Reviewing Key Terms

Choose the letter of the best answer.

1. The amount of work done on an object is obtained by multiplying
   a. input force and output force.
   b. force and distance.
   c. time and force.
   d. efficiency and work.

2. The rate at which work is done is called
   a. output force.
   b. efficiency.
   c. power.
   d. mechanical advantage.

3. One way a machine can make work easier for you is by
   a. decreasing the amount of work you do.
   b. changing the direction of your force.
   c. increasing the amount of work required for a task.
   d. decreasing the friction you encounter.

4. The output force is greater than the input force for a
   a. pizza cutter.
   b. hockey stick.
   c. single fixed pulley.
   d. screw.

5. An example of a second-class lever is a
   a. seesaw.
   b. shovel.
   c. paddle.
   d. wheelbarrow.

If the statement is true, write *true*. If it is false, change the underlined word or words to make the statement true.

6. The SI unit of work is the <u>newton</u>.

7. The work you do on a machine is called the <u>input work</u>.

8. The ratio of output work to input work is <u>mechanical advantage</u>.

9. An <u>inclined plane</u> is a flat, sloped surface.

10. A <u>pulley</u> can be thought of as an inclined plane wrapped around a cylinder.

Writing in Science

Proposed Solution A community of people in Pennsylvania known as the Old Order Amish can build a wooden barn in a single day—without using electricity. Suppose you were faced with this task. Propose how you would use simple machines to help with the construction.

Work and Machines
Video Preview
Video Field Trip
▶ Video Assessment

All in One Teaching Resources
- Transparency M45
- Chapter Test
- Performance Assessment Teacher Notes
- Performance Assessment Student Worksheet
- Performance Assessment Scoring Rubric

ExamView® Computer Test Bank CD-ROM

Review and Assessment

Organizing Information
Sample answer:
Title: Simple Machines
a. Wheel and axle
b. Radius of wheel ÷ Radius of axle
c. Screwdriver
Wedge: length of wedge ÷ width of wedge; ax
Screw: length around threads ÷ length of screw; screw
Lever: distance from fulcrum to input force ÷ distance from fulcrum to output force; seesaw
Pulley: number of sections of supporting rope; flag pole

Reviewing Key Terms

1. b **2.** c **3.** b **4.** d **5.** d
6. joule
7. true
8. efficiency
9. true
10. screw

DISCOVERY CHANNEL SCHOOL
Video Assessment

Work and Machines

Show the Video Assessment to review chapter content and as a prompt for the writing assignment. Discussion question: **Why did the inclined plane make the work easier for people trying to get the marble down the mountain?** *(The inclined plane made a uniform slope along the jagged mountain side to make the descent of the marble as smooth as possible.)*

Writing in Science

Writing Mode Exposition/How-To
Scoring Rubric
4 Exceeds criteria; gives a detailed and feasible proposal for constructing a barn without using electricity
3 Meets criteria
2 Proposal does not give enough details about the use of simple machines and/or includes some errors
1 Proposal is poorly thought out and/or does not mention the use of simple machines

M ● 141

Checking Concepts

11. No, because he does not move the sky, he only holds it. There is no work without motion.

12. 15 N (input force × actual mechanical advantage)

13. The longer wedge has a greater mechanical advantage (3 as opposed to 2) because ideal mechanical advantage = length of wedge ÷ width of wedge.

14. Decreasing the radius of the axle increases its mechanical advantage because the mechanical advantage of a wheel and axle is determined by dividing the radius of the wheel by the radius of the axle.

15. Sample answer: The lower leg is a lever, with the knee as the fulcrum, the thigh muscle supplying the input force, and the output force lifting the lower leg.

Thinking Critically

16. As friction increases, efficiency decreases.

17. A pulley or a wheel and axle

18. A door is a lever. The hinge is a fulcrum. The distance between the fulcrum and the output force remains the same. So if you decrease the distance between the input force and the fulcrum (by pushing in the center of the door rather than the edge), you decrease the mechanical advantage.

19. Ramp Y has an ideal mechanical advantage of 8 and Ramp Z has an ideal mechanical advantage of 3. Ramp Y has the greater ideal mechanical advantage.

Math Practice

20. 1,500 W

21. 4,400 J

Applying Skills

22. 3

23. 1, 2, 4

24. Students' graphs should show an increase in mechanical advantage as the distance from the input force to the fulcrum increases.

25. The greater the distance between the fulcrum and the input force, the greater the lever's ideal mechanical advantage.

Review and Assessment

Checking Concepts

11. The mythical god Atlas was believed to hold the weight of the sky on his shoulders. Was Atlas performing any work? Explain.

12. The mechanical advantage of a machine is 3. If you exert an input force of 5 N, what output force is exerted by the machine?

13. Which has a greater mechanical advantage, a wedge that is 6 cm long and 3 cm wide, or a wedge that is 12 cm long and 4 cm wide? Explain your answer.

14. Why will decreasing the radius of the axle improve the mechanical advantage of a wheel and axle?

15. Describe a lever in your body. Locate the input force, output force, and fulcrum.

Thinking Critically

16. Relating Cause and Effect Describe the relationship between friction and the efficiency of a machine.

17. Classifying What type of simple machine would be used to lower an empty bucket into a well and then lift the bucket full of water?

18. Applying Concepts To open a door, you push on the part of the door that is farthest from the hinges. Why would it be harder to open the door if you pushed on the center of it?

19. Interpreting Diagrams Which ramp has the greater ideal mechanical advantage?

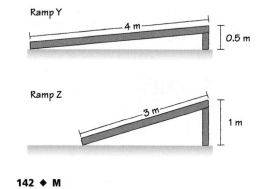

142 ◆ M

Math Practice

20. Calculating Power A bulldozer does 72,000 J of work in 48 seconds. How much power does the bulldozer use?

21. Calculating Efficiency A machine with 75% efficiency does 3,300 J of work. Using the machine, how much work did you do?

Applying Skills

Use the illustration to answer Questions 22–25.

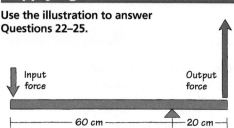

22. Calculating Use the input and output distances to calculate the ideal mechanical advantage of the lever.

23. Predicting What would the ideal mechanical advantage be if the distance from the fulcrum to the input force were 20 cm? 40 cm? 80 cm?

24. Graphing Use your answers to Questions 22 and 23 to graph the distance from the fulcrum to the input force on the *x*-axis and the ideal mechanical advantage on the *y*-axis.

25. Interpreting Data What does your graph show you about the relationship between the ideal mechanical advantage of a first-class lever and the distance between the fulcrum and the input force?

Lab zone Chapter **Project**

Performance Assessment Finalize your design and build your machine. Consider how you can improve the machine's efficiency. Check all measurements and calculations. Does it lift the soup can at least 5 cm? Is it made of two or more simple machines? When you show your machine to the class, explain why you built it as you did.

Lab zone Chapter **Project**   L3

Performance Assessment

Review the rules with students the day before presentations to prevent students from missing their goals because they overlooked a restriction of the project. For example, students may be so focused on mechanical advantage that they may not remember that their machines must lift the load at least 5 centimeters.

Consider any project successful if the student building the complex machine reached any level of success. A cooperative classroom climate makes this project a positive experience for more students than does a competitive climate. You can set an example by stressing each student's success rather than comparing students' results.

Standardized Test Prep

Choose the letter of the best answer.

1. What simple machine is used in *all* of the following jobs: moving a flag to the top of a flagpole, lifting equipment with a construction crane, and using a block and tackle to move a crate?
  A lever
  B pulley
  C wedge
  D wheel and axle

2. The table below shows the input work and output work for four different pulleys. Which pulley has the highest efficiency?

Work of Different Pulleys		
Pulley	**Input Work**	**Output Work**
Fixed pulley A	20,000 J	8,000 J
Fixed pulley B	20,000 J	10,000 J
Movable pulley	20,000 J	12,000 J
Block and tackle	20,000 J	16,000 J

  F Fixed pulley A   **H** Movable pulley
  G Fixed pulley B   **J** Block and tackle

3. Which is the *best* definition of a machine?
  A A machine is a time-saving device that uses motors and gears.
  B A machine changes the amount of input force.
  C A machine makes work easier by changing force, distance, or direction.
  D A machine can be either simple or compound.

4. Which of the following will increase the ideal mechanical advantage of a wheel and axle?
  F increasing the wheel's radius
  G decreasing the wheel's radius
  H increasing the axle's radius
  J increasing the wheel's radius and the axle's radius equally

5. Which activity describes work being done on an object?
  A walking a dog on a leash
  B lifting a bag of groceries
  C holding up an umbrella
  D pressing a stamp onto an envelope

Constructed Response

6. Explain why an engineer would design a road to wind around a mountain rather than go straight up the side. Show how this design would be better.

Standardized Test Practice

1. B   **2.** J   **3.** C   **4.** F   **5.** B

6. Sample response: A mountain road is an inclined plane. A road that winds around a mountain is much longer and is at less of an incline than a road that goes straight up the side. An engineer would design a road to wind around the mountain because by increasing the length of the road (or incline), the input force needed to reach the top of the mountain is reduced and the mechanical advantage is increased. For example, suppose a mountain is 1,000 m high. A road that goes straight up the side might be 4,000 m long. 4,000 m divided by 1,000 m gives a mechanical advantage of 4. A winding road on the same mountain might be 8,000 m long, which gives a mechanical advantage of 8. You would have to travel for a longer distance, but the journey would be much easier.

Chapter at a Glance

 PRENTICE HALL
TeacherEXPRESS™
Plan · Teach · Assess

 Chapter Project *Design and Build a Roller Coaster*

Technology

Local Standards

All in One Teaching Resources
- Chapter Project Teacher Notes, pp. 294–295
- Chapter Project Student Overview, pp. 296–297
- Chapter Project Student Worksheets, pp. 298–299
- Chapter Project Scoring Rubric, p. 300

Discovery SCHOOL
Video Preview

Section 1

What Is Energy?
1–2 periods
1/2–1 block
M.5.1.1 Describe how energy, work, and power are related.
M.5.1.2 Name and describe the two basic kinds of energy.

Go Online
SCiLINKS™ NSTA

Section 2

Forms of Energy
2–3 periods
1–1 1/2 blocks
M.5.2.1 Explain how an object's mechanical energy is determined.
M.5.2.2 Name some forms of energy associated with the particles that make up objects.

Go Online
SCiLINKS™ NSTA

Section 3

Energy Transformations and Conservation
3–4 periods
1 1/2–2 blocks
M.5.3.1 Describe how different forms of energy are related.
M.5.3.2 Name common energy transformations.
M.5.3.3 State the law of conservation of energy.

Go Online
active art

Discovery SCHOOL
Video Field Trip

Section 4

Energy and Fossil Fuels
1–2 periods
1/2–1 block
M.5.4.1 Identify the source of the energy stored in fossil fuels.
M.5.4.2 Describe how energy is transformed when fossil fuels are used.

Go Online
SCiLINKS™ NSTA

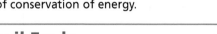 **Review and Assessment**

Test Preparation

All in One Teaching Resources
- Key Terms Review, p. 333
- Transparency M51
- Performance Assessment Teacher Notes, p. 341
- Performance Assessment Scoring Rubric, p. 342
- Performance Assessment Student Worksheet, p. 343
- Chapter Test, pp. 344–347

Discovery SCHOOL
Video Assessment

Go Online
PHSchool.com

Test Preparation Blackline Masters

Chapter Activities Planner

Student Edition	Inquiry	Time	Materials	Skills	Resources
Chapter Project, p. 145	Open-Ended	Ongoing (2 weeks)	**All In One Teaching Resources** p. 294	Making models, controlling variables	**Lab zone Easy Planner** **All In One Teaching Resources** pp. 294–295
Section 1					
Discover Activity, p. 146	Directed	10 minutes	Meter stick, tennis ball	Observing	**Lab zone Easy Planner**
Section 2					
Discover Activity, p.151	Directed	10 minutes	Flashlight, batteries	Inferring	**Lab zone Easy Planner**
Skills Lab, pp. 156–157	Guided	Prep: 20 minutes; Class: 40 minutes	Calculator; meter stick; stopwatch or clock with a second hand; board, about 2.5 cm × 30 cm × 120 cm; 8–10 books, each about 2 cm thick	Calculating, interpreting data	**Lab zone Easy Planner** **Lab Activity Video** **All In One Teaching Resources** Skills Lab: *Can You Feel the Power?*, pp. 313–315
Section 3					
Discover Activity, p. 158	Directed	10 minutes	3 × 5 index card, scissors, rubber band, safety goggles	Drawing conclusions	**Lab zone Easy Planner**
Skills Activity, p. 159	Guided	10 minutes		Classifying	**Lab zone Easy Planner**
Try This Activity, p. 162	Guided	15 minutes	Washers or rubber stoppers, string, ring stand, 2 clamps, meter stick	Observing	**Lab zone Easy Planner**
At-Home Activity, p.163	Directed	Home		Inferring	**Lab zone Easy Planner**
Skills Lab, pp.164–165	Guided	Prep: 15 minutes; Class: 40 minutes	Scissors, rubber band, 3 plastic straws, meter stick, marker, metric ruler, balance, masking tape, empty toilet paper tube	Controlling variables, graphing	**Lab zone Easy Planner** **Lab Activity Video** **All In One Teaching Resources** Skills Lab: *Soaring Straws*, pp. 323–326
Section 4					
Discover Activity, p. 166	Directed	20 minutes	Flask, ring stand, clamp, thermometer, water, wooden coffee stirrer, small aluminum pan, matches, safety goggles	Forming operational definitions	**Lab zone Easy Planner**
Skills Activity, p. 168	Directed	15 minutes	Graph paper, compass, protractor	Graphing	**Lab zone Easy Planner**
At-Home Activity, p. 169	Guided	Home		Classifying	**Lab zone Easy Planner**

Section 1 What Is Energy?

 1–2 periods, 1/2–1 block

ABILITY LEVELS
L1 Basic to Average
L2 For All Students
L3 Average to Advanced

Objectives

M.5.1.1 Describe how energy, work, and power are related.
M.5.1.2 Name and describe the two basic kinds of energy.

Key Terms

• energy • kinetic energy • potential energy • gravitational potential energy
• elastic potential energy

Local Standards

Preteach

Build Background Knowledge

Help students relate the everyday usage of the word *energy* with its scientific usage.

 **Discover Activity** *How High Does a Ball Bounce?* **L2**

Targeted Print and Technology Resources

All in One Teaching Resources

Reading Strategy Transparency
M46: Using Prior Knowledge

 PresentationExpress™ CD-ROM

Instruct

Energy, Work, and Power Students create a concept map relating the terms *work, energy,* and *power.*

Kinetic Energy Ask leading questions to help students understand that an object's kinetic energy is related to its mass and velocity.

Potential Energy Students use a Venn diagram to relate gravitational and elastic potential energy.

Targeted Print and Technology Resources

All in One Teaching Resources

L2 Guided Reading, pp. 303–304
L2 Transparency M47

www.SciLinks.org Web Code: scn-1351

⊙ **Student Edition on Audio CD**

Assess

Section Assessment Questions

Have students use their completed graphic organizers to answer the questions.

Reteach

Students write statements comparing and contrasting potential and kinetic energy.

Targeted Print and Technology Resources

All in One Teaching Resources

• Section Summary, p. 302
L1 Review and Reinforce, p. 305
L3 Enrich, p. 306

Section 2 Forms of Energy

 2–3 periods, 1–1 1/2 blocks

Objectives

M.5.2.1 Explain how an object's mechanical energy is determined.

M.5.2.2 Name some forms of energy associated with the particles that make up objects.

Local Standards

Key Terms

• mechanical energy • thermal energy • electrical energy • chemical energy
• nuclear energy • electromagnetic energy

Preteach

Build Background Knowledge

Students list everyday examples of various forms of energy.

 **Discover Activity** *What Makes a Flashlight Shine?* L1

Targeted Print and Technology Resources

 Teaching Resources

L2 Reading Strategy: Building Vocabulary

 PresentationExpress™ CD-ROM

Instruct

Mechanical Energy Students practice calculating mechanical energy by adding potential energy and kinetic energy.

Other Forms of Energy Have students describe and compare various forms of energy.

 **Skills Lab** *Can You Feel the Power?* L2

Targeted Print and Technology Resources

 Teaching Resources

L2 Guided Reading, pp. 309–310
L2 Skills Lab: *Can You Feel the Power?*, pp. 313–315

Lab Activity Video/DVD
Skills Lab: *Can You Feel the Power?*

www.SciLinks.org Web Code: scn-1352

 Student Edition on Audio CD

Assess

Section Assessment Questions

 Students use their definitions to help them answer questions.

Reteach

Students work in pairs to review the key terms from the section.

Targeted Print and Technology Resources

 **Teaching Resources**

• Section Summary, p. 308
L1 Review and Reinforce, p. 311
L3 Enrich, p. 312

Section 3 Energy Transformations and Conservation

ABILITY LEVELS
L1 Basic to Average
L2 For All Students
L3 Average to Advanced

 3–4 periods, 1 1/2–2 blocks

Objectives

M.5.3.1 Describe how different forms of energy are related.
M.5.3.2 Name common energy transformations.
M.5.3.3 State the law of conservation of energy.

Local Standards

Key Terms

• energy transformation • law of conservation of energy • matter

---

Preteach

Build Background Knowledge

Use everyday examples to introduce the idea of energy transformations.

 **Discover Activity** *What Would Make a Card Jump?* L2

Targeted Print and Technology Resources

All in One Teaching Resources

L2 Reading Strategy Transparency M48: Asking Questions

◉ **PresentationExpress™ CD-ROM**

Instruct

Energy Transformations Relate the concept of energy transformations to chemical energy in food being used by the body.

Transformations Between Potential and Kinetic Energy Use the figures to help students understand the transformation between potential and kinetic energy.

Conservation of Energy Relate that in most energy transformations, energy is conserved. However, in situations where mass is transformed into energy, matter and energy together are conserved.

 **Skills Lab** *Soaring Straws* L2

Targeted Print and Technology Resources

All in One Teaching Resources

L2 Guided Reading, pp. 318–320
L2 Transparency M49
L2 Skills Lab: *Soaring Straws*, pp. 323–326

📼 **Lab Activity Video/DVD**
Skills Lab: *Soaring Straws*

PHSchool.com Web Code: cgp-3053

Discovery CHANNEL SCHOOL
Video Field Trip

◉ **Student Edition on Audio CD**

Assess

Section Assessment Questions

↻ Have students use their completed questions and answers to answer the questions.

Reteach

Students work in pairs to review the reading checkpoint questions and caption questions in the section.

Targeted Print and Technology Resources

All in One Teaching Resources

• Section Summary, p. 317
L1 Review and Reinforce, p. 321
L3 Enrich, p. 322

Section 4 Energy and Fossil Fuels

 *1–2 periods, 1/2–1 block*

ABILITY LEVELS
L1 Basic to Average
L2 For All Students
L3 Average to Advanced

Objectives

Local Standards

M.5.4.1 Identify the source of the energy stored in fossil fuels.

M.5.4.2 Describe how energy is transformed when fossil fuels are used.

Key Terms

• fossil fuel • combustion

Preteach

Build Background Knowledge

Use a piece of coal to introduce fossil fuels.

 Discover Activity *What Is a Fuel?* L1

Targeted Print and Technology Resources

 Teaching Resources

L2 Reading Strategy Transparency
M50: Previewing Visuals

○ **PresentationExpress™ CD-ROM**

Instruct

Formation of Fossil Fuels Have students sequence the steps in the formation of fossil fuels.

Use of Fossil Fuels Ask leading questions to help students understand that energy transformations are required for the use of fossil fuels.

Targeted Print and Technology Resources

 Teaching Resources

L2 Guided Reading, pp. 329–330

www.SciLinks.org Web Code: scn-1354

○ **Student Edition on Audio CD**

Assess

Section Assessment Questions

 Have students use their questions and answers about Figure 18 to help them answer Question 2.

Reteach

Students use Figure 18 to review the energy transformations involved in the use of fossil fuels.

Targeted Print and Technology Resources

 Teaching Resources

• Section Summary, p. 328
L1 Review and Reinforce, p. 331
L3 Enrich, p. 332

Chapter 5 Content Refresher

Go Online

NSTA–PD LINKS

For: Professional development support
Visit: www.SciLinks.org/PDLinks
Web Code: scf-1350

Professional Development

Section 1 What Is Energy?

Kinetic Energy   Kinetic energy is the energy that an object has due to its motion. The translational kinetic energy (kinetic energy due to motion in one direction) of an object is defined as follows:

$$\text{Kinetic energy} = \tfrac{1}{2}mv^2$$

In this equation, m is mass, and v is velocity. Because the velocity is squared, kinetic energy is always positive. There are also other types of kinetic energy, such as vibrational kinetic energy.

Potential Energy   Potential energy is the energy due to the relative position of objects in a system or due to the shape of an object (e.g., an object that is stretched or compressed).

Elastic Potential Energy   The amount of elastic potential energy stored in an object is directly related to the amount the object is stretched or compressed. This is a familiar relationship; for example, the more a bow is bent, the farther the arrow flies. Springs are an example of objects that can store elastic potential energy. The elastic potential energy of a spring can be calculated using the following equation:

$$\text{Elastic potential energy} = \tfrac{1}{2}kx^2$$

In this equation, k is a constant—the spring constant, which depends on the stiffness of the spring. The amount the spring is stretched is represented by x in the equation. So, the elastic potential energy of a spring is related to both the stiffness of the spring and the distance it is stretched.

Elastic Potential Energy

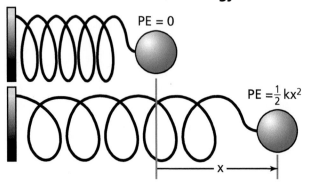

Gravitational Potential Energy

Gravitational Potential Energy   Gravitational potential energy is the energy an object has due to its position in a gravitational field. Near Earth's surface, gravitational potential energy can be calculated with the following formula:

$$\text{Gravitational potential energy} = mgh$$

In this equation, m is mass, g is the acceleration due to gravity, and h is the height relative to an arbitrary zero point. Since an object's weight is the product of its mass and the acceleration due to gravity, the equation above can be simplified to the form used in the text:

$$\text{Gravitational potential energy} = \text{Weight} \times \text{Height}$$

Section 2 Forms of Energy

Nuclear Energy   Nuclear energy, the energy stored in the nuclei of atoms, is a form of potential energy. The nucleus of an atom contains protons (each with a positive charge) and neutrons (each with no charge). Because like charges repel one another, one might ask how the protons, all with a positive charge, can remain packed together in the nucleus of the atom. A force called the *strong nuclear force* overcomes the repulsion between the protons and holds the nucleus together.

Nuclear fission is one way that nuclear energy can be released. Fission, or splitting, of the nucleus requires that the strong nuclear force holding the nucleus together is overcome. To initiate the process, a heavy nucleus (one that contains a large number of protons and neutrons) is struck by a neutron. The mass and energy of the additional neutron allows fission to occur, resulting in two or more smaller nuclei and a small number of individual neutrons.

Nuclear Fission

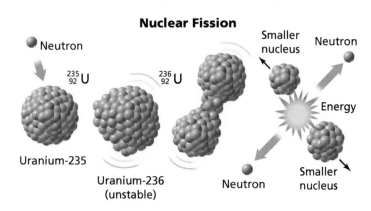

The mass of the resulting smaller particles does not add up to the mass of the original nucleus. The mass that is "missing" was converted to energy. The amount of energy produced can be calculated using the equation

$$E = mc^2$$

where E is energy, m is mass, and c is the speed of light.

Section 3 Energy Transformations and Conservation

Photosynthesis and Respiration The flow of energy through the living things in an ecosystem requires energy transformations. Photosynthesis is the process in which plants and certain other organisms transform electromagnetic energy from the sun into chemical energy, which is stored in the bonds of sugars and starches. Animals that eat the plants transform the stored chemical energy into heat and mechanical energy through the process of respiration.

Food chains show how energy is passed from one living thing to the next. A pyramid of energy shows how much energy is available at each level of an ecosystem. Plants form the base of the energy pyramid. About 10% of the energy transformed by plants is passed to the next level—animals that eat the plants. When these animals are eaten by other animals, only 10% of the energy is available to that next level.

Energy transformations in living things and the flow of energy in ecosystems follow the first and second laws of thermodynamics. The first law states that energy cannot be created or destroyed, but can be transformed. Although only 10% of the energy at any level of an ecosystem is passed to the next level, the other 90% is not lost or destroyed; it is used for body processes or given off as body heat.

The second law of thermodynamics states that energy transformations lead to increased entropy, or disorder. It might seem that a process such as photosynthesis, which builds more complex molecules, defies the second law of thermodynamics. However, the second law applies to closed systems, and living things, which are constantly interacting with the environment, are open systems. Building more complex molecules in photosynthesis is only a local decrease in entropy. These molecules are eventually broken down, and entropy increases.

 **Address Misconceptions**

Students might confuse the meanings of the phrases conservation of energy *and* conserving energy resources. *For a strategy for overcoming this misconception, see* **Address Misconceptions** *in the section* Energy Transformations and Conservation.

Section 4 Energy and Fossil Fuels

Environmental Consequences of Fossil Fuel Use Fossil fuels store the sun's energy in chemical bonds. In the process of combustion, the chemical energy in fossil fuels is transformed to thermal energy.

Although fossil fuels have many advantages as energy sources, the use of fossil fuels also has some negative consequences for the environment. Two of the main environmental problems associated with the use of fossil fuels are global warming and acid rain.

Global warming is due in part to the carbon dioxide given off when fossil fuels are burned. Carbon dioxide is one type of greenhouse gas. Greenhouse gases are gases that keep Earth warm by retaining solar energy. Without greenhouse gases, life on Earth would not exist. Problems arise when the amounts of greenhouse gases increase, causing more solar energy to be retained. Most scientists think that this process is causing average global temperatures to rise.

Acid rain is caused when the byproducts of fossil fuel combustion combine with oxygen and mix with precipitation. Acid rain causes damage to buildings and crops. Acid rain can also reduce the pH of bodies of water, harming the organisms that live in the water and altering or destroy aquatic ecosystems.

Help Students Read

Sequencing
Ordering the Steps of a Process

Strategy Guide students in visualizing the order in which events occur by using the strategy of sequencing. Cycle diagrams and flowcharts can be used to help students understand the steps in a process. Before introducing the strategy, locate an appropriate section of the text, such as the section *Energy Transformations and Conservation.*

Example
1. Have students read the passage, paying particular attention to the order in which events occur.
2. Students should determine whether a flowchart or a cycle diagram is best suited to sequence the events.
3. Have the students use the appropriate graphic organizer to order the steps of the process.
4. Have students apply the strategy of sequencing to other sections of the text, and share their completed graphic organizers with the class.

See the section *Energy Transformations and Conservation* for a script for using the Sequencing strategy with students.

The BIG Idea

The Big Idea is the major scientific concept of the chapter. It is followed by the Essential Question. Read aloud the question to students. As students study the chapter, tell them to think about the Essential Question. Explain that they will discover the answer to the question as they read. The chapter Study Guide provides a sample answer.

Objectives

This Chapter Project will give students a chance to design, build, and modify a model roller coaster to gain hands-on experience with conversion of potential energy into kinetic energy. After completing this Chapter Project, students will be able to

- create working models of roller coasters following specifications
- control variables as they experiment with different hill heights, turns, and loops
- evaluate their models in terms of kinetic energy, potential energy, and the law of conservation of energy
- communicate how their models illustrate energy transformations and conservation of energy

Skills Focus

Making models, controlling variables

Project Time Line   2 weeks

All in One   Teaching Resources

- Chapter Project Teacher Notes
- Chapter Project Overview
- Chapter Project Worksheet 1
- Chapter Project Worksheet 2
- Chapter Project Scoring Rubric

The BIG Idea
Energy Forms and Conservation

Q   **What is energy and how can it be transformed?**

Chapter Preview

❶ What Is Energy?
Discover How High Does a Ball Bounce?
Math Skills Exponents

❷ Forms of Energy
Discover What Makes a Flashlight Shine?
Analyzing Data Calculating Mechanical Energy
Skills Lab Can You Feel the Power?

❸ Energy Transformations and Conservation
Discover What Would Make a Card Jump?
Skills Activity Classifying
Active Art Energy Transformations
Try This Pendulum Swing
At-Home Activity Hot Wire
Skills Lab Soaring Straws

❹ Energy and Fossil Fuels
Discover What Is a Fuel?
Skills Activity Graphing
At-Home Activity Burning Fossils

▶ Cars powered by the sun's energy race in Suzuka, Japan.

Developing a Plan

During the first week, have students experiment with different materials to determine how they will construct their tracks and vehicles. During the second week, students should modify their tracks by changing hill heights and including turns and loops. When students present their roller coaster to the class, they should use key terms, such as *kinetic energy*, *potential energy*, and *law of conservation of energy*.

Possible Materials

Possible materials for tracks include cardboard, poster board, garden hoses, rubber tubing, foam pipe insulation, and drinking straws. Possible materials for vehicles include marbles, ball bearings, rubber balls, and toy cars. Students may also need string, tape, glue, paper clips, bricks, shoe boxes, blocks of wood, stopwatches, cups, and buckets.

Energy
▶ Video Preview
Video Field Trip
Video Assessment

Discovery CHANNEL SCHOOL
Video Preview

Energy

Show the Video Preview to introduce the chapter and provide an overview of chapter content. Discussion question: **How is gravitational potential energy transformed into electrical energy in a hydroelectric generator?** *(Sample answer: As water goes over the falls, its gravitational potential energy is transformed to kinetic energy, which turns turbines and is transformed to mechanical energy. The turbines in the generator transform mechanical energy to electrical energy.)*

Lab zone™ Chapter Project

Design and Build a Roller Coaster

In this chapter, you will learn about energy, the forms it takes, and how it is transformed and conserved. You will use what you learn to design and construct your own roller coaster.

Your Goal To design and construct a roller coaster that uses kinetic and potential energy to move

Your roller coaster must

- be no wider than 2 meters and be easily disassembled and reassembled
- have a first hill with a height of 1 meter and have at least two additional hills
- have an object that moves along the entire track without stopping
- follow the safety guidelines in Appendix A

Plan It! Brainstorm the characteristics of a fun roller coaster. Consider how fast a roller coaster moves and how its speed changes throughout the ride. Then choose materials for your roller coaster and sketch a design. When your teacher has approved your design, build your roller coaster. Experiment with different hill heights and inclines. Add turns and loops to determine their effect.

Chapter 5 **M ◆ 145**

Performance Assessment

The Chapter Project Scoring Rubric will help you evaluate how well students complete the Chapter Project. You may want to share the scoring rubric with your students so they will know what is expected. Students will be assessed on whether

- their roller coaster is no wider than 2 meters and has three hills, the first of which is 1 meter high
- their vehicle successfully completes the entire track without stopping
- their roller coaster is modified based on experimental results and application of concepts involving energy conversions
- their descriptions of their roller coaster apply concepts such as *kinetic energy, potential energy,* and *the law of conservation of energy*
- their presentation and written analysis are thorough and well-organized

Students can keep the designs and descriptions of their roller coasters in their portfolios.

Portfolio

Launching the Project

To introduce the project, begin with a class discussion about roller coasters. Ask: **Have you ever ridden a roller coaster?** Some students will say yes. Have them describe their experiences as the roller coaster rushed down a hill, climbed up a hill, and went around corners. Ask: **What features of a roller coaster would you include if you were going to build one?** *(Sample answer: Lots of hills)* Allow students time to read the project

description in the text. Encourage students to discuss potential energy and kinetic energy as they relate to a roller coaster.

Objectives

After this lesson, students will be able to

M.5.1.1 Describe how energy, work, and power are related.

M.5.1.2 Name and describe the two basic kinds of energy.

Target Reading Skill 🔄

Using Prior Knowledge Explain that using prior knowledge helps students connect what they already know to what they are about to read.

Answers

Sample graphic organizer:

What You Know

1. The joule is the unit of work.

2. Energy has different forms.

What You Learned

1. Power is the rate at which energy is transferred.

2. The two basic kinds of energy are potential energy and kinetic energy.

All in One Teaching Resources

• Transparency M46

Preteach

Build Background Knowledge   L2

Describing Energy

Ask: **What does it mean when you say someone has "a lot of energy"?** *(Sample answer: A person with lots of energy is active and gets things done.)* Help students connect this everyday usage of the word *energy* with the scientific definition of the word *energy* (the ability to do work or cause change).

Reading Preview

Key Concepts

• How are energy, work, and power related?

• What are the two basic kinds of energy?

Key Terms

• energy • kinetic energy
• potential energy
• gravitational potential energy
• elastic potential energy

🔄 Target Reading Skill

Using Prior Knowledge Before you read, look at the section headings and visuals to see what this section is about. Then write what you know about energy in a graphic organizer like the one below. As you read, write what you learn.

What You Know
1. The joule is the unit of work.
2.

What You Learned
1.
2.

Lab zone Discover **Activity**

How High Does a Ball Bounce?

1. Hold a meter stick vertically, with the zero end on the ground.

2. Drop a tennis ball from the 50-cm mark and record the height to which it bounces.

3. Drop the tennis ball from the 100-cm mark and record the height to which it bounces.

4. Predict how high the ball will bounce if dropped from the 75-cm mark. Test your prediction.

Think It Over

Observing How does the height from which you drop the ball relate to the height to which the ball bounces?

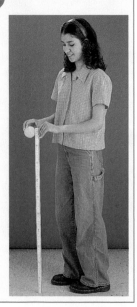

Brilliant streaks of lightning flash across the night sky. The wind howls, and thunder cracks and rumbles. Then a sound like a runaway locomotive approaches, growing louder each second. Whirling winds rush through the town. Roofs are lifted off of buildings. Cars are thrown about like toys. Then, in minutes, the tornado is gone.

The next morning, a light breeze carries leaves past the debris. The wind that destroyed buildings hours before is now barely strong enough to move a leaf. Wind is just moving air, but it has energy.

When a breeze does work lifting leaves, it transfers energy to them. ▶

Lab zone Discover **Activity**

Skills Focus Observing   L2

Materials meter stick, tennis ball

Time 10 minutes

Tips Students should work in pairs or small groups. Suggest that students perform several trials at each position and find the average height. Encourage students to use the same method of observation in every trial.

Expected Outcome The ball bounces the highest when it is dropped from the greatest height.

Think It Over The greater the height from which the ball is dropped, the higher the ball bounces.

Energy, Work, and Power

When wind moves a house, or even a leaf, it causes a change. In this case, the change is in the position of the object. Recall that work is done when a force moves an object through a distance. The ability to do work or cause change is called **energy.** So the wind has energy.

Work and Energy When an object or living thing does work on another object, some of its energy is transferred to that object. You can think of work, then, as the transfer of energy. When energy is transferred, the object upon which the work is done gains energy. Energy is measured in joules—the same units as work.

Power and Energy You may recall that power is the rate at which work is done. **If the transfer of energy is work, then power is the rate at which energy is transferred, or the amount of energy transferred in a unit of time.**

$$\text{Power} = \frac{\text{Energy transferred}}{\text{Time}}$$

Power is involved whenever energy is being transferred. For example, a calm breeze's power is its rate of energy transfer to lift a leaf a certain distance. The tornado in Figure 1 transfers the same amount of energy when it lifts the leaf the same distance. However, the tornado has a greater power than the breeze because it transfers energy to the leaf in less time.

Reading Checkpoint What is power in terms of energy?

Kinetic Energy

Two basic kinds of energy are kinetic energy and potential energy. Whether energy is kinetic or potential depends on whether an object is moving or not.

A moving object, such as the wind, can do work when it strikes another object and moves it some distance. Because the moving object does work, it has energy. The energy an object has due to its motion is called **kinetic energy.** The word *kinetic* comes from the Greek word *kinetos*, which means "moving."

FIGURE 1
Energy and Power
A tornado and a calm breeze each do the same amount of work if they transfer the same amount of energy to a leaf. However, the tornado has a greater power than the breeze because it transfers its energy in less time.
Drawing Conclusions *Why is the same amount of work done on the leaf?*

Mass, Velocity, and Kinetic Energy

Materials skateboards or toy trucks, 3 books

Time 15 min

Focus Ask: **How do you think mass affects the velocity at which an object moves after being pushed with the same force?** *(Sample answer: An object with greater mass might move more slowly.)*

Teach Have students place one book on the skateboard, push the skateboard, and observe the velocity at which the skateboard travels. Have the students place three books on the skateboard, push the skateboard with the same force, and observe its velocity.

Apply Ask: **What can you determine about the kinetic energy of the skateboard in the two trials?** *(The kinetic energy is about the same, because the skateboard was pushed with about the same force each time.)* **How would you compare the velocity in the two trials? Explain.** *(The velocity decreased in the second trial because the mass increased.)* **learning modality: kinesthetic**

Help Students Read   L1

Outlining Explain that using an outline format helps students organize information by main topic, subtopic, and details. Have students prepare an outline of the section, *What Is Energy?* The heads should serve as main ideas. Students can add details to their outlines as they read.

All in One Teaching Resources
• Transparency M47

Exponents

An exponent tells how many times a number is used as a factor. For example, 3×3 can be written as 3^2. You read this number as "three squared." An exponent of 2 indicates that the number 3 is used as a factor two times. To find the value of a squared number, multiply the number by itself.

$$3^2 = 3 \times 3 = 9$$

Practice Problem What is the value of the number 8^2?

FIGURE 2
Kinetic Energy
Kinetic energy increases as mass and velocity increase.
Predicting *In each example, which object will transfer more energy to the pins? Why?*

Factors Affecting Kinetic Energy The kinetic energy of an object depends on both its mass and its velocity. Kinetic energy increases as mass increases. For example, think about rolling a bowling ball and a golf ball down a bowling lane at the same velocity, as shown in Figure 2. The bowling ball has more mass than the golf ball. If both balls have the same velocity, the bowling ball is more likely to knock down the pins because it has more kinetic energy than the golf ball.

Kinetic energy also increases when velocity increases. For example, suppose you have two identical bowling balls and you roll one ball so it moves at a greater velocity than the other. You must throw the ball harder to give it the greater velocity. In other words, you transfer more energy to it. Therefore, the faster ball has more kinetic energy.

Calculating Kinetic Energy There is a mathematical relationship between kinetic energy, mass, and velocity.

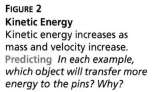

$$\text{Kinetic energy} = \frac{1}{2} \times \text{Mass} \times \text{Velocity}^2$$

Do changes in velocity and mass have the same effect on kinetic energy? No—changing the velocity of an object will have a greater effect on its kinetic energy than changing its mass by the same factor. This is because velocity is squared in the kinetic energy equation. For instance, doubling the mass of an object will double its kinetic energy. But doubling its velocity will quadruple its kinetic energy.

Reading Checkpoint Which has a greater effect on an object's kinetic energy—doubling its mass or doubling its velocity?

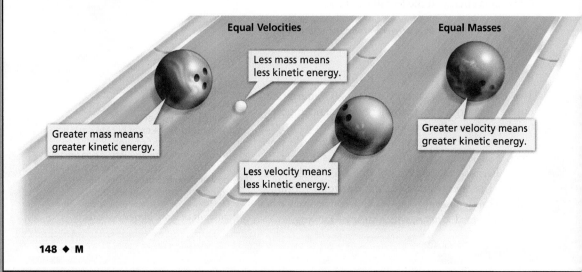

Equal Velocities

Less mass means less kinetic energy.

Greater mass means greater kinetic energy.

Less velocity means less kinetic energy.

Equal Masses

Greater velocity means greater kinetic energy.

Math Skill Exponents

Time 10 minutes

Tip Remind students that 3^2 is equal to 3×3, not 3×2.

Answer 64

Extend Have students determine the value of the term 3^3. *(27)*

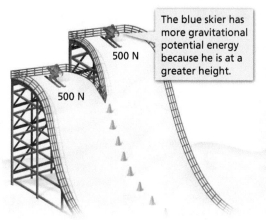

500 N

The blue skier has more gravitational potential energy because he is at a greater height.

500 N

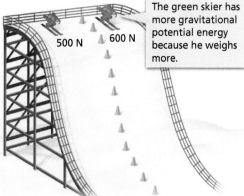

500 N   600 N

The green skier has more gravitational potential energy because he weighs more.

Potential Energy

An object does not have to be moving to have energy. Some objects have stored energy as a result of their positions or shapes. When you lift a book up to your desk from the floor or compress a spring to wind a toy, you transfer energy to it. The energy you transfer is stored, or held in readiness. It might be used later when the book falls to the floor or the spring unwinds. Stored energy that results from the position or shape of an object is called **potential energy.** This type of energy has the potential to do work.

Gravitational Potential Energy Potential energy related to an object's height is called **gravitational potential energy.** The gravitational potential energy of an object is equal to the work done to lift it. Remember that Work = Force × Distance. The force you use to lift the object is equal to its weight. The distance you move the object is its height. You can calculate an object's gravitational potential energy using this formula.

> **Gravitational potential energy = Weight × Height**

For example, the red skier on the left in Figure 3 weighs 500 newtons. If the ski jump is 40 meters high, then the skier has 500 newtons × 40 meters, or 20,000 J, of gravitational potential energy.

The more an object weighs, or the greater the object's height, the greater its gravitational potential energy. At the same height, a 600-newton skier has more gravitational potential energy than a 500-newton skier. Similarly, a 500-newton skier has more gravitational potential energy on a high ski jump than on a low one.

FIGURE 3
Gravitational Potential Energy
Gravitational potential energy increases as weight and height increase.
Interpreting Diagrams *Does the red skier have more gravitational potential energy on the higher ski jump or the lower one? Why?*

For: Links on energy
Visit: www.SciLinks.org
Web Code: scn-1351

Differentiated Instruction

English Learners/Beginning L1
Vocabulary: Science Glossary There are many confusingly similar terms in this section: *energy, kinetic energy, potential energy, gravitational potential energy,* and *elastic potential energy.* Have students add these terms to their science glossary with definitions written in their own words. Model this activity for students before they begin. **learning modality: verbal**

English Learners/Intermediate L2
Vocabulary: Science Glossary Have students extend the strategy for Beginning students by using each term in a written sentence. Model this activity for students before they begin. **learning modality: verbal**

Potential Energy

Teach Key Concepts   L2
Stored Energy

Focus Explain that potential energy is stored energy related to an object's position or shape.

Teach Draw a Venn diagram on the board to compare gravitational potential energy and elastic potential energy, which are both types of potential energy. Ask students to volunteer facts to place in the Venn diagram.

Apply Ask: **Which has a greater gravitational potential energy—a book lifted 1 meter off the ground or the same book lifted 10 meters off the ground?** *(The book lifted 10 meters)* **learning modality: logical/mathematical**

For: Links on energy
Visit: www.SciLinks.org
Web Code: scn-1351

Students can research energy online.

Monitor Progress   L2

Skills Check Have students explain the difference between kinetic energy and potential energy.

Answers
Figure 2 In the first example, the bowling ball will transfer more energy because it has more mass. In the second example, the bowling ball moving at the greater velocity will transfer more energy to the pins.
Figure 3 The red skier has more gravitational potential energy on the higher jump, because gravitational potential energy = weight × height.

 Reading Checkpoint Velocity affects kinetic energy more than mass.

Answers

Figure 4 The stored energy will be transferred to the arrow.

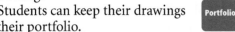 Elastic potential energy

Assess

Reviewing Key Concepts

1. a. Energy is the ability to do work or cause change. **b.** Energy and work are measured in the same units, joules. When work is done on an object, energy is transferred to the object. The amount of energy transferred or work done in a unit of time is power. **c.** The chainsaw has more power because it transfers energy to the log faster than the handsaw.

2. a. Kinetic energy is the energy an object has due to its motion. Potential energy is the stored energy an object has due to its position or shape. **b.** An object's mass and velocity affect its kinetic energy. **c.** You would need to know the sky diver's weight, height above Earth's surface, mass, and velocity. Potential energy = weight × height above Earth's surface; kinetic energy = $1/2 \times$ mass $\times$ velocity^2

Reteach L1

Have students write statements comparing and contrasting potential and kinetic energy.

Performance Assessment L2

Drawing Have students draw a sketch or diagram of playground equipment and label positions where a child would have potential energy and kinetic energy. Diagrams might include a slide, see-saw, climbing equipment, or a swing.

Students can keep their drawings in their portfolio. **Portfolio**

All in One Teaching Resources

- Section Summary: *What Is Energy?*
- Review and Reinforce: *What Is Energy?*
- Enrich: *What Is Energy?*

The farther the string is pulled, the greater the bow's elastic potential energy.

Pulling the string changes the bow's shape and stores elastic potential energy.

FIGURE 4
Elastic Potential Energy
The energy stored in a stretched object, such as a bow, is elastic potential energy. *Interpreting Photographs When the energy stored in the bow is released, how is it used?*

Elastic Potential Energy An object gains a different type of potential energy when it is stretched. The potential energy associated with objects that can be stretched or compressed is called **elastic potential energy.** For example, when an archer pulls back an arrow, the bow changes shape. The bow now has potential energy. When the archer releases the string, the stored energy sends the arrow flying to its target.

 What type of energy does a bow have when you pull back an arrow?

Section 1 Assessment

Target Reading Skill

Using Prior Knowledge Review your graphic organizer and revise it based on what you just learned in the section.

Reviewing Key Concepts

1. a. Defining What is energy?
  b. Describing How are energy, work, and power related?
  c. Applying Concepts If a handsaw does the same amount of work on a log as a chainsaw does, which has a greater power? Why?
2. a. Identifying What is kinetic energy? What is potential energy?

  b. Explaining What factors affect an object's kinetic energy?
  c. Problem Solving At a given height above Earth, how would you determine the potential energy of a sky diver? The kinetic energy of a sky diver?

Math Practice

3. Exponents What is the value of the number 10^2?

4. Exponents What number when squared gives you the value 36?

Math Practice

Math Skill Exponents
Answers
3. 100 ($10 \times 10 = 100$)
4. 6 ($6 \times 6 = 36$)

Lab zone Chapter Project

Keep Students on Track Have students experiment with different hill heights and inclines. Explain that the roller coaster car has the greatest gravitational potential energy at the top of hills. As the car travels downhill, potential energy is converted to kinetic energy.

Section 2 Forms of Energy

Reading Preview

Key Concepts
- How can you determine an object's mechanical energy?
- What are some forms of energy associated with the particles that make up objects?

Key Terms
- mechanical energy
- thermal energy
- electrical energy
- chemical energy
- nuclear energy
- electromagnetic energy

Target Reading Skill

Building Vocabulary After you read the section, reread the paragraphs that contain definitions of Key Terms. Use the information you have learned to write a definition of each Key Term in your own words.

Lab zone Discover Activity

What Makes a Flashlight Shine?

1. Remove the batteries from a flashlight and examine them. Think about what type of energy is stored in the batteries.
2. Replace the batteries and turn on the flashlight. What type of energy do you observe?
3. After a few minutes, place your hand near the bulb of the flashlight. What type of energy do you feel?

Think It Over

Inferring Describe how you think a flashlight works in terms of energy. Where does the energy come from? Where does the energy go?

You are on the edge of your seat as the quarterback drops back, steps forward, and then launches a deep pass. The ball soars down the field and drops into the receiver's hands. The electronic scoreboard flashes TOUCHDOWN. You jump to your feet and cheer!

As the crowd settles back down, you shiver. The sun is setting, and the afternoon is growing cool. A vendor hands you a hot dog, and its heat helps warm your hands. Suddenly, the stadium lights switch on. You can see the players more clearly as they line up for the next play.

The thrown football, the scoreboard, the sun, the hot dog, and the stadium lights all have energy. You have energy, too! Energy comes in many different forms.

Mechanical Energy

Think about the pass thrown by the quarterback. A football thrown by a quarterback has mechanical energy. So does a moving car or a trophy on a shelf. The form of energy associated with the position and motion of an object is called **mechanical energy.**

◀ A quarterback transfers mechanical energy to the football.

Chapter 5 M ◆ 151

Objectives

After this lesson, students will be able to

M.5.2.1 Explain how an object's mechanical energy is determined.

M.5.2.2 Name some forms of energy associated with the particles that make up objects.

Target Reading Skill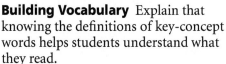

Building Vocabulary Explain that knowing the definitions of key-concept words helps students understand what they read.

As students read each passage that contains a key term, remind them to write a sentence in their own words. Encourage students to write one or two descriptive phrases to help them remember the key term. Call on students to share their definitions.

Preteach

Build Background Knowledge L2

Examples of Energy

Ask: **How did you get to school today?** *(Sample answer: Walked, rode a bike, rode the bus, rode in a car)* Make a list of different student responses on the board. Explain that each method involved energy. Walking and riding a bicycle require the chemical energy in food. Cars and buses are powered by engines that use the chemical energy stored in fuel.

Lab zone Discover Activity

Skills Focus Inferring

Materials flashlight, batteries

Time 10 minutes

Expected Outcome Students will observe light energy when the flashlight is turned on and feel thermal energy when they place their hand near the bulb.

L1 **Think It Over** Sample answer: Stored energy is released when the flashlight is turned on. The energy comes from the batteries and travels to the bulb, where it is released as light and heat.

Mechanical Energy

Teach Key Concepts L2
Calculating Mechanical Energy

Focus Direct students' attention to the formula for mechanical energy found in the text.

Teach Explain that the mechanical energy of an object is due to its position (potential energy) and its motion (kinetic energy).

Apply Ask: **If an object has 50 joules of kinetic energy and 237 joules of potential energy, what is its mechanical energy?** *(287 J)* **learning modality: logical/mathematical**

 **Teacher Demo** L2

Visualizing Mechanical Energy

Materials marble, clay, pie plate

Time 10 minutes

Focus Tell students that Mechanical energy = Kinetic energy + Potential energy.

Teach Drop a marble from 0.5 meter above a pie plate lined with clay. Have students observe the dent made by the marble. Then hold the marble 2 meters above the pie plate. Ask: **Does the marble have more or less gravitational potential energy than it did during the first trial?** *(More)* **How will this affect its mechanical energy?** *(It will be greater.)* Drop the marble. Students should see a deeper dent in the clay.

Apply Ask: **How does mechanical energy relate to the work an object can do?** *(As mechanical energy increases, so does the amount of work that can be done.)* **learning modality: visual**

Go Online
SciLINKS NSTA
For: Links on forms of energy
Visit: www.SciLinks.org
Web Code: scn-1352

Students can research forms of energy online.

Independent Practice L2

All in One Teaching Resources

• Guided Reading and Study Worksheet: *Forms of Energy*

○ **Student Edition on Audio CD**

Go Online
SciLINKS NSTA
For: Links on forms of energy
Visit: www.SciLinks.org
Web Code: scn-1352

An object's mechanical energy is a combination of its potential energy and kinetic energy. **You can find an object's mechanical energy by adding the object's kinetic energy and potential energy.**

> **Mechanical Energy = Potential energy + Kinetic energy**

For example, a football thrown by a quarterback has both potential energy and kinetic energy. The higher the football, the greater its potential energy. The faster the football moves, the greater its kinetic energy.

You can add the potential energy and kinetic energy of the football in Figure 5 to find its mechanical energy. The football has 32 joules of potential energy due to its position above the ground. It also has 45 joules of kinetic energy due to its motion. The total mechanical energy of the football is equal to 32 joules + 45 joules, or 77 joules.

An object with mechanical energy can do work on another object. In fact, you can think of mechanical energy as the ability to do work. The more mechanical energy an object has, the more work it can do.

 Reading Checkpoint **What two forms of energy combine to make mechanical energy?**

FIGURE 5
Mechanical Energy
To find the football's mechanical energy, add its kinetic energy to its potential energy. *Observing Why does the football have potential energy?*

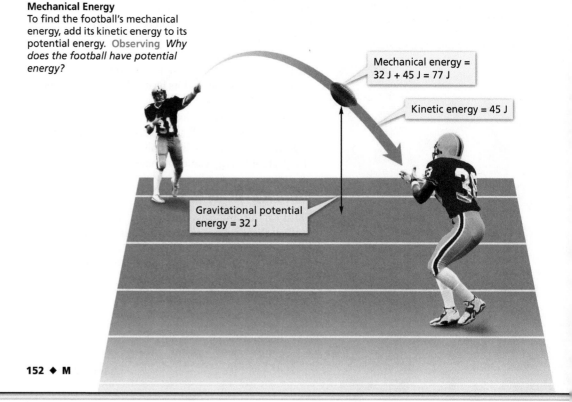

Mechanical energy = 32 J + 45 J = 77 J

Kinetic energy = 45 J

Gravitational potential energy = 32 J

152 ◆ M

Differentiated Instruction

Special Needs L1
Observing Energy Have students look around the classroom for examples of different forms of energy. Possible examples: chemical energy in food, thermal energy from heaters, and electromagnetic energy from the sun or lights. As each example is located have the students say aloud with you the correct term describing that type of energy. **learning modality: verbal**

Gifted and Talented L3
Persuasive Writing Have students research the use of nuclear fission to produce electrical energy for consumers. Have students list the positive and negative aspects of this source of energy. Then have students write a persuasive paragraph arguing for or against the use of nuclear fission reactors. **learning modality: verbal**

Math ▸ Analyzing Data

Calculating Mechanical Energy

The kinetic energy of a 500-N diver during a dive from a 10-m platform was measured. These data are shown in the graph.

1. **Reading Graphs** According to the graph, how much kinetic energy does the diver have at 8 m?

2. **Calculating** Using the graph, find the kinetic energy of the diver at 6 m. Then calculate the diver's potential energy at that point.

3. **Inferring** The mechanical energy of the diver is the same at every height. What is the mechanical energy of the diver?

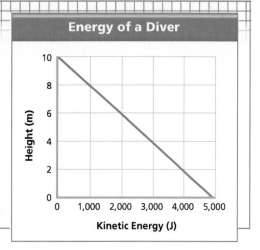

Energy of a Diver

Other Forms of Energy

So far in this chapter, you have read about energy that involves the motion and position of an object. But an object can have other forms of kinetic and potential energy. Most of these other forms are associated with the particles that make up objects. These particles are far too small to see. **Forms of energy associated with the particles of objects include thermal energy, electrical energy, chemical energy, nuclear energy, and electromagnetic energy.**

Thermal Energy All objects are made up of particles called atoms and molecules. Because these particles are constantly in motion, they have kinetic energy. The faster the particles move, the more kinetic energy they have. These particles are arranged in specific ways in different objects. Therefore, they also have potential energy. The total potential and kinetic energy of the particles in an object is called **thermal energy.** Look at Figure 6. Even though the lava may be flowing slowly down the volcano, its particles are moving quickly. Because the particles have a large amount of kinetic energy, the lava has a large amount of thermal energy.

If you've ever eaten ice cream on a hot day, you've experienced thermal energy. Fast-moving particles in the warm air make the particles of ice cream move faster. As the kinetic energy of the particles increases, so does the thermal energy of the ice cream. Eventually, the ice cream melts.

FIGURE 6
Thermal Energy
The lava flowing from this volcano has a large amount of thermal energy. *Predicting Will the thermal energy of the lava increase or decrease as it flows away from the volcano?*

M ◆ 153

M ● 153

FIGURE 7
Electrical Energy
Electric charges in lightning carry electrical energy.

Electrical Energy When you receive a shock from a metal doorknob, you are experiencing electrical energy. The energy of electric charges is **electrical energy.** Depending on whether the charges are moving or stored, electrical energy can be a form of kinetic or potential energy. The lightning in Figure 7 is a form of electrical energy. You rely on electrical energy from batteries or electrical lines to run devices such as flashlights, handheld games, and radios.

Chemical Energy Almost everything you see, touch, or taste is composed of chemical compounds. Chemical compounds are made up of atoms and molecules. Bonds between the atoms and molecules hold chemical compounds together. These bonds have chemical energy. **Chemical energy** is potential energy stored in the chemical bonds that hold chemical compounds together. Chemical energy is stored in the foods you eat, in the matches you can use to light a candle, and even in the cells of your body. When bonds in chemical compounds break, new chemical compounds may form. When this happens, chemical energy may be released.

FIGURE 8
Chemical Energy
The particles in these grapes contain chemical energy. Your body can use this energy after you eat them.

154 ◆ M

Nuclear Energy A type of potential energy called **nuclear energy** is stored in the nucleus of an atom. Nuclear energy is released during a nuclear reaction. One kind of nuclear reaction, known as nuclear fission, occurs when a nucleus splits. Nuclear power plants use fission reactions to produce electricity. Another kind of reaction, known as nuclear fusion, occurs when the nuclei of atoms fuse, or join together. Nuclear fusion reactions occur continuously in the sun, releasing tremendous amounts of energy.

Electromagnetic Energy The sunlight that you see each day is a form of **electromagnetic energy.** Electromagnetic energy travels in waves. These waves have some electrical properties and some magnetic properties.

The microwaves you use to cook your food and the X-rays doctors use to examine patients are types of electromagnetic energy. Other forms of electromagnetic energy include ultraviolet radiation, infrared radiation, and radio waves.

 What form of energy are microwaves?

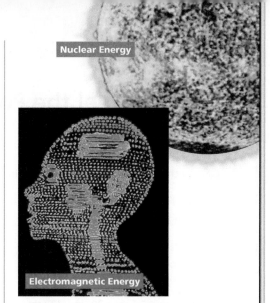
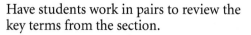

FIGURE 9
Nuclear and Electromagnetic Energy
The sun is a source of nuclear energy. Doctors use X-rays, a form of electromagnetic energy, when taking a CT scan to look for brain disorders. *Observing What other forms of energy from the sun can you observe?*

Section 2 Assessment

Target Reading Skill Building Vocabulary Use your definitions to help answer the questions.

Reviewing Key Concepts

1. a. Defining What is mechanical energy?
   b. Drawing Conclusions If an object's mechanical energy is equal to its potential energy, how much kinetic energy does the object have? How do you know?
   c. Calculating If the kinetic energy of a falling apple is 5.2 J and its potential energy is 3.5 J, what is its mechanical energy?

2. a. Listing List the five forms of energy associated with the particles that make up objects.
   b. Explaining Why do the particles of objects have both kinetic and potential energy?
   c. Classifying What kind of energy do you experience when you eat a peanut butter and jelly sandwich?

Writing in Science

Detailed Observation In terms of energy, think about what happens when you eat a hot meal. Describe all the different forms of energy that you experience. For example, if you are eating under a lamp, its electromagnetic energy helps you see the food. Explain the source of each form of energy.

Monitor Progress _____ L2
Answers
Figure 9 Electromagnetic energy, in the form of visible light

Reading Checkpoint Microwaves are a form of electromagnetic energy.

Assess

Reviewing Key Concepts

1. a. The form of energy related to the position and motion of an object. **b.** Its kinetic energy is zero because mechanical energy equals potential energy plus kinetic energy. **c.** Its mechanical energy is 8.7 J, the sum of its potential energy and kinetic energy.
2. a. Thermal energy, electrical energy, chemical energy, nuclear energy, electromagnetic energy **b.** These particles are constantly in motion, so they have kinetic energy. The particles also have potential energy as the result of their specific arrangement in objects. **c.** You experience the chemical energy stored in the sandwich.

Reteach L1
Have students work in pairs to review the key terms from the section.

Performance Assessment L2
Skills Check Ask: **What is the mechanical energy of a book that has 15 J of gravitational potential energy and is at rest on a table?** *(15 J)*

All in One Teaching Resources
• Section Summary: *Forms of Energy*
• Review and Reinforce: *Forms of Energy*
• Enrich: *Forms of Energy*

Writing in Science

Writing Mode Description
Scoring Rubric
4 Exceeds criteria
3 Meets criteria
2 Mentions only two forms of energy and/or includes some incorrect information
1 Includes information about only one form of energy and/or many incorrect statements

Can You Feel the Power?

Prepare for Inquiry

Key Concept
Power is the rate at which work is done.

Skills Objective
After this lab, students will be able to
- calculate work, gravitational potential energy, and power
- interpret data about the relationship between work and power

Prep Time 20 minutes

Class Time 40 minutes

Advance Planning
Have the boards, stopwatches, and meter sticks ready. Tell students to bring calculators and 2 cm-thick books to class on lab day.

Alternative Materials
Aerobic "steps" can be used in place of the boards and books.

Safety
Be sure partners hold the board steady and level throughout the investigations. Partners should "spot" for steppers. Review the safety guidelines in Appendix A.

All in One Teaching Resources
- Lab Worksheet: *Can You Feel the Power?*

Guide Inquiry

Invitation
Ask: **Does it take more work to walk up a flight of steps, or run up the same steps?** *(The amount of work is the same.)* **Which way requires increased power? Why?** *(Running, because more work is done in each unit of time)*

Introduce the Procedure
- Divide the class into groups of three students each.
- Ask: **Why are the body weights given in newtons and the distance measured in meters?** *(Work is measured in joules, which are newton-meters.)*

Can You Feel the Power?

Problem
Can you change your power while exercising?

Skills Focus
calculating, interpreting data

Materials
- calculator
- meter stick
- stopwatch or clock with a second hand
- board, about 2.5 cm × 30 cm × 120 cm
- 18–20 books, each about 2 cm thick

Procedure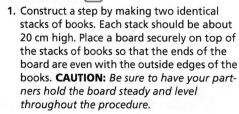

1. Construct a step by making two identical stacks of books. Each stack should be about 20 cm high. Place a board securely on top of the stacks of books so that the ends of the board are even with the outside edges of the books. **CAUTION:** *Be sure to have your partners hold the board steady and level throughout the procedure.*

2. Copy the data table into your notebook.

3. You gain gravitational potential energy every time you step up. Gaining energy requires work.

   Work = Weight × Height = Gravitational potential energy

   a. Assume your weight is 400 N and your partners' weights are 425 N and 450 N.

b. Measure the vertical distance in centimeters from the floor to the top of the board. Convert to meters by dividing by 100 and record this height in the data table.

4. Calculate the work you do in stepping up onto the board once. Then calculate the work you do stepping up onto the board 20 times. Record both answers in your data table.

5. Step up onto the board with both feet and then step backwards off the board onto the floor. This up and down motion is one repetition. Make sure you are comfortable with the motion.

6. Have one partner time how long it takes you to do 20 repetitions performed at a constant speed. Count out loud to help the timer keep track of the number of repetitions. Record the time in your data table.

7. Calculate the power over 20 repetitions. (Power = Energy transferred ÷ Time.) Predict how your results will change if you step up and down at different speeds.

8. Repeat Steps 6 and 7, but climb the step more slowly than you did the first time. Record the new data in the Trial 2 row of your data table.

9. Switch roles with your partners and repeat Steps 3 through 8 with a different weight from Step 3(a).

Data Table						
Trial	Weight (N)	Height of Board (m)	Time for 20 Repetitions (s)	Work for 1 Repetition (J)	Work for 20 Repetitions (J)	Power (W)
Student 1, Trial 1						
Student 1, Trial 2						

Troubleshooting the Experiment
Students should recognize that the work done during the downward motion is done by gravity and cannot be counted as work done by the student. A complete up-and-down cycle is counted as one repetition, not two.

Analyze and Conclude

1. **Calculating** What is the gravitational potential energy gained from stepping up onto the board? How does this compare to the amount of work required to step up onto the board?

2. **Interpreting Data** Compare the amount of work you did during your first and second trials.

3. **Interpreting Data** Compare the power during your first and second trials.

4. **Drawing Conclusions** Did you and your partners all do the same amount of work? Did you all do work at the same rate? Explain your answers.

5. **Communicating** Often, a physical therapist will want to increase a patient's power. Write a letter to a physical therapist suggesting how he or she could use music to change a patient's power.

Design an Experiment

Design an experiment to test two other ways a physical therapist could change the power output of her patients. *Obtain your teacher's permission before carrying out your investigation.*

Expected Outcome

Students' results should show that, for a given student, the work done for each repetition is the same because the step is the same height. However, slower repetitions mean lower power.

Students' results should show that the student with a weight of 400 N does less work for each repetition than the students with greater weights.

Analyze and Conclude

1. The gravitational potential energy gained equals 400 N × the height of the board in meters. It is equal to the work required to step up on the board.

2. The amount of work is the same.

3. The power in the first trial was greater because the work done was faster.

4. No. Partners with more weight do more work. No. The power depended on the student's weight and the time required to perform 20 repetitions.

5. Sample letter: You could regulate the rate at which your patients do work by having them perform their exercises to the beat of music. Using this method, you could increase a patient's power (work done per unit of time) by having the patient exercise to music with a faster beat.

Extend Inquiry

Design an Experiment Sample answer: The physical therapist could change a patient's power by having the patient take higher steps, use hand-held weights, or use ankle weights. Note: students should test only one variable at a time and should never work unsupervised in the lab.

Objectives

After this lesson, students will be able to

M.5.3.1 Describe how different forms of energy are related.

M.5.3.2 Name common energy transformations.

M.5.3.3 State the law of conservation of energy.

Target Reading Skill

Asking Questions Explain that changing a head into a question helps students anticipate the ideas, facts, and events they are about to read.

Answers

Sample graphic organizer:

What is an energy transformation? *(An energy transformation is a change from one form of energy to another.)* **What are some examples of transformations between potential and kinetic energy?** *(Juggling and pendulums show transformations between potential and kinetic energy.)* **What is conservation of energy?** *(The law of conservation of energy states that energy cannot be created or destroyed.)*

All in One Teaching Resources
- Transparency M48

Preteach

Build Background Knowledge L2

Introducing Energy Transformations

Ask: **What happens when you rub your hands together?** *(They feel warm.)* **When you're cold, what are some other ways you can get warm?** *(Sample answer: Jump up and down, stay in a heated area, use electric blankets, stand in the sunlight)*

Section 3 — Energy Transformations and Conservation

Reading Preview

Key Concepts
- How are different forms of energy related?
- What is a common energy transformation?
- What is the law of conservation of energy?

Key Terms
- energy transformation
- law of conservation of energy
- matter

Target Reading Skill
Asking Questions Before you read, preview the red headings and ask a *what* or *how* question for each heading. As you read, write the answers to your questions.

Energy Transformations

Question	Answer
What is an energy transformation?	An energy transformation is . . .

▼ Niagara Falls is more than 50 meters high.

158 ◆ M

Lab zone Discover **Activity**

What Would Make a Card Jump?

1. Fold an index card in half.
2. In the edge opposite the fold, cut two slits that are about 2 cm long and 2 cm apart.
3. Keep the card folded and loop a rubber band through the slits. With the fold toward you, gently open the card like a tent and flatten it against your desk.
4. Predict what will happen to the card if you let go. Then test your prediction.

Think It Over

Drawing Conclusions Describe what happened to the card. Based on your observations, what is the relationship between potential and kinetic energy?

The spray bounces off your raincoat as you look up at the millions of liters of water plunging toward you. The roar of the water is deafening. Are you doomed? Fortunately not—you are on a sightseeing boat at the foot of the mighty Niagara Falls. The waterfall carries the huge amount of water that drains from the upper Great Lakes. It lies on the border between Canada and the United States.

What many visitors don't know, however, is that Niagara Falls serves as much more than just a spectacular view. The Niagara Falls area is the center of a network of electrical power lines. Water that is diverted above the falls is used to generate electricity for much of the surrounding region.

Energy Transformations

What does flowing water have to do with electricity? You may already know that the mechanical energy of moving water can be transformed into electrical energy. **Most forms of energy can be transformed into other forms.** A change from one form of energy to another is called an **energy transformation.** Some energy changes involve single transformations, while others involve many transformations.

Lab zone Discover **Activity**

Skills Focus Drawing conclusions L2

Materials 3 × 5 index card, scissors, rubber band, safety goggles

Time 10 minutes

Tips The rubber band should be just large enough to stretch out when the card is flattened. Students should wear safety goggles.

Expected Outcome When the card is released, the rubber band will snap back and pull the card with it.

Think It Over Sample answer: When I flattened the card, I stretched the rubber band and gave it potential energy. When I released the card, the potential energy was converted to kinetic energy as the rubber band snapped back and pulled the card with it.

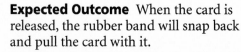

A cell phone transforms electrical energy to electromagnetic energy.

Your body transforms the chemical energy in food to mechanical energy.

A toaster transforms electrical energy to thermal energy.

FIGURE 10
Common Energy Transformations
Every day, energy transformations are all around you. Some of these transformations happen inside you! Observing *What other energy transformations do you observe every day?*

Single Transformations Sometimes, one form of energy needs to be transformed into another to get work done. You are already familiar with many such energy transformations. For example, a toaster transforms electrical energy to thermal energy to toast your bread. A cell phone transforms electrical energy to electromagnetic energy that travels to other phones.

Your body transforms the chemical energy in your food to mechanical energy you need to move your muscles. Chemical energy in food is also transformed to the thermal energy your body uses to maintain its temperature.

Multiple Transformations Often, a series of energy transformations is needed to do work. For example, the mechanical energy used to strike a match is transformed first to thermal energy. The thermal energy causes the particles in the match to release stored chemical energy, which is transformed to thermal energy and the electromagnetic energy you see as light.

In a car engine, another series of energy conversions occurs. Electrical energy produces a spark. The thermal energy of the spark releases chemical energy in the fuel. The fuel's chemical energy in turn becomes thermal energy. Thermal energy is converted to mechanical energy used to move the car, and to electrical energy to produce more sparks.

 Reading Checkpoint **What is an example of a multiple transformation of energy?**

Lab zone Skills **Activity**

Classifying
Many common devices transform electrical energy into other forms. Think about the following devices in terms of energy transformations.

• steam iron • ceiling fan
• digital clock • dryer

For each device, describe which form or forms of energy the electrical energy becomes. Do these devices produce single or multiple transformations of energy?

Lab zone Skills **Activity**

Skills Focus Classifying [L1]

Time 10 minutes

Expected Outcome Sample answer: Steam iron (electrical to thermal); ceiling fan (electrical to mechanical and perhaps thermal as the fan motor becomes warm); digital clock (electrical to electromagnetic); dryer (electrical to mechanical and thermal). These are single transformations.

Extend Have students brainstorm to create a list of other devices in their homes that transform energy. **learning modality: logical/mathematical**

Instruct

Energy Transformations

Teach Key Skills [L2]
Examples of Energy Transformations

Focus Tell students that life on Earth would not be possible without energy transformations.

Teach Have students list examples of energy transformations. Help students by asking questions, such as: **What happens to the chemical energy in the food you eat?** (*It is transformed to thermal energy and mechanical energy.*)

Apply Ask: **Why is food sometimes called fuel for your body?** (*Food contains chemical energy, which is transformed to thermal and mechanical energy. This is similar to the chemical energy in gasoline being transformed to mechanical and thermal energy in a car's engine.*) **learning modality: verbal**

Independent Practice [L2]

All in One **Teaching Resources**
• Guided Reading and Study Worksheet: *Energy Transformations and Conservation*

⊙ Student Edition on Audio CD

Monitor Progress [L2]

Drawing Have students illustrate an example of one of these energy transformations: mechanical to thermal energy, electrical to electromagnetic, or chemical to mechanical.

Answers
Figure 10 Sample answer: A lamp transforms electrical energy to electromagnetic energy.

 Reading Checkpoint Sample answer: The energy transformations in a car's engine are an example of multiple energy transformations.

M ● 159

Transformations Between Potential and Kinetic Energy

FIGURE 11
Juggling The kinetic energy of an orange thrown into the air becomes gravitational potential energy. Its potential energy becomes kinetic energy as it falls.

Go **Online**
active art

For: Energy Transformations activity
Visit: PHSchool.com
Web Code: cgp-3053

Transformations Between Potential and Kinetic Energy

One of the most common energy transformations is the transformation between potential energy and kinetic energy. In waterfalls such as Niagara Falls, potential energy is transformed to kinetic energy. The water at the top of the falls has gravitational potential energy. As the water plunges, its velocity increases. Its potential energy becomes kinetic energy.

Energy Transformation in Juggling Any object that rises or falls experiences a change in its kinetic and gravitational potential energy. Look at the orange in Figure 11. When it moves, the orange has kinetic energy. As it rises, it slows down. Its potential energy increases as its kinetic energy decreases. At the highest point in its path, it stops moving. Since there is no motion, the orange no longer has kinetic energy. But it does have potential energy. As the orange falls, the energy transformation is reversed. Kinetic energy increases while potential energy decreases.

Energy Transformation in a Pendulum In a pendulum, a continuous transformation between kinetic and potential energy takes place. At the highest point in its swing, the pendulum in Figure 12 has no movement, so it only has gravitational potential energy. As it swings downward, it speeds up. Its potential energy is transformed to kinetic energy. The pendulum is at its greatest speed at the bottom of its swing. There, all its energy is kinetic energy.

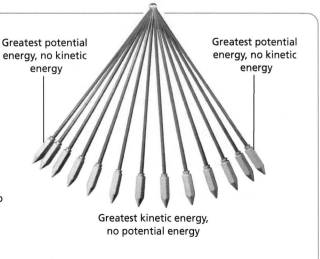

Greatest potential energy, no kinetic energy

Greatest potential energy, no kinetic energy

Greatest kinetic energy, no potential energy

FIGURE 12
Pendulum
A pendulum continuously transforms energy from kinetic to potential energy and back.
Interpreting Diagrams *At what two points is the pendulum's potential energy greatest?*

FIGURE 13
Pole Vault
Energy transformations enable
this athlete to vault more than
six meters into the air.

As the pendulum swings to the other side, its height increases. The pendulum regains gravitational potential energy and loses kinetic energy. At the top of its swing, it comes to a stop again. And so the pattern of energy transformation continues.

Energy Transformation in a Pole Vault A pole-vaulter transforms kinetic energy to elastic potential energy, which then becomes gravitational potential energy. The pole-vaulter you see in Figure 13 has kinetic energy as he runs forward. When the pole-vaulter plants the pole to jump, his velocity decreases and the pole bends. His kinetic energy is transformed to elastic potential energy in the pole. As the pole straightens out, the pole-vaulter is lifted high into the air. The elastic potential energy of the pole is transformed to the gravitational potential energy of the pole-vaulter. Once he is over the bar, the pole-vaulter's gravitational potential energy is transformed back into kinetic energy as he falls toward the safety cushion.

 Reading Checkpoint What kind of energy lifts a pole-vaulter over the bar?

Energy
Video Preview
▶ Video Field Trip
Video Assessment

Modeling Pole Vaulting

Materials modeling clay, plastic drinking straw

Time 10 min

Focus Direct students' attention to Figure 13. Tell students they will use a model to study the energy transformations in a pole vault.

Teach Have students stick one end of the straw in the clay and then gently push down on the other end. Ask: **What happens to the straw?** (*It bends.*) Ask: **What happens when you release the straw?** (*It straightens.*)

Apply Ask: **At what point does a pole-vaulter have the most gravitational potential energy?** (*When the pole-vaulter is at the highest point above Earth's surface*)
learning modality: kinesthetic

Video Field Trip

Energy

Show the Video Field Trip to let students experience the relationship of potential energy, kinetic energy, and thermal energy during skiing. Discussion question: **What is the difference between potential energy and kinetic energy?** (*Sample answer: Potential energy is energy due to position; kinetic energy is energy due to motion.*)

Differentiated Instruction

English Learners/Beginning Comprehension: Ask Questions L1 To help students understand the energy transformations in a pole vault, distribute a rewritten, simplified version of the text. Then ask students questions about the rewritten text. Possible questions include: **What kind of energy does the pole-vaulter have when he is running?** (*Kinetic energy*) **learning modality: verbal**

English Learners/Intermediate Comprehension: Ask Questions L2 Have students read the simplified text you wrote for Beginning students. Then, have students write the answers to the questions using complete sentences. Ask for volunteers to read their sentences aloud. **learning modality: verbal**

Monitor Progress L2

Oral Presentation Have students pretend they are swinging on a swing. Have them describe the energy transformations that take place.

Answers
Figure 12 Its potential energy is highest at the two high points of its swing.

 Reading Checkpoint Elastic potential energy lifts the pole-vaulter over the bar.

Conservation of Energy

Teach Key Concepts `L2`

Energy, Matter, and Conservation

Focus Tell students that the law of conservation of energy states that energy cannot be created or destroyed.

Teach In some nuclear reactions, matter is converted to energy. Students may have heard of Einstein's famous equation: $E = mc^2$ (Energy = Mass × Speed of light^2). Einstein showed that energy and mass are equivalent and can be converted into one another. Tell students that Einstein's equation is used to determine the amount of energy that is created when matter is destroyed.

Apply Ask: **To what form of energy is mechanical energy most often transformed?** *(Thermal energy)* **learning modality: logical/mathematical**

Address Misconceptions `L1`

Students may confuse conservation of energy with conserving an energy resource. Ask students to name an energy resource. Discuss the energy transformations that occur when an energy resource is used. Remind students that conserving an energy resource means using a resource wisely.

Lab zone Try This **Activity**

Pendulum Swing

1. Set up a pendulum using washers or a rubber stopper, string, a ring stand, and a clamp.
2. Pull the pendulum back so that it makes a 45° angle with the vertical. Measure the height of the stopper. Release it and observe how high it swings.

3. Use a second clamp to reduce the length of the pendulum as shown. The pendulum will run into the second clamp at the bottom of its swing.
4. Pull the pendulum back to the same height as you did the first time. Predict how high the pendulum will swing. Then set it in motion and observe.

Observing How high did the pendulum swing in each case? Explain your observations.

FIGURE 14
Conservation of Energy
A spinning top's kinetic energy is not lost. It is transformed into thermal energy through friction.
Applying Concepts *How much of the top's kinetic energy becomes thermal energy?*

Conservation of Energy

If you set a spinning top in motion, will the top remain in motion forever? No, it will not. Then what happens to its energy? Is the energy destroyed? Again, the answer is no. The **law of conservation of energy** states that when one form of energy is transformed to another, no energy is destroyed in the process. **According to the law of conservation of energy, energy cannot be created or destroyed.** So the total amount of energy is the same before and after any transformation. If you add up all the new forms of energy after a transformation, all of the original energy will be accounted for.

Energy and Friction So what happens to the energy of the top in Figure 14? As the top spins, it encounters friction with the floor and friction from the air. Whenever a moving object experiences friction, some of its kinetic energy is transformed into thermal energy. So, the mechanical energy of the spinning top is transformed to thermal energy. The top slows and eventually falls on its side, but its energy is not destroyed—it is transformed.

The fact that friction transforms mechanical energy to thermal energy should not surprise you. After all, you take advantage of such thermal energy when you rub your cold hands together to warm them up. The fact that friction transforms mechanical energy to thermal energy explains why no machine is 100 percent efficient. You may recall that the output work of any real machine is always less than the input work. This reduced efficiency occurs because some mechanical energy is always transformed into thermal energy due to friction.

Lab zone Try This **Activity**

Skills Focus Observing `L3`

Materials washers or rubber stoppers, string, ring stand, 2 clamps, meter stick

Time 15 minutes

Tips Suggest that students practice so they can get an accurate height measurement.

Expected Outcome In Step 2, the pendulum will swing to almost the same height from which it was released. In Steps 3 and 4, the pendulum will swing through a larger angle, but will still reach almost the same height it had when it was released. The original amount of potential energy is not affected by changing the length of the pendulum in mid-swing.

Extend Have students test how increasing mass affects the swing of the pendulum.
learning modality: kinesthetic

Energy and Matter You might have heard of Albert Einstein's theory of relativity. His theory stated that energy *can* sometimes be created—by destroying matter! **Matter** is anything that has mass and takes up space. All objects are made up of matter.

Just as one form of energy can be transformed to other forms, Einstein discovered that matter can be transformed to energy. In fact, destroying just a small amount of matter releases a huge amount of energy.

Einstein's discovery meant that the law of conservation of energy had to be adjusted. In some situations, energy alone is not conserved. However, since matter can be transformed to energy, scientists say matter and energy together are always conserved.

 Reading Checkpoint How can energy be created?

FIGURE 15
Albert Einstein
Einstein published his theory of special relativity in 1905.

Section 3 Assessment

Target Reading Skill Asking Questions Use the answers to the questions you wrote about the headings to help you answer the questions below.

Reviewing Key Concepts

1. a. Reviewing What is the relationship between different forms of energy?
   b. Relating Cause and Effect When you turn a toaster on, what happens to the electrical energy?
   c. Sequencing Describe the energy transformations that happen when you strike a match. List them in the order in which they occur.

2. a. Identifying What common energy transformation allows you to send a rubber band flying across the room?
   b. Describing Describe the energy transformations that occur when you bounce a ball.
   c. Interpreting Diagrams Describe the energy transformations that occur in the pendulum in Figure 12.

3. a. Summarizing State the law of conservation of energy in your own words.
   b. Explaining Thermal energy is produced when a firefighter slides down a pole. Where does it come from?
   c. Making Generalizations Based on the theory of relativity, what must always be conserved?

Lab zone At-Home **Activity**

Hot Wire Straighten a wire hanger. Have a family member feel the wire and observe whether it feels cool or warm. Then hold the ends of the wire and bend it back and forth several times. **CAUTION:** *If the wire breaks, it can be sharp.* Do not bend it more than a few times. After bending the wire, have your family member feel it again. Explain how energy transformations can produce a change in temperature.

Chapter 5 M ◆ 163

Lab zone At-Home **Activity**

Hot Wire L1 Students should find that the wire feels warm after it has been bent. Sample explanation: Some of the mechanical energy used to bend the wire is converted to thermal energy. The wire feels warmer after it has been bent because its increased thermal energy raises its temperature.

Monitor Progress _____ L2
Answers
Figure 14 All of the top's kinetic energy becomes thermal energy.
Reading Checkpoint By destroying matter

Assess

Reviewing Key Concepts

1. a. Most forms of energy can be transformed into other forms. **b.** The electrical energy is transformed to thermal energy. **c.** First, striking the match transforms mechanical energy to thermal energy. The thermal energy causes particles to release chemical energy. Finally, chemical energy is transformed to thermal and electromagnetic energy.
2. a. Elastic potential energy in the stretched band is transformed to kinetic energy. **b.** Sample answer: As the ball falls, potential energy is transformed to kinetic energy. While the ball is in contact with the floor or other surface (during the bounce), kinetic energy is transformed to elastic potential energy, which is transformed back to kinetic energy. As the ball travels upward, kinetic energy is transformed to potential energy. Some kinetic energy is transformed to thermal energy or sound during the bounce. **c.** Downswing—potential energy is transformed to kinetic energy; upswing—kinetic energy is transformed to potential energy.
3. a. Sample answer: No energy is created or destroyed as one form of energy is transformed to another form. **b.** Some of the firefighter's potential energy is transformed to thermal energy through friction. **c.** Energy and matter together are conserved.

Reteach L1
Have students work in pairs to review the reading checkpoint questions and the caption questions in the section.

Performance Assessment L2
Organizing Information Have students make flowcharts to show the energy transformations made by an electric fan.

All in One Teaching Resources
- Section Summary: *Energy Transformations and Conservation*
- Review and Reinforce: *Energy Transformations and Conservation*
- Enrich: *Energy Transformations and Conservation*

M ● 163

Soaring Straws L2

Prepare for Inquiry

Key Concept
As the amount of stretch (related to elastic potential energy) in a rocket launcher increases, the subsequent height that a rocket attains (related to gravitational potential energy) increases.

Skills Objective
After this lab, students will be able to
- control variables in an experiment to find the relationship between elastic potential energy and gravitational potential energy
- graph the results of the experiment

 Prep Time 15 minutes
Class Time 40 minutes

Advance Planning
Collect sufficient toilet paper tubes or ask students to bring them from home. Purchase rubber bands and straws, if necessary.

Alternative Materials
Any short tube can be used for a launcher, for example, a 5-cm diameter plastic or PVC pipe.

Safety
 Warn students not to point or shoot their rockets at another person. Review the safety guidelines in Appendix A.

All in One Teaching Resources
- Lab Worksheet: *Soaring Straws*

Guide Inquiry

Invitation
Shoot a straw into the air with the launcher. Ask students to describe the launch in terms of energy. *(The elastic potential energy of the rubber band was transformed into kinetic energy and then gravitational potential of the rocket.)*

Introduce the Procedure
Demonstrate the construction of the rocket and the launcher.

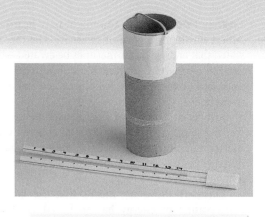

Soaring Straws

Problem
How does the gravitational potential energy of a straw rocket depend on the elastic potential energy of a rubber band launcher?

Skills Focus
controlling variables, graphing

Materials
- scissors
- rubber band
- 3 plastic straws
- meter stick
- marker
- metric ruler
- balance
- masking tape
- empty toilet paper tube

Procedure

1. Construct the rocket and launcher following the instructions in the box above. Use a balance to find the mass of the rocket in grams. Record the mass.
2. Hold the launcher in one hand with your fingers over the ends of the rubber band. Load the launcher by placing the straw rocket on the rubber band and pulling down from the other end as shown in the photograph. Let go and launch the rocket straight up. **CAUTION:** *Be sure to aim the straw rocket into the air, not at classmates.*
3. In your notebook, make a data table similar to the one on the next page.
4. Have your partner hold a meter stick, or tape it to the wall, so that its zero end is even with the top of the rocket launcher. Measure the height, in meters, to which the rocket rises. If the rocket goes higher than a single meter stick, use two meter sticks.

Making A Rocket and Launcher
A Cut a rubber band and tape it across the open end of a hollow cylinder, such as a toilet paper tube. The rubber band should be taut, but stretched only a tiny amount. This is the launcher.

B Cut about 3 cm off a plastic straw.

C Lay 2 full-length straws side by side on a flat surface with the 3-cm piece of straw between them. Arrange the straws so that their ends are even.

D Tape the straws together side by side. Starting from the untaped end, make marks every centimeter on one of the long straws. This is the rocket.

5. You can measure the amount of stretch of the rubber band by noting where the markings on the rocket line up with the bottom of the launching cylinder. Launch the rocket using five different amounts of stretch. Record your measurements.

6. For each amount of stretch, find the average height to which the rocket rises. Record the height in your data table.

7. Find the gravitational potential energy for each amount of stretch:

Gravitational potential energy =
Mass × Gravitational acceleration × Height

You have measured the mass in grams. So the unit of energy is the millijoule (mJ), which is one thousandth of a joule. Record the results in your data table.

Troubleshooting the Experiment
The straw rocket should be put on the rubber band the same way each time. The ends of the straw must be parallel when the straw is pulled down. If a toilet paper tube is used it may begin to collapse after several uses and should be replaced. Remind students not to twist the straw rocket as they read the stretch marking; the entire assembly should be rotated to see the marks.

Data Table					
Amount of Stretch (cm)	Height Trial 1 (m)	Height Trial 2 (m)	Height Trial 3 (m)	Average Height (m)	Gravitational Potential Energy (mJ)

Analyze and Conclude

1. **Controlling Variables** Which variable in your data table is the manipulated variable? The responding variable? How do you know?

2. **Graphing** Graph your results. Show gravitational potential energy on the vertical axis and amount of stretch on the horizontal axis.

3. **Measuring** In this experiment, what measurement is related to elastic potential energy?

4. **Drawing Conclusions** Look at the shape of the graph. What conclusions can you reach about the relationship between the gravitational potential energy of the rocket and the elastic potential energy of the rubber band?

5. **Inferring** When you release the rocket, what kind of energy does the rocket have just after takeoff? What are the elastic potential energy and the gravitational potential energy at this point?

6. **Developing Hypotheses** Make an additional column on the right side of your data table labeled Kinetic Energy (mJ). For each row, write down what you think the rocket's kinetic energy is right after takeoff.

7. **Communicating** Write an advertisement for your rocket launcher. Include a diagram explaining how the rocket gains potential energy, how its potential energy is transformed to kinetic energy, and how its kinetic energy is transformed back into potential energy.

Design an Experiment

How would the height and distance the rocket travels be affected by the angle of launch? Design an experiment to measure the height and distance resulting from different launch angles. Keep the amount of stretch constant. *Obtain your teacher's permission before carrying out your investigation.*

Expected Outcome

As the elastic potential energy of the rubber band increases, the subsequent gravitational potential energy of the rocket increases. This relationship is complex. If the band is stretched very tight, more stretching might have a progressively smaller effect.

Analyze and Conclude

1. Manipulated variable—the amount of stretch of the elastic; responding variable—the height the rocket reached. The rubber band was stretched to various lengths, and the height was measured in response to the stretch.

2. The curve should point up and to the right.

3. Amount of stretch

4. As the elastic potential energy of the rubber band increases, the gravitational potential energy of the rocket increases.

5. Just after takeoff, the rocket has kinetic energy only. The elastic potential energy and gravitational potential energy are zero.

6. Students should predict that the rocket's kinetic energy at takeoff is equal to its gravitational potential energy at its maximum height.

7. Students' explanations and diagrams should clearly describe how the rocket gains energy from the rubber band and describe the energy transformations the rocket undergoes during flight.

Extend Inquiry

Design an Experiment Students may propose various methods of determining the relationship between rocket height and distance and the angle at which it is launched. Be sure students' methods are safe before allowing them to perform their investigations.

Objectives

After this lesson, students will be able to
M.5.4.1 Identify the source of the energy stored in fossil fuels.
M.5.4.2 Describe how energy is transformed when fossil fuels are used.

Target Reading Skill

Previewing Visuals Explain that looking at the visuals before they read helps students activate prior knowledge and predict what they are about to read.

Answers

Sample graphic organizer:
What energy transformation occurs in the sun? (Nuclear energy to thermal energy and electromagnetic energy) **What energy transformation takes place when coal is burned?** (Chemical energy to thermal energy)

All in One Teaching Resources
• Transparency M50

Preteach

Build Background Knowledge L2

Identifying Fossil Fuels

Show students a piece of coal. Ask: **What is this, and what is it used for?** (Coal, it provides thermal energy.) **What happens when the coal is burned?** (The coal produces thermal energy.) **What does this tell you about coal?** (Sample: It contains potential energy.)

Go Online
SCiLINKS NSTA
For: Links on energy transformations
Visit: www.SciLinks.org
Web Code: scn-1354

Students can research energy transformations online.

Energy and Fossil Fuels

Reading Preview

Key Concepts
• What is the source of the energy stored in fossil fuels?
• How is energy transformed when fossil fuels are used?

Key Terms
• fossil fuel
• combustion

Target Reading Skill

Previewing Visuals When you preview, you look ahead at the material to be read. Preview Figure 18. Then write two questions that you have about the diagram in a graphic organizer like the one below. As you read, answer your questions.

Using Fossil Fuel Energy

Q.	What energy transformation occurs in the sun?
A.	
Q.	

Go Online
SCiLINKS NSTA
For: Links on energy transformations
Visit: www.SciLinks.org
Web Code: scn-1354

166 ◆ M

Lab zone Discover Activity

What Is a Fuel?

1. Put on your goggles. Attach a flask to a ring stand with a clamp. Then place a thermometer in the flask.
2. Add enough water to the flask to cover the thermometer bulb. Record the temperature of the water. Remove the thermometer.
3. Fold a wooden coffee stirrer in three places to look like a W. Stand it in a small aluminum pan so that the W is upright. Position the pan 4–5 cm directly below the flask.
4. Ignite the coffee stirrer at its center. **CAUTION:** Be careful when using matches.
5. When the coffee stirrer has stopped burning, read the temperature of the water again. Allow the flask to cool before cleaning up.

Think It Over
Forming Operational Definitions Gasoline in a car, kerosene in a lantern, and a piece of wood are all fuels. Based on your observations, what is a fuel?

Imagine a lush, green, swampy forest. Ferns as tall as trees block the view. Enormous dragonflies buzz through the warm, moist air. Huge cockroaches, some longer than your finger, crawl across the ground. Where is this place? Actually, a better question to ask would be, *when* is it? The time is more than 400 million years ago. That's even before the dinosaurs lived! But what does this ancient forest have to do with you?

Formation of Fossil Fuels

The plants of vast forests that once covered Earth provide the energy stored in fuels. A fuel is a material that contains stored potential energy. The gasoline used in vehicles and the propane used in a gas grill are examples of fuels. Some of the fuels used today were made from materials that formed hundreds of millions of years ago. These fuels, which include coal, petroleum, and natural gas, are known as **fossil fuels.**

Lab zone Discover Activity

Skills Focus Forming operational definitions **L1**

Materials flask, ring stand, clamp, thermometer, water, wooden coffee stirrer, small aluminum pan, matches, safety goggles

Time 20 minutes

Tip CAUTION: *Students should use care when working with matches and keep loose*

hair and clothing away from the burning wood. The flask will be hot.

Expected Outcome The temperature of the water is higher after the coffee stirrer is burned.

Think It Over Sample answer: A fuel is a material that contains stored energy and can be used to supply energy.

The vast, ancient forests were the source of coal. When plants and animals died, their remains piled up in thick layers in swamps and marshes. Clay and sand sediments covered their remains. The resulting pressure and high temperature turned the remains into coal.

Energy From the Sun Remember that energy is conserved. That means that fuels do not create energy. So if fossil fuels store energy, they must have gotten energy from somewhere else. But where did it come from? **Fossil fuels contain energy that came from the sun.** In fact, the sun is the source of energy for most of Earth's processes. Within the dense core of the sun, during the process of nuclear fusion, nuclear energy is transformed to electromagnetic energy as well as other forms. Some of this electromagnetic energy reaches Earth in the form of light.

FIGURE 16
Fossil Fuels
Offshore oil rigs drill for the fossil fuel petroleum under the ocean floor.

 Reading Checkpoint What is the source of the energy stored in fossil fuels?

FIGURE 17
Mining for Coal
Miners use heavy machinery to dig for coal. Developing Hypotheses *Why is coal usually found underground?*

M ◆ 167

Instruct

Formation of Fossil Fuels

Teach Key Concepts   L2
Fossil Fuels Store the Sun's Energy

Focus Tell students that fossils fuels are formed from the remains of once-living things.

Teach Have students state the steps in the formation of fossil fuels, and write their answers on the board. Have students review the steps, and insert or rearrange the steps as needed. (*Sample answer: Plants store the sun's energy, animals eat the plants, plants and animals die, remains are buried, heat and pressure turn remains into coal*)

Apply Ask: **Do fossil fuels have potential or kinetic energy?** (*Potential energy*) **learning modality: verbal**

Independent Practice   L2

All in One Teaching Resources

- Guided Reading and Study Worksheet: *Energy and Fossil Fuels*

◉ **Student Edition on Audio CD**

Differentiated Instruction

Less Proficient Readers   L1
Reviewing Key Concepts Have students read the boldface sentences in the section. Then ask the following questions: **Where did the energy in fossil fuels come from?** (*The sun*) **How is energy in fossil fuels released?** (*Burning, or combustion*)
learning modality: verbal

Gifted and Talented   L3
Displaying Information Have students research the use of fossil fuels in the United States. Possible topics include the increase or decrease in use of certain fuels or fuel consumption by state. Have students generate graphs and charts summarizing the data they have located. Students can display their graphs and charts in the classroom. **learning modality: logical/mathematical**

Monitor Progress   L2

Writing Have students write paragraphs describing how ancient plants were transformed to fossil fuels.

Students can save their writing in their portfolios.   Portfolio

Answers
Figure 17 Thick layers of sediments covered plant and animal remains, from which the coal was formed.

Reading Checkpoint The sun

Use of Fossil Fuels

Teach Key Concepts L2

Fossil Fuels and Energy Transformations

Focus Tell students that in order for the energy in fossils fuels to be useful, energy transformations must take place.

Teach Have students name some of the energy transformations that occur in the use of fossil fuel. Ask: **Why is chemical energy always involved in the use of a fossil fuel?** *(Fossil fuels store chemical energy.)*

Apply Ask: **How is the energy in coal transformed into electricity?** *(Chemical energy is released when coal is burned, which heats water to make steam. The thermal energy of the steam is transformed to mechanical energy by a turbine, which causes generators to spin and transform the mechanical energy to electrical energy.)* **learning modality: logical/ mathematical**

Lab zone Teacher **Demo** L1

Plants Store the Sun's Energy

Materials two seedlings, cups, water, potting soil

Time 5 min a day for several days

Focus Tell students that plants store the sun's energy.

Teach Place two seedlings in the classroom, one near a window and one in the dark. Have the students observe the plants for several days.

Apply Ask: **Which of these plants has received enough of the sun's energy to meet its energy needs?** *(The seedling near the window)* **learning modality: visual**

---

① The sun transforms nuclear energy to electromagnetic energy.

FIGURE 18
Using Fossil Fuel Energy
The chemical energy in fossil fuels comes from the sun. Millions of years later, power plants transform that chemical energy to the electrical energy that powers your hair dryer.
Interpreting Diagrams What does a turbine do?

③ Coal is burned to make steam, transforming stored chemical energy to thermal energy.

② Ancient plants and animals transform electromagnetic energy from the sun to stored chemical energy. Their remains become coal.

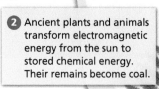

Lab zone Skills **Activity**

Graphing

The following list shows what percent of power used in the United States in a recent year came from each energy source: coal, 23%; nuclear, 8%; oil, 39%; natural gas, 24%; water, 3%; and biofuels, 3%. Prepare a circle graph that presents these data. (See the Skills Handbook for more on circle graphs.)

What power source does the United States rely on most? What percent of the country's total energy needs is met by coal, oil, and natural gas combined?

The Sun's Energy on Earth When the sun's energy reaches Earth, certain living things—plants, algae, and certain bacteria—transform some of it to chemical energy. Some of the energy in the chemical compounds they make is used for their daily energy needs. The rest is stored. Animals that eat plants store some of the plant's chemical energy in their own cells. When ancient animals and plants died, the chemical energy they had stored was trapped within them. This trapped energy is the chemical energy found in coal.

Use of Fossil Fuels

Fossil fuels can be burned to release the chemical energy stored millions of years ago. The process of burning fuels is known as **combustion.** During combustion, the fuel's chemical energy is transformed to thermal energy. This thermal energy can be used to heat water until the water boils and produces steam. In modern, coal-fired power plants, the steam is raised to a very high temperature in a boiler. When it leaves the boiler it has enough pressure to turn a turbine.

Lab zone Skills **Activity**

Skills Focus Graphing

Materials graph paper, compass, protractor

Time 15 minutes

Tips Demonstrate for students how to use the compass and protractor to complete the circle graph.

L2

Expected Outcome Students will find that the United States relies mostly on oil. Together, coal, oil, and natural gas met 86% of the total energy needs in the given year.

Extend Have students find out what fuel resources provide the energy used in their home. **learning modality: logical/ mathematical**

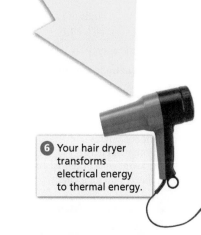

5 The turbines spin electric generators, transforming mechanical energy to electrical energy.

4 The steam turns turbines, transforming thermal energy to mechanical energy.

A turbine is like a fan, with blades attached to an axle. The pressure of the steam on the blades causes the turbine to spin very fast. In this process, the thermal energy of the steam is transformed to the mechanical energy of the moving turbine.

The turbines are connected to generators. When turbines spin them, generators produce electricity. As you can see in Figure 18, a power plant transforms chemical energy to thermal energy to mechanical energy to electrical energy. This electrical energy is then used to light your home and run other devices, such as a hair dryer.

6 Your hair dryer transforms electrical energy to thermal energy.

 Reading Checkpoint What energy transformations take place in a power plant?

Section 4 Assessment

Target Reading Skill Previewing Visuals Refer to your questions and answers about Figure 18 to help you answer Question 2 below.

Reviewing Key Concepts

1. **a.** Defining What are fossil fuels?
   b. Explaining What role did the sun play in making fossil fuels?
   c. Drawing Conclusions How did ancient animals receive stored energy from the sun?
2. **a.** Reviewing How is the chemical energy stored in coal released?
   b. Sequencing Describe the steps in which a power plant transforms the energy in fossil fuels to electrical energy.
   c. Inferring Which steps in the power plant process rely on potential energy? Which steps rely on kinetic energy? Why?

Lab zone At-Home **Activity**

Burning Fossils Some appliances in your home, such as ovens, grills, and water heaters, may use fossil fuels as an energy source. With a family member, search your home for appliances that use fossil fuels such as petroleum, coal, or natural gas as a source of energy. Explain to your family member what fossil fuels are and how they form.

Chapter 5 M ◆ 169

Lab zone At-Home **Activity**

Burning Fossils L2 Sample answer: I found that the hot water heater in my home was run using natural gas. Natural gas is a fossil fuel that has the sun's energy stored in the form of chemical potential energy. That energy is released through combustion, which transforms the chemical energy to thermal energy, which heats the water.

Lab zone Chapter **Project**

Keep Students on Track Make sure students can explain how the results of their experiments are related to the design of their roller coasters. Some students may have trouble with the performance of their roller coasters. Encourage them to simplify their designs until they find one that works, and add more detail slowly.

Monitor Progress ____ L2

Answers

Figure 18 A turbine transforms the thermal energy in steam to mechanical energy.

Reading Checkpoint A power plant that uses fossil fuels transforms chemical energy to thermal energy to mechanical energy to electrical energy.

Assess

Reviewing Key Concepts

1. **a.** Fuels made from materials that formed hundreds of millions of years ago, such as coal and petroleum, are fossil fuels. **b.** Some of the sun's energy reaches Earth as light, a form of electromagnetic energy. Some of that energy became stored in fossil fuels. **c.** Some of the sun's energy was transformed and stored in plants. Animals received the energy when they ate the plants.
2. **a.** It is released when coal is burned. **b.** A power plant transforms chemical energy to thermal energy when it burns a fossil fuel to make steam. The steam turns turbines that transform the thermal energy to mechanical energy. Turbines turn generators that supply electrical energy. **c.** When a fossil fuel is burned, chemical (potential) energy is transformed to thermal (kinetic and potential) energy. Boiling water and heating steam rely on a transfer of thermal (kinetic and potential) energy. When steam turns turbines, thermal (kinetic and potential) energy is transformed to mechanical (kinetic) energy. When turbines spin generators, mechanical (kinetic) energy is transformed to electrical (kinetic) energy.

Reteach L1

Have students review the energy transformations involved in the use of fossil fuels by reviewing Figure 18.

Performance Assessment L2

Writing Have students write a paragraph to describe how ancient plants were transformed into a fossil fuel.

All in One Teaching Resources

- Section Summary: *Energy and Fossil Fuels*
- Review and Reinforce: *Energy and Fossil Fuels*
- Enrich: *Energy and Fossil Fuels*

M ● 169

Study Guide

The BIG Idea

Have students read the answer to the Essential Question. Encourage them to evaluate and revise their own answers as needed.

Help Students Read

Building Vocabulary

Compare/Contrast Table Have students make a table that compares and contrasts various forms of energy. For example, chemical and nuclear energy are types of potential energy, while electrical energy is a type of kinetic energy.

Word/Part Analysis Tell students that the prefix *trans-* is a Latin word part meaning "across" or "through." Have students relate this to the term *energy transformation*. Ask students to name other words that contain the prefix *trans-*. Have the students relate the meaning of the prefix to the meaning of the word. *(Sample answer: Transparent, light can pass through)*

Connecting Concepts

Concept Maps Help students develop a concept map to show how the information in this chapter is related. Energy exists in many different forms including potential energy and kinetic energy, is measured in joules, and can be transformed without energy being created or destroyed. Have students brainstorm to identify the key concepts, key terms, details, and examples. Then, write each one on a self-sticking note and attach it at random on chart paper or on the board.

Tell students that this concept map will be organized in hierarchical order and to begin at the top with the key concepts. Ask students these questions to guide them to categorize the information on the self-sticking notes: **What is energy? What are some forms of energy? How is energy transformed and conserved? How is energy stored in fossil fuels?** Prompt students to use connecting words or phrases, such as "exists as" and "including," to indicate the

---

Energy Forms and Conservation Energy is the ability to do work or cause change. Energy can be transformed from one form into another, but it cannot be created or destroyed.

① What Is Energy?

Key Concepts

- If the transfer of energy is work, then power is the rate at which energy is transferred, or the amount of energy transferred in a unit of time.

- $\text{Power} = \dfrac{\text{Energy transferred}}{\text{Time}}$

- Two basic kinds of energy are kinetic energy and potential energy.

- $\text{Kinetic energy} = \frac{1}{2} \times \text{Mass} \times \text{Velocity}^2$

- Gravitational potential energy $=$
  $$\text{Weight} \times \text{Height}$$

Key Terms
energy
kinetic energy
potential energy
gravitational potential energy
elastic potential energy

② Forms of Energy

Key Concepts

- You can find an object's mechanical energy by adding the object's kinetic energy and potential energy.

  Mechanical energy $=$
  $$\text{Kinetic energy} + \text{Potential energy}$$

- Forms of energy associated with the particles of objects include thermal energy, electrical energy, chemical energy, nuclear energy, and electromagnetic energy.

Key Terms
mechanical energy
thermal energy
electrical energy
chemical energy
nuclear energy
electromagnetic energy

③ Energy Transformations and Conservation

Key Concepts

- Most forms of energy can be transformed into other forms.

- One of the most common energy transformations is the transformation between potential energy and kinetic energy.

- According to the law of conservation of energy, energy cannot be created or destroyed.

Key Terms
energy transformation
law of conservation of energy
matter

④ Energy and Fossil Fuels

Key Concepts

- Fossil fuels contain energy that came from the sun.

- Fossil fuels can be burned to release the chemical energy stored millions of years ago.

Key Terms
fossil fuel
combustion

---

basis for the connections in the map. The phrases should form a sentence between or among a set of concepts.

Answer

Accept logical presentations by students.

All in One Teaching Resources

- Key Terms Review: *Energy*
- Connecting Concepts: *Energy*

Review and Assessment

Go Online
PHSchool.com
For: Self-Assessment
Visit: PHSchool.com
Web Code: cga-3050

Organizing Information

Concept Mapping Copy the concept map about energy onto a separate sheet of paper. Then complete it and add a title. (For more on Concept Mapping, see the Skills Handbook.)

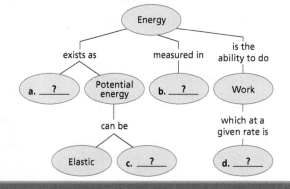

Reviewing Key Terms

Choose the letter of the best answer.

1. Energy of motion is called
   a. kinetic energy.
   b. elastic potential energy.
   c. gravitational potential energy.
   d. chemical energy.

2. When you stretch a rubber band, you give it
   a. kinetic energy.
   b. elastic potential energy.
   c. gravitational potential energy.
   d. electrical energy.

3. The energy associated with the position and motion of an object is called
   a. potential energy.
   b. nuclear energy.
   c. mechanical energy.
   d. thermal energy.

4. The energy stored in the nucleus of an atom is called
   a. electromagnetic energy.
   b. electrical energy.
   c. chemical energy.
   d. nuclear energy.

5. Fossil fuels store energy from the sun as
   a. chemical energy.
   b. thermal energy.
   c. electromagnetic energy.
   d. electrical energy.

If the statement is true, write *true*. If it is false, change the underlined word or words to make the statement true.

6. <u>Kinetic energy</u> is related to an object's height.

7. <u>Electrical energy</u> is the total kinetic and potential energy of the particles in an object.

8. The <u>law of conservation of energy</u> states that when one form of energy is transformed to another, no energy is destroyed.

9. <u>Energy</u> is anything that has mass and takes up space.

10. <u>Combustion</u> is the process of burning fuels.

Writing in Science

Interview You are preparing to interview an Olympic skier for a children's science magazine. Prepare a list of questions that you would ask the skier about the energy transformations that occur while skiing.

Discovery CHANNEL SCHOOL
Energy
Video Preview
Video Field Trip
▶ Video Assessment

Chapter 5 **M ◆ 171**

Go Online
PHSchool.com
For: Self-Assessment
Visit: PHSchool.com
Web Code: cga-3050

Students can take a practice test online that is automatically scored.

All in One Teaching Resources
- Transparency M51
- Chapter Test
- Performance Assessment Teacher Notes
- Performance Assessment Student Worksheet
- Performance Assessment Scoring Rubric

ExamView® Computer Test Bank CD-ROM

Review and Assessment

Organizing Information
a. Kinetic energy
b. Joules
c. Gravitational
d. Power

Reviewing Key Terms
1. a 2. b 3. c 4. d 5. a
6. Gravitational potential energy
7. Thermal energy
8. true
9. Matter
10. true

Discovery CHANNEL SCHOOL
Video Assessment

Energy

Show the Video Assessment to review chapter content and as a prompt for the writing assignment. Discussion questions: **Is potential energy or kinetic energy ever lost? Why or why not?** *(Sample answer: No, energy is not lost, but it can be transformed.)* **What force can transform kinetic energy into heat?** *(Friction)*

Writing in Science

Writing Mode Exposition/Interview
Scoring Rubric
4 Exceeds criteria; includes thoughtful and detailed questions related to energy transformations during skiing
3 Meets criteria
2 The list of interview questions is brief and/or does not show a strong relationship between skiing and energy transformations
1 The list of questions does not relate skiing to energy transformations and/or shows poor effort

Checking Concepts

11. Work can be thought of as the transfer of energy.

12. An object's mechanical energy is the sum of its potential energy and kinetic energy.

13. The walnut has mechanical energy (kinetic and gravitational potential energy). The burning candle has chemical energy and releases thermal energy and electromagnetic energy. The spring has elastic potential energy.

14. On the perch, the eagle has gravitational potential energy. Halfway to the ground, half of the gravitational potential energy transforms to kinetic energy. When the eagle reaches its prey, all its mechanical energy is kinetic energy. The eagle also transforms chemical energy from its food to mechanical energy when it flies.

15. Some of the sun's energy is transformed and stored in plants and in animals that ate the plants. When the remains of plants and animals pile up in layers in swamps and marshes and are covered by thick sediments of clay and sand, pressure and high temperature transform the remains to fossil fuels. Chemical (potential) energy is stored in a fossil fuel.

Thinking Critically

16. 50 watts

17. 97,200 J

18. The motorcycle has the least kinetic energy because it has the least mass. The red vehicle has the greatest kinetic energy because it has the greatest mass.

19. Her potential energy decreased by 950 J.

20. The energy is the same in both cases, but the power is double in the second case because the same energy transfer was done twice as quickly.

Math Practice

21. 144

22. 36

Checking Concepts

11. Define work in terms of energy.

12. How do you find an object's mechanical energy?

13. For each of the following, decide which forms of energy are present: a walnut falls from a tree; a candle burns; a spring is stretched.

14. An eagle flies from its perch in a tree to the ground to capture and eat its prey. Describe its energy transformations.

15. How does energy become stored in a fossil fuel? What kind of energy is stored?

Thinking Critically

16. **Calculating** Find the power of a machine that transfers 450 J of energy in 9 s.

17. **Calculating** A 1,350-kg car travels at 12 m/s. What is its kinetic energy?

18. **Comparing and Contrasting** In the illustration below, which vehicle has the least kinetic energy? The greatest kinetic energy? Explain your answers.

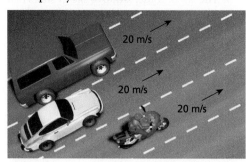

19. **Problem Solving** A 380-N girl walks down a flight of stairs so that she is 2.5 m below her starting level. What is the change in the girl's gravitational potential energy?

20. **Applying Concepts** One chef places a pie in the oven at a low setting so that it is baked in one hour. Another chef places a pie in the oven at a high setting so that the pie bakes in 30 minutes. Is the amount of energy the same in each case? Is the power the same?

Math Practice

21. **Exponents** What is the value of 12^2?

22. **Exponents** What is the value of $2^2 \times 3^2$?

Applying Skills

Use the photo to answer Questions 23–25.

The golfer in the photo is taking a swing. The golf club starts at Point A and ends at Point E.

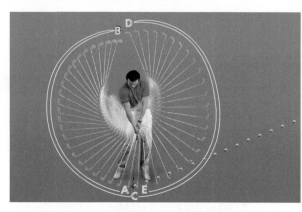

23. **Inferring** At which point(s) does the golf club have the greatest potential energy? At which point(s) does it have the greatest kinetic energy?

24. **Interpreting Diagrams** Describe the energy transformations from Point A to Point E.

25. **Drawing Conclusions** The kinetic energy of the club at Point C is more than the potential energy of the club at Point B. Does this mean that the law of conservation of energy is violated? Why or why not?

Lab zone Chapter **Project**

Performance Assessment Present your roller coaster to the class. Explain how you selected your materials, as well as the effect of hill height, incline, turns, and loops on the motion of the roller coaster. You should also explain how energy is transformed as the roller coaster moves along the tracks.

Lab zone Chapter **Project**   L3

Performance Assessment Students should present their roller coasters to the class either in an oral presentation with demonstrations or as a class exhibit. Ask the students to demonstrate how their roller coasters transform potential energy to kinetic energy.

Standardized Test Prep

Choose the letter of the best answer.

1. Wind has energy because
   - **A** it can change direction.
   - **B** it can do work.
   - **C** it has mass.
   - **D** it is electrically charged.

Use the table below and your knowledge of science to answer Questions 2 and 3.

Summer Classic Diving Competition

Name	Weight (N)	Height of Dive (m)
Clark	620	3
Simmons	640	3
Delgado	610	10
Chen	590	10

2. When standing on the diving board, which diver has the least gravitational potential energy?
   - **F** Clark
   - **G** Simmons
   - **H** Delgado
   - **J** Chen

3. In SI, which unit is used to express the divers' gravitational potential energy?
   - **A** newton
   - **B** kilowatt
   - **C** horsepower
   - **D** joule

4. A pendulum will eventually slow and stop because of
   - **F** friction.
   - **G** weight.
   - **H** kinetic energy.
   - **J** potential energy.

5. What energy transformation takes place when wood is burned?
   - **A** nuclear energy to thermal energy
   - **B** thermal energy to electrical energy
   - **C** chemical energy to thermal energy
   - **D** mechanical energy to thermal energy

Constructed Response

6. Explain the energy transformations involved in how fossil fuels formed and how they are used.

Applying Skills

23. The golf club has the greatest potential energy at D, and nearly as much potential energy at B, which is slighty lower. It has the greatest kinetic energy at C.

24. At A, when the club is at rest, the club has no potential or kinetic energy. At B it has near-maximum gravitational potential energy and no kinetic energy. At C it has maximum kinetic energy and no potential energy. At D it has maximum potential energy and no kinetic energy. At E, when it is brought back to rest, it has no potential or kinetic energy.

25. No, the man adds energy as he swings the club. Therefore, energy is conserved.

Standardized Test Practice

1. B **2.** F **3.** D **4.** F **5.** C

6. Much of the energy on Earth originally came from the sun. Millions of years ago, plants transformed the sun's electromagnetic energy to chemical energy through photosynthesis. Animals ate the plants and stored the plant's chemical energy in their own bodies. Eventually, both the plants and animals died. Over the centuries, their remains turned into fossil fuels such as coal, oil, and natural gas. Today, people transform the chemical energy in fossil fuels to thermal energy through combustion. In a power plant that burns fossil fuels, this thermal energy is transformed to mechanical energy and then to the electrical energy we use in our homes.

Chapter at a Glance

PRENTICE HALL
TeacherEXPRESS™
Plan • Teach • Assess

 **Chapter Project** *In Hot Water*

All in One Teaching Resources
- Chapter Project Teacher Notes, pp. 358–359
- Chapter Project Student Overview, pp. 360–361
- Chapter Project Student Worksheets, pp. 362–363
- Chapter Project Scoring Rubric, p. 364

Technology

Local Standards

Discovery CHANNEL SCHOOL
Video Preview

Section 1 — Temperature, Thermal Energy, and Heat

2–3 periods
1–1 1/2 blocks

M.6.1.1 Name the three common temperature scales.
M.6.1.2 Describe how thermal energy is related to temperature and heat.
M.6.1.3 Explain the significance of a high specific heat.

Go Online
SCi*LINKS*™ NSTA

Section 2 — The Transfer of Heat

M.6.2.1 Describe the three forms of heat transfer.
2–3 periods
1–1 1/2 blocks
M.6.2.2 Identify the direction in which heat moves.
M.6.2.3 Describe the differences between conductors and insulators.

Go Online
SCi*LINKS*™ NSTA

Section 3 — Thermal Energy and States of Matter

1–2 periods
1/2–1 block

M.6.3.1 Name the three states of matter.
M.6.3.2 Identify the cause of changes of state.
M.6.3.3 Describe what happens to a substance as its thermal energy increases.

Go Online
SCi*LINKS*™ NSTA

Discovery CHANNEL SCHOOL
Video Field Trip

Section 4 — Uses of Heat

1–2 periods
1/2–1 block

M.6.4.1 Describe how heat engines use thermal energy.
M.6.4.2 Describe how refrigerators keep things cold.

Go Online
active art

Review and Assessment

All in One Teaching Resources
- Key Terms Review, p. 399
- Transparency M60
- Performance Assessment Teacher Notes, p. 407
- Performance Assessment Scoring Rubric, p. 408
- Performance Assessment Student Worksheet, p. 409
- Chapter Test, pp. 410–413

Discovery CHANNEL SCHOOL
Video Assessment

Go Online
PHSchool.com

Test Preparation

Test Preparation Blackline Masters

Chapter Activities Planner

For more activities
LAB ZONE Easy Planner CD-ROM

Student Edition	Inquiry	Time	Materials	Skills	Resources
Chapter Project, p. 175	Open-Ended	Ongoing (1–2 weeks)	**All in One Teaching Resources** p. 358	Designing experiments, communicating	**Lab zone Easy Planner** **All in One Teaching Resources** pp. 358–359
Section 1					
Discover Activity, p. 176	Directed	10 minutes	3 large bowls, warm tap water, cold tap water, room temperature water, markers, paper	Observing	**Lab zone Easy Planner**
Technology Lab, p. 182	Open-ended	Prep: 30 minutes; Class: 40 minutes	Bowl of hot water, bowl of ice water, water of unknown temperature, tap water, food coloring, metric ruler, cooking oil, clear glass bottle, clear plastic straw, modeling clay, 500-mL beaker, plastic dropper, fine-point marker	Evaluating the design, troubleshooting	**Lab zone Easy Planner** **Lab Activity Video** **All in One Teaching Resources** Technology Lab: *Build Your Own Thermometer*, pp. 372–373
Section 2					
Discover Activity, p. 183	Directed	15 minutes	Frozen butter; glass beaker; hot water; utensils made of different materials, such as stainless steel, plastic, and wood	Observing	**Lab zone Easy Planner**
Try This Activity, p. 184	Directed	10 minutes	Lamp with a 60- or 75-W bulb, centimeter ruler, clock or stopwatch	Drawing conclusions	**Lab zone Easy Planner**
Skills Activity p. 186	Directed	10 minutes		Inferring	**Lab zone Easy Planner**
Skills Lab pp. 188–189	Guided	Prep: 15 minutes; Class: 40 minutes	Hot tap water, balance, scissors, pencil, 4 plastic foam cups, 2 thermometers or temperature probes, beaker of water kept in an ice bath	Observing, calculating, interpreting data	**Lab zone Easy Planner** **Lab Activity Video** **All in One Teaching Resources** Skills Lab: *Just Add Water*, pp. 381–383
Section 3					
Discover Activity, p. 190	Guided	15 minutes	1 m of thin metal wire, clamp, ring stand, 3 or 4 washers, matches, candle, oven mitt	Inferring	**Lab zone Easy Planner**
Skills Activity, p. 193	Directed	10 minutes	Tea kettle, hot plate, water	Observing	**Lab zone Easy Planner**
At-Home Activity, p. 194	Guided	Home		Measuring	
Section 4					
Discover Activity, p. 195	Directed	10 minutes	Bicycle pump, deflated basketball or soccer ball	Developing hypotheses	**Lab zone Easy Planner**
Try This Activity, p. 196	Directed	15 minutes	Dry sand, metal container such as a coffee can with a plastic lid, thermometer	Classifying	**Lab zone Easy Planner**

Section 1 Temperature, Thermal Energy, and Heat

ABILITY LEVELS
L1 Basic to Average
L2 For All Students
L3 Average to Advanced

 2–3 periods, 1–1 1/2 blocks

Objectives

Local Standards

M.6.1.1 Name the three common temperature scales.
M.6.1.2 Describe how thermal energy is related to temperature and heat.
M.6.1.3 Explain the significance of a high specific heat.

Key Terms

• temperature • Fahrenheit scale • Celsius scale • Kelvin scale • absolute zero
• heat • specific heat

Preteach

Build Background Knowledge

Have students locate temperature data in newspapers, and use the data to initiate a discussion about temperature.

 **Discover Activity** *How Cold Is the Water?*

Targeted Print and Technology Resources

 **Teaching Resources**

L2 Reading Strategy Transparency
M52: Comparing and Contrasting

⊙ **PresentationExpress™ CD-ROM**

Instruct

Temperature Ask leading questions to show the relationship between temperature and the average kinetic energy of the particles in matter.

Thermal Energy and Heat Use a fill-in-the-blank exercise to help students define temperature, thermal energy, and heat.

Specific Heat Use Figure 6 to help students understand specific heat.

 **Technology Lab** *Build Your Own Thermometer*

Targeted Print and Technology Resources

 **Teaching Resources**

L2 Guided Reading, pp. 367–369
L2 Transparency M53
L2 Technology Lab: *Build Your Own Thermometer*, pp. 372–373

▭ **Lab Activity Video/DVD**
Technology Lab: *Build Your Own Thermometer*

www.SciLinks.org Web Code: scn-1361

⊙ **Student Edition on Audio CD**

Assess

Section Assessment Questions

 Have students use their completed tables to answer the questions.

Reteach

Students state the main idea of each figure in the section.

Targeted Print and Technology Resources

 **Teaching Resources**

• Section Summary, p. 366
L1 Review and Reinforce, p. 370
L3 Enrich, p. 371

Section 2 The Transfer of Heat

 2–3 periods, 1–1 1/2 blocks

Objectives

M.6.2.1 Describe the three forms of heat transfer.

M.6.2.2 Identify the direction in which heat moves.

M.6.2.3 Describe the differences between conductors and insulators.

Local Standards

Key Terms

• conduction • convection • convection current • radiation • conductor
• insulator

Preteach

Build Background Knowledge

Ask questions about an everyday situation to introduce the idea of heat transfer.

 **Discover Activity** *What Does It Mean to Heat Up?* L2

Targeted Print and Technology Resources

 **Teaching Resources**

L2 Reading Strategy Transparency
M54: Identifying Main Ideas

 PresentationExpress™ CD-ROM

Instruct

How Is Heat Transferred? Students describe and list examples of each mode of heat transfer.

Heat Moves One Way Familiarize students with the direction of heat flow by using everyday examples.

Conductors and Insulators Ask leading questions to help students relate the properties of materials to their uses.

 **Skills Lab** *Just Add Water* L2

Targeted Print and Technology Resources

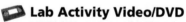 **Teaching Resources**

L2 Guided Reading, pp. 376–378
L2 Skills Lab: *Just Add Water*, pp. 381–383

Lab Activity Video/DVD
Skills Lab: *Just Add Water*

www.SciLinks.org Web Code: scn-1362

 Student Edition on Audio CD

Assess

Section Assessment Questions

 Have students use their completed graphic organizers to answer the questions.

Reteach

Students work in pairs to review the key terms from the section.

Targeted Print and Technology Resources

 **Teaching Resources**

• Section Summary, p. 375
L1 Review and Reinforce, p. 379
L3 Enrich, p. 380

Section 3 Thermal Energy and States of Matter

ABILITY LEVELS
L1 Basic to Average
L2 For All Students
L3 Average to Advanced

 1–2 periods, 1/2–1 block

Objectives

M.6.3.1 Name the three states of matter.

M.6.3.2 Identify the cause of changes of state.

M.6.3.3 Describe what happens to a substance as its thermal energy increases.

Local Standards

Key Terms

- state • change of state • melting • freezing • evaporation • boiling
- condensation • thermal expansion

Preteach

Build Background Knowledge

Use a glass of ice water to introduce states of matter.

 **Discover Activity** *What Happens to Heated Metal?* **L2**

Targeted Print and Technology Resources

 **Teaching Resources**

L2 Reading Strategy: Building Vocabulary

PresentationExpress™ CD-ROM

Instruct

Three States of Matter Challenge students to generate lists of facts about and examples of solids, liquids, and gases.

Changes of State Guide students in relating thermal energy to changes in state.

Thermal Expansion Relate changes in an object's thermal energy to expansion and contraction.

Targeted Print and Technology Resources

 **Teaching Resources**

L2 Guided Reading, pp. 386–389

L2 Transparency M55

www.SciLinks.org Web Code: scn-1363

 DISCOVERY CHANNEL SCHOOL
Video Field Trip

Student Edition on Audio CD

Assess

Section Assessment Questions

Have students use their completed sentences to answer the questions.

Reteach

Students restate the boldface sentences in the section in their own words.

Targeted Print and Technology Resources

 **Teaching Resources**

- Section Summary, p. 385

L1 Review and Reinforce, p. 390

L3 Enrich, p. 391

Section 4 Uses of Heat

 1–2 periods, 1/2–1 block

ABILITY LEVELS
L1 Basic to Average
L2 For All Students
L3 Average to Advanced

Objectives

M.6.4.1 Describe how heat engines use thermal energy.
M.6.4.2 Describe how refrigerators keep things cold.

Key Terms

• heat engine • external combustion engine • internal combustion engine
• refrigerant

Local Standards

Preteach

Build Background Knowledge

Ask questions to help students relate combustion to thermal energy.

 **Discover Activity** *What Happens at the Pump?*   **L1**

Targeted Print and Technology Resources

 **Teaching Resources**
L2 Reading Strategy Transparency
M56: Sequencing

◉ **PresentationExpress™ CD-ROM**

Instruct

Heat Engines Ask leading questions to help students identify the energy transformations in a heat engine.

Cooling Systems Use Figure 17 to help students understand how a refrigerator works.

Targeted Print and Technology Resources

Teaching Resources
L2 Guided Reading, pp. 394–396
L2 Transparencies M57, M58, M59

PHSchool.com Web Code: cgp-3064

◉ **Student Edition on Audio CD**

Assess

Section Assessment Questions

Have students use their completed cycle diagrams to answer Question 2.

Reteach

Students review heat engines and refrigerators using Figures 16 and 17.

Targeted Print and Technology Resources

Teaching Resources
• Section Summary, p. 393
L1 Review and Reinforce, p. 397
L3 Enrich, p. 398

Chapter 6 Content Refresher

Professional Development

Section 1 Temperature, Thermal Energy, and Heat

Measuring Temperature   There are many different devices, called temperature sensors, that can be used to measure temperature. Temperature sensors use properties, such as the volume of a liquid, that change with temperature.

Thermometers are a familiar type of temperature sensor. Thermometers require contact with a substance in order to measure its temperature. Thermal energy transfers until the temperature of the thermometer and the substance are the same. This is important because the temperature shown by a thermometer is actually its own temperature.

Other temperature sensors rely on other properties that change with temperature. A thermocouple, shown below, is a type of temperature sensor that uses two different types of metal. The voltage generated by the contact of the two dissimilar metals changes with temperature. Using a table that equates voltage to temperature allows thermocouples to be used to measure temperature.

> **⚑ Address Misconceptions**
>
> *Students may be confused about the scientific meaning of the word* heat. *For a strategy for overcoming this misconception, see* **Address Misconceptions** *in the section* Temperature, Thermal Energy, and Heat.

Thermocouple

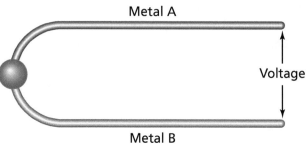

Metal A

Voltage

Metal B

Section 2 The Transfer of Heat

Methods of Heat Transfer   There are three methods by which heat can be transferred: convection, conduction, and radiation.

Heat transfers by convection when particles in a fluid move from one place to another. A fluid that is heated expands, becoming less dense than the surrounding fluid. The difference in densities causes the warm, less dense fluid to rise and the cooler, denser fluid to sink, creating a convection current.

In the process of conduction, the collisions between particles tranfer heat on average from particles with greater kinetic energy to particles with lower kinetic energy.

Heat is transferred by radiation via electromagnetic waves, which can travel through empty space. Absorption of radiation by matter increases the matter's thermal energy, while emission of radiation decreases the thermal energy of the matter.

Insulation   Insulators are substances that do not conduct heat well. Some substances (for example fiberglass) insulate well because they contain pockets of trapped air. Insulation is a consideration in the design and construction of buildings such as homes and schools. A properly insulated building reduces the cost and environmental impact of heating and cooling the building.

Insulating materials can be compared using R values. An R value is a numerical rating of a material's insulating ability, or thermal resistance. For any substance, the R value is the inverse of k, its heat conductivity. R values are usually given per one-inch thickness of a material. Since R values are additive, two inches of material will have double the R value of one inch of material.

Section 3 Thermal Energy and States of Matter

Latent Heat The thermal energy absorbed or released by a substance during a phase change is called latent heat. This thermal energy does not change the temperature of the substance, but it does change the arrangement of the molecules of the substance. The latent heat associated with the change in state between liquid and solid is called the *latent heat of fusion*. The *latent heat of vaporization* refers to the latent heat associated with change of state between liquid and gas.

The latent heat of fusion and the latent heat of vaporization are not the same for any given substance. In other words, a different amount of thermal energy is involved in the change of a given substance from a solid to a liquid than is involved in the change from a liquid to a gas. Water, for example, has a latent heat of fusion of 3.3×10^5 J/kg. So, a kilogram of ice must gain 3.3×10^5 J of thermal energy in order to change phase to liquid water. A kilogram of water must release 3.3×10^5 J of thermal energy to become ice. For a kilogram of water to become a gas, however, 2.3×10^6 J of thermal energy is needed for the phase change. In this case, the latent heat of vaporization of 2.3×10^6 J/kg is much higher than the latent heat of fusion.

The graph below shows the temperature and thermal energy of a substance as it undergoes phase changes. In the areas where the line is flat, the substance's thermal energy is changing but its temperature is not.

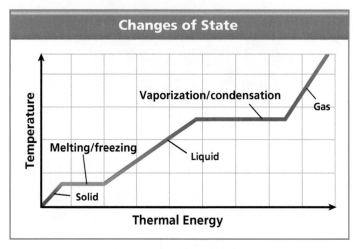

Changes of State

Note that the lengths of the two flat segments are different. This substance requires a greater change in thermal energy to change between a liquid and a gas than it does to change between a solid and a liquid.

Section 4 Uses of Heat

Refrigerants The operation of refrigerators and air conditioning systems relies on substances known as refrigerants. In a cooling system, a refrigerant undergoes changes in pressure and temperature, which cause changes in state.

Substances used as refrigerants must have certain properties. The latent heat of vaporization is the amount of thermal energy absorbed or released by a substance in the phase change between liquid and gas. Since refrigerants in their liquid state absorb thermal energy from the contents of the refrigerator, one property of an ideal refrigerant is a high latent heat of vaporization. This property allows the substance to absorb a great deal of thermal energy from the refrigerator's contents as it changes to a gas.

Other factors used to evaluate substances as refrigerants are their toxicity to humans and their effect on the environment. Ammonia was used as a refrigerant in some early cooling systems, but it is highly toxic. CFCs, which are substances containing chlorine, fluorine, and carbon, were used extensively as refrigerants until the mid 1970s. Although CFCs were thought to be ideal refrigerants because of their physical properties and lack of toxicity, research has linked CFCs to damage of the Earth's ozone layer. Today, compounds such as HFCs or HCFCs, which have little or no effect on the ozone layer, are used in most refrigerators.

Help Students Read

SQ3R
Survey, Question, Read, Recite, and Review

Strategy Using this strategy helps students remember what they have read by having them focus on the main topics in the reading assignment, such as the section *Temperature, Thermal Energy, and Heat*.

Example
1. Survey: Have students look over the section and note the headings, boldface sentences, and key terms.
2. Question: Have the students use each heading in the section to generate a question. Students should write the questions, leaving space after each question for a written answer.
3. Read: Have students read the section. While they read, they should locate the answers to their questions.
4. Recite: Have students recite their questions and answers.
5. Review: Have the students review the section content by writing the answers they recited in Step 4. After they have written their answers, have them answer each of the key concept questions found on the first page of the section.

See the section *Temperature, Thermal Energy, and Heat*, for a script using the SQ3R strategy with students.

The BIG Idea

The Big Idea is the major scientific concept of the chapter. It is followed by the Essential Question. Read aloud the question to students. As students study the chapter, tell them to think about the Essential Question. Explain that they will discover the answer to the question as they read. The chapter Study Guide provides a sample answer.

Lab zone Chapter **Project** L3

Objectives

This Chapter Project will challenge students to explore what is necessary to keep a can of hot water warm. After completing this Chapter Project, students will be able to

- design and analyze an experiment to measure the insulating capabilities of several materials
- build and test an insulating device
- communicate the insulating capabilities of their devices

Skills Focus

Designing experiments, communicating

Project Time Line 1–2 weeks

All in One Teaching Resources

- Chapter Project Teacher Notes
- Chapter Project Overview
- Chapter Project Worksheet 1
- Chapter Project Worksheet 2
- Chapter Project Scoring Rubric

Safety

Follow the safety guidelines in Appendix A.

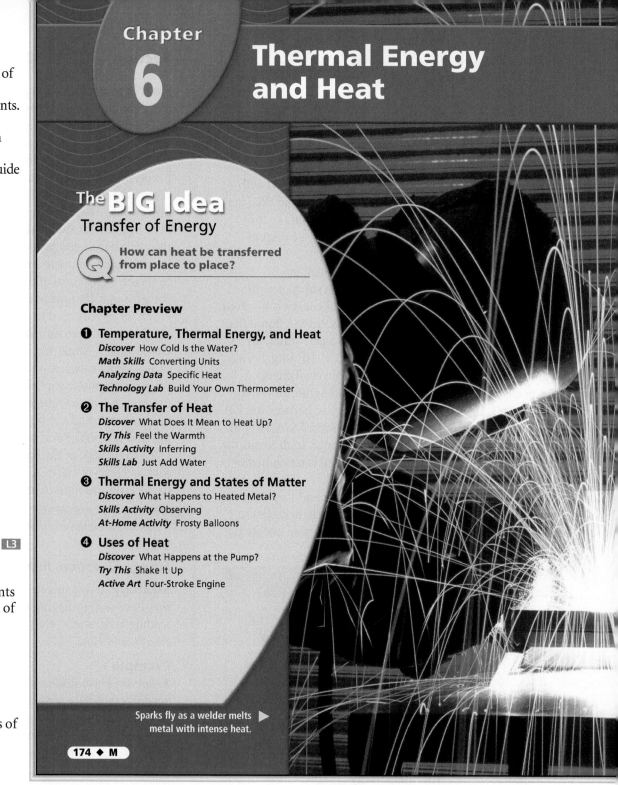

Chapter

6 Thermal Energy and Heat

The BIG Idea
Transfer of Energy

Q How can heat be transferred from place to place?
_____

Chapter Preview

❶ Temperature, Thermal Energy, and Heat
Discover How Cold Is the Water?
Math Skills Converting Units
Analyzing Data Specific Heat
Technology Lab Build Your Own Thermometer

❷ The Transfer of Heat
Discover What Does It Mean to Heat Up?
Try This Feel the Warmth
Skills Activity Inferring
Skills Lab Just Add Water

❸ Thermal Energy and States of Matter
Discover What Happens to Heated Metal?
Skills Activity Observing
At-Home Activity Frosty Balloons

❹ Uses of Heat
Discover What Happens at the Pump?
Try This Shake It Up
Active Art Four-Stroke Engine

► Sparks fly as a welder melts metal with intense heat.

Developing a Plan

After introducing the project, encourage students to spend two or three days designing and performing experiments to measure the insulating abilities of several different materials. Class time should be set aside to allow students access to thermometers. After students have obtained the results of their experiments, they should apply the results to design and build an insulating device. On the last day, students' devices will be tested for their ability to keep hot water warm.

Possible Materials

Empty aluminum soda cans, funnels, thermometers, tongs or hot pads, and a wide variety of materials for insulation, including aluminum foil, cardboard, newspaper, packing peanuts, nylon cloth, canvas cloth, plastic wrap, foam board, and wood chips. Encourage students to suggest and use other materials as well.

DISCOVERY CHANNEL SCHOOL™

Thermal Energy
and Heat
▶ Video Preview
Video Field Trip
Video Assessment

DISCOVERY CHANNEL SCHOOL™
Video Preview

Lab zone™ Chapter Project

In Hot Water

In this chapter, you will find out what heat is and how it relates to thermal energy and temperature. As you read the chapter, you will use what you learn to construct a device that will insulate a container of hot water.

Your Goal To build a container for a 355-mL aluminum can that keeps water hot

Your container must

● minimize the loss of thermal energy from the hot water
● be built from materials approved by your teacher
● have insulation no thicker than 3 cm
● not use electricity or heating chemicals
● follow the safety guidelines in Appendix A

Plan It! With a group of classmates, brainstorm different materials that prevent heat loss. Write a plan for how you will test these materials. Include a list of the variables you will control when doing your tests. Perform your tests to determine the best insulating materials. Keep a log of your results. Then build and test the device.

Chapter 6   **M** ◆ 175

Thermal Energy and Heat

Show the Video Preview to introduce the chapter and provide an overview of chapter content. Discussion question: **How do most materials, including steel, respond to exposure to hot and cold temperatures?** *(Sample answer: Most materials expand when they are heated and contract when they are cooled.)*

Performance Assessment

The Chapter Project Scoring Rubric will help you evaluate how well students complete the Chapter Project. You may want to share the scoring rubric with your students so they will know what is expected. Students will be assessed on

● their experimental design
● whether the experiment included controls
● whether the experiment tested different materials and designs
● the effectiveness of the completed design
● the accuracy of their predictions of the final temperatures of other students' devices
● their participation in their groups (if the project is assigned to groups)

Students can keep the designs and descriptions of their insulating devices in their portfolios.

Portfolio

Possible Shortcuts

Have students work in groups, or alternatively, perform the project as a class project.

Launching the Project

Introduce the project as a mystery to solve. Challenge students to find the best design to insulate a can of water. Before students begin, encourage discussion of experimental design, including controls and variables. Remind students they can use insulating materials other than those on the suggested materials list. Remind students that the shape of their container and whether it has a lid will also affect their results. Remind students that they need to have their experimental designs approved by you before they proceed.

M ● 175

Objectives

After this lesson, students will be able to

M.6.1.1 Name the three common temperature scales.

M.6.1.2 Describe how thermal energy is related to temperature and heat.

M.6.1.3 Explain the significance of a high specific heat.

Target Reading Skill

Comparing and Contrasting Explain that comparing and contrasting information shows how ideas, facts, and events are similar and different. The results of the comparison can increase students' understanding.

Answers

Temperature—Average kinetic energy of particles, Fahrenheit or Celsius degrees, kelvins

Thermal energy—Total energy of all particles in an object, Joule

Heat—Energy transferred, Joule

All in One Teaching Resources

• Transparency M52

Preteach

Build Background Knowledge   L2

Temperature Measures Kinetic Energy

Have students use newspapers to locate the daily high and low temperatures for the past week. Invite students to describe the hottest and coldest temperatures they have experienced. Ask: **When the temperature of a substance is 25°C, what is that a measure of?** *(Sample answer: How hot or cold something is)* List the answers and use them as a basis for assessing misconceptions about temperature.

Section
1
Temperature, Thermal Energy, and Heat

Reading Preview

Key Concepts

• What are the three common temperature scales?

• How is thermal energy related to temperature and heat?

• What does having a high specific heat mean?

Key Terms

• temperature
• Fahrenheit scale
• Celsius scale
• Kelvin scale
• absolute zero
• heat
• specific heat

Target Reading Skill

Comparing and Contrasting
As you read, compare and contrast temperature, thermal energy, and heat by completing a table like the one below.

	Energy Measured	Units
Temp.	Average kinetic energy of particles	
Thermal energy		
Heat		

176 ◆ M

Lab zone Discover **Activity**

How Cold Is the Water?

1. Fill a plastic bowl with cold water, another with warm water, and a third with water at room temperature. Label each bowl and line them up.

2. Place your right hand in the cold water and your left hand in the warm water.

3. After about a minute, place both your hands in the third bowl at the same time.

Think It Over
Observing How did the water in the third bowl feel when you touched it? Did the water feel the same on both hands? If not, explain why.

The radio weather report says that today's high temperature will be 25 degrees. What should you wear? Do you need a coat to keep warm, or only shorts and a T-shirt? What you decide depends on what "25 degrees" means.

Temperature

You don't need a science book to tell you that the word *hot* means higher temperatures or the word *cold* means lower temperatures. When scientists think about high and low temperatures, however, they do not think about "hot" and "cold." Instead, they think about particles of matter in motion.

Recall that all matter is made up of tiny particles. These particles are always moving even if the matter they make up is stationary. Recall that the energy of motion is called kinetic energy. So all particles of matter have kinetic energy. The faster particles move, the more kinetic energy they have. **Temperature** is a measure of the average kinetic energy of the individual particles in matter.

Lab zone Discover **Activity**

Skills Focus Observing   L1

Materials 3 large bowls, warm tap water, cold tap water, room temperature water, markers, paper

Time 10 minutes

Tips Keep paper towels on hand to clean up any water spills. **CAUTION:** *Students should not use water with a temperature greater than 45°C.*

Expected Outcome The water in the third bowl will feel warm to the hand that was in the cold water and cold to the hand that was in the warm water.

Think It Over The water in the third bowl (room temperature water) felt warm to the hand that was in the cold water and cold to the hand that was in warm water. The sense of temperature by the body is relative.

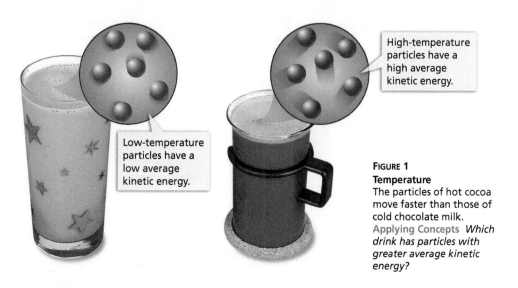

Low-temperature particles have a low average kinetic energy.

High-temperature particles have a high average kinetic energy.

FIGURE 1
Temperature
The particles of hot cocoa move faster than those of cold chocolate milk.
Applying Concepts Which drink has particles with greater average kinetic energy?

In Figure 1, the hot cocoa has a higher temperature than the cold chocolate milk. The cocoa's particles are moving faster, so they have greater average kinetic energy. If the milk is heated, its particles will move faster, so their kinetic energy will increase. The temperature of the milk will rise.

Measuring Temperature To measure the temperature of the heated milk, you would probably use a thermometer like the one shown in Figure 2. A thermometer usually consists of a liquid such as alcohol sealed inside a narrow glass tube. When the tube is heated, the particles of the liquid speed up and spread out so the particles take up more space, or volume. You see the level of the liquid move up the tube. The reverse happens when the tube is cooled. The particles of the liquid slow down and move closer, taking up less volume. You see the level of the liquid move down in the tube.

A thermometer has numbers and units, or a scale, on it. When you read the scale on a thermometer, you read the temperature of the surrounding matter. Thermometers can have different scales. The temperature reading you see depends on the thermometer's scale.

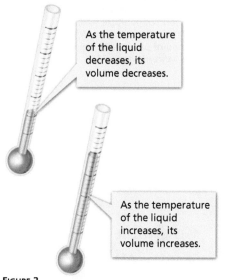

As the temperature of the liquid decreases, its volume decreases.

As the temperature of the liquid increases, its volume increases.

FIGURE 2
How a Thermometer Works
Temperature changes cause the level of the liquid inside a thermometer to rise and fall.

 Reading Checkpoint What happens to the liquid particles inside a thermometer when it is heated?

Chapter 6   M ◆ 177

Instruct

Temperature

Teach Key Concepts   L2
Describing and Measuring Temperature

Focus Tell students that in science the term *temperature* refers to the average kinetic energy of the tiny particles that make up matter.

Teach Ask: **If the kinetic energy of the particles in an object increases, what happens to the temperature of the object?** *(The temperature increases.)* **If the kinetic energy of the particles in an object decreases, what happens to the temperature of the object?** *(The temperature decreases.)* Tell students that temperature is measured using a thermometer. The higher the level of the liquid in the thermometer, the higher the temperature.

Apply Ask: **What temperature scale are you most familiar with?** *(Sample answer: Fahrenheit)* **Why?** *(Sample answer: It is used in weather forecasts and recipes.)* **learning modality: logical/mathematical**

Independent Practice   L2

All in One Teaching Resources

• Guided Reading and Study Worksheet: *Temperature, Thermal Energy, and Heat*

⊙ **Student Edition on Audio CD**

Differentiated Instruction

English Learners/Beginning L1
Comprehension: Prior Knowledge
Students from countries other than the United States will most likely be familiar with hearing the temperature in weather reports given using the Celsius scale, rather than the Fahrenheit scale. Ask students to describe the typical high and low temperatures, in Celsius degrees, found in their home country. **learning modality: verbal**

English Learners/Intermediate L2
Comprehension: Prior Knowledge
Extend the Beginning activity by asking students to write several sentences describing the weather conditions, including temperatures, in their home country. Ask for volunteers to read their answers aloud. **learning modality: verbal**

Monitor Progress   L2

Writing Have students write a paragraph comparing the water particles in a pot of boiling water to those in an ice cube tray in the freezer.

Answers
Figure 1 The hot cocoa has particles with greater average kinetic energy.

Reading Checkpoint The liquid particles speed up and spread out, so the liquid takes up more volume.

M ● 177

Thermal Energy and Heat

Teach Key Concepts L2

Differentiating Between Temperature, Thermal Energy, and Heat

Focus Tell students that the terms *temperature*, *thermal energy*, and *heat* are related, but not identical, in meaning.

Teach Write the following sentences on the board: _____ *(Thermal energy)* is the total energy of all the particles in an object. _____ *(Temperature)* is the measure of the average kinetic energy of the particles in an object. The transfer of thermal energy is called _____. *(heat)* Ask for volunteers to supply the answer for each blank.

Apply Ask: **Can two objects have the same temperature but different amounts of thermal energy? Explain.** *(Yes, if the two objects have different numbers of particles, they can have the same temperature but different amounts of thermal energy.)*
learning modality: logical/mathematical

Help Students Read L1

SQ3R Refer to the Content Refresher in this chapter, which provides guidelines for using the SQ3R strategy.

Have students survey the section, noting the headings. Students should generate one written question for each heading, for example: *How are thermal energy and heat related?* Then have students read the section and look for answers to their questions. When students have completed reading they should recite, or state aloud, their questions and answers. As a review, have students write the answers to their questions. **learning modality: verbal**

 **Teaching Resources**

• Transparency M53

For: Links on temperature and heat
Visit: www.SciLinks.org
Web Code: scn-1361

Download a worksheet that will guide students' review of Internet sources on temperature and heat.

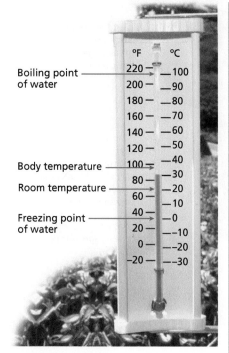

FIGURE 3
Temperature Scales
Many thermometers have both Celsius and Fahrenheit temperature scales.
Interpreting Photographs What is the boiling point of water on the Celsius scale? On the Fahrenheit scale?

For: Links on temperature and heat
Visit: www.SciLinks.org
Web Code: scn-1361

Temperature Scales The three common scales for measuring temperature are the Fahrenheit, Celsius, and Kelvin scales. Each of these scales is divided into regular intervals.

The temperature scale you are probably most familiar with is the Fahrenheit scale. In the United States, the **Fahrenheit scale** is the most common temperature scale. The scale is divided into degrees Fahrenheit (°F). On this scale, the freezing point of water is 32°F and the boiling point is 212°F.

In nearly all other countries, however, the most common temperature scale is the **Celsius scale.** The Celsius scale is divided into degrees Celsius (°C), which are larger units than degrees Fahrenheit. On the Celsius scale, the freezing point of water is 0°C and the boiling point is 100°C.

The temperature scale commonly used in physical science is the **Kelvin scale.** Units on the Kelvin scale, called kelvins (K), are the same size as degrees on the Celsius scale. So, an increase of 1 K equals an increase of 1°C. The freezing point of water on the Kelvin scale is 273 K, and the boiling point is 373 K. The number 273 is special. Scientists have concluded from experiments that −273°C is the lowest temperature possible. No more thermal energy can be removed from matter at −273°C. Zero on the Kelvin scale represents −273°C and is called **absolute zero.**

Thermal Energy and Heat

Different objects at the same temperature can have different energies. To understand this, you need to know about thermal energy and about heat. You may be used to thinking about thermal energy as heat, but they are not the same thing. Temperature, thermal energy, and heat are closely related, but they are all different.

Thermal Energy You may recall that the total energy of all of the particles in an object is called thermal energy, or sometimes internal energy. The thermal energy of an object depends on the number of particles in the object, the temperature of the object, and the arrangement of the object's particles. You will learn about how the arrangement of particles affects thermal energy in Section 3.

The more particles an object has at a given temperature, the more thermal energy it has. For example, a 1-liter pot of hot cocoa at 75°C has more thermal energy than a 0.2-liter mug of hot cocoa at 75°C because the pot contains more cocoa particles. On the other hand, the higher the temperature of an object, the more thermal energy the object has. Therefore, if two 1-liter pots of hot cocoa have different temperatures, the pot with the higher temperature has more thermal energy. In Section 3, you will learn about how thermal energies differ for solids, liquids, and gases.

Heat Thermal energy that is transferred from matter at a higher temperature to matter at a lower temperature is called **heat.** The scientific definition of heat is different from its everyday use. In a conversation, you might say that an object contains heat. However, objects contain thermal energy, not heat. Only when thermal energy is transferred is it called heat. **Heat is thermal energy moving from a warmer object to a cooler object.** For example, when you hold an ice cube in your hand, as shown in Figure 4, the ice cube melts because thermal energy is transferred from your hand to the ice cube.

Recall that work also involves the transfer of energy. Since work and heat are both energy transfers, they are both measured in the same unit—joules.

 Reading Checkpoint Why does an ice cube melt in your hand?

FIGURE 4
Heat Your hand transfers thermal energy to the ice cube. Even though your hand is cold, this transfer is called heat. Your hand feels cold because it is losing thermal energy.

Heat is transferred from the hand to the ice cubes.

Chapter 6 M ◆ 179

 Math Skills

Converting Units

To convert a Fahrenheit temperature to a Celsius temperature, use the following formula.

$$°C = \frac{5}{9}(°F - 32)$$

For example, if the temperature in your classroom is 68°F, what is the temperature in degrees Celsius?

$$°C = \frac{5}{9}(68 - 32)$$

$$°C = \frac{5}{9} \times 36$$

$$°C = 20$$

The temperature of your classroom is 20°C.

Practice Problem While at the beach, you measure the ocean temperature as 77°F. What is the temperature of the ocean in degrees Celsius?

 **Lab zone Teacher Demo** L2

Comparing and Contrasting Temperature and Thermal Energy

Materials mug, bucket, 2 thermometers
Time 10 min

Focus Ask: **What is temperature?** (*The measure of the average kinetic energy of the particles in a substance*) **What is thermal energy?** (*The total energy of all the particles in an object*)

Teach Fill the bucket and the mug with water of the same temperature. Show students both containers with the thermometers inserted. Ask: **Which contains water with a greater temperature?** (*The temperature of the water in the containers is equal.*) Ask: **Which contains a greater thermal energy? Why?** (*The bucket, because there are a greater number of particles*)

Apply Ask: **What can you determine about the average kinetic energy of the individual particles in these containers?** (*The average kinetic energy of the particles is equal.*)
learning modality: visual

🚩 Address Misconceptions L2
What Is Heat?
Students may have misconceptions about the meaning of the word *heat*. Some of these misconceptions are fostered by the everyday uses of the word that differ from the scientific usage. Write the word *heat* on the board. Ask: **In science, what does the term *heat* refer to?** (*The transfer of thermal energy*) **Can an object contain heat?** (*No*)
learning modality: verbal

 **Math Skills**

Math Skill Converting units
Time 10 minutes
Tip Remind students to insert known values into the formula. They can then solve for the unknown values.

Answer 25°C
Extend Have students determine the ocean temperature in degrees Celsius if the ocean temperature drops to 59°F. (*15°C*)

Monitor Progress _____ L2

Skills Check Have students calculate the temperature in degrees Celsius if the outdoor thermometer on a summer day reads 95°F. (*35°C*)

Answers
Figure 3 100°C, 212°F

Reading Checkpoint An ice cube melts in your hand because thermal energy is transferred from your hand to the ice cube.

M ● 179

Specific Heat

Teach Key Concepts `L2`
Specific Heat and Temperature Change

Focus Remind students that a material's specific heat is how much energy is required to raise the temperature of 1 kilogram of the material by 1 kelvin.

Teach Tell students that different materials have different specific heats. Direct students' attention to Figure 6. Ask: **Which material listed in the table has the lowest specific heat?** *(Silver)* **If 1 kilogram of each of the listed materials absorbed the same amount of energy, how would the temperature change of the silver compare with the temperature change of the other materials?** *(Silver would have a greater temperature change than any other listed material.)*

Apply Ask: **Why do foods that contain lots of water stay hot longer than those that don't contain much water?** *(Water changes temperature more slowly than many other substances, so foods containing lots of water stay warm longer than those that don't contain much water.)* **learning modality: logical/mathematical**

![Math] **Analyzing Data**

Math Skill Making and interpreting graphs

Focus Tell students that a bar graph is used to show information about separate but related items.

Teach Call students' attention to the graph. Explain that the lower the specific heat, the smaller the amount of heat required to raise the temperature of the material. A higher bar on the graph represents a greater specific heat. Of the materials shown, water has the highest specific heat. Ask: **Which material shown has the lowest specific heat?** *(Sand)*

Answers
1. water, sand, and iron
2. About 4,200 J would be required.
3. sand

FIGURE 5
Specific Heat of Sand and Water
The specific heat of water is greater than the specific heat of sand. On a sunny day the water feels cooler than the sand.

Specific Heat

Imagine running across hot sand toward the ocean. You run to the water's edge, but you don't go any farther—the water is too cold. How can the sand be so hot and the water so cold? After all, the sun heats both of them. The answer is that water requires more heat to raise its temperature than sand does.

When an object is heated, its temperature rises. But the temperature does not rise at the same rate for all objects. The amount of heat required to raise the temperature of an object depends on the object's chemical makeup. To change the temperature of different objects by the same amount, different amounts of heat are required.

Scientists have defined a quantity to measure the relationship between heat and temperature change. The amount of energy required to raise the temperature of 1 kilogram of a material by 1 kelvin is called its **specific heat.** The unit of measure for specific heat is joules per kilogram-kelvin, or J/(kg·K).

![Math] **Analyzing Data**

Specific Heat
The specific heat of three different materials was measured. These data are shown in the graph.

1. **Reading Graphs** What three materials are compared in the graph?
2. **Interpreting Data** About how much heat is required to raise 1 kg of water by 1 K?
3. **Drawing Conclusions** According to the graph, which material requires more heat to raise its temperature by 1 K, iron or sand?

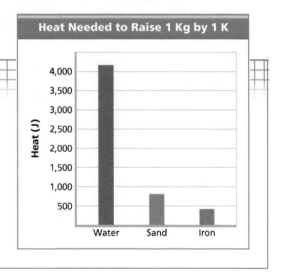

Heat Needed to Raise 1 Kg by 1 K

Heat (J): 4,000 / 3,500 / 3,000 / 2,500 / 2,000 / 1,500 / 1,000 / 500

Water · Sand · Iron

Differentiated Instruction

Gifted and Talented `L3`
Making a Game Have students create a board game that can be used to review the material in this section. Possible game topics include definitions of key terms, calculations of specific heat, and questions based on the key concepts. When the games are complete, have students share their games with the class. **learning modality: logical/mathematical**

Less Proficient Readers `L1`
Reviewing Key Terms Have students listen to this section of the chapter on the **Student Edition on Audio CD**. After they have completed listening, ask them to write the key terms from the section on index cards. Then pair students and have one display an index card, and the other define the term aloud. Students can take turns displaying cards and defining terms. **learning modality: verbal**

Look at the specific heats of the materials listed in Figure 6. Notice that the specific heat of water is quite high. One kilogram of water requires 4,180 joules of energy to raise its temperature 1 kelvin.

A material with a high specific heat can absorb a great deal of thermal energy without a great change in temperature. On the other hand, a material with a low specific heat would have a large temperature change after absorbing the same amount of thermal energy.

The energy gained or lost by a material is related to its mass, change in temperature, and specific heat. You can calculate thermal energy changes with the following formula.

Change in energy =
Mass × Specific heat × Change in temperature

How much heat is required to raise the temperature of 5 kilograms of water by 10 kelvins?

$$\text{Change in energy} = 5\text{ kg} \times 4{,}180\text{ J/(kg}\cdot\text{K)} \times 10\text{ K}$$
$$= 209{,}000\text{ J}$$

You need to transfer 209,000 joules to the water to increase its temperature by 10 kelvins.

Reading Checkpoint **What formula allows you to determine an object's change in thermal energy?**

Specific Heat of Common Materials

Material	Specific Heat (J/(kg•K))
Aluminum	903
Copper	385
Glass	837
Ice	2,060
Iron	450
Sand	800
Silver	235
Water	4,180

FIGURE 6
This table lists the specific heats of several common materials.
Interpreting Tables *How much more energy is required to raise the temperature of 1 kg of iron by 1 K than to raise the temperature of 1 kg of copper by 1 K?*

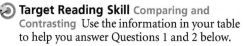

Section 1 Assessment

Target Reading Skill **Comparing and Contrasting** Use the information in your table to help you answer Questions 1 and 2 below.

Reviewing Key Concepts

1. a. **Identifying** What is temperature?
   b. **Describing** How do thermometers measure temperature?
   c. **Comparing and Contrasting** How are the three temperature scales alike? How are they different?
2. a. **Defining** What is heat?
   b. **Explaining** What is the relationship between thermal energy and temperature? Between thermal energy and heat?
   c. **Relating Cause and Effect** What happens to the motion of an object's particles as the object's thermal energy increases? What happens to the temperature of the object?
3. a. **Reviewing** Why do some materials get hot more quickly than others?
   b. **Calculating** You stir your hot cocoa with a silver spoon that has a mass of 0.032 kg. The spoon's temperature increases from 20 K to 60 K. What is the change in the spoon's thermal energy? (*Hint:* Use the table in Figure 6 to find the specific heat of silver.)

Math Practice

4. **Converting Units** Convert 5.0°F to degrees Celsius.
5. **Converting Units** The surface temperature on the planet Venus can reach 860°F. Convert this temperature to degrees Celsius.

Math Practice

Math Skill Converting units

Answers

4. –15°C (°C = 5/9(°F – 32); °C = 5/9(5.0 – 32); °C = –15)
5. 460°C (°C = 5/9(860 – 32); °C = 460)

All in One Teaching Resources

- Section Summary: *Temperature, Thermal Energy, and Heat*
- Review and Reinforce: *Temperature, Thermal Energy, and Heat*
- Enrich: *Temperature, Thermal Energy, and Heat*

Monitor Progress L2

Answers

Figure 6 It requires 65 joules more energy to raise 1 kg of iron by 1 K than to raise 1 kg of copper by the same amount.

Reading Checkpoint Change in energy = Mass × Specific Heat × Change in temperature

Assess

Reviewing Key Concepts

1. a. Temperature is a measure of the average kinetic energy of the individual particles in matter. **b.** Sample answer: When a thermometer is heated, the liquid level rises because particles of the liquid speed up and spread out. When the thermometer is cooled, the liquid level falls because particles of the liquid slow down and move closer together. **c.** Each of the three temperature scales is divided into degrees. Celsius degrees are the same size as Kelvin degrees, and both are larger than Fahrenheit degrees. The three scales give different readings for all temperatures, including absolute zero, the freezing point of water, and the boiling point of water.

2. a. Heat is thermal energy moving from a warmer object to a cooler object.
b. Temperature is one of the factors that determine an object's thermal energy. The others are the number of particles and the arrangement of the particles. Heat is the flow of thermal energy between objects. **c.** When the motion of an object's particles increase, its temperature rises. All else equal, this will result in an increase in the object's thermal energy.

3. a. Materials with smaller specific heats need less heat to change temperature by a given amount. **b.** 300.8 J (0.032 kg × 235 J/kg•K × 40 K)

Reteach L1

Have students review the figures in the section. Then ask volunteers to state the main idea of each figure. Review the caption questions and answers aloud with students.

Performance Assessment L2

Skills Check Have students determine the energy gained by 10 kilograms of copper when its temperature increases by 15 kelvins. *(57,750 J)*

Build Your Own Thermometer

Prepare for Inquiry

Skills Objective

After this lab, students will be able to
- evaluate the design of a thermometer
- troubleshoot a technical design
- redesign and improve their thermometer based on the results of their testing

 Prep Time 30 minutes
Class Time 40 minutes

Advance Planning

Gather required materials. Soften the clay to make it easier to work with. Set up a common hot water bath and ice bath.

Alternative Materials

One-hole rubber stoppers, glass flask, plastic tubing, index cards, plastic bottles

Safety

Caution students to be careful using thermometers, glass soda bottles, and hot water. Review the safety guidelines in Appendix A.

All in One Teaching Resources

- Lab Worksheet: *Build Your Own Thermometer*

Guide Inquiry

Introduce the Procedure

Prepare and display a sample of the thermometer for Part 1. Have students review the procedure and ask any questions they may have. Review the concept of thermal expansion.

Troubleshooting the Experiment

Be certain students obtain an airtight seal with the clay. Tilt the bottle and straw when adding water to the straw in Step 3.

Expected Outcome

When the thermometer was placed in cold water, the water in the straw decreased. When the thermometer was placed in the hot water, the water in the straw increased.

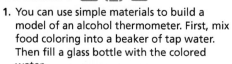

Build Your Own Thermometer

Problem

Can you build a thermometer out of simple materials?

Design Skills

evaluating the design, measuring, making models

Materials

- bowl of hot water • bowl of ice water
- water of unknown temperature
- tap water • 500-mL beaker
- clear glass juice or soda bottle, 20–25 cm
- clear plastic straw, 18–20 cm • food coloring
- plastic dropper • cooking oil
- modeling clay
- metric ruler
- fine-point marker

Procedure

1. You can use simple materials to build a model of an alcohol thermometer. First, mix food coloring into a beaker of tap water. Then fill a glass bottle with the colored water.

2. Place a straw in the bottle. Use modeling clay to position the straw so that it extends at least 10 cm above the bottle mouth. Do not let the straw touch the bottom. The clay should completely seal off the bottle mouth. Make sure there is no air in the bottle.

3. Using a dropper, add colored water into the straw to a level 5 cm above the bottle. Place a drop of cooking oil in the straw to prevent evaporation.

4. Place your thermometer into a bowl of hot water. When the colored water reaches its highest level, place a mark on the straw.

5. Place your thermometer in the bowl of ice water. Place a mark on the straw when the water reaches its lowest level.

6. Create a scale for your model thermometer. Divide the distance between the two marks into 5-mm intervals. Starting with the lowest point, label the intervals on the straw 0, 1, 2, 3, and so on.

7. Measure the temperature of two unknown samples with your thermometer. Record both temperatures.

Analyze and Conclude

1. **Evaluating the Design** Do you think your model accurately represents an alcohol thermometer? How is it like a real thermometer? How is it different?

2. **Inferring** How can you use the concepts of matter and the kinetic energy of particles to explain the way your model works?

3. **Measuring** Approximately what Celsius temperatures do you think your model measures? Explain your estimate.

4. **Making Models** Examine the structure and materials used in your model. Propose a change that would improve the model. Explain your choice.

Communicate

Create a poster to show how an alcohol thermometer works. Explain how the Celsius and Fahrenheit scales compare. For example, does 0° have the same meaning on both scales? Use a diagram with labels and captions to communicate your ideas.

Analyze and Conclude

1. Sample answer: The thermometer is a reasonable model of a real thermometer. It is like a real thermometer in that it has a scale that can be used to measure temperatures. The actual scale intervals are different than in a real thermometer. Water expands when it is heated, like alcohol, but not to the same extent.

2. When the thermometer is placed in hot water, thermal energy is transferred to the particles in the thermometer and these particles speed up and spread out (their kinetic energy increases). The opposite occurs when the thermometer is placed in ice water.

3. The thermometer measures temperatures between 0°C and 100°C.

4. Possible answers may include using a different liquid, using a finer scale, changing the thickness of the column of liquid, or changing the size of the reservoir of liquid.

Reading Preview

Key Concepts
- What are the three forms of heat transfer?
- In what direction does heat move?
- How are conductors and insulators different?

Key Terms
- conduction • convection
- convection current • radiation
- conductor • insulator

Target Reading Skill
Identifying Main Ideas As you read the How Is Heat Transferred? section, write the main idea in a graphic organizer like the one below. Then write three supporting details that give examples of the main idea.

Main Idea

Heat can be transferred in three ways . . .

Detail	Detail	Detail

Lab zone Discover **Activity**

What Does It Mean to Heat Up?

1. Obtain several utensils made of different materials, such as silver, stainless steel, plastic, and wood.
2. Stand the utensils in a beaker so that they do not touch each other.
3. Press a small gob of frozen butter on the handle of each utensil. Make sure that when the utensils stand on end, the butter is at the same height on each one.
4. Pour hot water into the beaker until it is about 6 cm below the butter. Watch the butter on the utensils for several minutes. What happens?
5. Wash the utensils in soapy water when you finish.

Think It Over

Observing What happened to the butter? Did the same thing happen on every utensil? How can you account for your observations?

Blacksmithing is hot work. A piece of iron held in the fire of the forge becomes warmer and begins to glow. At the same time, the blacksmith feels hot air rising from the forge, and his face and arms begin to feel warmer. Each of these movements of energy is a transfer of heat.

◀ A blacksmith at work

M ◆ 183

Lab zone Discover **Activity**

Skills Focus Observing   L2

Materials frozen butter, glass beaker, hot water, utensils made of different materials

Time 15 minutes

Tips CAUTION: *Remind students to avoid touching the hot water and tasting the butter.* Have students record the order in which the butter melts on the utensils.

Expected Outcome The butter will melt more quickly on metal utensils than on the wood or plastic utensils.

Think It Over Sample answer: The butter melted. It melted faster on metal utensils than on wooden or plastic ones. Heat from the hot water moved along the utensils, but at a different rate for each material.

Objectives
After this lesson, students will be able to

M.6.2.1 Describe the three forms of heat transfer.

M.6.2.2 Identify the direction in which heat moves.

M.6.2.3 Describe the differences between conductors and insulators.

Target Reading Skill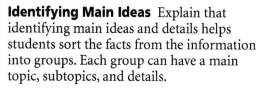

Identifying Main Ideas Explain that identifying main ideas and details helps students sort the facts from the information into groups. Each group can have a main topic, subtopics, and details.

Answers
Sample graphic organizer:

Main Idea: Heat can be transferred in three ways.

Detail: Conduction—transfer of heat between particles without the movement of matter

Detail: Convection—transfer of heat by the movement of currents in a fluid

Detail: Radiation—transfer of energy by electromagnetic waves

All in One Teaching Resources
- Transparency M54

Preteach

Build Background Knowledge   L2
Heat Transfer

Ask: **How would you safely remove a tray of hot cookies from the oven?** *(Sample answer: I would use an oven mitt.)* **What is the function of the oven mitt?** *(It keeps the cookies and tray from burning my hands.)* Tell students that in this section they will learn how the oven mitt protects their hands.

Instruct

How Is Heat Transferred?

Teach Key Concepts `L2`
Conduction, Convection, and Radiation

Focus Tell students that heat can be transferred in three ways—conduction, convection, and radiation.

Teach On the board write three headings: *conduction, convection,* and *radiation.* Ask for a volunteer to describe each type of heat transfer. Then, ask students to give examples of each kind of heat transfer. Write their answers on the board under the correct heading.

Apply Ask: **What type of heat transfer occurs when you burn your feet on hot sand at the beach?** *(Conduction)* **learning modality: verbal**

Go Online
SciLINKS NSTA

For: Links on heat transfer
Visit: www.SciLinks.org
Web Code: scn-1362

Students can research heat transfer online.

Help Students Read `L1`
Comparing and Contrasting Have students use the information in the text to create a table that compares and contrasts the three ways in which heat is transferred. Remind students that comparing and contrasting means looking for similarities and differences.

Independent Practice `L2`

 All in One Teaching Resources

- Guided Reading and Study Worksheet: *The Transfer of Heat*

Student Edition on Audio CD

Go Online
SciLINKS NSTA

For: Links on heat transfer
Visit: www.SciLinks.org
Web Code: scn-1362

Lab zone Try This **Activity**

Feel the Warmth
How is heat transferred from a light bulb?

1. Turn on a lamp without the shade. Wait about a minute.
2. Hold the palm of your hand about 10 cm from the side of the bulb for about 15 seconds. **CAUTION:** *Do not touch the bulb. Remove your hand sooner if it gets too warm.*
3. Now hold the palm of your hand about 10 cm above the top of the bulb for about 15 seconds.

Drawing Conclusions
In which location did your hand feel warmer? Explain your observations in terms of heat transfer.

How Is Heat Transferred?

There are three ways that heat can move. **Heat is transferred by conduction, convection, and radiation.** The blacksmith experiences all three.

Conduction In the process of **conduction,** heat is transferred from one particle of matter to another without the movement of the matter. Think of a metal spoon in a pot of water on an electric stove. The fast-moving particles in the hot electric coil collide with the slow-moving particles in the cool pot. The transfer of heat causes the pot's particles to move faster. Then the pot's particles collide with the water's particles, which in turn collide with the particles in the spoon. As the particles move faster, the metal spoon becomes hotter.

If you were to touch the spoon, heat would be transferred to your fingers. Too much heat transferred this way can cause a burn!

In Figure 7, heat from the fire is transferred to the stone beneath it. Then it is transferred from the stone to the metal tools. This transfer of heat from the fire to the tools is due to conduction.

Convection If you watch a pot of hot water on a stove, you will see the water moving. This movement transfers heat within the water. In **convection,** heat is transferred by the movement of currents within a fluid.

When the water at the bottom of the pot is heated, its particles move faster. The particles also move farther apart. As a result, the heated water becomes less dense. You may remember that a less dense fluid will float on top of a denser one. So the heated water rises. The surrounding, cooler water flows into its place. This flow creates a circular motion known as a **convection current.**

Convection currents can transfer heated air. As the air above the fire in Figure 7 is heated, it becomes less dense and rises up the chimney. When the warm air rises, cool air flows into its place.

Radiation **Radiation** is the transfer of energy by electromagnetic waves. You can feel the radiation from a fire in a fireplace all the way across the room. Unlike conduction and convection, radiation does not require matter to transfer thermal energy. All of the sun's energy that reaches Earth travels through millions of kilometers of empty space.

Reading Checkpoint **How does radiation transfer thermal energy?**

Lab zone Try This **Activity**

Skills Focus Drawing conclusions `L1`

Materials lamp with a 60- or 75-W bulb, centimeter ruler, clock or stopwatch

Time 10 minutes

Tips CAUTION: Do not touch the light bulb. Tell students to withdraw their hands if they become uncomfortable.

Drawing Conclusions Students' palms should feel considerably warmer when held above the bulb. Many students may mention that air heated by the bulb is rising and that makes their hand feel warmer.

Extend Have students wrap a 2 cm × 2 cm piece of black paper around the base of a thermometer and tape it into

place. Then repeat the experiment with the bulb of the thermometer held 10 cm away from the light. Increase the time if necessary.
learning modality: kinesthetic

FIGURE 7

Methods of Heat Transfer

Heat can be transferred by conduction, convection, or radiation. Heat from a fire is transferred by all three methods.
Interpreting Diagrams Which of these methods requires the movement of currents with a fluid?

Convection
When the air around the fire is heated, it becomes less dense than the cooler air nearby. The warm air rises up the chimney, and cool air flows in to take its place.

Radiation
The fire transforms chemical energy in the wood to electromagnetic energy, which radiates heat across the room.

Conduction
Fast-moving particles in the fire transfer heat as they collide with slow-moving particles in the stone hearth. Eventually the heat conducts through the stones to the metal tools.

M ◆ 185

Differentiated Instruction

Special Needs L1
Observing Conduction Have students hold an ice cube for a brief period. Tell them to put down the ice if they become uncomfortable. Remind students that this is an example of heat transfer by conduction. Thermal energy from their hand is transferred to the ice cube, causing the ice cube to become warmer and their hand to become cooler. **learning modality: kinesthetic**

Gifted and Talented L3
Researching Weather Have students research El Niño and La Niña, weather patterns caused by convection currents. Students should write a short report describing their findings. **learning modality: verbal**

Lab zone **Build Inquiry**   L2

Visualizing Convection Currents

Materials 2 test tubes, test tube holder, 2 beakers, red and blue food coloring, cold water, hot water, large dropper

Time 20 minutes

Focus Tell students they will use hot and cold water to visualize convection currents.

Teach Prepare hot water with red food coloring and cold water with blue food coloring. Have students place cold water in one test tube and hot water in the other. Then, demonstrate how to place one layer of water on top of the other by gently squeezing a full dropper against the side of the test tube. Students should add a layer of cold water to the tube containing hot water, and a layer of hot water to the tube containing cold water.

Apply Ask: **What happened when you placed cold water on top of hot water? Why?** *(The hot water floated on top of the cold water because it is less dense.)* **learning modality: visual**

Integrating Earth Science L2
Convection currents in Earth's oceans and atmosphere cause major weather patterns. Convection currents also occur in Earth's mantle, causing Earth's plates to slowly move. Ask: **In what type of material does convection occur? Why?** *(Fluids, because they can flow)* **learning modality: verbal**

Monitor Progress _____ L2

Drawing Have students draw a kettle of water being heated on a burner and label the convection currents and the path of heat conduction.

Students can keep their drawings in their portfolios. **Portfolio**

Answers
Figure 7 Convection requires movement of currents within a fluid.

 Reading Checkpoint Radiation transfers thermal energy by electromagnetic waves.

Heat Moves One Way

Teach Key Concepts
The Direction of Heat Flow

Focus Explain that heat can flow spontaneously in one direction only: from a warmer object to a colder object.

Teach Write on the board the following pairs of terms, leaving a space between the terms in each pair: ice, lemonade; cool air, warm bath water; hot clothes dryer, cold clothes. Tell students you will draw an arrow between the terms indicating the direction of heat flow. Ask for volunteers to indicate the direction each arrow should point. (Arrows should point to *ice, cool air,* and *cold clothes.*)

Apply Ask: **Your friend asks if you want some ice to transfer coldness to your lemonade. What is incorrect about your friend's question?** (*There is no such thing as coldness, therefore it can't be transferred. Instead, heat flows from the lemonade to the ice, cooling the lemonade.*) **learning modality: visual**

Conductors and Insulators

Teach Key Concepts

Uses of Conductors and Insulators

Focus Ask: **Have you ever packed a picnic lunch in a cooler?** (*Some students will say yes.*) **What was the function of the cooler?** (*Sample answer: It kept our food cool even though it was hot outside.*)

Teach Explain that insulators are materials that do not transfer thermal energy well; conductors are materials that do conduct thermal energy well. Tell students that materials are selected for certain applications based on how well they conduct thermal energy.

Apply Ask: **Based on what you know about insulators and conductors, which type of material is a picnic cooler made of? Why?** (*An insulator, to keep thermal energy from the hot surroundings from being transferred to the cold food inside*) **learning modality: logical/mathematical**

FIGURE 8
Heat Transfer From Food
The soup's heat is transferred to the bowl, the spoon, and the air.
Predicting If the soup is not eaten, what will happen to its temperature?

Heat Moves One Way

If two objects have different temperatures, heat will flow from the warmer object to the colder one. When heat flows into matter, the thermal energy of the matter increases. As the thermal energy increases, the temperature increases. At the same time, the temperature of the matter losing the heat decreases. Heat will flow from one object to the other until the two objects have the same temperature. You have probably seen this happen to your food. The bowl of hot soup shown in Figure 8, for example, cools to room temperature if you don't eat it quickly.

What happens when something becomes cold, such as when ice cream is made? The ingredients used to make it, such as milk and sugar, are not nearly as cold as the finished ice cream. In an ice cream maker, the ingredients are put into a metal can that is packed in ice. You might think that the ice transfers cold to the ingredients in the can. But this is not the case. There is no such thing as "coldness." Instead, the ingredients grow colder as thermal energy flows from them to the ice. Heat transfer occurs in only one direction.

 Reading Checkpoint **Can heat flow from one object to a warmer object? Why or why not?**

Conductors and Insulators

Have you ever stepped from a rug to a tile floor on a cold morning? The tile floor feels colder than the rug. Yet if you measured their temperatures, they would be the same—room temperature. The difference between them has to do with how materials conduct heat. A material can be either a conductor or an insulator. **A conductor transfers thermal energy well. An insulator does not transfer thermal energy well.**

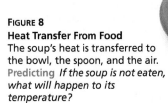

Lab zone Skills **Activity**

Inferring

You pull some clothes out of the dryer as soon as they are dry. You grab your shirt without a problem, but when you pull out your jeans, you quickly drop them. The metal zipper is too hot to touch! What can you infer about which material in your jeans conducts thermal energy better? Explain.

Lab zone Skills **Activity**

Skills Focus Inferring

Time 10 minutes

Answer Sample answer: The metal zipper feels much hotter because metal conducts thermal energy better than the material of the jeans.

Extend Have the students infer which would conduct thermal energy better—metal buttons or plastic buttons. (*metal buttons*) **learning modality: logical/mathematical**

Conductors A material that conducts heat well is called a **conductor.** Metals such as silver and stainless steel are good conductors. A metal spoon conducts heat better than a wooden spoon. Some materials are good conductors because of the particles they contain and how those particles are arranged. A good conductor, such as a tile floor, feels cool to the touch because it easily transfers heat away from your skin.

Insulators A material that does not conduct heat well is called an **insulator.** Wood, wool, straw, and paper are good insulators. So are the gases in air. Clothes and blankets are insulators that slow the transfer of heat out of your body.

A well-insulated building is comfortable inside whether it is hot or cold outdoors. Insulation prevents heat from entering the building in hot weather and from escaping in cold weather. Much of the heat transfer in a building occurs through the windows. For this reason, insulating windows have two panes of glass with a thin space of air between them. The trapped air does not transfer heat well.

Glass
Air space

FIGURE 9
Insulating Windows
Air between the panes of this window acts as an insulator to slow the transfer of heat.

 Reading Checkpoint Is air better as an insulator or as a conductor?

Section 2 Assessment

Target Reading Skill
Identifying Main Ideas Use your graphic organizer to help you answer Question 1 below.

Reviewing Key Concepts

1. a. Describing What are conduction, convection, and radiation?
b. Classifying Identify each example of heat transfer as conduction, convection, or radiation: opening the windows in a hot room; a lizard basking in the sun; putting ice on a sprained ankle.
c. Inferring How can heat be transferred across empty space?

2. a. Reviewing In what direction will heat flow between two objects with different temperatures?
b. Applying Concepts How does a glass of lemonade become cold when you put ice in it?

3. a. Identifying What kind of substance conducts thermal energy well?
b. Making Judgments Would a copper pipe work better as a conductor or an insulator? Why do you think so?
c. Interpreting Diagrams Why are two panes of glass used in the window in Figure 9?

Writing in Science

Explanation Suppose you are camping on a mountain, and the air temperature is very cold. How would you keep warm? Would you build a fire or set up a tent? Write an explanation for each action you would take. Tell whether conduction, convection, or radiation is involved with each heat transfer.

Monitor Progress L2

Answers
Figure 8 The soup's temperature will decrease as it transfers heat to materials around it.

✓ **Reading Checkpoint** No. Heat transfer occurs spontaneously in only one direction—from a warmer object or material to a colder one.

✓ **Reading Checkpoint** Air is a better insulator than a conductor.

Assess

Reviewing Key Concepts

1. a. Conduction, convection, and radiation are three means by which heat may be transferred. **b.** Convection; radiation; conduction **c.** By electromagnetic waves, which do not require matter to transfer thermal energy
2. a. Heat flows spontaneously from the warmer object to the colder object.
b. Thermal energy flows from the lemonade to the ice.
3. a. A conductor transfers thermal energy well. **b.** A conductor because copper is a metal. **c.** Because air is a good insulator, the air trapped between the two panes slows the transfer of heat into and out of the building.

Reteach L1
Have students work in pairs to review the key terms from section.

Performance Assessment L2
Writing Ask students to make lists of situations in which materials that are good insulators of thermal energy are helpful and situations in which good conductors of thermal energy are helpful.

All in One Teaching Resources
• Section Summary: *The Transfer of Heat*
• Review and Reinforce: *The Transfer of Heat*
• Enrich: *The Transfer of Heat*

Lab zone Chapter Project

Keep Students on Track Instruct students to review the steps for designing an experiment in the Skills Handbook. Have students prepare a short summary of their experimental plan that includes identifying variables and controls. After students have completed their plans and you have approved them, have them begin their tests.

Writing in Science

Writing Mode Exposition/ How-To
Scoring Rubric
4 Exceeds criteria
3 Meets criteria
2 Meets most, but not all criteria; explanation lacks details and/or includes some incorrect information
1 Meets few criteria; includes few details and/or incorrect statements

Just Add Water L2

Prepare for Inquiry

Skills Objectives

After this lab, students will be able to
- observe the transfer of thermal energy from hot water to cold water
- calculate the heat transferred from hot water to cold water in a calorimeter
- interpret data about the conservation of thermal energy in a calorimeter

 Prep Time 15 minutes
Class Time 40 minutes

Advance Planning

Before the lab, gather the materials students will need. Provide sponges or paper towels to mop up spills.

Alternative Materials

Any kind of disposable, insulated cup can be used instead of plastic foam cups.

Safety

Caution students to be careful using thermometers. Review the safety guidelines in Appendix A.

All in One Teaching Resources
- Lab Worksheet: *Just Add Water*

Guide Inquiry

Invitation

Ask: **What would you do if you got in a bath and found that the water was too hot?**
(*Sample answer: Add cold water*) **When you add cold water, what happens to the heat?**
(*Heat is transferred from the hot water to the cold water.*)

Introduce the Procedure

- Describe the lab to students. Explain that they will calculate the amount of heat transferred when hot water and cold water are mixed.
- Set up and display a calorimeter.
- Help students understand how to use the equation for calculating the change in thermal energy in the hot water and the cold water.

Just Add Water

Problem

Can you build a calorimeter—a device that measures changes in thermal energy—and use it to determine how much thermal energy is transferred from hot water to cold water?

Skills Focus

observing, calculating, interpreting data

Materials

- hot tap water • balance • scissors
- pencil • 4 plastic foam cups
- 2 thermometers or temperature probes
- beaker of water kept in an ice bath

Procedure

1. Predict how the amount of thermal energy lost by hot water will be related to the amount of thermal energy gained by cold water.

2. Copy the data table into your notebook.

3. Follow the instructions in the box to make two calorimeters. Find the mass of each empty calorimeter (including the cover) on a balance and record each mass in your data table.

4. From a beaker of water that has been sitting in an ice bath, add water (no ice cubes) to the cold-water calorimeter. Fill it about one-third full. Put the cover on, find the total mass, and record the mass in your data table.

5. Add hot tap water to the hot-water calorimeter. **CAUTION:** *Hot tap water can cause burns.* Fill the calorimeter about one-third full. Put the cover on, find the total mass, and record the mass in your data table.

6. Calculate the mass of the water in each calorimeter. Record the results in your data table.

7. Put thermometers through the holes in the covers of both calorimeters. Wait a minute or two and then record the temperatures. If you are using temperature probes, see your teacher for instructions.

> **MAKING A CALORIMETER**
>
> **A** Label a plastic foam cup with the letter C, which stands for cold water.
>
> **B** Cut 2 to 3 cm from the top of a second plastic foam cup. Invert the second cup inside the first. Label the cover with a C also. The cup and cover are your cold-water calorimeter.
>
> **C** Using a pencil, poke a hole in the cover large enough for a thermometer to fit into snugly.
>
> **D** Repeat Steps A, B, and C with two other plastic foam cups. This time, label both cup and cover with an H. This is your hot-water calorimeter.

	Data Table					
Calorimeter	Mass of Empty Cup (g)	Mass of Cup and Water (g)	Mass of Water (g)	Starting Temp. (°C)	Final Temp. (°C)	Change in Temp. (°C)
Cold Water						
Hot Water						

Troubleshooting the Experiment

- In the cold-water calorimeter, students may need to pull the thermometer up a bit to read it.
- Students should read the thermometer to the nearest half degree.
- In Step 8, students should wait a minute or two before recording the final

temperature. Do not allow students to use the thermometers to stir the water.

- Remind students to use the final temperature to calculate the temperature change for both the hot and cold water.

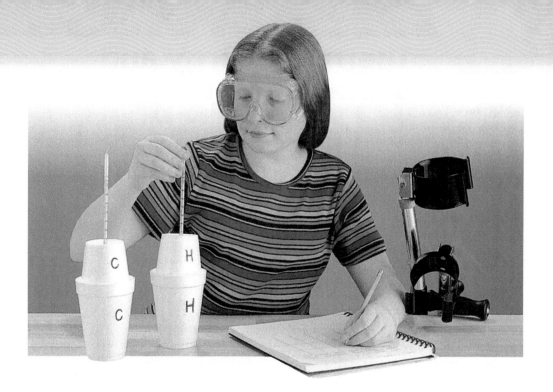

8. Remove both thermometers and covers. Pour the water from the cold-water calorimeter into the hot-water calorimeter. Put the cover back on the hot-water calorimeter, and insert a thermometer. Record the final temperature as the final temperature for both calorimeters.

Analyze and Conclude

1. **Observing** What is the temperature change of the cold water? Record your answer in the data table.

2. **Observing** What is the temperature change of the hot water? Record your answer in the data table.

3. **Calculating** Calculate the amount of thermal energy that enters the cold water by using the formula for the transfer of thermal energy. The specific heat of water is 4.18 J/(g·K).
   Thermal energy transferred =
      4.18 J/(g·K) × Mass of cold water ×
      Temperature change of cold water
   Remember that a change of 1°C is equal to a change of 1 K.

4. **Calculating** Now use the same formula to calculate the amount of thermal energy leaving the hot water.

5. **Calculating** What unit should you use for your results for Questions 3 and 4?

6. **Interpreting Data** Was your prediction from Step 1 confirmed? How do you know?

7. **Communicating** What sources of error might have affected your results? Write a paragraph explaining how the lab could be redesigned in order to reduce the errors.

Design an Experiment

How would your results be affected if you started with much more hot water than cold? If you used more cold water than hot? Make a prediction. Then design a procedure to test your prediction. *Obtain your teacher's permission before carrying out your investigation.*

Expected Outcome

The final temperature will be greater than the initial temperature of the cold water and less than the initial temperature of the hot water. The amount of thermal energy transferred to the cold water should be approximately equal to the thermal energy transferred from the hot water. Some heat will be lost to the surroundings during transfer.

Analyze and Conclude

1. Sample data: The temperature of the cold water increased by 14.5°C.

2. Sample data: The temperature of the hot water decreased by 24°C.

3. Answer for sample data: Thermal energy gained = 6300 J.

4. Answer for sample data: Thermal energy lost = 6840 J.

5. The unit should be joules.

6. Students' answers will depend on their original predictions. Sample answer: I predicted that the thermal energy lost by the hot water would be neary equal to the thermal energy gained by the cold water. Considering reasonable experimental error, 6840 J and 6300 J are nearly equal. I believe my prediction was confirmed.

7. Sample answer: Thermal energy in the form of heat was lost or gained through the sides or tops of the cups. Thermometers or balances may have been misread. I could have used thicker cups or better insulating materials, nested two or more cups together, or repeated the procedure several times and averaged the results.

Extend Inquiry

Design an Experiment Sample answer: With more hot water, the mixture would end up hotter; with more cold water, it would end up colder. In either case, however, the thermal energy lost by the hot water should be approximately equal to the thermal energy gained by the cold water.

Objectives

After this lesson, students will be able to

M.6.3.1 Name the three states of matter.

M.6.3.2 Identify the cause of changes of state.

M.6.3.3 Describe what happens to a substance as its thermal energy increases.

Target Reading Skill

Building Vocabulary Explain that knowing the definitions of key-concept words helps students understand what they read.

As students read each passage that contains a key term, remind them to write a sentence in their own words. Encourage students to write one or two descriptive phrases to help them remember the key term. Call on students to share their definitions.

Preteach

Build Background Knowledge   L2

Introducing States of Matter

Show students a glass containing water and ice cubes. Ask: **What substance is in this glass?** *(Water)* **What forms of water are in this glass?** *(Liquid water and ice, a solid)* **What will happen to the ice if it sits at room temperature?** *(It will melt and turn into liquid water.)*

Reading Preview

Key Concepts
- What are three states of matter?
- What causes matter to change state?
- What happens to a substance as its thermal energy increases?

Key Terms
- state • change of state
- melting • freezing
- evaporation • boiling
- condensation
- thermal expansion

Target Reading Skill

Building Vocabulary Using a word in a sentence helps you think about how best to explain the word. After you read the section, reread the paragraphs that contain definitions of Key Terms. Use all the information you have learned to write a meaningful sentence for each Key Term.

Lab zone | Discover **Activity**

What Happens to Heated Metal?

1. Wrap one end of a one-meter-long metal wire around a clamp on a ring stand.
2. Tie the other end through several washers. Adjust the clamp so that the washers swing freely, but nearly touch the floor.
3. Light a candle. Hold the candle with an oven mitt, and heat the wire. **CAUTION:** *Be careful near the flame, and avoid dripping hot wax on yourself.* Predict how heat from the candle will affect the wire.
4. With your hand in the oven mitt, swing the wire. Observe any changes in the motion of the washers.
5. Blow out the candle and allow the wire to cool. After several minutes, swing the wire again and observe its motion.

Think It Over
Inferring Based on your observations, what can you conclude about the effect of heating a solid?

Throughout the day, the temperature at an orange grove drops steadily. The anxious farmer awaits the updated weather forecast. The news is not good. The temperature is expected to fall even further during the night. Low temperatures could wipe out the entire crop. He considers picking the crop early, but the oranges are not yet ripe.

Instead, the farmer tells his workers to haul in hoses and spray the orange trees with water. As the temperature drops, the water begins to freeze. The ice keeps the oranges warm!

How can ice possibly keep anything warm? The answer has to do with how thermal energy is transferred as water becomes ice.

◀ Oranges at 0°C sprayed with water

Lab zone | Discover **Activity**

Skills Focus Inferring   L2

Materials 1 m of thin metal wire, clamp, ring stand, 3 or 4 washers, matches, candle, oven mitt

Time 15 minutes

Tips CAUTION: *Students should keep loose hair and clothes away from the flame.* In Step 4, suggest that students swing the wire gently.

Expected Outcome As the metal wire is heated, its length increases and the washers drag on the floor. As it cools, the wire returns to its original length and the washers can swing.

Think It Over Sample answer: Solids expand when heated and contract when cooled.

States of Matter

What happens when you hold an ice cube in your hand? It melts. The solid and the liquid are both the same material—water. Water can exist in three different **states,** or forms. **In fact, most matter on Earth can exist in three states—solid, liquid, and gas.** Although the chemical composition of matter remains the same, the arrangement of the particles that make up the matter differs from one state to another.

Solids The particles that make up a solid are packed together in relatively fixed positions. Particles of a solid cannot move out of their positions. They can only vibrate back and forth. This is why solids retain a fixed shape and volume. Because the shape and volume of the plastic helmets shown in Figure 10 do not change, the plastic is a solid.

Liquids The particles that make up a liquid are close together, but they are not held together as tightly as those of a solid. Because liquid particles can move around, liquids don't have a definite shape. But liquids do have a definite volume. In Figure 10, notice how the river water changes shape.

Gases In gases, the particles are moving so fast that they don't even stay close together. Gases expand to fill all the space available. They don't have a fixed shape or volume. Because air is a gas, it can expand to fill the raft in Figure 10 and also take the raft's shape.

Go Online
SCi LINKS™ NSTA

For: Links on changes of state
Visit: www.SciLinks.org
Web Code: scn-1363

FIGURE 10
Three States of Matter
The plastic helmets, the water in the river, and the air that fills the raft are examples of three states of matter—solid, liquid, and gas.
Classifying Which state of matter is represented by the plastic oars?

Solid: plastic helmet

Liquid: river water

Gas: air inside raft

M ◆ 191

Instruct

States of Matter

Teach Key Concepts   L2
Solids, Liquids, and Gases

Focus State that almost all matter on Earth exists as a solid, a liquid or a gas.

Teach Write three headings on the board: *solid, liquid, gas.* Ask students to state facts about each state of matter, and list their responses under the correct heading on the board. After the facts have been collected, ask students to list examples of common substances for each state of matter. Record the examples on the board.

Apply Ask: **In which state of matter do substances have a definite shape? Why?** *(Solids, because the particles that make up a solid are not free to move out of their positions.)* **learning modality: logical/mathematical**

Go Online
SCi LINKS™ NSTA

For: Links on changes of state
Visit: www.SciLinks.org
Web Code: scn-1363

Students can explore internet sources about changes of state.

Independent Practice   L2

All in One Teaching Resources

• Guided Reading and Study Worksheet: *Thermal Energy and States of Matter*

⊙ **Student Edition on Audio CD**

Monitor Progress _____   L2

Oral Presentation Have students give a description of the motion of particles in solids, liquids, and gases.

Answer
Figure 10 The plastic oars are an example of a solid.

Differentiated Instruction

English Learners/Beginning L1
Comprehension: Link to Visual Call students' attention to the inset drawings in Figure 10. Have students copy the three inset drawings on a blank sheet of paper. Then have students add the labels *solid, liquid,* and *gas* to the correct drawing.
learning modality: visual

English Learners/Intermediate L2
Comprehension: Link to Visual Call students' attention to the inset drawings in Figure 10. Have students copy the three inset drawings on a blank sheet of paper. Then, have students write a sentence next to each drawing describing the particles in that state of matter, for example, *The particles in a solid are close together.* Model this activity for students before they begin.
learning modality: visual

Changes of State

Thermal Energy Causes Changes of State

Focus Ask: **What happens to an ice cube at room temperature?** *(It melts.)*

Teach Point out that the ice cube melting, like any change of state, is caused by a change in the thermal energy of the substance. Explain that thermal energy flows from the air in the room to the ice cube. When the ice cube absorbs a certain amount of thermal energy, it melts, or changes from a solid to a liquid.

Apply Ask: **What happens to liquid water when it is placed in the freezer? Why?** *(It changes state from a liquid to a solid because it releases thermal energy.)* **learning modality: verbal**

 **Teaching Resources**

• Transparency M55

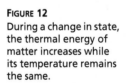 **Teacher Demo**

Observing the Freezing Point of Paraffin L1

Materials hot plate, two blocks of paraffin, thermometer, saucepan

Time 20 minutes

Focus Tell students that different substances have different freezing points.

Teach Place the paraffin in a saucepan on a hot plate. Gently warm the paraffin over low heat until it is completely melted. Remove the saucepan from the hot plate. Turn off the hot plate. Place a thermometer into the liquid paraffin and record the temperature every minute until the paraffin is once again solid. Note the temperature at which the paraffin begins to solidify.

Apply Ask: **Is the freezing point of paraffin the same as the freezing point of water?** *(No)* **Is it higher or lower?** *(Higher)* **learning modality: visual**

FIGURE 11
Melted Chocolate
Though normally a solid at room temperature, this chocolate has absorbed enough thermal energy to become a liquid.

FIGURE 12
During a change in state, the thermal energy of matter increases while its temperature remains the same.

Changes of State

The physical change from one state of matter to another is called a **change of state.** The state of matter depends on the amount of thermal energy it has. The more thermal energy matter has, the faster its particles move. Since a gas has more thermal energy than a liquid, the particles of a gas move faster than the particles of the same matter in the liquid state.

Matter can change from one state to another when thermal energy is absorbed or released. The graph in Figure 12 shows that as thermal energy increases, matter changes from a solid to a liquid and then to a gas. A gas changes to a liquid and then to a solid as thermal energy is removed from it.

The flat regions of the graph show conditions under which thermal energy is changing but temperature remains the same. Under these conditions, matter is changing from one state to another. During a change of state, the addition or loss of thermal energy changes the arrangement of the particles. However, the average kinetic energy of those particles does not change. Since temperature is a measure of average kinetic energy, temperature does not change as the state of matter changes.

Solid–Liquid Changes of State The change of state from a solid to a liquid is called **melting.** Melting occurs when a solid absorbs thermal energy. As the thermal energy of the solid increases, the structure of its particles breaks down. The particles become freer to move around. The temperature at which a solid changes to a liquid is called the melting point.

The change of state from a liquid to a solid is called **freezing.** Freezing occurs when matter releases thermal energy. The temperature at which matter changes from a liquid to a solid is called its freezing point.

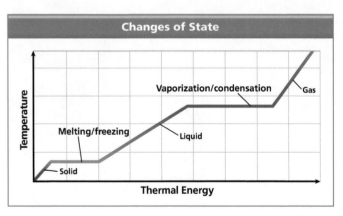

Changes of State

Vaporization/condensation — Gas

Melting/freezing — Liquid

Solid

Temperature (vertical axis) — Thermal Energy (horizontal axis)

Differentiated Instruction

Gifted and Talented L3
Researching Have students research the use of road salt to prevent slippery roads in cold climates. Students should relate the use of road salt to freezing point and changes of state. When students have completed their research, they can present their findings to the class. **learning modality: verbal**

Special Needs L1
Displaying Information Have students use drawings or magazine clippings of substances that are solids, liquids, and gases to create a three-part poster. Each part of the poster should have an appropriate label. **learning modality: visual**

For a given type of matter, the freezing point and melting point are the same. The difference between the two is whether the matter is gaining or releasing thermal energy. The farmer had his workers spray the orange trees with water because the freezing water releases thermal energy into the oranges.

Liquid–Gas Changes of State The process by which matter changes from the liquid to the gas state is called vaporization. During this process, particles in a liquid absorb thermal energy and move faster. Eventually they move fast enough to escape the liquid as gas particles. If vaporization takes place at the surface of a liquid, it is called **evaporation.** At higher temperatures, vaporization can occur below the surface of a liquid as well. This process is called **boiling.** When a liquid boils, gas bubbles that form within the liquid rise to the surface. The temperature at which a liquid boils is called its boiling point.

When a gas loses a certain amount of thermal energy, it will change into a liquid. A change from the gas state to the liquid state is called **condensation.** You have probably seen beads of water appear on the outside of a cold drinking glass. This occurs because water vapor that is present in the air loses thermal energy when it comes in contact with the cold glass.

 Reading Checkpoint What change of state occurs in evaporation?

FIGURE 13
Condensation
Under certain weather conditions, water vapor in the air can condense into fog.
Applying Concepts *As it condenses, does water absorb or release thermal energy?*

M ◆ 193

Lab zone Skills Activity

Observing

Put a teakettle on a stove or a lab burner and bring the water to a boil. Look carefully at the white vapor coming out of the spout. **CAUTION:** *Steam and boiling water can cause serious burns.* In what state of matter is the white vapor that you see? What is present, but not visible, in the small space between the white vapor and the spout?

Lab zone Skills Activity

Skills Focus Observing L2
Materials tea kettle, hot plate, water
Time 10 minutes
Tips CAUTION: *Students stand clear of the boiling water and steam.*
Expected Outcome Students will see steam coming from the teakettle. Sample answer: The visible steam is condensation,

a liquid. Water vapor, a gas, is present but not visible.

Extend Have students apply what they have observed in this activity to infer the role of condensation in cloud formation. (*Clouds are formed when water vapor undergoes condensation on particulate matter in the air.*) **learning modality: visual**

M ● 193

Thermal Energy and Heat

Show the Video Field Trip to let students understand how thermal expansion affects bridges. Discussion question: **Why is knowledge of heat transfer important in the construction of bridges?** *(Sample answer: The materials used to construct bridges are subject to expansion and contraction as the surrounding temperature changes. Engineers and bridge designers must consider possible expansion or contraction of bridge materials so the bridge is safe at all temperatures.)*

Assess

Reviewing Key Concepts

1. a. Solids, liquids, and gases **b.** Only solids have definite shapes. Solids and liquids have definite volumes. Gases have neither definite shapes nor definite volumes.

2. a. At certain temperatures, matter changes from one state to another when thermal energy is absorbed or released. **b.** The addition or loss of thermal energy changes the arrangement of the particles, not their average kinetic energy. **c.** Melting occurs when a solid absorbs enough thermal energy to reach its melting point.

3. a. A liquid can expand without changing state if the thermal energy it absorbs does not cause it to reach the temperature at which it vaporizes. **b.** The water in the potato will change state as the potato is baked. The holes allow the water vapor and steam to escape. **c.** A thermostat uses a bimetallic strip. When the strip is heated, one side expands more than the other, operating the switch that turns the heating system on and off.

Reteach   L1

Have students locate the boldface sentences in the section, and restate each in their own words.

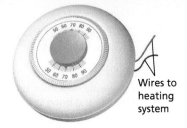

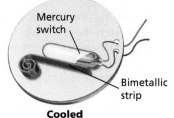

Mercury switch

Wires to heating system

Bimetallic strip

Cooled   **Heated**

FIGURE 14
Thermostat
A bimetallic strip controls many thermostats. When it cools, the strip curls up and lowers the switch, allowing mercury to flow over the wires. When the strip warms up, it uncurls and raises the switch.

Thermal Energy and Heat

Video Preview
▶ Video Field Trip
Video Assessment

Thermal Expansion

Have you ever loosened a tight jar lid by holding it under a stream of hot water? This works because the metal lid expands a little. Do you know why? **As the thermal energy of matter increases, its particles spread out and the substance expands.** With a few exceptions, this is true for all matter, even when the matter is not changing state. The expanding of matter when it is heated is known as **thermal expansion.**

When matter is cooled, thermal energy is released. The motion of the particles slows down and the particles move closer together. In nearly all cases, as matter is cooled, it contracts, or decreases in volume.

Heat-regulating devices called thermostats use thermal expansion to work. Many thermostats contain bimetallic strips, which are strips of two different metals joined together. Different metals expand at different rates. When the bimetallic strip is heated, one side expands more than the other. This causes the strip to uncurl. The movement of the strip operates a switch, which can turn a heating system on or off.

Section 3 Assessment

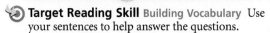

Target Reading Skill Building Vocabulary Use your sentences to help answer the questions.

Reviewing Key Concepts

1. a. Identifying Name three states of matter.
  b. Comparing and Contrasting How are the three states of matter different from each other? How are they the same?
2. a. Reviewing What causes a change in state?
  b. Describing Why does the temperature of matter remain the same while the matter changes state?
  c. Relating Cause and Effect What causes a solid to melt?
3. a. Defining How can a liquid expand without changing state?

b. Applying Concepts Why should you poke holes in a potato before baking it?
c. Interpreting Diagrams How does a thermostat make use of thermal expansion?

Lab zone At-Home Activity

Frosty Balloons Blow up two balloons so that they are the same size. Have a family member use a measuring tape to measure the circumference of the balloons. Place one of the balloons in the freezer for 15 to 20 minutes. Then measure both balloons again. Explain how changes in thermal energy cause the change in size.

Performance Assessment   L2

Drawing Have students make labeled diagrams that show the change of state of a container of water that starts cold and is heated until it boils and vaporizes.

All in One Teaching Resources

• Section Summary: *Thermal Energy and Heat*
• Review and Reinforce: *Thermal Energy and Heat*
• Enrich: *Thermal Energy and Heat*

Lab zone At-Home Activity

Frosty Balloons L1 Suggest that students mark the location of the measuring tape on the balloon, so they can measure the same part of the balloon each time. Do not use Mylar™ balloons. Students should note that placing the balloon in the freezer causes the particles of the gas in the balloon to lose thermal energy. This causes the gas to contract, so that the balloon's circumference becomes smaller.

Section 4 Uses of Heat

Reading Preview

Key Concepts
- How do heat engines use thermal energy?
- How do refrigerators keep things cold?

Key Terms
- heat engine
- external combustion engine
- internal combustion engine
- refrigerant

Target Reading Skill
Sequencing A sequence is the order in which the steps in a process occur. As you read, make a cycle diagram that shows how refrigerators work. Write each phase of the cooling system's cycle in a separate circle.

How Refrigerators Work

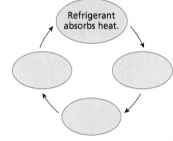

Refrigerant absorbs heat.

Lab zone Discover **Activity**

What Happens at the Pump?

1. Obtain a bicycle pump and a deflated basketball or soccer ball.
2. Feel the pump with your hand. Note whether it feels cool or warm to the touch.
3. Use the pump to inflate the ball to the recommended pressure.
4. As soon as you stop pumping, feel the pump again. Observe any changes in temperature.

Think It Over
Developing Hypotheses Propose an explanation for any changes that you observed.

For more than 100 years, the steam locomotive was a symbol of power and speed. It first came into use in the 1830s, and was soon hauling hundreds of tons of freight faster than a horse could gallop. Today, many trains are pulled by diesel locomotives that are far more efficient than steam locomotives.

Heat Engines

To power a coal-burning steam locomotive, coal is shoveled into a roaring fire. Heat is then transferred from the fire to water in the boiler. But how can heat move a train?

The thermal energy of the coal fire must be transformed to the mechanical energy, or energy of motion, of the moving train. You already know about the reverse process, the transformation of mechanical energy to thermal energy. It happens when you rub your hands together to make them warm.

The transformation of thermal energy to mechanical energy requires a device called a **heat engine.** Heat engines usually make use of combustion. You may recall that combustion is the process of burning a fuel, such as coal or gasoline. During combustion, chemical energy that is stored in fuel is transformed to thermal energy. **Heat engines transform thermal energy to mechanical energy.** Heat engines are classified according to whether combustion takes place outside the engine or inside the engine.

Lab zone Discover **Activity**

Skills Focus Developing hypotheses L1

Materials bicycle pump, deflated basketball or soccer ball

Time 10 minutes

Tip Caution students to avoid over-inflating the ball, which could cause it to burst. Remind students that the pump uses mechanical energy to inflate the ball.

Expected Outcome Students should find that the temperature of the pump has increased after pumping.

Think It Over Sample answer: The pump's temperature increased because work done by the piston went into the thermal energy of the gas (due to compression) and the thermal energy of the pump (due to friction).

Section 4 Uses of Heat

Objectives
After this lesson, students will be able to
M.6.4.1 Describe how heat engines use thermal energy.
M.6.4.2 Describe how refrigerators keep things cold.

Target Reading Skill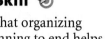

Sequencing Explain that organizing information from beginning to end helps students understand a step-by-step process.

Answers
Sample cycle diagram: Refrigerant absorbs heat. Compressor increases refrigerant's temperature. Refrigerant releases heat. Expansion valve decreases refrigerant's temperature.

All in One Teaching Resources
- Transparency M56

Preteach

Build Background Knowledge L2

Heat Engines Use Thermal Energy
Ask: **How does the hood of a car that has just been driven feel?** *(It feels warm.)* **Where does the heat come from?** *(Combustion in the engine releases thermal energy.)*

Instruct

Heat Engines

Teach Key Concepts L2
Energy Conversions in Heat Engines

Focus Tell students that most heat engines convert thermal energy to mechanical energy.

Teach Direct students' attention to Figures 15 and 16. Have them note the location of the combustion in each engine.

Apply Ask: **What type of energy is stored in gasoline?** *(Chemical energy)* **What type of energy is this converted to during combustion?** *(Thermal energy)* **What type of energy is this converted to by the engine?** *(Mechanical energy)* **learning modality: logical/mathematical**

Mechanical Energy From Steam L2

Materials teakettle, water, hot plate, pinwheel

Time 10 minutes

Focus Tell students that steam is used in some external combustion engines.

Teach Fill the teakettle with water, and place it on the hot plate. Heat the water until it boils and steam escapes from the spout. Hold the pinwheel in the escaping steam, so students can see the blades of the pinwheel turn. Explain that the hot plate is used in place of combustion in this demonstration.

Apply Ask: **What type of energy does the moving pinwheel have?** *(Mechanical energy, or kinetic energy)* **learning modality: visual**

Independent Practice L2

All in One **Teaching Resources**

- Guided Reading and Study Worksheet: *Uses of Heat*
- Transparency M57

 Student Edition on Audio CD

FIGURE 15

External Combustion Engine

In a steam-powered external combustion engine, expanding steam pushes a piston back and forth inside a cylinder. The steam's thermal energy is transformed to mechanical energy.

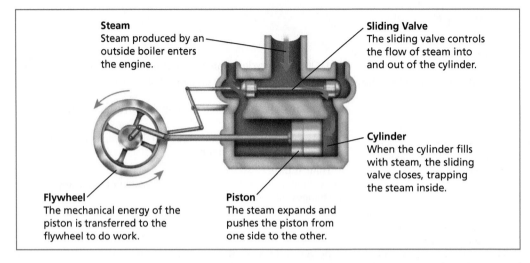

Steam
Steam produced by an outside boiler enters the engine.

Sliding Valve
The sliding valve controls the flow of steam into and out of the cylinder.

Cylinder
When the cylinder fills with steam, the sliding valve closes, trapping the steam inside.

Flywheel
The mechanical energy of the piston is transferred to the flywheel to do work.

Piston
The steam expands and pushes the piston from one side to the other.

External Combustion Engines Engines that burn fuel outside the engine in a boiler are called **external combustion engines.** A steam engine, like the one shown in Figure 15, is an example of an external combustion engine. The combustion of wood, coal, or oil heats water in a boiler. As its thermal energy increases, the liquid water turns to water vapor, or steam. The steam is then passed through a sliding valve into the engine, where it pushes against a metal plunger called a piston. Work is done on the piston as it moves back and forth in a tube called a cylinder. The piston's motion turns a flywheel.

Internal Combustion Engines Engines that burn fuel in cylinders inside the engine are called **internal combustion engines.** Diesel and gasoline engines, which power most automobiles, are internal combustion engines. A piston inside a cylinder moves up and down, turning a crankshaft. The motion of the crankshaft is transferred to the wheels of the car.

Each up or down movement by a piston is called a stroke. Most diesel and gasoline engines are four-stroke engines, as shown in Figure 16. Automobile engines usually have four, six, or eight cylinders. The four-stroke process occurs in each cylinder, and is repeated many times each second.

Reading Checkpoint **How many cylinders do automobiles usually have?**

Lab zone **Try This Activity**

Shake It Up

How does work relate to temperature?

1. Place a handful of dry sand in a metal container that has a cover.
2. Measure the temperature of the sand with a thermometer.
3. Cover the can and shake it vigorously for a minute or two.
4. Predict any change in the temperature of the sand. Was your prediction correct?

Classifying Identify any energy transformations and use them to explain your observations.

Lab zone **Try This Activity**

Skills Focus Classifying L3

Materials dry sand, metal container such as a coffee can with a plastic lid, thermometer

Time 15 minutes

Tips Caution students not to force the thermometer into the sand. Remind students that some thermal energy escapes when they open the lid.

Expected Outcome The sand's temperature should increase slightly from shaking because mechanical energy is converted to thermal energy.

Extend Challenge students to find a way to reduce heat loss when the temperature is checked. *(Insert the thermometer into the lid)* **learning modality: kinesthetic**

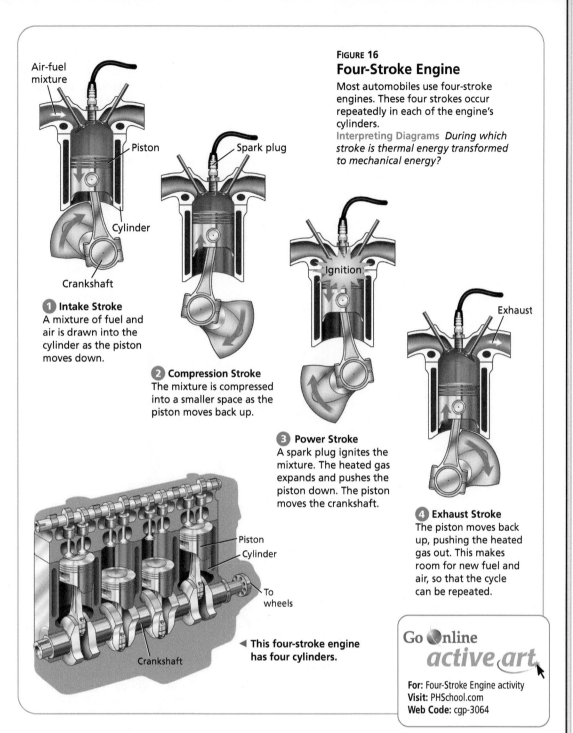

Air-fuel mixture

Piston

Spark plug

Cylinder

Crankshaft

Ignition

Exhaust

① **Intake Stroke**
A mixture of fuel and air is drawn into the cylinder as the piston moves down.

② **Compression Stroke**
The mixture is compressed into a smaller space as the piston moves back up.

③ **Power Stroke**
A spark plug ignites the mixture. The heated gas expands and pushes the piston down. The piston moves the crankshaft.

④ **Exhaust Stroke**
The piston moves back up, pushing the heated gas out. This makes room for new fuel and air, so that the cycle can be repeated.

Piston
Cylinder

To wheels

Crankshaft

◀ This four-stroke engine has four cylinders.

FIGURE 16
Four-Stroke Engine
Most automobiles use four-stroke engines. These four strokes occur repeatedly in each of the engine's cylinders.
Interpreting Diagrams During which stroke is thermal energy transformed to mechanical energy?

Go **Online**
active art

For: Four-Stroke Engine activity
Visit: PHSchool.com
Web Code: cgp-3064

Chapter 6 M ◆ 197

Use Visuals   L2
Four-Stroke Engine

Focus Tell students that most automobiles use four-stroke engines.

Teach Have students read the numbered descriptions within the figure. Ask volunteers to describe each step in their own words while the other students follow the diagrams in Figure 16.

Apply Ask: **In what step shown in the figure does combustion take place?** *(In Step 3, when the spark plug ignites the mixture of fuel and air)* **learning modality: visual**

 **Teaching Resources**
• Transparency M58

Go **Online**
active art

For: Four-Stroke Engine activity
Visit: PHSchool.com
Web Code: cgp-3064

Students can interact with diagrams of a four-stroke engine online.

Differentiated Instruction

Less Proficient Readers   L1
Organizing Information Have students organize the information in Figure 16 onto four index cards. Students should name the stroke on the front of each card and describe the stroke on the back. Students can use the cards for review or to quiz others. **learning modality: verbal**

Special Needs   L1
Reviewing Key Concepts Have students listen to the section on the **Student Edition on Audio CD.** When the students have finished listening, have them locate and read the boldface sentences in the section. Students can work with a partner to complete this activity. **learning modality: verbal**

Monitor Progress   L2

Skills Check Ask students to predict what will happen in a four-stroke engine if a spark plug does not fire. *(The fuel-air mixture will not be ignited, and the heated gas will not push down on the piston.)*

Answers
Figure 16 Thermal energy is transformed to mechanical energy during the power stroke.

 Four, six, or eight

Cooling Systems

Teach Key Concepts `L2`
How Cooling Systems Work

Focus Ask: **In what direction does thermal energy flow?** *(From warm substances to cooler substances)*

Teach Tell students that refrigerators and air conditioners work by transferring thermal energy from a cool area to a warm area using a substance called a refrigerant. Direct students' attention to Figure 17. Ask: **What happens to the state of the refrigerant as it passes through the steps shown in Figure 17?** *(It undergoes phase changes, from a liquid to a gas, and then from a gas to a liquid.)*

Apply Ask: **Why does keeping the refrigerator open for long time periods of time cause the refrigerator to use more electricity?** *(When the door is open, the temperature inside the refrigerator rises; therefore, there is more thermal energy to be removed.)* **learning modality: visual**

All in One Teaching Resources

• Transparency M59

Help Students Read `L1`
Relating Cause and Effect Have students examine Figure 17 to determine a cause and an effect within each numbered step in the diagram. Model this for students by showing the following example, for Step 1: Cause: Liquid refrigerant absorbs heat from food. Effect: Liquid refrigerant changes to a gas. Have the students complete this exercise for Steps 2, 3, and 4. *(Step 2: Cause: The compressor increases the pressure on the refrigerant. Effect: The refrigerant's temperature rises higher than room temperature. Step 3: Cause: The gas refrigerant releases heat into the room. Effect: The gas refrigerant changes to a liquid. Step 4: Cause: The expansion valve causes a drop in the pressure on the refrigerant. Effect: The refrigerant's temperature drops lower than the temperature of the food.)*

Cooling Systems

The transfer of heat can sometimes be used to keep things cool. Are you surprised? After all, heat naturally flows from a warm area to a cold area—not the other way around. But some devices, such as refrigerators, can transfer heat from cold areas to warm areas.

Refrigerators A refrigerator is cold inside. So where does the heat in the warm air rising from the back of a refrigerator come from? You may be surprised to learn that part of the heat actually comes from food in the refrigerator! **A refrigerator is a device that transfers thermal energy from inside the refrigerator to the room outside.** In doing so, the refrigerator transfers thermal energy from a cool area to a warm area.

FIGURE 17
Refrigerator
Inside a refrigerator, refrigerant moves through a system of pipes, transferring thermal energy from inside the refrigerator to the surrounding air. *Inferring Why must the temperature of the refrigerant be lower than that of the food to absorb the food's thermal energy?*

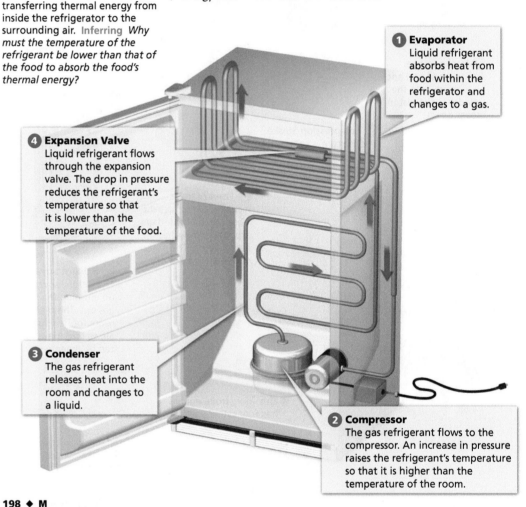

❶ Evaporator
Liquid refrigerant absorbs heat from food within the refrigerator and changes to a gas.

❹ Expansion Valve
Liquid refrigerant flows through the expansion valve. The drop in pressure reduces the refrigerant's temperature so that it is lower than the temperature of the food.

❸ Condenser
The gas refrigerant releases heat into the room and changes to a liquid.

❷ Compressor
The gas refrigerant flows to the compressor. An increase in pressure raises the refrigerant's temperature so that it is higher than the temperature of the room.

198 ◆ M

Differentiated Instruction

Less Proficient Readers `L1`
Active Listening Read aloud the text found in the insets in Figure 17. Ask students to follow along in their book as you read. When you have completed reading, challenge students to state facts or ask questions about the text. **learning modality: verbal**

Gifted and Talented `L3`
Communicating Information Have students research the history of refrigeration. Students can share what they have learned with the class in an oral presentation. **learning modality: verbal**

A substance called a **refrigerant** absorbs and releases heat in a refrigerator. As shown in Figure 17, the refrigerant moves through a closed system of pipes. These pipes run along the back of the refrigerator and inside where food is stored. The coiled pipes inside make up the evaporator. As the refrigerant enters the evaporator, it is a liquid. Because it is colder than the food, it absorbs the thermal energy of the food. The food's thermal energy raises the refrigerant's temperature, causing it to evaporate. Then, the gas refrigerant enters an electric pump called a compressor. The compressor increases the refrigerant's pressure, further raising its temperature.

From the compressor, the gas refrigerant flows to the coiled pipes at the back of the refrigerator that make up the condenser. When it enters the condenser, the refrigerant is warmer than the air in the room. It releases heat into the air and its temperature drops, causing the refrigerant to condense. The pressure of the liquid refrigerant is decreased as it flows into a narrow opening called an expansion valve. The decreased pressure lowers the refrigerant's temperature further. The refrigerant recycles as it flows back to the evaporator.

Air Conditioners The air conditioners used in homes, schools, and cars cool air in the same way that a refrigerator cools food. Refrigerant in a system of pipes changes from a liquid to a gas and back again to transfer heat. Unlike a refrigerator, however, an air conditioner absorbs heat from the air inside a room or car and transfers it to the outdoors.

 Reading Checkpoint How are air conditioners and refrigerators similar?

Section 4 Assessment

Target Reading Skill Sequencing Refer to your cycle diagram about cooling systems as you answer Question 2.

Reviewing Key Concepts

1. **a.** Describing What does a heat engine do?
   b. Comparing and Contrasting How are internal combustion engines different from external combustion engines? How are they similar?
   c. Making Generalizations Why do you think modern cars use internal rather than external combustion engines?

2. **a.** Identifying What changes of state occur in the refrigerant of a refrigerator?

   b. Explaining Where do the changes of state occur?
   c. Predicting If the compressor in a refrigerator stopped working, how would its failure affect the heat transfer cycle?

Cause-and-Effect Paragraph The invention of the heat engine and refrigerator both had a great impact on society. Write about how daily life might be different if either system had not been invented.

Answers

Figure 17 Because thermal energy moves spontaneously from a warmer object to a cooler one

 Reading Checkpoint Both devices transfer heat to keep an area cool.

Assess

Reviewing Key Concepts

1. **a.** A heat engine transforms thermal energy to mechanical energy. **b.** In an internal combustion engine, fuel is burned inside the engine; in an external combustion engine, fuel is burned outside the engine. Both transform thermal energy to mechanical energy. **c.** Sample answer: Internal combustion engines are more efficient.

2. **a.** Condensation and evaporation **b.** Condensation occurs in the condenser; evaporation occurs in the evaporator. **c.** The refrigerant's pressure and temperature would not be increased sufficiently before it entered the condenser. Therefore, the refrigerant would not release enough heat (to the air outside the refrigerator) to condense. If the refrigerant did not condense, it could not evaporate later to cool items inside the refrigerator.

Reteach **L1**

Have students use Figures 16 and 17 to review the processes involved in the function of a heat engine and a cooling system.

Performance Assessment **L2**

Writing Ask students to write advertisements for an air conditioning system. The advertisement should describe how the air conditioner cools a hot room.

All in One Teaching Resources
- Section Summary: *Uses of Heat*
- Review and Reinforce: *Uses of Heat*
- Enrich: *Uses of Heat*

Lab zone Chapter **Project**

Keep Students on Track Students should build and test their containers. Make sure that students consider that they will need to access the aluminum can at the beginning of the test to add water and at the end of the test to measure the water's temperature.

Writing in Science

Writing Mode Exposition/Cause and Effect
Scoring Rubric
4 Exceeds criteria
3 Meets criteria
2 Includes little information on heat engines and refrigerators
1 Shows little effort and/or includes serious errors

The **BIG Idea**   **Transfer of Energy** Heat can be transferred by conduction, convection, or radiation.

The BIG Idea

Have students read the answer to the Essential Question. Encourage them to evaluate and revise their own answers as needed.

Help Students Read
Building Vocabulary

Paraphrasing Have students rewrite the boldface sentences from Thermal Energy and States of Matter in their own words. Have the students use their rewritten statements when they review the section content.

Word/Part Analysis Tell students that the suffix *-tion* changes a verb into a noun. For example, the word *vaporize* means "to turn into a gas." The word *vaporization* thus means "the process of turning into a gas." Have students apply this concept to the words *evaporation* and *condensation*.

Connecting Concepts
Concept Maps Help students develop a concept map to show how the information in this chapter is related. Thermal energy, temperature, and heat are related to the energy in particles in matter, can be used to explain energy transfer and changes of state, and are applied in the design of heat engines and cooling systems. Have students brainstorm to identify the key concepts, key terms, details, and examples. Then, write each one on a self-sticking note and attach it at random on chart paper or on the board.

Tell students that this concept map will be organized in hierarchical order and to begin at the top with the key concepts. Ask students these questions to guide them to categorize the information on the self-sticking notes: **How are temperature, thermal energy, and heat related? What are the three ways in which heat is transferred? How does thermal energy relate to an object's state of matter? What are some common uses of heat?** Prompt students to use connecting words or phrases, such as "are related to" and "can be used to explain," to indicate the basis for the connections in

the map. The phrases should form a sentence between or among a set of concepts.

Answer
Accept logical presentations by students.

1 Temperature, Thermal Energy, and Heat

Key Concepts
- The three common scales for measuring temperature are the Fahrenheit, Celsius, and Kelvin scales.
- Heat is thermal energy moving from a warmer object to a cooler object.
- A material with a high specific heat can absorb a great deal of thermal energy without a great change in temperature.
- Change in energy = Mass × Specific heat × Change in temperature

Key Terms
temperature
Fahrenheit scale
Celsius scale
Kelvin scale
absolute zero
heat
specific heat

2 The Transfer of Heat
Key Concepts
- Heat is transferred by conduction, convection, and radiation.
- If two objects have different temperatures, heat will flow from the warmer object to the colder one.
- A conductor transfers thermal energy well. An insulator does not transfer thermal energy well.

Key Terms
conduction
convection
convection current
radiation
conductor
insulator

3 Thermal Energy and States of Matter

Key Concepts
- Most matter on Earth can exist in three states—solid, liquid, and gas.
- Matter can change from one state to another when thermal energy is absorbed or released.
- As the thermal energy of matter increases, its particles spread out and the substance expands.

Key Terms
state
change of state
melting
freezing
evaporation
boiling
condensation
thermal expansion

4 Uses of Heat
Key Concepts
- Heat engines transform thermal energy to mechanical energy.
- A refrigerator is a device that transfers thermal energy from inside the refrigerator to the room outside.

Key Terms
heat engine
external combustion engine
internal combustion engine
refrigerant

All in One Teaching Resources
- Key Terms Review: *Thermal Energy and Heat*
- Connecting Concepts: *Thermal Energy and Heat*

Review and Assessment

Organizing Information

Concept Mapping Copy the concept map about heat onto a separate sheet of paper. Then complete it and add a title. (For more on Concept Mapping, see the Skills Handbook.)

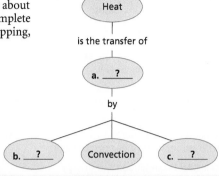

Reviewing Key Terms

Choose the letter of the best answer.

1. A measure of the average kinetic energy of the particles of an object is its
   a. heat.
   b. temperature.
   c. specific heat.
   d. thermal energy.

2. If you want to know the amount of heat needed to raise the temperature of 2 kg of steel by 10°C, you need to know steel's
   a. temperature.   b. thermal energy.
   c. state.   d. specific heat.

3. The process by which heat moves from one particle of matter to another without the movement of matter itself is called
   a. convection.
   b. conduction.
   c. radiation.
   d. thermal expansion.

4. Vaporization that occurs below the surface of a liquid is called
   a. evaporation.   b. melting.
   c. boiling.   d. freezing.

5. The process of burning a fuel is called
   a. combustion.
   b. thermal expansion.
   c. radiation.
   d. boiling.

If the statement is true, write *true*. If it is false, change the underlined word or words to make the statement true.

6. A temperature reading of zero on the <u>Celsius scale</u> is equal to absolute zero.

7. A <u>convection current</u> is the circular motion of a fluid caused by the rising of heated fluid.

8. An <u>insulator</u> conducts heat well.

9. When a substance is <u>freezing</u>, the thermal energy of the substance decreases.

10. In an <u>external combustion engine</u>, the fuel is burned inside the engine.

Writing in Science

Proposed Solution You have been asked to design a bridge for an area that is quite hot in the summer and cold in the winter. Propose a design plan for the bridge. Include in your plan how expansion joints will help the bridge react in hot and cold temperatures.

Discovery CHANNEL SCHOOL

Thermal Energy and Heat
Video Preview
Video Field Trip
▶ Video Assessment

Chapter 6   M ◆ 201

Review and Assessment

Organizing Information
a. Thermal energy
b. Conduction or radiation
c. Radiation or conduction

Reviewing Key Terms
1. b 2. d 3. b 4. c 5. a
6. Kelvin scale
7. true
8. conductor
9. true
10. internal combustion engine

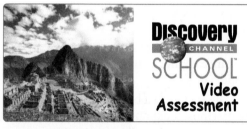

Discovery CHANNEL SCHOOL Video Assessment

Thermal Energy and Heat

Show the Video Assessment to review chapter content and as a prompt for the writing assignment. Discussion questions: **What are the three ways in which heat is transferred?** *(The three ways in which heat is transferred are conduction, convection, and radiation.)* **How does heat transfer affect bridge structures?** *(Heat transfer affects bridge structures by causing expansion and contraction of the materials.)*

Writing in Science

Writing Mode Exposition/Problem-solution

Scoring Rubric
4 Exceeds criteria; includes a detailed plan and an extensive description of how the expansion joints will function
3 Meets criteria
2 Includes few details and/or some incorrect information
1 Fails to correctly explain how expansion joints are important to the bridge design

---

Go Online
PHSchool.com

For: Self-Assessment
Visit: PHSchool.com
Web Code: cga-3060

Students can take a practice test online that is automatically scored.

All in One Teaching Resources
- Transparency M60
- Chapter Test
- Performance Assessment Teacher Notes
- Performance Assessment Student Worksheet
- Performance Assessment Scoring Rubric

ExamView® Computer Test Bank CD-ROM

Checking Concepts

11. The particles remain in fairly fixed positions until sufficient thermal energy has been absorbed to break down the solid's structure. At that point, melting takes place and the particles become freer to move around.

12. No. Air has a much lower specific heat than water. Loss of the same amount of thermal energy by the water will result in a smaller temperature drop.

13. The water near the heat source is warmed. The warm water expands and rises while cool water sinks to take its place. The circular flow is a convection current.

14. You could add more particles of the substance at the same temperature. Also, during some changes of state, thermal energy increases while temperature stays the same.

15. Thermal energy is released when a substance changes phase from a liquid to a solid.

16. The metals in a bimetallic strip inside the thermostat expand and contract by different amounts as the temperature changes. This causes the strip to curve, and allows it to control a switch connected to the heating or cooling system.

Thinking Critically

17. The air in the tires gets warmer as the car is driven. The increase in temperature causes the air particles to move faster and hit the inside of the tire with greater average force, which produces greater air pressure.

18. The lines expand in the summer and contract in the winter. If they did not sag, they would contract and pull away from the poles during cold winters.

19. Solid: B; liquid: C; gas: A

20. Inside the open refrigerator, the system is transferring thermal energy from the air to the refrigerant. Outside the open refrigerator, the system is transferring that same amount of thermal energy from the refrigerant back to the room.

Math Practice

21. 135°C

22. 30°C

Review and Assessment

Checking Concepts

11. What happens to the particles of a solid as the thermal energy of the solid increases?

12. During a summer night, the air temperature drops by 10°C. Will the temperature of the water in a nearby lake change by the same amount? Explain why or why not.

13. When you heat a pot of water on the stove, a convection current is formed. Explain how this happens.

14. How can you add thermal energy to a substance without increasing its temperature?

15. When molten steel becomes solid, is energy absorbed or released by the steel? Explain.

16. Describe how a thermostat controls the temperature in a building.

Thinking Critically

17. Relating Cause and Effect Why is the air pressure in a car's tires different before and after the car has been driven for an hour?

18. Applying Concepts When they are hung, telephone lines are allowed to sag. Can you think of a reason why?

19. Interpreting Diagrams The three illustrations below represent the molecules in three different materials. Which is a solid? A liquid? A gas?

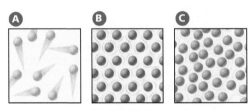

20. Developing Hypotheses A refrigerator is running in a small room. The refrigerator door is open, but the room does not grow any cooler. Use the law of conservation of energy to explain why the temperature does not drop.

Math Practice

21. Converting Units A recipe says to preheat your oven to 275°F. What is this temperature in degrees Celsius?

22. Converting Units The temperature in a greenhouse is 86°F. Convert this temperature to degrees Celsius.

Applying Skills

Use the illustration of three containers of water to answer Questions 23–25.

23. Interpreting Data Compare the average motion of the molecules in the three containers. Explain your answer.

24. Drawing Conclusions Compare the total amount of thermal energy in the three containers. Explain your answer.

25. Calculating Which container would need the least amount of thermal energy to raise its temperature by 1 K? The specific heat of water is 4,180 J/(kg·K).

Lab zone Chapter **Project**

Performance Assessment Talk with your classmates about their container designs. When you've had a chance to look them over, predict the final water temperature for each container. Record the starting temperature for each one, including your own. Record the final temperatures at the end of each demonstration. Which insulating materials seemed to work the best? Describe how you could improve your container, based on what you learned.

Lab zone Chapter **Project**   L3

Performance Assessment Students' predictions should be based on what they have learned in the chapter. Students should explain how their experimental results affected their design and choice of materials. While the class is waiting for final temperatures, predictions can be posted. Ask students to explain the reasoning behind their predictions. Encourage students to compare their designs to the best-insulated design in the class.

Standardized Test Prep

Test-Taking Tip

Using Formulas

For some questions, you will need to use a formula to find the correct answer. It is important to know which formula to use. Look for key words in the question to help you decide which formula will help you answer the question. Then substitute the values provided to make your calculations.

Sample Question

The specific heat of iron is 450 J/(kg·K). How much heat must be transferred to 15 kg of iron to raise its temperature by 4.0 K?

   A 450 J
   B 2,700 J
   C 5,400 J
   D 27,000 J

Answer

The question deals with the amount of heat needed to change the temperature of a material. The specific heat of that material, iron, is provided. You need to use the formula for calculating thermal energy changes.

Change in energy =
  Mass × Specific heat × Change in temperature

Change in energy = 15 kg × 450 J/(kg·K) × 4.0 K
Change in energy = 27,000 J

The correct answer is **D**.

Choose the letter of the best answer.

1. When cold, dry air passes over a much warmer body of water, a type of fog called sea smoke is produced. Which process explains why this occurs?
  A melting
  B condensation
  C boiling
  D freezing

2. The table below shows the specific heat of four metals. If 1,540 J of heat is transferred to 4 kg of each metal, which metal will increase in temperature by 1 K?

Specific Heat of Metals	
Metal	**Specific Heat (J/(kg·K))**
Silver	235
Iron	450
Copper	385
Aluminum	903

  F Silver
  G Copper
  H Iron
  J Aluminum

3. A student wants to measure the temperature at which several different liquids freeze. In the student's experiment, temperature is the
  A hypothesis.
  B responding variable.
  C manipulated variable.
  D operational definition.

4. Two solid metal blocks are placed in a container. If there is a transfer of heat between the blocks, then they must have different
  F boiling points.
  G melting points.
  H specific heats.
  J temperatures.

5. A thermometer measures
  A temperature.
  B thermal energy.
  C heat.
  D specific heat.

Constructed Response

6. Explain how heat is transferred by conduction, convection, and radiation. Give an example of each.

Applying Skills

23. The average motion of the molecules is greater at higher temperatures. The average motion is the same for the two containers on the left and at the center, and greater for the container on the right.

24. The total thermal energy in the middle container is twice the thermal energy in the container on the left because it has twice as many particles at the same temperature. The thermal energy in the container on the right is greater than the middle container. It has the same number of particles, but the average energy of each particle is greater.

25. The left container would require the least amount of thermal energy (418 J) to raise its temperature by 1 K because it has the least mass.

Standardized Test Practice

1. B **2.** G **3.** B **4.** J **5.** A

6. In conduction, heat is transferred from one particle to another without the movement of the matter itself. If you leave an iron poker in the fireplace while a fire is burning, the poker will get hot. This is an example of conduction. Convection is movement within a fluid that transfers heat. For example, when hot air rises, cool air descends to take its place. Hawks take advantage of convection to soar upward. In radiation, energy is transferred by electromagnetic waves. Matter is not required to transfer the energy. A microwave oven cooks food by radiation.

Bridges—From Vines to Steel

This interdisciplinary feature presents the central theme of bridges by connecting four different disciplines: science, social studies, mathematics, and language arts. The four explorations are designed to capture students' interest and help them see how the content they are studying in science relates to other school subjects and to real-world events. The unit is particularly suitable for team teaching.

All in One Teaching Resources

- Interdisciplinary Exploration: *Science*
- Interdisciplinary Exploration: *Language Arts*
- Interdisciplinary Exploration: *Mathematics*
- Interdisciplinary Exploration: *Social Studies*

Build Background Knowledge
Recalling Science Concepts
Help students recall what they learned in the chapter, Forces. Ask: **What does Newton's third law say about action and reaction forces?** *(For every action force, there is an equal and opposite reaction force.)* **If the weight of a truck pushes down on a bridge, what is the reaction force?** *(The bridge pushing back on the truck)* Invite students to describe bridges they have seen.

Introduce the Exploration
Ask: **What is the basic purpose of a bridge?** *(Sample answer: Bridges allow people and vehicles to cross bodies of water.)* Point out that bridges must be strong enough to support the weight of vehicles. Many bridges must be designed to allow boats to pass under the bridge. Ask: **Why are bridges important for trade?** *(Sample answer: Bridges make it easier to transport goods.)* List all reasonable responses on the board.

Bridges— From Vines to Steel

Have you ever
- balanced on a branch or log to cross a brook?
- jumped from rock to rock in a streambed?
- swung on a vine or rope over a river?

Vine Footbridge
A girl crosses over the Hunza River in northern Pakistan.

Then you have used the same ways that early people used to get over obstacles. Fallen trees, twisted vines, and natural stones formed the first bridges.

Bridges provide easy ways of getting over difficult obstacles. For thousands of years, bridges have also served as forts for defense, scenes of great battles, and homes for shops and churches. They have also been sites of mystery, love, and intrigue. They span history—linking cities, nations, and empires and encouraging trade and travel.

But bridges have not always been as elaborate as they are today. The earliest ones were made of materials that were free and plentiful. In deep forests, people used beams made from small trees. In tropical regions where vegetation was thick, people wove together vines and grasses, then hung them to make walkways over rivers and gorges.

No matter what the structures or materials, bridges reflect the people who built them. The ancient civilizations of China, Egypt, Greece, and Rome all designed strong, graceful bridges to connect and control their empires.

Roman Arch Bridge
Ponte Sant'Angelo is in Rome.

The Balance of Forces

What keeps a bridge from falling down? How does it support its own weight and the weight of people and traffic on it? Builders found the answers by considering the various forces that act on a bridge.

The weight of the bridge and the traffic on it are called the *load*. When a heavy truck crosses a beam bridge, the weight of the load forces the beam to curve downward. This creates tension forces that stretch the bottom of the beam. At the same time, the load also creates compression forces at the top of the beam.

Since the bridge doesn't collapse under the load, there must be upward forces to balance the downward forces. In simple beam bridges, builders anchor the beam to the ground or to end supports called abutments. To cross longer spans or distances, they construct piers under the middle span. Piers and abutments are structures that act as upward forces—reaction forces.

Another type of bridge, the arch bridge, supports its load by compression. A heavy load on a stone arch bridge squeezes or pushes the stones together, creating compression throughout the structure. Weight on the arch bridge pushes down to the ends of the arch. The side walls and abutments act as reaction forces.

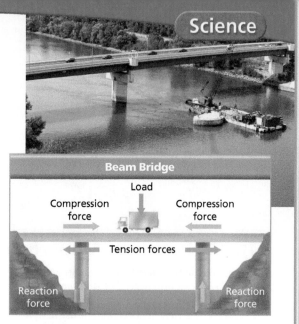

Beam Bridge
A beam bridge spans the Rhone River in France (top).

Early engineers discovered that arch bridges made of stone could span wider distances than simple beam bridges. Arch bridges are also stronger and more durable. Although the Romans were not the first to build arch bridges, they perfected the form in their massive, elegant structures. Early Roman arch bridges were built without mortar, or "glue." The arch held together because the stones were skillfully shaped to work in compression. After nearly 2,000 years, some of these Roman arch bridges are still standing.

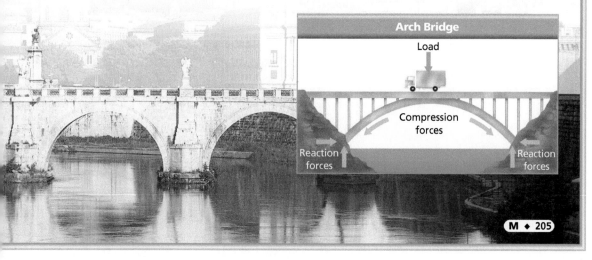

Explore Science Concepts

Use Visuals Have volunteers each read one paragraph aloud. As they are reading, direct students' attention to the diagrams.

Discuss Point out that it would be too expensive and dangerous for builders to use trial and error to find out how many supports a bridge needs. Ask: **How can builders determine how many supports a bridge needs?** *(Sample answer: Builders can use a scale model to test their bridge design.)*

Review Point out that the title of this page is "The Balance of Forces." Ask: **What does this mean?** *(The downward force of the load on the bridge is balanced by the upward force of the bridge on the load.)* **What might happen if the forces were not balanced?** *(Sample answer: The bridge might collapse.)*

Demonstrate Model a beam bridge by laying a meter stick between two desks. Show how the meter stick bends as you add weight to the center of the meter stick.

Use Visuals Invite a volunteer to find a diagram of the parts of a bridge in an encyclopedia or visual dictionary. In particular, have the student find illustrations of abutments to share with the class.

M ◆ 205

Background

Facts and Figures The oldest bridge still in use today with a construction date that can be accurately determined is in Turkey. This stone arch bridge over the River Meles in Izmar dates from about B.C. 850.

The longest stone arch bridge in the world is the Rockville Bridge in Pennsylvania. The bridge has 48 spans and is 1,161 meters long. This type of bridge is no longer built in the United States because of the expense.

Early bridge builders worked with stone, which is very strong in compression but very weak when bent. Early bridges were designed so that the forces of the load could be transferred to compression forces in the stone. Bridges, buildings, and aqueducts were all built by the Romans using arches, because arches take advantage of the high compression strength of stone.

Science

Explore Science Concepts

Use Visuals Challenge an interested student to find a drawing or photograph of a woven bridge. Have students compare the picture of the woven bridge to the picture of the suspension bridge in the text. Ask: **Woven bridges sway in the wind. What does this tell you about suspension bridges?** *(Suspension bridges also sway in the wind.)* Point out that suspension bridges are designed to allow for some movement in high winds. The shape of some valleys causes them to be windy so bridge designers have to consider wind when they make their designs.

Discuss Point out to students that the towers of a suspension bridge do not support the roadway. The towers support the cables from which the road hangs.

Use Visuals As the class reads the text, direct students' attention to the bridge diagrams. Point out the different forces, and help students understand how they counterbalance each other.

Discuss Point out that the text mentions several materials that have been used for bridge construction. Ask: **Why would bridge builders rather work with steel than iron?** *(Sample answer: Steel is less dense than iron, so a bridge of a given strength can be built with less dense materials using steel.)*

The Structure of Modern Bridges

By the 1800s in the United States, bridge builders began to use cast iron instead of stone and wood. By the late 1800s, they were using steel, which was strong and relatively lightweight. The use of new building materials was not the only change. Engineers began designing different types of bridges as well. They found that they could build longer, larger bridges by using a suspension structure.

Suspension bridges are modern versions of long, narrow, woven bridges found in tropical regions. These simple, woven suspension bridges can span long distances. Crossing one of these natural structures is like walking a tightrope. The weight of people and animals traveling over the bridge pushes down on the ropes, stretching them and creating tension forces.

Modern suspension bridges follow the same principles of tension as do woven bridges. A suspension bridge is strong in tension. In suspension bridges, parallel cables are stretched the entire length of the bridge—over giant towers. The cables are anchored at each end of the bridge. The roadway hangs from the cables, attached by wire suspenders. The weight of the bridge and the load on it act to pull apart or stretch the cables. This pulling apart creates tension forces.

The towers of a suspension bridge act as supports for the bridge cables. The abutments that anchor the cables exert reaction forces as well. So forces in balance keep a suspension bridge from collapsing.

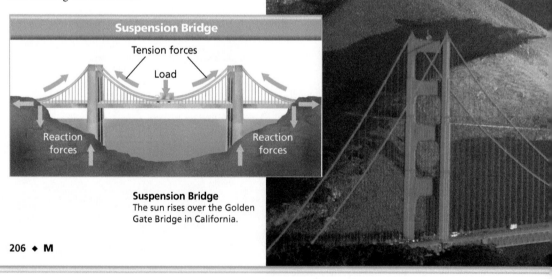

Suspension Bridge
The sun rises over the Golden Gate Bridge in California.

Background

Facts and Figures Iron, steel, and other metals are more flexible than stone, and they are also very strong in tension. So it is possible to design a bridge that takes advantage of the strength of wire in tension to build higher and longer bridges than would be practical with stone (or the modern equivalent of stone, concrete).

Suspension bridges can span greater distances than beam or arch bridges because the strong steel cables transfer force to the tall towers. The towers can be built high enough to allow huge ocean liners to sail underneath. The tallest masted ships can still sail under the Brooklyn Bridge.

Cable-Stayed Bridge
The Sunshine Skyway Bridge spans a broad section of Tampa Bay in Florida. The cables, attached to the center of the roadway, enable travelers to have a clear view.

When the Brooklyn Bridge opened in New York City in 1883, it was the longest suspension bridge in the world. The Golden Gate Bridge in San Francisco, which was opened in 1937, was another great engineering feat.

Recently, engineers have developed a new bridge design called the cable-stayed bridge. It looks similar to a suspension bridge because both are built with towers and cables. But the two bridges are quite different. The cables on the cable-stayed bridge attach to the towers, so the towers bear the weight of the bridge and the load on it. In contrast, the cables on a suspension bridge ride over the towers and anchor at the abutments. So on a suspension bridge, both the towers and abutments bear the load.

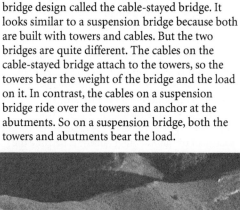

Science Activity

Work in groups to make a suspension bridge, using two chairs, a wooden plank, rope, and some books.

- Place two chairs back-to-back and stretch 2 ropes over the backs of the chairs. Hold the ropes at both ends.
- Tie three pieces of rope to the longer ropes. Place the plank through the loops.
- With a partner, hold the ropes tightly at each end. Load books on top of the plank to see how much it will hold.

Why is it important to anchor the ropes tightly at each end?

M ◆ 207

Explore Social Studies Concepts

Research Ask: **How might bridge workers die on the job?** *(Sample answer: Falling from the bridge)* Have students research other hazards that were faced by bridge builders during the construction of the Brooklyn Bridge. Students should share their findings with the class.

Extend Construction on the Brooklyn Bridge began in 1869. The bridge was completed 14 years later, in 1883. Have students research events that occurred in the United States and throughout the world between 1869 and 1883. After students have completed their research, have each student add an event to a timeline that spans from 1869 to 1883.

Social Studies Activity

Focus Have students brainstorm a list of ways in which a bridge could change the lives of people in the surrounding area. List the students' answers on the board.

Teach Assign each group a different kind of bridge to research (for example, suspension, arch, beam). Tell students to begin by planning what questions each student will be responsible for researching. Suggest that students locate information about the bridge they are researching by reading about the city in which it is located.

Events connected to the bridge may be famous accidents, celebrations, or significant historical dates. Schedule times for students to make their presentations to the class.

Scoring Rubric

4 Exceeds criteria; presentation shows creativity and detail and includes many photos or drawings; research shows extra effort and thoroughness
3 Meets criteria
2 Includes few details; presentation is brief and/or includes few drawings and photos
1 Shows little effort; is incomplete and/or includes serious errors

---

Brooklyn Bridge
This bridge connects Brooklyn and Manhattan (above). It took 14 years for workers to complete the bridge (left).

Against All Odds

When John Roebling was hired in 1868 to build the Brooklyn Bridge, he was already a skilled suspension bridge engineer. He had been working on plans for the bridge since 1855.

But before bridge construction even began in 1869, John Roebling died in a construction accident. Fortunately, he had worked out his bridge design to the last detail. His son, Colonel Washington Roebling, who was also a skilled engineer, dedicated himself to carrying out his father's plans.

The construction dragged on for 14 years and cost nearly 30 lives. Colonel Roebling himself became so disabled that he was forced to direct construction from his home. Using a telescope, Colonel Roebling followed every detail. His remarkable, energetic wife, Emily Warren Roebling, learned enough engineering principles to deliver and explain his orders to the workers.

As soon as the giant towers were up, workers unrolled the steel wire back and forth across the towers to weave the cables. The next step was to twist the wires together. But the workmen were terrified of hanging so high on the bridge and refused to work.

Finally, Frank Farrington, the chief mechanic, crossed the river on a small chair dangling from a wheel that ran across an overhead line. Farrington completed his journey to the roar of the crowd. Somewhat reassured, the builders returned to work. But it took two more years to string the cables. The bridge was one of the greatest engineering achievements of its time.

In the end, the Brooklyn Bridge project succeeded only because of the determination and sacrifices of the Roebling family. It became the model for hundreds of other suspension bridges.

Social Studies Activity

How do you think the Brooklyn Bridge changed the lives of New Yorkers? In groups, research the history of another famous bridge. Present your findings to your class along with drawings and photos. Find out

- when and why the bridge was built
- what type of bridge it is
- what effects the bridge has on people's lives—on trade, travel, and population
- how landforms affected the bridge building
- about events connected to the bridge

Background

Integrating Science and Technology Roebling designed his bridge using steel wire instead of iron wire, which had traditionally been used for bridges. Steel wire was a relatively new material then and had not yet proven itself. The wire for the Brooklyn Bridge was supplied by a contractor. After the workers began reeling the wire to make cables, they discovered that the wire did not match the bid specifications. The contractor had committed fraud by substituting cheaper and weaker wire. Fortunately, Roebling initially designed the bridge using steel wire that would be six times stronger than necessary. The cheaper wire that had been substituted was still five times stronger than necessary, so it was used on the bridge.

TWO GREAT CITIES UNITED

MAY 25, 1883—The Brooklyn Bridge was successfully opened yesterday. The pleasant weather brought visitors by the thousands from all around. Spectators were packed in masses through which it was almost impossible to pass, and those who had tickets to attend the ceremonies had hard work to reach the bridge. Every available house-top and window was filled, and an adventurous party occupied a tall telegraph pole. It required the utmost efforts of the police to keep clear the necessary space.

After the exercises at the bridge were completed the Brooklyn procession was immediately re-formed and the march was taken up to Col. Roebling's residence. From the back study on the second floor of his house Col. Roebling had watched through his telescope the procession as it proceeded along from the New York side until the Brooklyn tower was reached. Mrs. Roebling received at her husband's side and accepted her share of the honors of the bridge.

For blocks and blocks on either side of the bridge there was scarcely a foot of room to spare. Many persons crossed and re-crossed the river on the ferry boats, and in that way watched the display. Almost every ship along the river front was converted into a grand stand.

The final ceremonies of the opening of the great bridge began at eight o'clock, when the first rocket was sent from the center of the great structure, and ended at nine o'clock, when a flight of 500 rockets illuminated the sky. The river-front was one blaze of light, and on the yachts and smaller vessels blue fires were burning and illuminating dark waters around them.

———Excerpted from
The New York Times

Brooklyn Bridge
This historic painting shows fireworks at the opening of the bridge in 1883.

THE GRAND DISPLAY OF FIREWORKS AND ILLUMINATIONS

Language Arts Activity

A reporter's goal is to inform and entertain the reader. Using a catchy opening line draws interest. Then the reader wants to know the facts—who, what, where, when, why, and how (5 W's and H).

You are a school reporter. Write about the opening of a bridge in your area. It could be a highway overpass or a bridge over water, a valley, or railroad tracks.

• Include some of the 5 W's and H.

• Add interesting details and descriptions.

Explore Language Arts Concepts

Extend Have students write a paragraph telling where in or near their town they think a bridge would be useful. Have students consider what type of bridge would be most suitable for the location.

Oral Presentation Have students read the description of the bridge opening in the text. Then call on volunteers to give an oral presentation describing the bridge opening from the point of view of a person who was there. Students should use varied vocabulary and descriptive phrases in their presentations. Their presentations should describe some of the scientific aspects of the bridge design as well as the sights and sounds associated with the bridge opening celebration.

Language Arts Activity

Focus Have students describe the characteristics of newspaper articles. List correct responses on the board.

Teach Students probably have not been present when a bridge was opened, so have them think of a bridge in or near your town. Then have them imagine how the town was different before the bridge was built. Students could talk to long-term residents to find out what public opinion was during the construction and how town life changed as a result. Have pairs of students check each other's work to ensure that the main facts are included in the article.

Scoring Rubric
4 Exceeds criteria; includes all required elements and extra material such as drawings or interviews
3 Meets criteria
2 Article is brief and/or includes few details
1 Article is incomplete and/or flawed

Background

Integrating Science and Technology In 1940, a new bridge was built over the narrows of Puget Sound, uniting two cities, Tacoma and Seattle. Four months later the bridge collapsed. The effects of wind on bridges were not well understood in 1940. The bridge was simply too flexible. It was also built with plate girders, which provided a flat wall of steel on which the wind could exert force. The combination proved disastrous when a 42-mile-per-hour wind caused vibrations of the bridge that eventually tore the suspenders, causing the bridge to collapse. When the bridge was rebuilt, open trusses were used instead of plate girders. The wind can blow through the trusses, thus reducing the force exerted by wind on the bridge.

Explore Mathematics Concepts

Demonstrate Cut four 10 cm **x** 1 cm strips of heavy cardboard. Punch a hole 0.5 cm from the end of each strip. Attach the strips end to end with brads to form a closed, rectangular figure. Show students how the shape of the figure can be altered. Now remove one of the strips so that a triangle is formed. Show students how the triangle has a fixed shape. Ask: **Which shape would be better to use in bridge supports?** (*The triangle, because of its fixed shape*)

Focus Direct students' attention to the picture of the truss bridge in the text. Have students name geometric shapes they see in the figure.

Teach Review with students the definitions of the terms *parallel* and *intersect*. Urge students to record their answers slowly and carefully.

Answers

1. AE and IF are parallel. AI, BH, CG, and DF are parallel to each other. BG and CF are parallel. CH, DG, and EF are parallel.
2. All pairs of lines that are not parallel intersect.
3. Rectangle
4. Triangle
5. Obtuse
6. Acute
7. Right triangle; it has a 90° angle
8. A square does not have a rigid shape, but a triangle does.

Mathematics

Bridge Geometry

As railroad traffic increased in the late 1800s, truss bridges became popular. Designed with thin vertical and diagonal supports to add strength, truss bridges were actually reinforced beam bridge structures. Many of the early wood truss bridges couldn't support the trains that rumbled over them. Cast iron and steel trusses soon replaced wood trusses.

Using basic triangular structures, engineers went to work on more scientific truss bridge designs. The accuracy of the design is crucial to handling the stress from heavy train loads and constant vibrations. As in all bridge structures, each steel piece has to be measured and fitted accurately—including widths, lengths, angles, and points of intersection and attachment.

Geometric Angles and Figures
Engineers use various geometric figures in drawing bridge plans. Figures that have right angles are squares, rectangles, and right triangles. Figures that have acute angles and obtuse angles can be triangles and parallelograms.

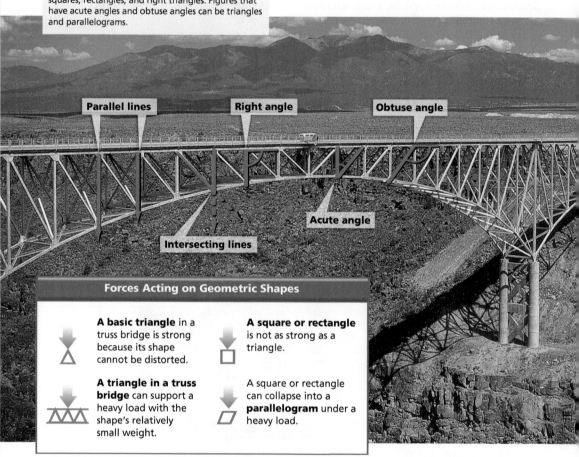

Parallel lines

Right angle

Obtuse angle

Acute angle

Intersecting lines

Forces Acting on Geometric Shapes

A basic triangle in a truss bridge is strong because its shape cannot be distorted.

A square or rectangle is not as strong as a triangle.

A triangle in a truss bridge can support a heavy load with the shape's relatively small weight.

A square or rectangle can collapse into a **parallelogram** under a heavy load.

Background

Integrating Science and Technology When engineers have distances to measure that cannot be measured directly, they use trigonometry. Trigonometry is a branch of mathematics that deals with relationships between the sides and angles of triangles. A distance can be measured by representing it as one side of a triangle, measuring other sides or angles in the triangle, and then using trigonometric formulas to calculate the length of the side to be measured. Trigonometry has many applications in engineering, such as studying vibrations in a building or bridge.

Math Activity

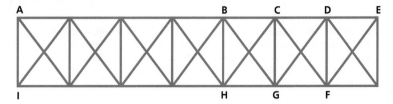

The chief building engineer has asked you to draw up exact plans for a new truss bridge. How well will you do as an assistant? Review the captions and labels on the previous page. Then answer these questions:

1. Which lines are parallel?
2. Which lines intersect?
3. What kind of figure is formed by *ABHI*?

4. What kind of figure is formed by *HCF*?
5. What kind of angle is *BGF*—obtuse or right?
6. What kind of angle is *CHG*?
7. What kind of triangle is *BHG*? What makes it this kind of triangle?
8. Why is a triangle stronger than a square?

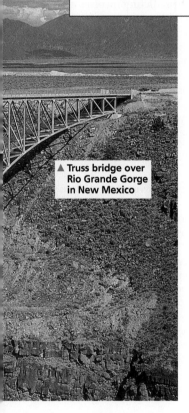

▲ **Truss bridge over Rio Grande Gorge in New Mexico**

Tie It Together

Work in small groups to build a model of a bridge out of a box of spaghetti and a roll of masking tape. Meet as a group to choose the type of bridge you will build. Each bridge should be strong enough to hold a brick. You can build

- a beam bridge
- a truss bridge
- an arch bridge
- a suspension bridge (This one is challenging.)

After drawing a sketch of the bridge design, assign jobs for each team member. Then

- decide how long the bridge span will be
- measure and cut the materials
- build the roadway first for beam, truss, and suspension bridges
- build the arch first in an arch bridge

When your bridge is complete, display it in the classroom. Test the strength of each bridge by placing a brick on the roadway. Discuss the difference in bridge structures. Determine which bridge design is the strongest.

M ◆ 211

Tie It Together

Time 2 class periods (1 period for planning and building; 1 period to test the design, examine other groups' work, and cleaning up) You may want to add an extra day so students can test whether their bridges could stay standing overnight.

Tips Divide the class into four groups. Assign each group a type of bridge.
- Make sure students understand that because their bridges are different design, some groups will take longer than others. Students should not try to race.
- Have students spend 15 minutes planning their designs before you hand out the building materials. Urge students to plan first, and not begin building by trial and error.
- You may wish to line each work area with newspaper to make cleanup easier.
- If bridges will be sitting overnight, have students work in parts of the room where their construction will not be disturbed.
- Groups making the suspension bridges may need the most help. Suggest that they make the towers from spaghetti and the cables from rolled lengths of tape.

Other Resources
- Oxlade, Chris, *Bridges*, Raintree/Steck Vaugn, 1997.
- Mann, Elizabeth B. and Witschonke, Alan, *The Brooklyn Bridge: A Wonders of the World Book*, Mikaya Press, 1996.
- Levy, Matthys and Panchyk, Richard, *Engineering the City*, Chicago Review Press, 2000.

Extend As an alternative to building four different types of bridges, have all groups build the same type of bridge. To encourage students to use their materials as efficiently as possible, assign costs to all materials (such as $1 million for each length of spaghetti and $5 million for each meter of masking tape). Assign a volunteer to "sell" materials and keep track of how much money each group spends on materials.

Think Like a Scientist

The Skills Handbook is designed as a reference for students to use whenever they need to review inquiry, reading, or math skills. You can use the activities in this part of the Skills Handbook to teach or reinforce inquiry skills.

Observing

Focus Remind students that an observation is what they can see, hear, smell, taste, or feel.

Teach Invite students to make observations of the classroom. List these observations on the board. Challenge students to identify the senses they used to make each observation. Then, ask: **Which senses will you use to make observations from the photograph on this page?** *(Sight is the only sense that can be used to make observations from the photograph.)*

Activity

Some observations that students might make include that the boy is skateboarding, wearing a white helmet, and flying in the air. Make sure that students' observations are confined to only things that they can actually see in the photograph.

Inferring

Focus Choose one or two of the classroom observations listed on the board, and challenge students to interpret them. Guide students by asking why something appears as it does.

Teach Encourage students to describe their thought processes in making their inferences. Point out where they used their knowledge and experience to interpret the observations. Then invite students to suggest other possible interpretations for the observations. Ask: **How can you find out whether an inference is correct?** *(By further investigation)*

Activity

One possible inference is that the boy just skated off a ramp at a skate park. Invite students to share their experiences that helped them make the inference.

Predicting

Focus Discuss the weather forecast for the next day. Point out that this prediction is an inference about what will happen in the

Think Like a Scientist

Scientists have a particular way of looking at the world, or scientific habits of mind. Whenever you ask a question and explore possible answers, you use many of the same skills that scientists do. Some of these skills are described on this page.

Observing

When you use one or more of your five senses to gather information about the world, you are **observing.** Hearing a dog bark, counting twelve green seeds, and smelling smoke are all observations. To increase the power of their senses, scientists sometimes use microscopes, telescopes, or other instruments that help them make more detailed observations.

An observation must be an accurate report of what your senses detect. It is important to keep careful records of your observations in science class by writing or drawing in a notebook. The information collected through observations is called evidence, or data.

Inferring

When you interpret an observation, you are **inferring,** or making an inference. For example, if you hear your dog barking, you may infer that someone is at your front door. To make this inference, you combine the evidence—the barking dog—and your experience or knowledge—you know that your dog barks when strangers approach—to reach a logical conclusion.

Notice that an inference is not a fact; it is only one of many possible interpretations for an observation. For example, your dog may be barking because it wants to go for a walk. An inference may turn out to be incorrect even if it is based on accurate observations and logical reasoning. The only way to find out if an inference is correct is to investigate further.

Predicting

When you listen to the weather forecast, you hear many predictions about the next day's weather—what the temperature will be, whether it will rain, and how windy it will be. Weather forecasters use observations and knowledge of weather patterns to predict the weather. The skill of **predicting** involves making an inference about a future event based on current evidence or past experience.

Because a prediction is an inference, it may prove to be false. In science class, you can test some of your predictions by doing experiments. For example, suppose you predict that larger paper airplanes can fly farther than smaller airplanes. How could you test your prediction?

Activity

Use the photograph to answer the questions below.

Observing Look closely at the photograph. List at least three observations.

Inferring Use your observations to make an inference about what has happened. What experience or knowledge did you use to make the inference?

Predicting Predict what will happen next. On what evidence or experience do you base your prediction?

future based on observations and experience.

Teach Help students differentiate between a prediction and an inference. You might organize the similarities and differences in a Venn diagram on the board. Both are interpretations of observations using experience and knowledge, and both can be incorrect. Inferences describe current or past events. Predictions describe future events.

Activity

Students might predict that the boy will land and skate to the other side. Others might predict that the boy will fall. Students should also describe the evidence or experience on which they based their predictions.

Classifying

Could you imagine searching for a book in the library if the books were shelved in no particular order? Your trip to the library would be an all-day event! Luckily, librarians group together books on similar topics or by the same author. Grouping together items that are alike in some way is called **classifying.** You can classify items in many ways: by size, by shape, by use, and by other important characteristics.

Like librarians, scientists use the skill of classifying to organize information and objects. When things are sorted into groups, the relationships among them become easier to understand.

Activity

Classify the objects in the photograph into two groups based on any characteristic you choose. Then use another characteristic to classify the objects into three groups.

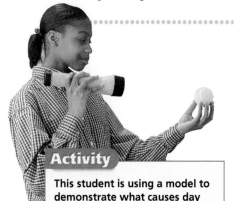

Activity

This student is using a model to demonstrate what causes day and night on Earth. What do the flashlight and the tennis ball in the model represent?

Making Models

Have you ever drawn a picture to help someone understand what you were saying? Such a drawing is one type of model. A model is a picture, diagram, computer image, or other representation of a complex object or process. **Making models** helps people understand things that they cannot observe directly.

Scientists often use models to represent things that are either very large or very small, such as the planets in the solar system, or the parts of a cell. Such models are physical models—drawings or three-dimensional structures that look like the real thing. Other models are mental models—mathematical equations or words that describe how something works.

Communicating

Whenever you talk on the phone, write a report, or listen to your teacher at school, you are communicating. **Communicating** is the process of sharing ideas and information with other people. Communicating effectively requires many skills, including writing, reading, speaking, listening, and making models.

Scientists communicate to share results, information, and opinions. Scientists often communicate about their work in journals, over the telephone, in letters, and on the Internet.

They also attend scientific meetings where they share their ideas with one another in person.

Activity

On a sheet of paper, write out clear, detailed directions for tying your shoe. Then exchange directions with a partner. Follow your partner's directions exactly. How successful were you at tying your shoe? How could your partner have communicated more clearly?

Skills Handbook ◆ 213

Classifying

Focus Encourage students to think of common things that are classified.

Teach Ask: **What things at home are classified?** (*Clothing might be classified in order to place it in the appropriate dresser drawer; glasses, plates, and silverware are grouped in different parts of the kitchen; screws, nuts, bolts, washers, and nails might be separated into small containers.*) **What are some things that scientists classify?** (*Scientists classify many things they study, including organisms, geological features and processes, and kinds of machines.*)

Activity

Some characteristics students might use include color, pattern of color, use of balls, and size. Students' criteria for classification should clearly divide the balls into two, and then three, distinct groups.

Making Models

Focus Ask: **What are some models you have used to study science?** (*Students might have used human anatomical models, solar system models, maps, or stream tables.*) **How have these models helped you?** (*Models can help you learn about things that are difficult to study because they are very large, very small, or highly complex.*)

Teach Be sure students understand that a model does not have to be three-dimensional. For example, a map is a model, as is a mathematical equation. Have students look at the photograph of the student modeling the causes of day and night on Earth. Ask: **What quality of each item makes this a good model?** (*The flashlight gives off light, and the ball is round and can be rotated by the student.*)

Activity

The flashlight represents the sun and the ball represents Earth.

Communicating

Focus Have students identify the methods of communication they have used today.

Teach Ask: **How is the way you communicate with a friend similar to and different from the way scientists communicate about their work to other scientists?** (*Both may communicate using various methods, but scientists must be very detailed and precise, whereas communication between friends may be less detailed and*

precise.) Encourage students to communicate like a scientist as they carry out the activity.

Activity

Students' answers will vary but should identify a step-by-step process for tying a shoe. Help students identify communication errors such as leaving out a step, putting steps in the wrong order, or disregarding the person's handedness.

Making Measurements

Students can refer to this part of the Skills Handbook whenever they need to review how to make measurements with SI units. You can use the activities here to teach or reinforce SI units.

Measuring in SI

Focus Review SI units with students. Begin by providing metric rulers, graduated cylinders, balances, and Celsius thermometers. Use these tools to reinforce that the meter is the unit of length, the liter is the unit of volume, the gram is the unit of mass, and the degree Celsius is the unit of temperature.

Teach Ask: **If you want to measure the length and the width of the classroom, which SI unit would you use?** (*Meter*) **Which unit would you use to measure the amount of mass in your textbook?** (*Gram*) **Which would you use to measure how much water a drinking glass holds?** (*Liter*) **When would you use the Celsius scale?** (*To measure the temperature of something*) Then use the measuring equipment to review SI prefixes. For example, ask: **What are the smallest units on the metric ruler?** (*Millimeters*) **How many millimeters are there in one centimeter?** (*10 millimeters*) **How many in 10 centimeters?** (*100 millimeters*) **How many centimeters are there in one meter?** (*100 centimeters*) **What does 1,000 meters equal?** (*One kilometer*)

> **Activity**
>
> **Length** The length of the shell is 7.8 centimeters, or 78 millimeters. If students need more practice measuring length, have them use meter sticks and metric rulers to measure various objects in the classroom.

> **Activity**
>
> **Liquid Volume** The volume of water in the graduated cylinder is 62 milliliters. If students need more practice, have them use a graduated cylinder to measure different volumes of water.

Making Measurements

By measuring, scientists can express their observations more precisely and communicate more information about what they observe.

Measuring in SI

The standard system of measurement used by scientists around the world is known as the International System of Units, which is abbreviated as SI (**Système International d'Unités,** in French). SI units are easy to use because they are based on powers of 10. Each unit is ten times larger than the next smallest unit and one tenth the size of the next largest unit. The table lists the prefixes used to name the most common SI units.

Common SI Prefixes		
Prefix	**Symbol**	**Meaning**
kilo-	k	1,000
hecto-	h	100
deka-	da	10
deci-	d	0.1 (one tenth)
centi-	c	0.01 (one hundredth)
milli-	m	0.001 (one thousandth)

Length To measure length, or the distance between two points, the unit of measure is the **meter (m).** The distance from the floor to a doorknob is approximately one meter. Long distances, such as the distance between two cities, are measured in kilometers (km). Small lengths are measured in centimeters (cm) or millimeters (mm). Scientists use metric rulers and meter sticks to measure length.

Common Conversions	
1 km	= 1,000 m
1 m	= 100 cm
1 m	= 1,000 mm
1 cm	= 10 mm

> **Activity**
>
> The larger lines on the metric ruler in the picture show centimeter divisions, while the smaller, unnumbered lines show millimeter divisions. How many centimeters long is the shell? How many millimeters long is it?

Liquid Volume To measure the volume of a liquid, or the amount of space it takes up, you will use a unit of measure known as the **liter (L).** One liter is the approximate volume of a medium-size carton of milk. Smaller volumes are measured in milliliters (mL). Scientists use graduated cylinders to measure liquid volume.

> **Activity**
>
> The graduated cylinder in the picture is marked in milliliter divisions. Notice that the water in the cylinder has a curved surface. This curved surface is called the *meniscus*. To measure the volume, you must read the level at the lowest point of the meniscus. What is the volume of water in this graduated cylinder?
>
> | Common Conversion |
> |---|
> | 1 L = 1,000 mL |

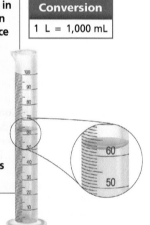

Mass To measure mass, or the amount of matter in an object, you will use a unit of measure known as the **gram (g).** One gram is approximately the mass of a paper clip. Larger masses are measured in kilograms (kg). Scientists use a balance to find the mass of an object.

Common Conversion

1 kg = 1,000 g

Activity

The mass of the potato in the picture is measured in kilograms. What is the mass of the potato? Suppose a recipe for potato salad called for one kilogram of potatoes. About how many potatoes would you need?

0.25 KG

Temperature To measure the temperature of a substance, you will use the **Celsius scale.** Temperature is measured in degrees Celsius (°C) using a Celsius thermometer. Water freezes at 0°C and boils at 100°C.

Time The unit scientists use to measure time is the **second (s).**

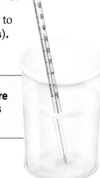

Activity

What is the temperature of the liquid in degrees Celsius?

Converting SI Units

To use the SI system, you must know how to convert between units. Converting from one unit to another involves the skill of **calculating,** or using mathematical operations. Converting between SI units is similar to converting between dollars and dimes because both systems are based on powers of ten.

Suppose you want to convert a length of 80 centimeters to meters. Follow these steps to convert between units.

1. Begin by writing down the measurement you want to convert—in this example, 80 centimeters.

2. Write a conversion factor that represents the relationship between the two units you are converting. In this example, the relationship is 1 meter = 100 centimeters. Write this conversion factor as a fraction, making sure to place the units you are converting from (centimeters, in this example) in the denominator.

3. Multiply the measurement you want to convert by the fraction. When you do this, the units in the first measurement will cancel out with the units in the denominator. Your answer will be in the units you are converting to (meters, in this example).

Example

80 centimeters = ■ meters

$$80 \text{ centimeters} \times \frac{1 \text{ meter}}{100 \text{ centimeters}} = \frac{80 \text{ meters}}{100}$$

$$= 0.8 \text{ meters}$$

Activity

Convert between the following units.
1. 600 millimeters = ■ meters
2. 0.35 liters = ■ milliliters
3. 1,050 grams = ■ kilograms

Skills Handbook ◆ 215

Activity

Mass The mass of the potato is 0.25 kilograms. You would need 4 potatoes to make one kilogram. If students need more practice, give them various objects, such as coins, paper clips, and books, to measure mass.

Activity

Temperature The temperature of the liquid is 35°C. Students who need more practice can measure the temperatures of various water samples.

Converting SI Units

Focus Review the steps for converting SI units, and work through the example with students.

Teach Ask: **How many millimeters are in 80 centimeters?** *(With the relationship 10 millimeters = 1 centimeter, students should follow the steps to calculate that 80 centimeters is equal to 800 millimeters.)* Have students do the conversion problems in the activity.

Activity

1. 600 millimeters = 0.6 meters
2. 0.35 liters = 350 milliliters
3. 1,050 grams = 1.05 kilograms
If students need more practice converting SI units, have them make up conversion problems to trade with partners.

M ● 215

Conducting a Scientific Investigation

Students can refer to this part of the Skills Handbook whenever they need to review the steps of a scientific investigation. You can use the activities here to teach or reinforce these steps.

Posing Questions

Focus Ask: **What do you do when you want to learn about something?** (*Answers might include asking questions about it or looking for information in books or on the Internet.*) Explain that scientists go through the same process to learn about something.

Teach Tell students that the questions scientists ask may have no answers or many different answers. To answer their questions, scientists often conduct experiments. Ask: **Why is a scientific question important to a scientific investigation?** (*It helps the scientist decide if an experiment is necessary; the answer might already be known. It also helps focus the idea so that the scientist can form a hypothesis.*) **What is the scientific question in the activity on the next page?** (*Is a ball's bounce affected by the height from which it is dropped?*)

Developing a Hypothesis

Focus Emphasize that a hypothesis is one possible explanation for a set of observations. It is *not* a guess. It is often based on an inference.

Teach Ask: **On what information do scientists base their hypotheses?** (*Their observations and previous knowledge or experience*) Point out that a hypothesis does not always turn out to be correct. Ask: **When a hypothesis turns out to be incorrect, do you think the scientist wasted his or her time? Explain.** (*No. The scientist learned from the investigation and will develop another hypothesis that could prove to be correct.*)

Designing an Experiment

Focus Have a volunteer read the Experimental Procedure in the box. Invite students to identify the manipulated variable (*amount of table salt*), the variables kept constant (*amount and starting temperature of water, location of containers*), the control (*Container 3*), and the responding variable (*the temperature at which water freezes*).

Conducting a Scientific Investigation

In some ways, scientists are like detectives, piecing together clues to learn about a process or event. One way that scientists gather clues is by carrying out experiments. An experiment tests an idea in a careful, orderly manner. Although experiments do not all follow the same steps in the same order, many follow a pattern similar to the one described here.

Posing Questions

Experiments begin by asking a scientific question. A scientific question is one that can be answered by gathering evidence. For example, the question "Which freezes faster—fresh water or salt water?" is a scientific question because you can carry out an investigation and gather information to answer the question.

Developing a Hypothesis

The next step is to form a hypothesis. A **hypothesis** is a possible explanation for a set of observations or answer to a scientific question. In science, a hypothesis must be something that can be tested. A hypothesis can be worded as an *If . . . then . . .* statement. For example, a hypothesis might be *"If I add table salt to fresh water, then the water will freeze at a lower temperature."* A hypothesis worded this way serves as a rough outline of the experiment you should perform.

216 ◆ M

Teach Ask: **How might the experiment be affected if Container 1 had only 100 milliliters of water?** (*It wouldn't be an accurate comparison with the containers that have more water.*) Also make sure that students understand the importance of the control. Then, ask: **What operational definition is used in this experiment?** (*"Frozen" means the condition when the wooden stick can no longer move in a container.*)

Designing an Experiment

Next you need to plan a way to test your hypothesis. Your plan should be written out as a step-by-step procedure and should describe the observations or measurements you will make.

Two important steps involved in designing an experiment are controlling variables and forming operational definitions.

Controlling Variables In a well-designed experiment, you need to keep all variables the same except for one. A **variable** is any factor that can change in an experiment. The factor that you change is called the **manipulated variable**. In this experiment, the manipulated variable is the amount of table salt added to the water. Other factors, such as the amount of water or the starting temperature, are kept constant.

The factor that changes as a result of the manipulated variable is called the **responding variable.** The responding variable is what you measure or observe to obtain your results. In this experiment, the responding variable is the temperature at which the water freezes.

An experiment in which all factors except one are kept constant is called a **controlled experiment.** Most controlled experiments include a test called the control. In this experiment, Container 3 is the control. Because no salt is added to Container 3, you can compare the results from the other containers to it. Any difference in results must be due to the addition of salt alone.

Forming Operational Definitions Another important aspect of a well-designed experiment is having clear operational definitions. An **operational definition** is a statement that describes how a particular variable is to be measured or how a term is to be defined. For example, in this experiment, how will you determine if the water has frozen? You might decide to insert a stick in each container at the start of the experiment. Your operational definition of "frozen" would be the time at which the stick can no longer move.

Experimental Procedure

1. Fill 3 containers with 300 milliliters of cold tap water.

2. Add 10 grams of salt to Container 1; stir.
   Add 20 grams of salt to Container 2; stir.
   Add no salt to Container 3.

3. Place the 3 containers in a freezer.

4. Check the containers every 15 minutes.
   Record your observations.

Interpreting Data

The observations and measurements you make in an experiment are called **data.** At the end of an experiment, you need to analyze the data to look for any patterns or trends. Patterns often become clear if you organize your data in a data table or graph. Then think through what the data reveal. Do they support your hypothesis? Do they point out a flaw in your experiment? Do you need to collect more data?

Drawing Conclusions

A **conclusion** is a statement that sums up what you have learned from an experiment. When you draw a conclusion, you need to decide whether the data you collected support your hypothesis or not. You may need to repeat an experiment several times before you can draw any conclusions from it. Conclusions often lead you to pose new questions and plan new experiments to answer them.

Activity

Is a ball's bounce affected by the height from which it is dropped? Using the steps just described, plan a controlled experiment to investigate this problem.

Skills Handbook ◆ 217

Interpreting Data

Focus Ask: **What kind of data would you collect from the experiment with freezing salt water?** (*Amount of salt and temperature when the water freezes*)

Teach Ask: **What if you forgot to record some data during an investigation?** (*You wouldn't be able to draw valid conclusions because some data are missing.*) Then, ask: **Why are data tables and graphs a good way to organize data?** (*They make it easier to record data accurately, as well as compare and analyze data.*) **What kind of data table and graph might you use for this experiment?** (*A table would have a row for each container and a column in which the freezing temperature of the water is recorded. A bar graph would show the temperature at which the water froze in each container.*)

Drawing Conclusions

Focus Help students understand that a conclusion is not necessarily the end of a scientific investigation. A conclusion about one experiment may lead right into another experiment.

Teach Point out that in scientific investigations, a conclusion is a summary and explanation of the results of an experiment. For the Experimental Procedure described on this page, tell students to suppose that they obtained the following results: Container 3 froze at about 0°C, Container 1 froze at a slightly lower temperature, and Container 2 froze at the lowest temperature. Ask: **What conclusions can you draw from this experiment?** (*Students might conclude that the more table salt there is in the water, the lower the temperature at which the water freezes. The hypothesis is supported, and the question of which freezes at a lower temperature is answered—salt water.*)

Activity

You might wish to have students work in pairs to plan the controlled experiment. Students should develop a hypothesis, such as, "If I increase the height from which a ball is dropped, then the height of its bounce will increase." They can test the hypothesis by dropping a ball from varying heights (the manipulated variable). All trials should be done with the same kind of ball and on the same surface (constants). For each trial, they should measure the height of the bounce (responding variable). After students have designed the experiment, provide rubber balls, and invite them to carry out the experiment so they can collect and interpret data and draw conclusions.

Technology Design Skills

Students can refer to this part of the Skills Handbook whenever they need to review the process of designing new technologies. You can use the activities here to teach or reinforce the steps in this process.

Identify a Need

Focus Solicit from students any situations in which they have thought that a tool, machine, or other object would be really helpful to them or others. Explain that this is the first step in the design of new products.

Teach Point out that identifying specific needs is very important to the design process. Ask: **If it was specified that the toy boat be wind-powered, how might that affect the design?** (*The boat would likely be designed with sails.*)

Research the Problem

Focus Explain that research focuses the problem so that the design is more specific.

Teach Ask: **What might happen if you didn't research the problem before designing the solution?** (*Answers include developing a design that has already been found to fail, using materials that aren't the best, or designing a solution that already exists.*) **What would you research before designing your toy boat?** (*Students might research designs and materials.*)

Design a Solution

Focus Emphasize the importance of a design team. Ask: **Why are brainstorming sessions important in product design?** (*A group will propose more new ideas than one person.*)

Teach Divide the class into teams to design the toy boat. Instruct them to brainstorm design ideas. Then, ask: **Why do you think engineers evaluate constraints after brainstorming?** (*Evaluating constraints while brainstorming often stops the flow of new ideas.*) **What design constraints do you have for your toy boat?** (*Materials must be readily available and teacher-approved. The boat must be 15 centimeters or less in length and must travel 2 meters in a straight line carrying a load of 20 pennies.*)

Technology Design Skills

Engineers are people who use scientific and technological knowledge to solve practical problems. To design new products, engineers usually follow the process described here, even though they may not follow these steps in the exact order. As you read the steps, think about how you might apply them in technology labs.

Identify a Need

Before engineers begin designing a new product, they must first identify the need they are trying to meet. For example, suppose you are a member of a design team in a company that makes toys. Your team has identified a need: a toy boat that is inexpensive and easy to assemble.

Research the Problem

Engineers often begin by gathering information that will help them with their new design. This research may include finding articles in books, magazines, or on the Internet. It may also include talking to other engineers who have solved similar problems. Engineers often perform experiments related to the product they want to design.

For your toy boat, you could look at toys that are similar to the one you want to design. You might do research on the Internet. You could also test some materials to see whether they will work well in a toy boat.

Drawing for a boat design ▼

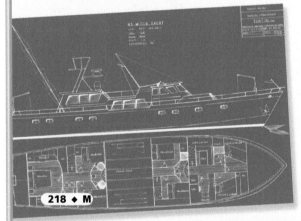

218 ◆ M

Design a Solution

Research gives engineers information that helps them design a product. When engineers design new products, they usually work in teams.

Generating Ideas Often design teams hold brainstorming meetings in which any team member can contribute ideas. **Brainstorming** is a creative process in which one team member's suggestions often spark ideas in other group members. Brainstorming can lead to new approaches to solving a design problem.

Evaluating Constraints During brainstorming, a design team will often come up with several possible designs. The team must then evaluate each one.

As part of their evaluation, engineers consider constraints. **Constraints** are factors that limit or restrict a product design. Physical characteristics, such as the properties of materials used to make your toy boat, are constraints. Money and time are also constraints. If the materials in a product cost a lot, or if the product takes a long time to make, the design may be impractical.

Making Trade-offs Design teams usually need to make trade-offs. In a **trade-off,** engineers give up one benefit of a proposed design in order to obtain another. In designing your toy boat, you will have to make trade-offs. For example, suppose one material is sturdy but not fully waterproof. Another material is more waterproof, but breakable. You may decide to give up the benefit of sturdiness in order to obtain the benefit of waterproofing.

Build and Evaluate a Prototype

Once the team has chosen a design plan, the engineers build a prototype of the product. A **prototype** is a working model used to test a design. Engineers evaluate the prototype to see whether it works well, is easy to operate, is safe to use, and holds up to repeated use.

Think of your toy boat. What would the prototype be like? Of what materials would it be made? How would you test it?

Troubleshoot and Redesign

Few prototypes work perfectly, which is why they need to be tested. Once a design team has tested a prototype, the members analyze the results and identify any problems. The team then tries to **troubleshoot,** or fix the design problems. For example, if your toy boat leaks or wobbles, the boat should be redesigned to eliminate those problems.

Communicate the Solution

A team needs to communicate the final design to the people who will manufacture and use the product. To do this, teams may use sketches, detailed drawings, computer simulations, and word descriptions.

Activity

You can use the technology design process to design and build a toy boat.

Research and Investigate

1. Visit the library or go online to research toy boats.
2. Investigate how a toy boat can be powered, including wind, rubber bands, or baking soda and vinegar.
3. Brainstorm materials, shapes, and steering for your boat.

Design and Build

4. Based on your research, design a toy boat that
   • is made of readily available materials
   • is no larger than 15 cm long and 10 cm wide

   • includes a power system, a rudder, and an area for cargo
   • travels 2 meters in a straight line carrying a load of 20 pennies

5. Sketch your design and write a step-by-step plan for building your boat. After your teacher approves your plan, build your boat.

Evaluate and Redesign

6. Test your boat, evaluate the results, and troubleshoot any problems.
7. Based on your evaluation, redesign your toy boat so it performs better.

Skills Handbook ◆ 219

Build and Evaluate a Prototype

Focus Explain that building a prototype enables engineers to test design ideas.

Teach Relate building and testing a prototype to conducting an experiment. Explain that engineers set up controlled experiments to test the prototype. Ask: **Why do you think engineers set up controlled experiments?** (From the data, they can determine which component of the design is working and which is failing.) **How would you test your prototype of the toy boat?** (Answers will vary depending on the toy boat's propulsion system.)

Troubleshoot and Redesign

Focus Make sure students know what it means to troubleshoot. If necessary, give an example. One example is a stapler that isn't working. In that case, you would check to see if it is out of staples or if the staples are jammed. Then you would fix the problem and try stapling again. If it still didn't work, you might check the position of staples and try again.

Teach Explain that engineers often are not surprised if the prototype doesn't work. Ask: **Why isn't it a failure if the prototype doesn't work?** (Engineers learn from the problems and make changes to address the problems. This process makes the design better.) Emphasize that prototypes are completely tested before the product is made in the factory.

Communicate the Solution

Focus Inquire whether students have ever read the instruction manual that comes with a new toy or electronic device.

Teach Emphasize the importance of good communication in the design process. Ask: **What might happen if engineers did not communicate their design ideas clearly?** (The product might not be manufactured correctly or used properly.)

Activity

The design possibilities are endless. Students might use small plastic containers, wood, foil, or plastic drinking cups for the boat. Materials may also include toothpicks, straws, or small wooden dowels. Brainstorm with students the different ways in which a toy boat can be propelled. The boats may be any shape, but must be no longer than 15 centimeters.

As student groups follow the steps in the design process, have them record their sources, brainstorming ideas, and prototype design in a logbook. Also give them time to troubleshoot and redesign their boats. When students turn in their boats, they should include assembly directions with a diagram, as well as instructions for use.

Creating Data Tables and Graphs

Students can refer to this part of the Skills Handbook whenever they need to review the skills required to create data tables and graphs. You can use the activities provided here to teach or reinforce these skills.

Data Tables

Focus Emphasize the importance of organizing data. Ask: **What might happen if you didn't use a data table for an experiment?** *(Possible answers include that data might not be collected or they might be forgotten.)*

Teach Have students create a data table to show how much time they spend on different activities during one week. Suggest that students first list the main activities they do every week. Then they should determine the amount of time they spend on each activity each day. Remind students to give the data table a title. A sample data table is shown below.

Bar Graphs

Focus Have students compare and contrast the data table and the bar graph on this page. Ask: **Why would you make a bar graph if the data are already organized in a table?** *(The bar graph organizes the data in a visual way that makes them easier to interpret.)*

Teach Students can use the data from the data table they created to make a bar graph that shows the amount of time they spend on different activities during a week. The vertical axis should be divided into units of time, such as hours. Remind students to label both axes and give their graph a title. A sample bar graph is shown below.

Creating Data Tables and Graphs

How can you make sense of the data in a science experiment? The first step is to organize the data to help you understand them. Data tables and graphs are helpful tools for organizing data.

Data Tables

You have gathered your materials and set up your experiment. But before you start, you need to plan a way to record what happens during the experiment. By creating a data table, you can record your observations and measurements in an orderly way.

Suppose, for example, that a scientist conducted an experiment to find out how many Calories people of different body masses burn while doing various activities. The data table shows the results.

Notice in this data table that the manipulated variable (body mass) is the heading of one column. The responding variable (for

Calories Burned in 30 Minutes			
Body Mass	Experiment 1: Bicycling	Experiment 2: Playing Basketball	Experiment 3: Watching Television
30 kg	60 Calories	120 Calories	21 Calories
40 kg	77 Calories	164 Calories	27 Calories
50 kg	95 Calories	206 Calories	33 Calories
60 kg	114 Calories	248 Calories	38 Calories

Experiment 1, the number of Calories burned while bicycling) is the heading of the next column. Additional columns were added for related experiments.

Bar Graphs

To compare how many Calories a person burns doing various activities, you could create a bar graph. A bar graph is used to display data in a number of separate, or distinct, categories. In this example, bicycling, playing basketball, and watching television are the three categories.

To create a bar graph, follow these steps.

1. On graph paper, draw a horizontal, or *x*-, axis and a vertical, or *y*-, axis.

2. Write the names of the categories to be graphed along the horizontal axis. Include an overall label for the axis as well.

3. Label the vertical axis with the name of the responding variable. Include units of measurement. Then create a scale along the axis by marking off equally spaced numbers that cover the range of the data collected.

4. For each category, draw a solid bar using the scale on the vertical axis to determine the height. Make all the bars the same width.

5. Add a title that describes the graph.

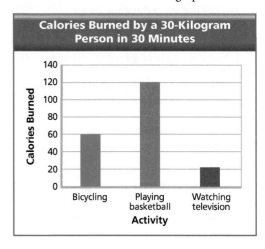

Time Spent on Different Activities in a Week				
	Going to Classes	Eating Meals	Playing Soccer	Watching Television
Monday	6	2	2	0.5
Tuesday	6	1.5	1.5	1.5
Wednesday	6	2	1	2
Thursday	6	2	2	1.5
Friday	6	2	2	0.5
Saturday	0	2.5	2.5	1
Sunday	0	3	1	2

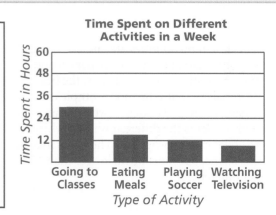

Line Graphs

To see whether a relationship exists between body mass and the number of Calories burned while bicycling, you could create a line graph. A line graph is used to display data that show how one variable (the responding variable) changes in response to another variable (the manipulated variable). You can use a line graph when your manipulated variable is **continuous,** that is, when there are other points between the ones that you tested. In this example, body mass is a continuous variable because there are other body masses between 30 and 40 kilograms (for example, 31 kilograms). Time is another example of a continuous variable.

Line graphs are powerful tools because they allow you to estimate values for conditions that you did not test in the experiment. For example, you can use the line graph to estimate that a 35-kilogram person would burn 68 Calories while bicycling.

To create a line graph, follow these steps.

1. On graph paper, draw a horizontal, or *x*-, axis and a vertical, or *y*-, axis.

2. Label the horizontal axis with the name of the manipulated variable. Label the vertical axis with the name of the responding variable. Include units of measurement.

3. Create a scale on each axis by marking off equally spaced numbers that cover the range of the data collected.

4. Plot a point on the graph for each piece of data. In the line graph above, the dotted lines show how to plot the first data point (30 kilograms and 60 Calories). Follow an imaginary vertical line extending up from the horizontal axis at the 30-kilogram mark. Then follow an imaginary horizontal line extending across from the vertical axis at the 60-Calorie mark. Plot the point where the two lines intersect.

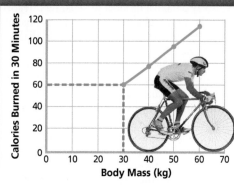

Effect of Body Mass on Calories Burned While Bicycling

5. Connect the plotted points with a solid line. (In some cases, it may be more appropriate to draw a line that shows the general trend of the plotted points. In those cases, some of the points may fall above or below the line. Also, not all graphs are linear. It may be more appropriate to draw a curve to connect the points.)

6. Add a title that identifies the variables or relationship in the graph.

Activity

Create line graphs to display the data from Experiment 2 and Experiment 3 in the data table.

Activity

You read in the newspaper that a total of 4 centimeters of rain fell in your area in June, 2.5 centimeters fell in July, and 1.5 centimeters fell in August. What type of graph would you use to display these data? Use graph paper to create the graph.

Skills Handbook ◆ 221

Line Graphs

Focus Ask: **Would a bar graph show the relationship between body mass and the number of Calories burned in 30 minutes?** (*No. Bar graphs can only show data in distinct categories.*) Explain that line graphs are used to show how one variable changes in response to another variable.

Teach Walk students through the steps involved in creating a line graph using the example illustrated on the page. For example, ask: **What is the label on the horizontal axis? On the vertical axis?** (*Body Mass (kg); Calories Burned in 30 Minutes*) **What scale is used on each axis?** (*10 kg on the* x-*axis and 20 Calories on the* y-*axis*) **What does the second data point represent?** (*77 Calories burned for a body mass of 40 kg*) **What trend or pattern does the graph show?** (*The number of Calories burned in 30 minutes of cycling increases with body mass.*)

Activity

Students should make a different graph for each experiment. Each graph should have a different *x*-axis scale that is appropriate for the data. See sample graphs below.

Activity

Students should conclude that a bar graph would be best for displaying the data.

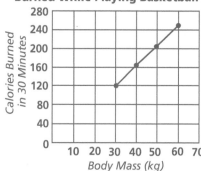

Effect of Body Mass on Calories Burned While Playing Basketball

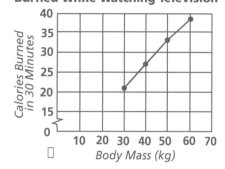

Effect of Body Mass on Calories Burned While Watching Television

Circle Graphs

Focus Emphasize that a circle graph must include 100 percent of the categories for the topic being graphed. For example, ask: **Could the data in the bar graph titled "Calories Burned by a 30-kilogram Person in Various Activities" (on the previous page) be shown in a circle graph? Why or why not?** *(No. It does not include all the possible ways a 30-kilogram person can burn Calories.)*

Teach Walk students through the steps for making a circle graph. If necessary, help them with the compass and the protractor. Use the protractor to illustrate that a circle has 360 degrees. Make sure students understand the mathematical calculations involved in making a circle graph.

You might have students work in pairs to complete the activity. Students' circle graphs should look like the graph below.

Ways Students Get to School

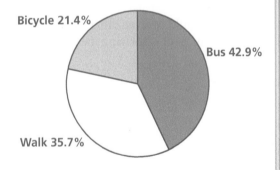

Bicycle 21.4%

Bus 42.9%

Walk 35.7%

Circle Graphs

Like bar graphs, circle graphs can be used to display data in a number of separate categories. Unlike bar graphs, however, circle graphs can only be used when you have data for *all* the categories that make up a given topic. A circle graph is sometimes called a pie chart. The pie represents the entire topic, while the slices represent the individual categories. The size of a slice indicates what percentage of the whole a particular category makes up.

The data table below shows the results of a survey in which 24 teenagers were asked to identify their favorite sport. The data were then used to create the circle graph at the right.

Favorite Sports	
Sport	Students
Soccer	8
Basketball	6
Bicycling	6
Swimming	4

To create a circle graph, follow these steps.

1. Use a compass to draw a circle. Mark the center with a point. Then draw a line from the center point to the top of the circle.

2. Determine the size of each "slice" by setting up a proportion where *x* equals the number of degrees in a slice. (*Note:* A circle contains 360 degrees.) For example, to find the number of degrees in the "soccer" slice, set up the following proportion:

$$\frac{\text{Students who prefer soccer}}{\text{Total number of students}} = \frac{x}{\text{Total number of degrees in a circle}}$$

$$\frac{8}{24} = \frac{x}{360}$$

Cross-multiply and solve for *x*.

$$24x = 8 \times 360$$
$$x = 120$$

The "soccer" slice should contain 120 degrees.

Sports That Teens Prefer

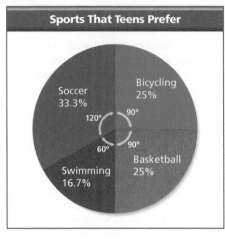

Soccer 33.3%

Bicycling 25%

Swimming 16.7%

Basketball 25%

120° 90° 60° 90°

3. Use a protractor to measure the angle of the first slice, using the line you drew to the top of the circle as the 0° line. Draw a line from the center of the circle to the edge for the angle you measured.

4. Continue around the circle by measuring the size of each slice with the protractor. Start measuring from the edge of the previous slice so the wedges do not overlap. When you are done, the entire circle should be filled in.

5. Determine the percentage of the whole circle that each slice represents. To do this, divide the number of degrees in a slice by the total number of degrees in a circle (360), and multiply by 100%. For the "soccer" slice, you can find the percentage as follows:

$$\frac{120}{360} \times 100\% = 33.3\%$$

6. Use a different color for each slice. Label each slice with the category and with the percentage of the whole it represents.

7. Add a title to the circle graph.

In a class of 28 students, 12 students take the bus to school, 10 students walk, and 6 students ride their bicycles. Create a circle graph to display these data.

Math Review

Scientists use math to organize, analyze, and present data. This appendix will help you review some basic math skills.

Mean, Median, and Mode

The **mean** is the average, or the sum of the data divided by the number of data items. The middle number in a set of ordered data is called the **median**. The **mode** is the number that appears most often in a set of data.

Example

A scientist counted the number of distinct songs sung by seven different male birds and collected the data shown below.

Male Bird Songs							
Bird	A	B	C	D	E	F	G
Number of Songs	36	29	40	35	28	36	27

To determine the mean number of songs, add the total number of songs and divide by the number of data items—in this case, the number of male birds.

$$\text{Mean} = \frac{231}{7} = 33 \text{ songs}$$

To find the median number of songs, arrange the data in numerical order and find the number in the middle of the series.

27 28 29 35 36 36 40

The number in the middle is 35, so the median number of songs is 35.

The mode is the value that appears most frequently. In the data, 36 appears twice, while each other item appears only once. Therefore, 36 songs is the mode.

Practice

Find out how many minutes it takes each student in your class to get to school. Then find the mean, median, and mode for the data.

Probability

Probability is the chance that an event will occur. Probability can be expressed as a ratio, a fraction, or a percentage. For example, when you flip a coin, the probability that the coin will land heads up is 1 in 2, or $\frac{1}{2}$, or 50 percent.

The probability that an event will happen can be expressed in the following formula.

$$P(\text{event}) = \frac{\text{Number of times the event can occur}}{\text{Total number of possible events}}$$

Example

A paper bag contains 25 blue marbles, 5 green marbles, 5 orange marbles, and 15 yellow marbles. If you close your eyes and pick a marble from the bag, what is the probability that it will be yellow?

$$P(\text{yellow marbles}) = \frac{15 \text{ yellow marbles}}{50 \text{ marbles total}}$$

$$P = \frac{15}{50}, \text{ or } \frac{3}{10}, \text{ or } 30\%$$

Practice

Each side of a cube has a letter on it. Two sides have *A*, three sides have *B*, and one side has *C*. If you roll the cube, what is the probability that *A* will land on top?

Math Review

Students can refer to this part of the Skills Handbook whenever they need to review some basic math skills. You can use the activities provided here to teach or reinforce these skills.

Mean, Median, and Mode

Focus Remind students that data from an experiment might consist of hundreds or thousands of numbers. Unless analyzed, the numbers likely will not be helpful.

Teach Work through the process of determining mean, median, and mode using the example in the book. Make sure students realize that these three numbers do not always equal each other. Point out that taken together, these three numbers give more information about the data than just one of the numbers alone.

Practice

Answers will vary based on class data. The mean should equal the total number of minutes divided by the number of students. The median should equal the number in the middle after arranging the data in numerical order. The mode should equal the number of minutes that is given most frequently.

Probability

Focus Show students a coin and ask: **What is the chance that I will get tails when I flip the coin?** (*Some students might know that there is a 1 in 2, or 50 percent, chance of getting tails.*)

Teach Set up a bag of marbles like the one in the example. Allow students to practice determining the probabilities of picking marbles of different colors. Then, encourage them to actually pick marbles and compare their actual results with those results predicted by probability.

Practice

$P(A) = 2 \text{ sides with } \frac{A}{6} \text{ sides total}$

$P = \frac{2}{6}, \text{ or } \frac{1}{3}, \text{ or } 33\%$

Area

Focus Ask: **Who knows what area is?** (*Area is equal to the number of square units needed to cover a certain shape or object.*) On the board, write the formulas for the area of a rectangle and a circle.

Teach Give students various objects of different shapes. Have them measure each object and determine its area based on the measurements. Point out that the units of the answer are squared because they are multiplied together. If students are interested, you might also explain that π is equal to the ratio of the circumference of a circle to its diameter. For circles of all sizes, π is approximately equal to the number 3.14, or $\frac{22}{7}$.

Practice

The area of the circle is equal to
$21 \text{ m} \times 21 \text{ m} \times \frac{22}{7}$, or $1{,}386 \text{ m}^2$.

Circumference

Focus Draw a circle on the board. Then trace the outline with your finger and explain that this is the circumference of the circle, or the distance around it.

Teach Show students that the radius is equal to the distance from the center of the circle to any point on it. Point out that the diameter of a circle is equal to two times the radius. Give students paper circles of various sizes, and have them calculate the circumference of each.

Practice

The circumference is equal to $2 \times 28 \text{ m} \times \frac{22}{7}$, or 176 m.

Volume

Focus Fill a beaker with 100 milliliters of water. Ask: **What is the volume of water?** (*100 milliliters*) Explain that volume is the amount of space that something takes up. Then point out that one milliliter is equal to one cubic centimeter (cm^3).

Teach Write on the board the formulas for calculating the volumes of a rectangle and a cylinder. Point out that volume is equal to the area of an object multiplied by its height. Then measure the beaker to show students the relationship between liquid volume (100 milliliters) and the number of cubic units it contains (100 cubic centimeters).

Area

The **area** of a surface is the number of square units that cover it. The front cover of your textbook has an area of about 600 cm^2.

Area of a Rectangle and a Square To find the area of a rectangle, multiply its length times its width. The formula for the area of a rectangle is

$$A = \ell \times w, \text{ or } A = \ell w$$

Since all four sides of a square have the same length, the area of a square is the length of one side multiplied by itself, or squared.

$$A = s \times s, \text{ or } A = s^2$$

Example

A scientist is studying the plants in a field that measures 75 m × 45 m. What is the area of the field?

$$A = \ell \times w$$
$$A = 75 \text{ m} \times 45 \text{ m}$$
$$A = 3{,}375 \text{ m}^2$$

Area of a Circle The formula for the area of a circle is

$$A = \pi \times r \times r, \text{ or } A = \pi r^2$$

The length of the radius is represented by r, and the value of π is approximately $\frac{22}{7}$.

Example

Find the area of a circle with a radius of 14 cm.

$$A = \pi r^2$$
$$A = 14 \times 14 \times \frac{22}{7}$$
$$A = 616 \text{ cm}^2$$

Practice

Find the area of a circle that has a radius of 21 m.

Circumference

The distance around a circle is called the circumference. The formula for finding the circumference of a circle is

$$C = 2 \times \pi \times r, \text{ or } C = 2\pi r$$

Example

The radius of a circle is 35 cm. What is its circumference?

$$C = 2\pi r$$
$$C = 2 \times 35 \times \frac{22}{7}$$
$$C = 220 \text{ cm}$$

Practice

What is the circumference of a circle with a radius of 28 m?

Volume

The volume of an object is the number of cubic units it contains. The volume of a wastebasket, for example, might be about 26,000 cm^3.

Volume of a Rectangular Object To find the volume of a rectangular object, multiply the object's length times its width times its height.

$$V = \ell \times w \times h, \text{ or } V = \ell w h$$

Example

Find the volume of a box with length 24 cm, width 12 cm, and height 9 cm.

$$V = \ell w h$$
$$V = 24 \text{ cm} \times 12 \text{ cm} \times 9 \text{ cm}$$
$$V = 2{,}592 \text{ cm}^3$$

Practice

What is the volume of a rectangular object with length 17 cm, width 11 cm, and height 6 cm?

Practice

The volume of the rectangular object is equal to
$17 \text{ cm} \times 11 \text{ cm} \times 6 \text{ cm}$, or $1{,}122 \text{ cm}^3$.

Fractions

A **fraction** is a way to express a part of a whole. In the fraction $\frac{4}{7}$, 4 is the numerator and 7 is the denominator.

Adding and Subtracting Fractions To add or subtract two or more fractions that have a common denominator, first add or subtract the numerators. Then write the sum or difference over the common denominator.

To find the sum or difference of fractions with different denominators, first find the least common multiple of the denominators. This is known as the least common denominator. Then convert each fraction to equivalent fractions with the least common denominator. Add or subtract the numerators. Then write the sum or difference over the common denominator.

Example
$$\frac{5}{6} - \frac{3}{4} = \frac{10}{12} - \frac{9}{12} = \frac{10-9}{12} = \frac{1}{12}$$

Multiplying Fractions To multiply two fractions, first multiply the two numerators, then multiply the two denominators.

Example
$$\frac{5}{6} \times \frac{2}{3} = \frac{5 \times 2}{6 \times 3} = \frac{10}{18} = \frac{5}{9}$$

Dividing Fractions Dividing by a fraction is the same as multiplying by its reciprocal. Reciprocals are numbers whose numerators and denominators have been switched. To divide one fraction by another, first invert the fraction you are dividing by—in other words, turn it upside down. Then multiply the two fractions.

Example
$$\frac{2}{5} \div \frac{7}{8} = \frac{2}{5} \times \frac{8}{7} = \frac{2 \times 8}{5 \times 7} = \frac{16}{35}$$

Practice
Solve the following: $\frac{3}{7} \div \frac{4}{5}$.

Decimals

Fractions whose denominators are 10, 100, or some other power of 10 are often expressed as decimals. For example, the fraction $\frac{9}{10}$ can be expressed as the decimal 0.9, and the fraction $\frac{7}{100}$ can be written as 0.07.

Adding and Subtracting With Decimals To add or subtract decimals, line up the decimal points before you carry out the operation.

Example

$$\begin{array}{r} 27.4 \\ + 6.19 \\ \hline 33.59 \end{array} \qquad \begin{array}{r} 278.635 \\ - 191.4 \\ \hline 87.235 \end{array}$$

Multiplying With Decimals When you multiply two numbers with decimals, the number of decimal places in the product is equal to the total number of decimal places in each number being multiplied.

Example

$$\begin{array}{r} 46.2 \text{ (one decimal place)} \\ \times\ 2.37 \text{ (two decimal places)} \\ \hline 109.494 \text{ (three decimal places)} \end{array}$$

Dividing With Decimals To divide a decimal by a whole number, put the decimal point in the quotient above the decimal point in the dividend.

Example

$$15.5 \div 5$$
$$\begin{array}{r} 3.1 \\ 5\overline{)15.5} \end{array}$$

To divide a decimal by a decimal, you need to rewrite the divisor as a whole number. Do this by multiplying both the divisor and dividend by the same multiple of 10.

Example

$$1.68 \div 4.2 = 16.8 \div 42$$
$$\begin{array}{r} 0.4 \\ 42\overline{)16.8} \end{array}$$

Practice
Multiply 6.21 by 8.5.

Fractions

Focus Draw a circle on the board, and divide it into eight equal sections. Shade in one of the sections, and explain that one out of eight, or one eighth, of the sections is shaded. Also use the circle to show that four eighths is the same as one half.

Teach Write the fraction $\frac{3}{4}$ on the board. Ask: **What is the numerator?** *(Three)* **What is the denominator?** *(Four)* Emphasize that when adding and subtracting fractions, the denominators of the two fractions must be the same. If necessary, review how to find the least common denominator. Remind students that when multiplying and dividing, the denominators do not have to be the same.

Practice

$$\frac{3}{7} \div \frac{4}{5} = \frac{3}{7} \times \frac{5}{4} = \frac{15}{28}$$

Decimals

Focus Write the number *129.835* on the board. Ask: **What number is in the ones position?** *(9)* **The tenths position?** *(8)* **The hundredths position?** *(3)* Make sure students know that 0.8 is equal to $\frac{8}{10}$ and 0.03 is equal to $\frac{3}{100}$.

Teach Use the examples in the book to review addition, subtraction, multiplication, and division with decimals. Make up a worksheet of similar problems to give students additional practice. Also show students how a fraction is converted to a decimal by dividing the numerator by the denominator. For example, $\frac{1}{2}$ is equal to 0.5.

Practice

$6.21 \times 8.5 = 52.785$

Ratio and Proportion

Focus Differentiate a ratio from a fraction. Remind students that a fraction tells how many parts of the whole. In contrast, a ratio compares two different numbers. For example, $\frac{12}{22}$, or $\frac{6}{11}$, of a class are girls. But the ratio of boys to girls in the class is 10 to 12, or $\frac{5}{6}$.

Teach Use the example in the book to explain how to use a proportion to find an unknown quantity. Provide students with additional practice problems, if needed.

Practice

$6 \times 49 = 7x$
$294 = 7x$
$294 \div 7 = x$
$x = 42$

Percentage

Focus On the board, write $50\% = \frac{50}{100}$. Explain that a percentage is a ratio that compares a number to 100.

Teach Point out that when calculating percentages, you are usually using numbers other than 100. In this case, you set up a proportion. Go over the example in the book. Emphasize that the number representing the total goes on the bottom of the ratio, as does the 100%.

Practice

Students should set up the proportion

$$\frac{42}{300} = \frac{x\%}{100\%}$$

$42 \times 100 = 300x$

$4200 = 300x$

$4200 \div 300 = 14\%$

Ratio and Proportion

A **ratio** compares two numbers by division. For example, suppose a scientist counts 800 wolves and 1,200 moose on an island. The ratio of wolves to moose can be written as a fraction, $\frac{800}{1,200}$, which can be reduced to $\frac{2}{3}$. The same ratio can also be expressed as 2 to 3 or 2 : 3.

A **proportion** is a mathematical sentence saying that two ratios are equivalent. For example, a proportion could state that $\frac{800 \text{ wolves}}{1,200 \text{ moose}} = \frac{2 \text{ wolves}}{3 \text{ moose}}$. You can sometimes set up a proportion to determine or estimate an unknown quantity. For example, suppose a scientist counts 25 beetles in an area of 10 square meters. The scientist wants to estimate the number of beetles in 100 square meters.

Example

1. Express the relationship between beetles and area as a ratio: $\frac{25}{10}$, simplified to $\frac{5}{2}$.
2. Set up a proportion, with x representing the number of beetles. The proportion can be stated as $\frac{5}{2} = \frac{x}{100}$.
3. Begin by cross-multiplying. In other words, multiply each fraction's numerator by the other fraction's denominator.

   $5 \times 100 = 2 \times x$, or $500 = 2x$

4. To find the value of x, divide both sides by 2. The result is 250, or 250 beetles in 100 square meters.

Practice

Find the value of x in the following proportion: $\frac{6}{7} = \frac{x}{49}$.

Percentage

A **percentage** is a ratio that compares a number to 100. For example, there are 37 granite rocks in a collection that consists of 100 rocks. The ratio $\frac{37}{100}$ can be written as 37%. Granite rocks make up 37% of the rock collection.

You can calculate percentages of numbers other than 100 by setting up a proportion.

Example

Rain falls on 9 days out of 30 in June. What percentage of the days in June were rainy?

$$\frac{9 \text{ days}}{30 \text{ days}} = \frac{d\%}{100\%}$$

To find the value of d, begin by cross-multiplying, as for any proportion:

$9 \times 100 = 30 \times d$ $d = \frac{900}{30}$ $d = 30$

Practice

There are 300 marbles in a jar, and 42 of those marbles are blue. What percentage of the marbles are blue?

Significant Figures

The **precision** of a measurement depends on the instrument you use to take the measurement. For example, if the smallest unit on the ruler is millimeters, then the most precise measurement you can make will be in millimeters.

The sum or difference of measurements can only be as precise as the least precise measurement being added or subtracted. Round your answer so that it has the same number of digits after the decimal as the least precise measurement. Round up if the last digit is 5 or more, and round down if the last digit is 4 or less.

> **Example**
>
> Subtract a temperature of 5.2°C from the temperature 75.46°C.
>
> **75.46 − 5.2 = 70.26**
>
> 5.2 has the fewest digits after the decimal, so it is the least precise measurement. Since the last digit of the answer is 6, round up to 3. The most precise difference between the measurements is 70.3°C.

> **Practice**
>
> Add 26.4 m to 8.37 m. Round your answer according to the precision of the measurements.

Significant figures are the number of nonzero digits in a measurement. Zeroes between nonzero digits are also significant. For example, the measurements 12,500 L, 0.125 cm, and 2.05 kg all have three significant figures. When you multiply and divide measurements, the one with the fewest significant figures determines the number of significant figures in your answer.

> **Example**
>
> Multiply 110 g by 5.75 g.
>
> **110 × 5.75 = 632.5**
>
> Because 110 has only two significant figures, round the answer to 630 g.

Scientific Notation

A **factor** is a number that divides into another number with no remainder. In the example, the number 3 is used as a factor four times.

An **exponent** tells how many times a number is used as a factor. For example, $3 \times 3 \times 3 \times 3$ can be written as 3^4. The exponent 4 indicates that the number 3 is used as a factor four times. Another way of expressing this is to say that 81 is equal to 3 to the fourth power.

> **Example**
>
> $3^4 = 3 \times 3 \times 3 \times 3 = 81$

Scientific notation uses exponents and powers of ten to write very large or very small numbers in shorter form. When you write a number in scientific notation, you write the number as two factors. The first factor is any number between 1 and 10. The second factor is a power of 10, such as 10^3 or 10^6.

> **Example**
>
> The average distance between the planet Mercury and the sun is 58,000,000 km. To write the first factor in scientific notation, insert a decimal point in the original number so that you have a number between 1 and 10. In the case of 58,000,000, the number is 5.8.
>
> To determine the power of 10, count the number of places that the decimal point moved. In this case, it moved 7 places.
>
> $58{,}000{,}000 \text{ km} = 5.8 \times 10^7 \text{ km}$

> **Practice**
>
> Express 6,590,000 in scientific notation.

Significant Figures

Focus Measure the length of a paper clip using two different rulers. Use one ruler that is less precise than the other. Compare the two measurements. Ask: **Which measurement is more precise?** (*The ruler with the smallest units will give the more precise measurement.*)

Teach Give students the opportunity to take measurements of an object using tools with different precision. Encourage students to add and subtract their measurements, making sure that they round the answers to reflect the precision of the instruments. Go over the example for significant digits. Check for understanding by asking: **How many significant digits are in the number 324,000?** (*Three*) **In the number 5, 901?** (*Four*) **In the number 0.706?** (*Three*) If students need additional practice, create a worksheet with problems in multiplying and dividing numbers with various significant digits.

> **Practice**
>
> 26.4 m + 8.37 m = 34.77 m
> This answer should be rounded to 34.8 m because the least precise measurement has only one digit after the decimal. This number is rounded up to 8 because the last digit is more than 5.

Scientific Notation

Focus Write a very large number on the board, such as 100 million, using all the zeros. Then, write the number using scientific notation. Ask: **Why do you think scientists prefer to write very large numbers using scientific notation?** (*Possible answers include that it is easier to do calculations, convert units, and make comparisons with other numbers.*)

Teach Go over the examples, and ask: **In the second example, which numbers are the factors?** (*5.8 and 10^7*) **Which number is the exponent?** (^{7}) Explain that very small numbers have a negative exponent because the decimal point is moved to the right to produce the first factor. For example, 0.00000628 is equal to 6.28×10^{-6}.

> **Practice**
>
> $6{,}590{,}000 = 6.59 \times 10^6$

Reading Comprehension Skills

Students can refer to this part of the Skills Handbook whenever they need to review a reading skill. You can use the activities provided here to teach or reinforce these skills.

All in One Teaching Resources
• Target Reading Skills Handbook

Using Prior Knowledge

Focus Explain to students that using prior knowledge helps connect what they already know to what they are about to read.

Teach Point out that prior knowledge might not be accurate because memories have faded or perspectives have changed. Encourage students to ask questions to resolve discrepancies between their prior knowledge and what they have learned.

Asking Questions

Focus Demonstrate to students how to change a text heading into a question to help them anticipate the concepts, facts, and events they will read about.

Teach Encourage students to use this reading skill for the next section they read. Instruct them to turn the text headings into questions. Also challenge students to write at least four *what, how, why, who, when,* or *where* questions. Then, have students evaluate the skill. Ask: **Did asking questions about the text help you focus on the reading and remember what you read?** *(Answers will vary, but encourage honesty.)* If this reading skill didn't help, challenge them to assess why not.

Previewing Visuals

Focus Explain to students that looking at the visuals before reading will help them activate prior knowledge and predict what they are about to read.

Teach Assign a section for students to preview the visuals. First, instruct them to write a sentence describing what the section will be about. Then, encourage them to write one or two questions for each visual to give purpose to their reading. Also have them list any prior knowledge about the subject.

Reading Comprehension Skills

Each section in your textbook introduces a Target Reading Skill. You will improve your reading comprehension by using the Target Reading Skills described below.

Using Prior Knowledge

Your prior knowledge is what you already know before you begin to read about a topic. Building on what you already know gives you a head start on learning new information. Before you begin a new assignment, think about what you know. You might look at the headings and the visuals to spark your memory. You can list what you know. Then, as you read, consider questions like these.

• How does what you learn relate to what you know?
• How did something you already know help you learn something new?
• Did your original ideas agree with what you have just learned?

Asking Questions

Asking yourself questions is an excellent way to focus on and remember new information in your textbook. For example, you can turn the text headings into questions. Then your questions can guide you to identify the important information as you read. Look at these examples:

> **Heading:** Using Seismographic Data
> **Question:** How are seismographic data used?
> **Heading:** Kinds of Faults
> **Question:** What are the kinds of faults?

You do not have to limit your questions to text headings. Ask questions about anything that you need to clarify or that will help you understand the content. *What* and *how* are probably the most common question words, but you may also ask *why, who, when,* or *where* questions.

Previewing Visuals

Visuals are photographs, graphs, tables, diagrams, and illustrations. Visuals contain important information. Before you read, look at visuals and their labels and captions. This preview will help you prepare for what you will be reading.

Often you will be asked what you want to learn about a visual. For example, after you look at the normal fault diagram below, you might ask: What is the movement along a normal fault? Questions about visuals give you a purpose for reading—to answer your questions.

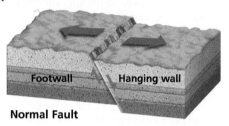

Footwall   Hanging wall

Normal Fault

Outlining

An outline shows the relationship between main ideas and supporting ideas. An outline has a formal structure. You write the main ideas, called topics, next to Roman numerals. The supporting ideas, called subtopics, are written under the main ideas and labeled A, B, C, and so on. An outline looks like this:

Technology and Society
I. Technology through history
II. The impact of technology on society
A.
B.

Outlining

Focus Explain that using an outline format helps organize information by main topic, subtopic, and details.

Teach Choose a section in the book, and demonstrate how to make an outline for it. Make sure students understand the structure of the outline by asking: **Is this a topic or a subtopic? Where does this information go in the outline? Would I write this heading next to a Roman numeral or a capital letter?** *(Answers depend on the section being outlined.)* Also show them how to indent and add details to the outline using numerals and lowercase letters.

Identifying Main Ideas

When you are reading science material, it is important to try to understand the ideas and concepts that are in a passage. Each paragraph has a lot of information and detail. Good readers try to identify the most important—or biggest—idea in every paragraph or section. That's the main idea. The other information in the paragraph supports or further explains the main idea.

Sometimes main ideas are stated directly. In this book, some main ideas are identified for you as key concepts. These are printed in boldface type. However, you must identify other main ideas yourself. In order to do this, you must identify all the ideas within a paragraph or section. Then ask yourself which idea is big enough to include all the other ideas.

Comparing and Contrasting

When you compare and contrast, you examine the similarities and differences between things. You can compare and contrast in a Venn diagram or in a table.

Venn Diagram A Venn diagram consists of two overlapping circles. In the space where the circles overlap, you write the characteristics that the two items have in common. In one of the circles outside the area of overlap, you write the differing features or characteristics of one of the items. In the other circle outside the area of overlap, you write the differing characteristics of the other item.

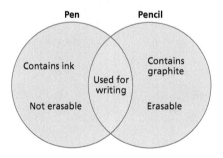

Table In a compare/contrast table, you list the characteristics or features to be compared across the top of the table. Then list the items to be compared in the left column. Complete the table by filling in information about each characteristic or feature.

Blood Vessel	Function	Structure of Wall
Artery	Carries blood away from heart	
Capillary		
Vein		

Identifying Supporting Evidence

A hypothesis is a possible explanation for observations made by scientists or an answer to a scientific question. Scientists must carry out investigations and gather evidence that either supports or disproves the hypothesis.

Identifying the supporting evidence for a hypothesis or theory can help you understand the hypothesis or theory. Evidence consists of facts—information whose accuracy can be confirmed by testing or observation.

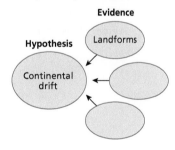

Identifying Main Ideas

Focus Explain that identifying main ideas and details helps sort the facts from the information into groups. Each group can have a main topic, subtopics, and details.

Teach Tell students that paragraphs are often written so that the main idea is in the first or second sentence, or in the last sentence. Assign students a page in the book. Instruct them to write the main idea for each paragraph on that page. If students have difficulty finding the main idea, suggest that they list all of the ideas given in the paragraph, and then choose the idea that is big enough to include all the others.

Comparing and Contrasting

Focus Explain that comparing and contrasting information shows how concepts, facts, and events are similar or different. The results of the comparison can have importance.

Teach Point out that Venn diagrams work best when comparing two things. To compare more than two things, students should use a compare/contrast table. Have students make a Venn diagram or compare/contrast table using two or more different sports or other activities, such as playing musical instruments. Emphasize that students should select characteristics that highlight the similarities and differences in the activities.

Identifying Supporting Evidence

Focus Explain to students that identifying the supporting evidence will help them to understand the relationship between the facts and the hypothesis.

Teach Remind students that a hypothesis is neither right nor wrong, but it is either supported or not supported by the evidence from testing or observation. If evidence is found that does not support a hypothesis, the hypothesis can be changed to accommodate the new evidence, or it can be dropped.

Sequencing

Focus Tell students that organizing information from beginning to end will help them understand a step-by-step process.

Teach Encourage students to create a flowchart to show the things they did this morning to get ready for school. Remind students that a flowchart should show the correct order in which events occur. *(A typical flowchart might include: got up ➤ took a shower ➤ got dressed ➤ ate breakfast ➤ brushed teeth ➤ gathered books and homework ➤ put on jacket.)*

Then explain that a cycle diagram shows a sequence of events that is continuous. Point out the cycle diagram that shows how the weather changes with the seasons of the year. Ask: **Why is a cycle diagram used instead of a flowchart to show the sequence of the seasons?** *(A cycle diagram shows that the sequence is continuous, not just a series of events.)* Challenge students to make a sequence diagram for a section of the text. Have them explain why they chose either a cycle diagram or a flowchart. Remind them to include at least four steps in the sequence.

Relating Cause and Effect

Focus Explain to students that cause is the reason for what happens. The effect is what happens in response to the cause. Relating cause and effect helps students relate the reason for what happens to what happens as a result.

Teach Emphasize that not all events that occur together have a cause-and-effect relationship. For example, tell students that you went to the grocery store and your car stalled. Ask: **Is there a cause-and-effect relationship in this situation? Explain.** *(No. Going to the grocery store could not cause a car to stall. There must be another cause to make the car stall.)*

Sequencing

A sequence is the order in which a series of events occurs. A flowchart or a cycle diagram can help you visualize a sequence.

Flowchart To make a flowchart, write a brief description of each step or event in a box. Place the boxes in order, with the first event at the top of the chart. Then draw an arrow to connect each step or event to the next.

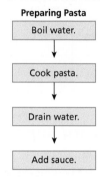

Preparing Pasta

Boil water.

Cook pasta.

Drain water.

Add sauce.

Cycle Diagram A cycle diagram shows a sequence that is continuous, or cyclical. A continuous sequence does not have an end because when the final event is over, the first event begins again. To create a cycle diagram, write the starting event in a box placed at the top of a page in the center. Then, moving in a clockwise direction, write each event in a box in its proper sequence. Draw arrows that connect each event to the one that occurs next.

Seasons of the Year

Winter · Spring · Summer · Fall

Relating Cause and Effect

Science involves many cause-and-effect relationships. A cause makes something happen. An effect is what happens. When you recognize that one event causes another, you are relating cause and effect.

Words like *cause, because, effect, affect,* and *result* often signal a cause or an effect. Sometimes an effect can have more than one cause, or a cause can produce several effects.

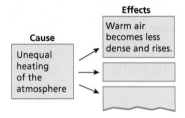

Cause

Unequal heating of the atmosphere

Effects

Warm air becomes less dense and rises.

Concept Mapping

Concept maps are useful tools for organizing information on any topic. A concept map begins with a main idea or core concept and shows how the idea can be subdivided into related subconcepts or smaller ideas.

You construct a concept map by placing concepts (usually nouns) in ovals and connecting them with linking words (usually verbs). The biggest concept or idea is placed in an oval at the top of the map. Related concepts are arranged in ovals below the big idea. The linking words connect the ovals.

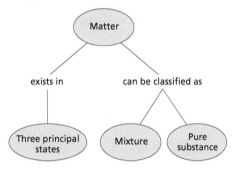

Matter

exists in — Three principal states

can be classified as — Mixture · Pure substance

Concept Mapping

Focus Elicit from students how a map shows the relationship of one geographic area to another. Connect this idea to how a concept map shows the relationship between terms and concepts.

Teach Challenge students to make a concept map with at least three levels of concepts to organize information about types of transportation. All students should start with the phrase *Types of transportation* at the top of the concept map. After that point, their concepts may vary. *(For example, some students might place* private transportation *and* public transportation *at the next level, while other students might choose* human-powered *and* gas-powered.*)* Make sure students connect the concepts with linking words.

Building Vocabulary

Knowing the meaning of these prefixes, suffixes, and roots will help you understand the meaning of words you do not recognize.

Word Origins Many science words come to English from other languages, such as Greek and Latin. By learning the meaning of a few common Greek and Latin roots, you can determine the meaning of unfamiliar science words.

Prefixes A prefix is a word part that is added at the beginning of a root or base word to change its meaning.

Suffixes A suffix is a word part that is added at the end of a root word to change the meaning.

Greek and Latin Roots		
Greek Roots	**Meaning**	**Example**
ast-	star	astronaut
geo-	Earth	geology
metron-	measure	kilometer
opt-	eye	optician
photo-	light	photograph
scop-	see	microscope
therm-	heat	thermostat
Latin Roots	**Meaning**	**Example**
aqua-	water	aquarium
aud-	hear	auditorium
duc-, duct-	lead	conduct
flect-	bend	reflect
fract-, frag-	break	fracture
ject-	throw	reject
luc-	light	lucid
spec-	see	inspect

Prefixes and Suffixes		
Prefix	**Meaning**	**Example**
com-, con-	with	communicate, concert
de-	from; down	decay
di-	two	divide
ex-, exo-	out	exhaust
in-, im-	in, into; not	inject, impossible
re-	again; back	reflect, recall
trans-	across	transfer
Suffix	**Meaning**	**Example**
-al	relating to	natural
-er, -or	one who	teacher, doctor
-ist	one who practices	scientist
-ity	state of	equality
-ology	study of	biology
-tion, -sion	state or quality of	reaction, tension

Skills Handbook ♦ 231

Building Vocabulary

Reading in a content area presents challenges different from those encountered when reading fiction. Science texts often have more new vocabulary and more unfamiliar concepts that place greater emphasis on inferential reasoning. Students who can apply vocabulary strategies will be more successful in reading and understanding a science textbook. Challenge students to use Greek and Latin word origins and the meanings of prefixes and suffixes to learn the Key Terms in each section.

Word Origins

Focus Explain that word origins describe the older, foreign words that many modern English words have come from. Many science words come from Greek and Latin.

Teach Tell students that most dictionaries give the word origin just before the definition. Choose a section that has a Key Term with a Greek or Latin word origin. Encourage students to learn the meaning of the root word. Ask: **How does knowing the word origin help you remember the meaning of the Key Term?** (*Answers will vary, but the meaning of the Latin or Greek root should provide a clue to the definition of the Key Term.*) Ask: **What other words do you know that come from the same word origin?** (*Students may mention other words related to the Key Term.*) Challenge students to use word origins to figure out the meanings of unfamiliar words as they read. Students should confirm their definitions as necessary by checking a dictionary.

Prefixes

Focus Tell students that learning the meaning of common prefixes can help them determine the meaning of words they don't recognize. They will also increase their vocabulary.

Teach Remind students that a prefix is a word part that is added at the beginning of a root word to change its meaning. List some of the familiar prefixes and meanings, such as *de-* and *re-*, on the chalkboard. Ask: **What words do you know that use these same prefixes?** (*Students should list at least two words for each prefix.*) Ask: **How does the prefix affect the meaning of the root word?** (*Students should explain how it changes the meaning.*) Challenge students to learn the meaning of common prefixes and to use the skill to increase their vocabulary.

Suffixes

Focus Explain to students that learning the meanings of common suffixes and recognizing them in words are two effective strategies for learning word meanings and building vocabulary.

Teach Remind students that a suffix is added to the end of a word to change its meaning. In addition, students can use suffixes to discover the part of speech of an unfamiliar word. On the chalkboard, draw a four-column chart. Label the columns Noun, Verb, Adjective, and Adverb. Choose a Key Term that has a familiar base word, such as *tension.* Ask: **What are the noun, verb, adjective, and adverb forms of this word?** (*Students should give all possible answers, which may include only two forms of the word.*) Ask: **What endings signal that the word is a noun, adjective, or adverb?** (*Students should list the suffixes.*) Challenge students to learn meanings of suffixes and to use them to decode new words.

M ● 231

Interactive Textbook

- Complete student edition
- Video and audio
- Simulations and activities
- Section and chapter activities

Laboratory Safety

Laboratory safety is an essential element of a successful science class. Students need to understand exactly what is safe and unsafe behavior and what the rationale is behind each safety rule.

All in One Teaching Resources

- Laboratory Safety Teacher Notes
- Laboratory Safety Rules
- Laboratory Safety Symbols
- Laboratory Safety Contract

General Precautions

- Post safety rules in the classroom, and review them regularly with students before beginning every science activity.
- Familiarize yourself with the safety procedures for each activity before introducing it to your students.
- For open-ended activities like Chapter Projects, have students submit their procedures or design plans in writing and check them for safety considerations.
- Always act as an exemplary role model by displaying safe behavior.
- Know how to use safety equipment, such as fire extinguishers and fire blankets, and always have it accessible.
- Have students practice leaving the classroom quickly and orderly to prepare them for emergencies.
- Explain to students how to use the intercom or other available means of communication to get help during an emergency.
- Never leave students unattended while they are engaged in science activities.
- Provide enough space for students to safely carry out science activities.
- Instruct students to report all accidents and injuries to you immediately.

Safety Symbols

These symbols warn of possible dangers in the laboratory and remind you to work carefully.

 Safety Goggles Wear safety goggles to protect your eyes in any activity involving chemicals, flames or heating, or glassware.

 Lab Apron Wear a laboratory apron to protect your skin and clothing from damage.

 Breakage Handle breakable materials, such as glassware, with care. Do not touch broken glassware.

 Heat-Resistant Gloves Use an oven mitt or other hand protection when handling hot materials such as hot plates or hot glassware.

 Plastic Gloves Wear disposable plastic gloves when working with harmful chemicals and organisms. Keep your hands away from your face, and dispose of the gloves according to your teacher's instructions.

 Heating Use a clamp or tongs to pick up hot glassware. Do not touch hot objects with your bare hands.

 Flames Before you work with flames, tie back loose hair and clothing. Follow instructions from your teacher about lighting and extinguishing flames.

 No Flames When using flammable materials, make sure there are no flames, sparks, or other exposed heat sources present.

 Corrosive Chemical Avoid getting acid or other corrosive chemicals on your skin or clothing or in your eyes. Do not inhale the vapors. Wash your hands after the activity.

 Poison Do not let any poisonous chemical come into contact with your skin, and do not inhale its vapors. Wash your hands when you are finished with the activity.

 Fumes Work in a ventilated area when harmful vapors may be involved. Avoid inhaling vapors directly. Only test an odor when directed to do so by your teacher, and use a wafting motion to direct the vapor toward your nose.

 Sharp Object Scissors, scalpels, knives, needles, pins, and tacks can cut your skin. Always direct a sharp edge or point away from yourself and others.

 Animal Safety Treat live or preserved animals or animal parts with care to avoid harming the animals or yourself. Wash your hands when you are finished with the activity.

 Plant Safety Handle plants only as directed by your teacher. If you are allergic to certain plants, tell your teacher; do not do an activity involving those plants. Avoid touching harmful plants such as poison ivy. Wash your hands when you are finished with the activity.

 Electric Shock To avoid electric shock, never use electrical equipment around water, or when the equipment is wet or your hands are wet. Be sure cords are untangled and cannot trip anyone. Unplug equipment not in use.

 Physical Safety When an experiment involves physical activity, avoid injuring yourself or others. Alert your teacher if there is any reason you should not participate.

 Disposal Dispose of chemicals and other laboratory materials safely. Follow the instructions from your teacher.

 Hand Washing Wash your hands thoroughly when finished with the activity. Use soap and warm water. Rinse well.

General Safety Awareness When this symbol appears, follow the instructions provided. When you are asked to develop your own procedure in a lab, have your teacher approve your plan before you go further.

End-of-Experiment Rules

- Always have students use warm water and soap for washing their hands.

Heating and Fire Safety

- No flammable substances should be in use around hot plates, light bulbs, or open flames.
- Test tubes should be heated only in water baths.

- Students should be permitted to strike matches to light candles or burners *only* with strict supervision. When possible, you should light the flames, especially when working with younger students.
- Be sure to have proper ventilation when fumes are produced during a procedure.
- All electrical equipment used in the lab should have GFI (Ground Fault Interrupter) switches.

Science Safety Rules

General Precautions

Follow all instructions. Never perform activities without the approval and supervision of your teacher. Do not engage in horseplay. Never eat or drink in the laboratory. Keep work areas clean and uncluttered.

Dress Code

Wear safety goggles whenever you work with chemicals, glassware, heat sources such as burners, or any substance that might get into your eyes. If you wear contact lenses, notify your teacher.

Wear a lab apron or coat whenever you work with corrosive chemicals or substances that can stain. Wear disposable plastic gloves when working with organisms and harmful chemicals. Tie back long hair. Remove or tie back any article of clothing or jewelry that can hang down and touch chemicals, flames, or equipment. Roll up long sleeves. Never wear open shoes or sandals.

First Aid

Report all accidents, injuries, or fires to your teacher, no matter how minor. Be aware of the location of the first-aid kit, emergency equipment such as the fire extinguisher and fire blanket, and the nearest telephone. Know whom to contact in an emergency.

Heating and Fire Safety

Keep all combustible materials away from flames. When heating a substance in a test tube, make sure that the mouth of the tube is not pointed at you or anyone else. Never heat a liquid in a closed container. Use an oven mitt to pick up a container that has been heated.

Using Chemicals Safely

Never put your face near the mouth of a container that holds chemicals. Never touch, taste, or smell a chemical unless your teacher tells you to.

Use only those chemicals needed in the activity. Keep all containers closed when chemicals are not being used. Pour all chemicals over the sink or a container, not over your work surface. Dispose of excess chemicals as instructed by your teacher.

Be extra careful when working with acids or bases. When mixing an acid and water, always pour the water into the container first and then add the acid to the water. Never pour water into an acid. Wash chemical spills and splashes immediately with plenty of water.

Using Glassware Safely

If glassware is broken or chipped, notify your teacher immediately. Never handle broken or chipped glass with your bare hands.

Never force glass tubing or thermometers into a rubber stopper or rubber tubing. Have your teacher insert the glass tubing or thermometer if required for an activity.

Using Sharp Instruments

Handle sharp instruments with extreme care. Never cut material toward you; cut away from you.

Animal and Plant Safety

Never perform experiments that cause pain, discomfort, or harm to animals. Only handle animals if absolutely necessary. If you know that you are allergic to certain plants, molds, or animals, tell your teacher before doing an activity in which these are used. Wash your hands thoroughly after any activity involving animals, animal parts, plants, plant parts, or soil.

During field work, wear long pants, long sleeves, socks, and closed shoes. Avoid poisonous plants and fungi as well as plants with thorns.

End-of-Experiment Rules

Unplug all electrical equipment. Clean up your work area. Dispose of waste materials as instructed by your teacher. Wash your hands after every experiment.

Handling Organisms Safely

- In an activity where students are directed to taste something, be sure to store the material in clean, *nonscience* containers. Distribute the material to students in *new* plastic or paper dispensables, which should be discarded after the tasting. Tasting or eating should never be done in a lab classroom.

- When growing bacterial cultures, use only disposable petri dishes. After streaking, the dishes should be sealed and not opened again by students. After the lab, students should return the unopened dishes to you.

- Two methods are recommended for the safe disposal of bacterial cultures. *First method:* Autoclave the petri dishes and discard them without opening. *Second method:* If no autoclave is available, carefully open the dishes (never have a student do this), pour full-strength bleach into the dishes, and let them stand for a day. Then pour the bleach from the petri dishes down a drain, and flush the drain with lots of water. Tape the petri dishes back together, and place them in a sealed plastic bag. Wrap the plastic bag with a brown paper bag or newspaper, and tape securely. Throw the sealed package in the trash. Thoroughly disinfect the work area with bleach.

- To grow mold, use a new, sealable plastic bag that is two to three times larger than the material to be placed inside. Seal the bag and tape it shut. After the bag is sealed, students should not open it. To dispose of the bag and mold culture, make a small cut near an edge of the bag, and cook the bag in a microwave oven on a high setting for at least one minute. Discard the bag according to local ordinance, usually in the trash.

- Students should wear disposable nitrile, latex, or food-handling gloves when handling live animals or nonliving specimens.

Using Glassware Safely

- Use plastic containers, graduated cylinders, and beakers whenever possible. If using glass, students should wear safety goggles.
- Use only nonmercury thermometers with anti-roll protectors.

Using Chemicals Safely

- When students use both chemicals and microscopes in one activity, microscopes should be in a separate part of the room from the chemicals so that when students remove their goggles to use the microscopes, their eyes are not at risk.

English and Spanish Glossary

A

absolute zero The temperature at which no more energy can be removed from matter. (p. 178)
cero absoluto Temperatura a la cual no se puede quitar más energía a la materia.

acceleration The rate at which velocity changes. (p. 22)
acelaración Razón a la que cambia la velocidad.

air resistance The fluid friction experienced by objects falling through the air. (p. 49)
resistencia del aire Fricción de fluido experimentada por los objetos que caen a través del aire.

Archimedes' principle The rule that the buoyant force on an object is equal to the weight of the fluid the object displaces. (p. 84)
principio de Arquímedes Regla que enuncia que la fuerza de flotación que actúa sobre un objeto es igual al peso del líquido que desaloja.

average speed The overall rate of speed at which an object moves; calculated by dividing the total distance an object travels by the total time. (p. 11)
rapidez media Velocidad general a la que se mueve un objeto; se calcula dividiendo la distancia total recorrida por el tiempo total empleado.

B

balanced forces Equal forces acting on an object in opposite directions. (p. 38)
fuerzas equilibradas Fuerzas iguales que actúan sobre un objeto en direcciones opuestas.

barometer An instrument used to measure atmospheric pressure. (p. 80)
barómetro Instrumento que se usa para medir la presión atmosférica.

Bernoulli's principle The rule that a stream of fast-moving fluid exerts less pressure than the surrounding fluid. (p. 96)
principio de Bernoulli Regla que enuncia que la corriente de un fluido de rápido movimiento ejerce menor presión que el fluido del entorno.

boiling Vaporization that occurs on and below the surface of a liquid. (p. 193)
ebullición Evaporación que ocurre sobre y bajo la superficie de un líquido.

buoyant force The upward force exerted by a fluid on a submerged object. (p. 83)
fuerza de flotación Fuerza ascendente que ejerce un líquido sobre un objeto sumergido.

C

Celsius scale The temperature scale on which water freezes at 0 degrees and boils at 100 degrees. (p. 178)
escala Celsius Escala de temperatura en la cual el agua se congela a los 0 grados y hierve a los 100 grados.

centripetal force A force that causes an object to move in a circle. (p. 65)
fuerza centrípeta Fuerza que causa que un objeto se mueva en círculos.

change of state The physical change of matter from one state to another. (p. 192)
cambio de estado Cambio físico de la materia de un estado a otro.

chemical energy The potential energy stored in chemical bonds. (p. 154)
energía química Energía potencial almacenada en los enlaces químicos.

combustion The process of burning a fuel to produce thermal energy. (p. 168)
combustión Proceso de quemado de un combustible para producir energía térmica.

compound machine A device that combines two or more simple machines. (p. 135)
máquina compuesta Dispositivo que combina dos o más máquinas simples.

condensation The change from the gaseous to the liquid state of matter. (p. 193)
condensación Cambio de la materia del estado gaseoso al estado líquido.

conduction The transfer of heat from one particle of matter to another. (p. 184)
conducción Transferencia de calor desde una partícula de materia a otra.

conductor A material that conducts heat well. (p. 187)
conductor Material que puede conducir bien el calor.

convection The transfer of heat by the movement of currents within a fluid. (p. 184)
convección Transferencia del calor a través del movimiento de las corrientes dentro de un líquido.

convection current A current caused by the rising of heated fluid and sinking of cooled fluid. (p. 184)
corriente de convección Movimiento circular causado por el ascenso de un líquido calentado y el descenso de un líquido enfriado.

density The mass of a substance contained in a unit of volume. (p. 85)
densidad Masa de una sustancia contenida en una unidad de volumen.

efficiency The percentage of the input work that is converted to output work. (p. 119)
eficiencia Porcentaje del trabajo aportado que se convierte en trabajo producido.

elastic potential energy The energy of stretched or compressed objects. (p. 150)
energía elástica potencial Energía de los objetos estirados o comprimidos.

electrical energy The energy of electric charges. (p. 154)
energía eléctrica Energía de las cargas eléctricas.

electromagnetic energy The energy of light and other forms of radiation. (p. 155)
energía electromagnética Energía de la luz y otras formas de radiación.

energy The ability to do work or cause change. (p. 147)
energía Capacidad para realizar trabajo o causar un cambio.

energy transformation The process of changing one form of energy to another. (p. 158)
transformación energética Proceso de cambio de una forma de energía a otra.

evaporation Vaporization that occurs at the surface of a liquid. (p. 193)
evaporación Vaporización que ocurre en la superficie de un líquido.

external combustion engine An engine powered by fuel burned outside the engine. (p. 196)
motor de combustión externa Motor alimentado por combustible que se quema fuera del motor.

Fahrenheit scale The temperature scale on which water freezes at 32 degrees and boils at 212 degrees. (p. 178)
escala Fahrenheit Escala de temperatura en la cual el agua se congela a los 32 grados y hierve a los 212 grados.

fluid A material that can easily flow. (p. 76)
fluido Sustancia que puede fluir con facilidad.

fluid friction Friction that occurs as an object moves through a fluid. (p. 44)
fricción de fluido Fricción que ocurre cuando un objeto se mueve a través de un fluido.

force A push or pull exerted on an object. (p. 36)
fuerza Empuje o atracción que se ejerce sobre un objeto.

fossil fuel A material such as coal that forms over millions of years from the remains of ancient plants and animals; burned to release chemical energy. (p. 166)
combustible fósil Material, como el carbón de piedra, que se forma durante millones de años a partir de los restos de animales y vegetales; se quema para liberar la energía química.

free fall The motion of a falling object when the only force acting on it is gravity. (p. 48)
caída libre Movimiento de un objeto que cae cuando la única fuerza que actúa sobre el mismo es la gravedad.

freezing The change from the liquid to the solid state of matter. (p. 192)
congelación Cambio de la materia del estado líquido al estado sólido.

friction The force that one surface exerts on another when the two surfaces rub against each other. (p. 43)
fricción Fuerza que ejerce una superficie sobre otra cuando se frotan una contra otra.

fulcrum The fixed point around which a lever pivots. (p. 128)
fulcro Punto fijo en torno al cual gira una palanca.

gravitational potential energy Potential energy that depends on the height of an object. (p. 149)
energía potencial gravitatoria Energía potencial que depende de la altura de un objeto.

gravity The force that pulls objects toward each other. (p. 46)
gravedad Fuerza que atrae objetos entre sí.

heat Thermal energy that is transferred from matter at a higher temperature to matter at a lower temperature. (p. 179)
calor Energía térmica que se transfiere desde una materia a mayor temperatura a una materia a menor temperatura.

heat engine A device that converts thermal energy into mechanical energy. (p. 195)
motor térmico Máquina que convierte la energía térmica en energía mecánica.

hydraulic system A system that multiplies force by transmitting pressure from a small surface area through a confined fluid to a larger surface area. (p. 93)
sistema hidráulico Sistema que multiplica la fuerza transmitiendo la presión de un área total pequeña a un área total mayor a través de un fluido confinado.

inclined plane A simple machine that is a flat, sloped surface. (p. 125)
plano inclinado Máquina simple que consiste en una superficie plana con pendiente.

inertia The tendency of an object to resist any change in its motion. (p. 52)
inercia Tendencia de un objeto a resistir cualquier cambio en su movimiento.

input force The force exerted on a machine. (p. 115)
fuerza aplicada Fuerza que se ejerce sobre una máquina.

input work The work done on a machine as the input force acts through the input distance. (p. 115)
trabajo aportado Trabajo realizado sobre una máquina mientras la fuerza aplicada actúa a lo largo de la distancia de aplicación.

instantaneous speed The speed of an object at one instant of time. (p. 11)
rapidez instantánea Velocidad de un objeto en un instante de tiempo.

insulator A material that does not conduct heat well. (p. 187)
aislante Material que no conduce bien el calor.

internal combustion engine An engine that burns fuel inside cylinders within the engine. (p. 196)
motor de combustión interna Motor que quema el combustible dentro de cilindros, dentro del motor.

International System of Units (SI) A system of measurement based on multiples of ten and on established measures of mass, length, and time. (p. 9)
Sistema Internacional de Unidades (SI) Sistema de medidas basado en múltiplos de diez y en medidas establecidas de masa, longitud y tiempo.

joule A unit of work equal to one newton-meter. (p. 111)
julio Unidad de trabajo igual a un newton-metro.

Kelvin scale The temperature scale on which zero is the temperature at which no more energy can be removed from matter. (p. 178)
escala Kelvin Escala de temperatura en la cual el cero es la temperatura a la cual no se puede quitar más energía de la materia.

kinetic energy Energy that an object has due to its motion. (p. 147)
energía cinética Energía que tiene un objeto debido a su movimiento.

law of conservation of energy The rule that energy cannot be created or destroyed. (p. 162)
ley de la conservación de la energía Regla que dice que la energía no se puede crear ni destruir.

law of conservation of momentum The rule that in the absence of outside forces the total momentum of objects that interact does not change. (p. 59)
ley de la conservación del momento Regla según la cual en ausencia de fuerzas externas, el momento total de los objetos no cambia en su interacción.

lever A simple machine that consists of a rigid bar that pivots about a fixed point. (p. 128)
palanca Máquina simple que consiste en una barra rígida que gira en torno a un punto fijo.

lift An upward force. (p. 97)
fuerza de elevación Fuerza ascendente.

machine A device that changes the amount of force exerted, the distance over which a force is exerted, or the direction in which force is exerted. (p. 115)
máquina Dispositivo que altera la cantidad de fuerza ejercida, la distancia sobre la que se ejerce la fuerza o la dirección en la que se ejerce la fuerza.

mass The amount of matter in an object. (p. 46)
masa Cantidad de materia en un objeto.

matter Anything that has mass and takes up space. (p. 163)
materia Cualquier cosa que tiene masa y ocupa un espacio.

mechanical advantage The number of times a machine increases a force exerted on it. (p. 118)
ventaja mecánica Número de veces que una máquina amplifica la fuerza que se ejerce sobre ella.

mechanical energy Kinetic or potential energy associated with the motion or position of an object. (p. 151)
energía mecánica Energía cinética o potencial asociada con el movimiento o posición de un objeto.

melting The change from the solid to the liquid state of matter. (p. 192)
fusión Cambio en el estado de la materia de sólido a líquido.

meter The basic SI unit of length. (p. 9)
metro Unidad básica de longitud del SI.

momentum The product of an object's mass and velocity. (p. 58)
momento Producto de la masa de un objeto por su velocidad.

motion The state in which one object's distance from another is changing. (p. 7)
movimiento Estado en el que la distancia entre un objeto y otro va cambiando.

N

net force The overall force on an object when all the individual forces acting on it are added together. (p. 37)
fuerza neta Fuerza total que actúa sobre un objeto cuando se suman las fuerzas individuales que actúan sobre él.

newton A unit of measure that equals the force required to accelerate 1 kilogram of mass at 1 meter per second per second. (p. 37)
newton Unidad de medida que es igual a la fuerza necesaria para acelerar 1 kilogramo de masa 1 metro por segundo cada segundo.

nuclear energy The potential energy stored in the nucleus of an atom. (p. 155)
energía nuclear Energía potencial almacenada en el núcleo de un átomo.

O

output force The force exerted on an object by a machine. (p. 115)
fuerza desarrollada Fuerza que una máquina ejerce sobre un objeto.

output work The work done by a machine as the output force acts through the output distance. (p. 115)
trabajo producido Trabajo que una máquina efectúa mientras la fuerza desarrollada actúa a lo largo de la distancia desarrollada.

P

pascal A unit of pressure equal to 1 newton per square meter. (p. 75)
pascal Unidad de presión igual a 1 newton por metro cuadrado.

Pascal's principle The rule that when force is applied to a confined fluid, the increase in pressure is transmitted equally to all parts of the fluid. (p. 91)
principio de Pascal Regla que enuncia que cuando se aplica una fuerza a un fluido confinado, el aumento en la presión es transmitida por igual a todas las partes del fluido.

plate One of the major pieces that make up Earth's upper layer. (p. 18)
placa Una de las partes principales que forman la capa exterior de la Tierra.

potential energy Stored energy that results from the position or shape of an object. (p. 149)
energía potencial Energía almacenada que es el resultado de la posición o forma de un objeto.

power The rate at which work is done. (p. 111)
potencia Razón a la que se realiza trabajo.

pressure The force exerted on a surface divided by the total area over which the force is exerted. (p. 75)
presión Fuerza ejercida sobre una superficie dividida por el área total sobre la cual se ejerce la fuerza.

projectile An object that is thrown. (p. 50)
proyectil Objeto que es lanzado.

pulley A simple machine that consists of a grooved wheel with a rope or cable wrapped around it. (p. 132)
polea Máquina simple que consiste en una rueda con un surco en el que entra una cuerda o cable.

R

radiation The transfer of energy by electromagnetic waves. (p. 184)
radiación Transferencia de energía a través de ondas electromagnéticas.

reference point A place or object used for comparison to determine if an object is in motion. (p. 7)
punto de referencia Lugar u objeto usado como punto de comparación para determinar si un objeto está en movimiento.

refrigerant The substance that absorbs and releases heat in a cooling system. (p. 199)
refrigerante Sustancia que absorbe y elimina calor en un sistema de enfriamiento.

rolling friction Friction that occurs when an object rolls over a surface. (p. 44)
fricción de rodamiento Fricción que ocurre cuando un objeto rueda sobre una superficie.

S

satellite Any object that orbits around another object in space. (p. 65)
satélite Cualquier objeto que orbita alrededor de otro objeto en el espacio.

screw A simple machine that is an inclined plane wrapped around a central cylinder to form a spiral. (p. 127)
tornillo Máquina simple que consiste en un plano inclinado enrollado en un cilindro central para formar una espiral.

sliding friction Friction that occurs when one solid surface slides over another. (p. 44)
fricción de deslizamiento Fricción que ocurre cuando una superficie sólida se desliza sobre otra.

slope The steepness of a line on a graph, equal to its vertical change divided by its horizontal change. (p. 14)
pendiente Inclinación de una recta en una gráfica, igual a su cambio vertical dividido por su cambio horizontal.

specific heat The amount of heat required to raise the temperature of 1 kilogram of a material by 1 kelvin. (p. 180)
calor específico Cantidad de calor que se requiere para elevar la temperatura de 1 kilogramo de material 1 grado Kelvin.

speed The distance an object travels per unit of time. (p. 10)
rapidez Distancia que viaja un objeto por unidad de tiempo.

state One of the three forms—solid, liquid, or gas—in which most matter on Earth exists. (p. 191)
estado Una de las tres formas (sólido, líquido o gas) en las que existe la materia en la Tierra.

static friction Friction that acts on objects that are not moving. (p. 44)
fricción estática Fricción que actúa sobre los objetos que no se mueven.

temperature The measure of the average kinetic energy of the particles in matter. (p. 176)
temperatura Medida de la energía cinética promedio de la partículas de la materia.

terminal velocity The greatest velocity a falling object can achieve. (p. 49)
velocidad terminal La máxima velocidad que puede alcanzar un objeto que cae.

theory of plate tectonics The theory that pieces of Earth's outer layer are in constant motion. (p. 19)
teoría de la tectónica de placas Teoría que enuncia que las partes de la capa exterior de la Tierra están en constante movimiento.

thermal energy The total potential and kinetic energy of the particles in an object. (p. 153)
energía térmica Energía cinética y potencial total de las partículas de un objeto.

thermal expansion The expansion of matter when it is heated. (p. 194)
expansión térmica Expansión de la materia cuando se calienta.

unbalanced forces Forces that produce a nonzero net force, which changes an object's motion. (p. 38)
fuerzas desequilibradas Fuerzas que producen una fuerza neta diferente de cero, lo cual cambia el movimiento de un objeto.

velocity Speed in a given direction. (p. 12)
velocidad Rapidez en una dirección dada.

wedge A simple machine that is an inclined plane that moves. (p. 126)
cuña Máquina simple que consiste en un plano inclinado en movimiento.

weight The force of gravity on an object at the surface of a planet. (p. 47)
peso Fuerza de gravedad ejercida sobre un objeto en la superficie de un planeta.

wheel and axle A simple machine that consists of two attached circular or cylindrical objects that rotate about a common axis, each one with a different radius. (p. 130)
rueda y eje Máquina simple que consiste en dos objetos circulares o cilíndricos unidos, de diferente radio, que giran en torno a un eje común.

work Force exerted on an object that causes it to move. (p. 108)
trabajo Fuerza ejercida sobre un objeto para moverlo.

Index

Teacher's Edition entries appear in **blue type.** The page on which a term is defined is indicated in **boldface** type.

Index

Page numbers for key terms are printed in **boldface** type.
Page numbers for illustrations, maps, and charts are printed in *italics*.

Index

Page numbers for key terms are printed in **boldface** type.
Page numbers for illustrations, maps, and charts are printed in *italics*.

Acknowledgments

Staff Credits

Diane Alimena, Michele Angelucci, Scott Andrews, Jennifer Angel, Laura Baselice, Carolyn Belanger, Barbara A. Bertell, Suzanne Biron, Peggy Bliss, Stephanie Bradley, James Brady, Anne M. Bray, Sarah M. Carroll, Kerry Cashman, Jonathan Cheney, Joshua D. Clapper, Lisa J. Clark, Bob Craton, Patricia Cully, Patricia M. Dambry, Kathy Dempsey, Leanne Esterly, Emily Ellen, Thomas Ferreira, Jonathan Fisher, Patricia Fromkin, Paul Gagnon, Kathy Gavilanes, Holly Gordon, Robert Graham, Ellen Granter, Diane Grossman, Barbara Hollingdale, Linda Johnson, Anne Jones, John Judge, Kevin Keane, Kelly Kelliher, Toby Klang, Sue Langan, Russ Lappa, Carolyn Lock, Rebecca Loveys, Constance J. McCarty, Carolyn B. McGuire, Ranida Touranont McKneally, Anne McLaughlin, Eve Melnechuk, Natania Mlawer, Janet Morris, Karyl Murray, Francine Neumann, Baljit Nijjar, Marie Opera, Jill Ort, Kim Ortell, Joan Paley, Dorothy Preston, Maureen Raymond, Laura Ross, Rashid Ross, Siri Schwartzman, Melissa Shustyk, Laurel Smith, Emily Soltanoff, Jennifer A. Teece, Elizabeth Torjussen, Amanda M. Watters, Merce Wilczek, Amy Winchester, Char Lyn Yeakley. **Additional Credits** Tara Alamilla, Louise Gachet, Allen Gold, Andrea Golden, Terence Hegarty, Etta Jacobs, Meg Montgomery, Stephanie Rogers, Kim Schmidt, Adam Teller, Joan Tobin.

Illustration

David Corrente: 105; **John Edwards and Associates:** 66, 92, 197; **Andrea Golden:** 204–211; **Kevin Jones Associates:** 94; **Rob Schuster:** 97; **J/B Woolsey Associates:** 1, 3, 49, 70b; **All other artwork developed by Morgan Cain & Associates.**

Photography

Photo Research Sue McDermott
Cover Image top, David Madison/Getty Images, Inc.; **net,** Ian Walton/Getty Images, Inc.; **ball,** Royalty-Free/Corbis.

Page vi t, Richard Haynes; **vi-vii b,** Prisma Dia/Index Stock Imagery, Inc.; **vii t,** Richard Haynes; **viii,** Richard Haynes; **ix,** Richard Haynes; **xi,** Richard Haynes; **xii,** Courtesy of Museum of Science; **1,** Stephen G. Maka/DRK Photo; **2l,** Brian Smale/Discover Magazine; **2r,** Helen Ghiradella/Discover Magazine; **3,** Courtesy of Museum of Science.

Chapter 1
Pages 4–5, Mark Barrett/Index Stock Imagery/PictureQuest; **5r,** PhotoDisc/Getty Images, Inc.; **6t,** Richard Haynes; **6–7b,** Prisma Dia/Index Stock Imagery, Inc.; **7t,** Sat Yip/SuperStock; **8t,** Chris Sorensen; **8b,** Digital Vision/Getty Images Inc.; **9,** Kim Taylor/Bruce Coleman Inc.; **10–11,** Robert LaBerge/Getty Images, Inc.; **12t,** Topham/The Image Works; **12m,** North Wind Picture Archives; **12b,** National Motor Museum, Beaulieu, England; **13l,** Bettmann/Corbis; **13r,** Fritz Hoffmann/documentCHINA; **14,** Bob Daemmrich Photography; **17,** Richard Haynes; **18t,** Russ Lappa; **18b,** Earth Imaging/Getty Images, Inc.; **21,** Richard Haynes; **22t,** Richard Haynes; **22b,** Jamie Squire/Getty Images Inc.; **23l,** Ezra Shaw/Getty Images Inc.; **23m,** Adam Pretty/Getty Images Inc.; **23r,** Nick Wilson/Getty Images Inc.; **25,** Kwame Zikomo/SuperStock; **26,** Eyewire Collection/Getty Images Inc.; **28,** Richard Haynes; **29,** Lou Jones/Image Bank/Getty Images, Inc.; **30,** Robert LaBerge/Getty Images, Inc.

Chapter 2
Pages 34–35, Stephen Munday/Getty Images, Inc.; **35r,** Richard Haynes; **36,** Richard Haynes; **37,** Duomo/Corbis; **38 all,** Richard Haynes; **39,** Richard Haynes; **40,** Richard Haynes; **41,** Ken O'Donaghue; **42t,** Richard Haynes; **42b,** Kindra Clineff/Index Stock Imagery, Inc.; **43t,** B & C Alexander/Photo Researchers, Inc.; **43b,** Jan Hinsch/Photo Researchers, Inc.; **44,** Russ Lappa; **45tl,** Michael Newman/PhotoEdit; **45tr,** Michael Newman/PhotoEdit; **45bl,** David Young-Wolff/PhotoEdit; **45br,** Kelly-Mooney Photography/Corbis; **46,** Joe McBride/Corbis; **47,** NASA; **48,** Megna/Peticolas/Fundamental Photographs; **50,** Richard Megna/Fundamental Photographs; **51t,** Russ Lappa; **51b,** Bettmann/Corbis; **52 all,** Richard Haynes; **53,** David Madison Sports Photography; **54,** Richard Haynes; **55,** Richard Haynes; **56tl,** David Madison Sports Photography; **56tr,** Omni Photo Communicatons, Inc./Index Stock Imagery, Inc.; **56b,** Lawrence Manning/Corbis; **57l,** Syracuse/Dick Blume/The Image Works; **57r,** Michael Devin Daly/Corbis Stock Market; **58,** Superstock; **59tl,** David Davis/Index Stock Imagery, Inc.; **59tr,** Image Source/Alamy Images; **59b,** Russ Lappa; **63,** Richard Haynes; **64t,** Richard Haynes; **64b,** Courtesy of Homer Hickam; **65,** Jeff Hunter/Getty Images, Inc.; **66,** Richard Haynes; **68,** David Young-Wolff/PhotoEdit.

Chapter 3
Pages 72–73, Getty Images, Inc.; **73r,** Richard Haynes; **74t,** Richard Haynes; **74bl,** Milton Feinberg/Stock Boston; **74br,** Chlaus Lotscher/Stock Boston; **75 all,** Richard Haynes; **76,** PhotoDisc/Getty Images, Inc.; **77 both,** Richard Megna/Fundamental Photographs; **80,** Paul Seheult-Eye Ubiquitous/Corbis; **82t,** Russ Lappa; **82b,** Ken Marshall/Madison Press. Ltd.; **83,** Bill Wood/Bruce Coleman, Inc.; **84 both,** Richard Haynes; **85,** Runk/Schoenberger/Grant Heilman Photography, Inc.; **86t,** Russ Lappa; **86b,** Ralph A. Clevenger/Corbis; **89,** Richard Haynes; **90t,** Richard Haynes; **90b,** Stephen Frink/Corbis; **91,** Richard Haynes; **95t,** Richard Haynes; **95b,** Mercury Archives/Getty Images, Inc.; **96 both,** Richard Haynes; **99,** Maxime Laurent/Digital Vision; **102t,** Stephen Frink/Corbis; **102b,** Paul Seheult-Eye Ubiquitous/Corbis; **104,** Russ Lappa.

Chapter 4
Pages 106–107, The G. R. "Dick" Roberts Photo Library; **107r,** Corbis; **108 both,** Richard Haynes; **109 all,** Richard Haynes; **110 both,** Richard Haynes; **111 both,** MVR Photo; **112,** Shelley Rotner/Omni-Photo Communications, Inc.; **113,** The Granger Collection, NY; **114t,** Corel Corp.; **114b,** Jim West/The Image Works; **115,** PhotoDisc/Getty Images, Inc.; **116,** Richard Haynes; **117t,** Thinkstock/SuperStock; **117m,** Richard Haynes; **117b,** MVR Photo; **118,** Sergio Piumatti; **119,** Richard Haynes; **120,** Russ Lappa; **121,** Charles D. Winters/Photo Researchers, Inc.; **122,** Richard Haynes; **124t,** Richard Haynes; **124b,** Russ Lappa; **125,** Richard Haynes; **126t,** Tony Freeman/PhotoEdit; **126b,** Russ Lappa; **127l,** Russ Lappa; **127r,** Richard Haynes; **129t,** Richard Haynes; **129m,** David Brownell; **129b,** Karl Weatherly/Corbis; **130l,** Sylvain Grandadam/Getty Images, Inc.; **130r,** Gerard Champion/Getty Images, Inc.; **131l,** Michael S. Yamashita/Corbis; **131m,** Jeffrey Aaronson/Network Aspen; **131r,** Ortelius; **132,** Prentice Hall School Division; **133,** Sandra Baker/Getty Images, Inc.; **134t all,** Richard Haynes; **134b,** David Young-Wolff/PhotoEdit; **135,** Russ Lappa; **136,** Cleo Photography/PhotoEdit; **137,** Richard Haynes; **138t,** Mark Gibson; **138m,** Royalty-Free/Corbis; **138b,** Bettmann/Corbis; **139,** Mark Gibson; **140,** Russ Lappa.

Chapter 5
Pages 144–145, Reuters/Toshiyuki Aizawa/Corbis; **145r,** Richard Haynes; **146t,** Richard Haynes; **146b,** Corel Corp./Mike Chambers; **147,** Paul and Lindamarie Ambrose/Getty Images, Inc.; **150,** Andy Wheeler/Alamy Images; **151,** AP/Wide World Photos; **151 football,** Reuters/Corbis; **152l,** AP/Wide World Photos; **152r,** Paine Stock Photos; **153,** Soames Summerhays/Photo Researchers, Inc.; **154t,** William L. Wantland/Tom Stack & Associates, Inc.; **154b,** Dorling Kindersley; **155t,** NASA; **155b,** Howard Sochurek/Corbis; **157,** Richard Haynes; **158t,** Richard Haynes; **158b,** Ken Straiton/Corbis; **160t,** Richard Haynes; **160b,** Richard Megna/Fundamental Photographs; **161,** Gilbert Iundt; TempSport/Corbis; **162t,** Russ Lappa; **162b,** Brand X Pictures/Getty Images, Inc.; **163,** Courtesy of the Archives, California Institute of Technology; **164,** Richard Haynes; **165,** Richard Haynes; **166,** Russ Lappa; **167t,** Glenn Short/Getty Images, Inc.; **167b,** Melvin Grubb/Grubb Photo Service, Inc.; **168l,** Robert Harding Picture Library/Alamy Images; **168m,** Richard M. Busch; **168r,** Nicholas DeVore/Bruce Coleman, Inc.; **169tl,** Brownie Harris/Corbis; **169tr,** Don Klumpp/Photographer's Choice/Getty Images, Inc.; **169b,** Clive Streeter/Dorling Kindersley; **170,** Brand X Pictures/Getty Images, Inc.; **172,** Globus, Holway & Lobel/Corbis.

Chapter 6
Pages 174–175, Roy Ooms/Masterfile; **175r,** Russ Lappa; **176,** Richard Haynes; **177,** Russ Lappa; **178,** Spencer Grant/PhotoEdit; **179,** Richard Haynes; **180,** IT International, Ltd./eStock Photo; **182,** Richard Haynes; **183t,** Russ Lappa; **183b,** Michael Mancuso/Omni-Photo Communications, Inc.; **185,** Melanie Acevedo/Getty Images, Inc.; **186t,** Russ Lappa; **186b,** Richard Haynes; **189,** Richard Haynes; **190,** Wayne Eastep/Getty Images, Inc.; **191,** David Stoecklein/Corbis; **192,** Richard Haynes; **193,** R. Knolan Benfield, Jr./Visuals Unlimited; **197,** Xenophon A. Beake/Corbis; **200,** Michael Mancuso/Omni-Photo Communications, Inc.

Page 204t, Martin Puddy/Getty Images, Inc.; **204–205b,** Chris Warren/International Stock; **205t,** PhotoDisc/Getty Images, Inc.; **206–207t,** David Lawrence; **206–207b,** Mitchell Funk/Photographer's Choice/Getty Images, Inc.; **207r,** Richard Haynes; **208l,** Corbis; **208r,** Joseph Pobereskin/Getty Images, Inc.; **209,** Bettmann/Corbis; **210–211,** Richard Weiss/Peter Arnold, Inc.; **212,** Tony Freeman/PhotoEdit; **213t,** Russ Lappa; **213m,** Richard Haynes; **213b,** Russ Lappa; **214,** Richard Haynes; **216,** Richard Haynes; **218,** Tanton Yachts; **219,** Richard Haynes; **221t,** Dorling Kidersley; **221b,** Richard Haynes; **223,** Image Stop/Phototake; **226,** Richard Haynes; **233,** Richard Haynes; **234,** Paul Seheult-Eye Ubiquitous/Corbis; **235,** David Stoecklein/Corbis; **237,** Richard Haynes; **239l,** Russ Lappa; **238b,** Stephen Frink/Corbis; **234,** Paul Seheult-Eye Ubiquitous/Corbis; **235,** David Stoecklein/Corbis; **237,** Richard Haynes; **238b,** Stephen Frink/Corbis; **239l,** Russ Lappa.